Fundamentals of MATHEMATICS

Fundamentals of MATHEMATICS

Third Edition

MOSES RICHARDSON

Professor of Mathematics, Brooklyn College
The City University of New York

The Macmillan Company, New York
Collier-Macmillan Limited, London

First Printing

Library of Congress catalog card number: 65–20177

THE MACMILLAN COMPANY, NEW YORK

COLLIER–MACMILLAN CANADA, LTD., TORONTO, ONTARIO

Printed in the United States of America

Preface to the Third Edition

In this third edition, many parts of the book have been thoroughly rewritten to conform with current changes in emphasis in the mathematical curriculum. Thus, there is increased stress on the language of sets, which has been introduced at an earlier stage, and considerable amplification of the material in many chapters, including a more complete discussion of rational, real, and complex numbers. The chapter on calculus has been expanded to include discussion of the completeness of the real numbers, the archimedean property, limits, and volumes of solids of revolution. The sections on graphs or networks have also been expanded. The principal obstacle encountered by students of the social sciences when they attempt to read current mathematical work in their respective fields is their lack of familiarity with vectors, matrices, and linear systems. Hence a new Chapter 14 on this subject has been included, introducing the student to techniques applicable to sociology (adjacency matrices of graphs), economics (the simplex method for linear programming), and psychology (Markov chains). It is hoped that the book will provide a year's course in mathematics suitable either as a terminal course for students of the liberal arts and social sciences or as an introductory course for those students, such as prospective teachers of secondary mathematics, who decide to go on with the study of mathematics.

In addition to the acknowledgements already made in the preface to the second edition, I wish to acknowledge here my indebtedness to Prentice-Hall, Inc., Englewood Cliffs, New Jersey, for permission to use approximately 50 pages of scattered material taken verbatim from Richardson, *College Algebra*, Third Edition, © 1966, of which they are the publishers. I am also indebted to Mr. Barry M. Glotzer for his conscientious assistance in typing the manuscript and checking the answers.

M. R.

Brooklyn, New York.

Preface for the Second Edition

Since 1941 when the first edition of this book was published, much new mathematics has been developed in the direction of the social and behavioral sciences. In this edition, an attempt is made to bring the most elementary aspects of some of these new developments within the reach of college students whose major interests are in the arts and social sciences rather than in mathematics or the physical sciences. Hence, there is new material on such topics as:

(1) Electronic computers;
(2) Information theory;
(3) Algebra of propositions and truth tables;
(4) Application of Boolean algebra to electrical networks;
(5) Political structures;
(6) Inequalities;
(7) Linear programming;
(8) Theory of games of strategy;
(9) Individual and social preferences.

None of this material is developed to the point where it becomes technically difficult. All students of the social sciences should learn how to use mathematicians even if only a few learn how to use mathematics. That is, they should learn the nature and concepts of mathematics well enough to know what they can expect mathematicians to do for them.

Some of the topics included in the first edition have been omitted, and some of what has been retained has been drastically rewritten. For example, the material on probability has been presented so as to avoid the impression that the assumption of equally likely cases is a necessity. The material on the number system has been somewhat simplified. The chapter on probability and statistics has been expanded, and the sections on the definite integral have been rewritten. The exercise lists have been reworked, and much minor rewriting has taken place. Bibliographical references have, of course, been brought up to date, although they are not intended to be complete. Supplementary reading in some of the stimulating literature about mathematics should be encouraged.

A boldface star ★ attached to an exercise indicates that it is more difficult than most others and should probably be expected only of "star" students. **It is not necessary to take all sections as they appear.** The instructor should use his own judgment in selecting the path to be taken throughout the entire book. In particular, the instructor in a short course may wish to be more sketchy than the text in Chapters 3 and 4 on the number system. The instructor should also feel free to rearrange the order of the chapters to suit his taste; for example, much of the chapter on probability could follow Chapter 7 on the algebra of sets immediately, if desired.

The general character and attitude of the book have not changed. Its principal objectives are still to give the student:

(1) An appreciation of the natural origin and evolutionary growth of the basic mathematical ideas from antiquity to the present;

(2) A critical, logical attitude, a wholesome respect for correct reasoning, precise definitions, and a clear grasp of underlying assumptions;

(3) An understanding of the rôle of mathematics as one of the major branches of human endeavor and its relations with other branches of the accumulated wisdom of the human race;

(4) A discussion of some of the simpler important problems of pure mathematics and its applications, including some which often come to the attention of the educated layman and cause him needless confusion;

(5) An understanding of the nature and practical importance of postulational thinking.

While it is assumed that the student has had some previous acquaintance with elementary algebra and plane geometry, almost no accurate recollection of the details of these subjects is prerequisite for this book. The table of contents indicates the topics chosen as vehicles by means of which the stated aims are to be reached. It no longer seems necessary, as it did in the 1941 edition, to defend the position that the early stages of a so-called "advanced" subject, presented at the proper level, may be easier to grasp as well as more important, meaningful, and interesting than the technically complicated stages of what has traditionally passed for an "elementary" subject. This idea now seems to be widely accepted.

The book attempts to provide a suitable terminal course for students of the arts and social sciences, stressing the fundamental concepts and applications of mathematics rather than its formal techniques. However, considerations of this kind would also be beneficial for students of the sciences and prospective teachers of secondary school mathematics who are commonly and naively supposed to acquire an understanding of the reasonableness and relevance of mathematics by osmosis during courses devoted largely to memorized and regurgitated techniques. A student of this text should be able to go on with a sophomore course in analytic geometry and calculus with a little supplementary material, largely analytic trigonometry, which is readily available elsewhere and best discussed when needed. The book is not merely an expository essay or a sugar-coated and worthless course for incompetents. It intends to provide a course in genuine (not necessarily traditional) mathematics which will emphasize the distinction between familiarity and understanding, between logical proof and routine manipulation, between a critical attitude of mind and habitual unquestioning belief, between scientific knowledge and both encyclopedic collections of facts and mere opinion and conjecture.

Applications are discussed throughout, but the discussion is restricted to matters within the student's reach to prevent the discussion from degenerating into a Sunday supplement article on "The Wonders of Science." Enough historical and biographical remarks are included to give the student a feeling for the evolution of the subject in response to human needs, for the fact that its progress is due to the efforts of human beings, and for the fact that it is still a living subject at which living human beings work. However, strict chronology is often sacrificed in the interests of logical presentation.

Needless to say, *complete logical rigor, according to present standards, is to be neither expected nor desired at this level.* One of the most puzzling tasks confronting the instructor, as well as the author, is that of deciding what logical inadequacies are to be permitted at this level of instruction. This is more puzzling in connection with numbers and algebra than with plane geometry where a long-standing tradition exists sanctioning logical gaps of well-known kinds in the proofs. In general, leniency is recommended since *it is a sufficient achievement for many students if they are brought to realize in some degree that algebra is a logical subject* and not a branch of black magic. It will, of course, be easy for the instructor to modify the amount of rigor according to his taste or the needs of any particular class; if less rigor is desired, it can be achieved simply by omission.

The statement that mathematics is basic to all sciences is correct partly in the sense of mathematics as the science of space and quantity but even more, and much more profoundly, in the sense of mathematics as the totality of logical (hypothetico-deductive) systems and their applications. *The unifying theme of the book is the fact that logical reasoning and logical structure are common features of all subjects forming part of the search for truth.* These are the common features concerning which one may hope for some transfer of training, if mathematics is taught with that end in view. Certainly they have a better chance for transfer than mere routine techniques. In particular the student should be brought to see mathematics as an embodiment of persistent intellectual honesty. While the objectives of this course will not be realized completely with every student, any more than will the objectives of any course, it is hoped that even partial realization will be of more lasting benefit to the student than are the more traditional courses.

Acknowledgments. For several exercises and examples in connection with the new material in this edition, I am indebted to Professor A. W. Tucker of Princeton University and to many other members of the Logistics Project at Princeton University, with whom I enjoyed a pleasant association during 1953–1956, including Professor H. W. Kuhn, Professor R. D. Luce, Dr. H. D. Mills, Dr. L. S. Shapley, Dr. M. Shubik, Professor G. L. Thompson, and others. Some of these exercises have been taken or adapted from mimeographed material circulated within the project, and others were absorbed during conversations. I am indebted to my colleague Professor W. Prenowitz for reading parts of the manuscript critically, to many friends and colleagues who have sent me helpful suggestions and corrections, and to Miss Irene Levine for her conscientious assistance in typing the manuscript and checking the answers.

For material retained from the first edition, I am indebted to Professor W. Prenowitz for communicating to me a sketch of the intuitively simple proofs of the theorems of Lobachevskian geometry in Chapter 17; to Professor C. B. Boyer for checking some of the historical comments; to Professor A. Church of Princeton University for some helpful remarks concerning consistency proofs; and to Professor J. Singer for his assistance with some illustrations.

I am also indebted to Professor E. T. Bell of the California Institute of Technology for permission to use portraits from his book *Men of Mathematics*; to Professor D. C. Miller of the Case School of Applied Science for permission to use the illustration in Fig. 235, taken from his book *The Science of Musical Sounds*; to the editors of *Scripta Mathematica* for permission to use portraits from Professor D. E. Smith's portfolio of famous mathematicians; to the Burroughs Adding Machine Company for permission to use the illustrations in Figs. 35 and 36; to the Keuffel and Esser Company for permission to use the illustrations in Figs. 201, 37, and 38; and to International Business Machines Corporation for permission to use Figs. 39, 40, and 41. Finally, I wish to thank The Macmillan Company for their cooperation and efficiency.

M. R.

Brooklyn, New York.

Table of Contents

1
Introduction

2
Logic, Mathematics, and Science

3
The Simplest Numbers

6

Arithmetical Computation and Its Relief

7

The Algebra of Logic and Related Topics

8

Impossibilities and Unsolved Problems

9

Analytic Geometry

10

Functions

11

Limits and the Calculus

12

Trigonometric Functions

13

Probability and Statistics

14

Vectors and Matrices

List of Symbols

References are to pages on which the symbol is introduced, or defined, or illustrated.

Symbol	Meaning or Name	Page
Not-P	Negation or contradictory of statement P	16
$>$	Is greater than	64, 104
$<$	Is less than	64, 104
$\neq$	Is not equal to	99
$\geqq$	Is greater than or equal to	104
$\leqq$	Is less than or equal to	104
$\pm$	Plus or minus	146
I	Basic collection or universal set	40
$\varnothing$	Empty set	40
$\cup$	Union of sets, "cup"	40
$\cap$	Intersection of sets, "cap"	41
$\subset$	Is contained in	41
$\supset$	Contains	41
A'	Complement of set A	198
$\sim p$	Negation or contradictory of p, "not-p"	205
$\vee$	Disjunction, "or"	205
$\wedge$	Conjunction, "and"	206
$\rightarrow$	Implies	207

1
Introduction

1. AIMS AND PROGRAM OF THE BOOK

Whatever a liberal education may be, it should involve some acquaintance with the principal achievements of human endeavor. The search for truth is an important branch of human endeavor, and in it mathematics has played a major role. What is mathematics? What is its role and what are its relations with other branches of knowledge? Why is it important? How did it arise and develop? These are some of the questions we shall discuss here.

Since you studied mathematics in secondary school for at least two years, it would seem fair to ask *you* "What is mathematics?" Or at least, "What are its outstanding characteristics?" Often, students answer by saying something about the study of useful relations among numbers, quantities, measurements of geometric figures, and methods of solution of problems concerning these things. Even some dictionaries still give such definitions. Indeed, in the student's previous experience with mathematics, it is true that the *objects* which he studied were numbers and geometric figures. But let us think rather of the distinctive characteristics of the *methods* by which these things were studied as compared with other subjects. You will remember that in geometry you proved assertions logically, one after another, on the basis of certain fundamental assertions (called *axioms*, *assumptions*, or *postulates*) which were taken for granted. Most of your education, aside from this, was a matter of memory and acceptance of authority as it must be, for example, in the elementary study of languages. In fact, while the idea of logical proof was brought home to you strongly in geometry, you may well be unable to recall anything of the sort in algebra. This is so because, in algebra, you were probably taught to solve certain types of problems according to prescribed rules which involved moving letters and numbers around the paper or blackboard in peculiar ways. Unfortunately, "transposition," "cancellation," etc., meant very little, to some of you, except a curious collection of rules of thumb, like a glorified game of tick-tack-toe, whose correctness was justified not by reasoning but by the teacher's authority. Can you, for example, justify logically the queer maneuvers you have learned to go through in the processes of multiplication or long division of numbers? It must be said that to some extent it was inevitable that you should learn to do many things in arithmetic, say, before you were old enough to understand them. But it should be understood that algebra is not merely a compendium of tricks for solving catchy problems. If it were, it would deserve to be called "a low form of cunning." On the contrary, algebra has the same logical structure as geometry or any other branch of mathematics, as you will see later. Mathematical problems assuredly have at least as much "puzzle appeal" as more popular hobbies such as card games, cross-word puzzles and the like, and are at the same time more valuable. But mathematics has a far deeper significance than could possibly be possessed by a mere collection of puzzles.

In the early part of the course we shall discuss many things in algebra and geometry which you have already studied in your high school courses, but from a very different point of view. We shall seldom ask you to remember accurately any of the techniques you took up in the past, and even arithmetic will be discussed here from a logical standpoint. In fact, in some parts of the book, you will find it necessary to forget many things which you have learned to do by habit in order to be able to consider their logical justification without prejudice. Later in the course you will be introduced to some of the easier fundamental ideas of many fascinating, modern, and so-called advanced branches of mathematics, although we shall never develop these subjects far enough to make stringent demands on your technical equipment. While there is no easy road to mastery of the mathematical sciences, many of the fundamental ideas, about which the intelligent layman is often curious, can be grasped readily without too much technique. We think that these will prove more interesting to you and will be of greater value to your mental development and your appreciation and understanding of all the subjects forming part of the search for truth than would, for example, the study of complicated equations.

While most people are somewhat aware of the importance of the technical applications of mathematics to the civilized world, many who do not intend to become technicians are inclined to doubt the value of the study of mathematics to themselves. This attitude may be due partly to the widespread failure to understand the nature of mathematics and to grasp the distinction between mathematics and its applications. At the end of this course, when you understand better the nature of both pure and applied mathematics, we hope you will be more inclined to agree with Benjamin Franklin who wrote,* "Whatever may have been imputed to some other studies under the notion of insignificancy and loss of time, yet these [mathematics] I believe, never caused repentance in any, except it was for their remissness in the prosecution of them."

2. ADVICE TO THE STUDENT

This book should not be used merely as a collection of homework exercises; it should be read. *You should read each section at least twice; once to get the general idea and then carefully, checking on each detail. A third reading is advisable.* Conciseness and accuracy of statement are characteristic of mathematical writing. Therefore, read slowly and make an earnest effort to grasp what you read. *Reading with a pencil and paper in hand is strongly recommended; work out the illustrative examples in the book and make up similar illustrations for yourself.* Your chief burden will be the necessity for sustained attention and a sincere desire to understand. Approach the subject without the dislike you may have felt for it previously. Its treatment may be so different that it may be, at times, difficult to recognize it as the same subject. Many people are fascinated by mathematics; it will be worth your while to give it a fresh chance.

Please do not approach even the most elementary parts of our work with the cock-sure, sophisticated attitude that you "know this because you have already had it" and therefore do not have to read it carefully. Even the person who does not take the familiar radio, for example, for granted and who realizes that an understanding of radio depends on the mathematical and physical work of many centuries may still take arithmetic for granted without realizing the long, blundering struggle of the human race to evolve a suitable arithmetic. In this age of mechanical wonders, you must guard against subconsciously assuming that you understand something merely because you are familiar with it, or that things are true merely because you have habitually believed them. A wholesome, naïve honesty is essential to the study of the fundamentals of science.

On the other hand, do not approach the subject with an unreasonable fear. Although there is no lack of unsolved problems at the frontier of mathematical research, there are no mysteries in a completed chapter of mathematics. It is all simple, honest reasoning which anybody can follow, with a little effort and concentration, if it is explained step by step. Often a student has difficulty in following a mathematical explanation only because the author skips steps with which he assumes the student to be familiar. If you do not recall the missing

* On the Usefulness of Mathematics, *Complete Works of Benjamin Franklin*, Vol. I, G. P. Putnam, N. Y., 1887, p. 421.

steps, you may be faced with an unbridgeable gap in the reasoning, and the author's conclusion may appear mysterious to you. We shall try to avoid such gaps here.

Another difficulty found by beginners in mathematics is the necessity for mastering the symbolism and technical vocabulary. This is to some extent unavoidable. The symbols are introduced to clarify and simplify statements and ideas which would seem very complicated if expressed in ordinary language. When you have learned to read the symbolism freely and fluently you can concentrate instead on the flow of ideas expressed therein. The situation is quite analogous to that of a beginner in music who cannot read and appreciate a great musical composition because he has to concentrate painfully on the meaning of individual notes, or a beginner in a foreign language who cannot appreciate the beauty of a great piece of writing because he has to concentrate painfully on the meaning of the individual words. Algebraic language, like any language, is merely a collection of symbols which we agree to interpret and combine in convenient ways. Therefore, to appreciate the great story of mathematical thinking, *learn carefully the definitions of whatever symbols or unfamiliar terms we introduce*, and thereby leave your mind free to grasp the larger, fundamental ideas of the subject. Even where familiar words are used, their meaning in mathematical usage is often entirely different from their meaning in every-day usage. For example, no one who is unacquainted with the technical definitions can understand the mathematical meaning of the words "power," "root," "coordinate," "function," "group," "rational," "differentiate," "integrate," all of which will be used in this book. A person who persists in using words, which have been defined precisely, without understanding their definitions, literally does not know what he is talking about.

Keep in mind that it requires no unusual ability to follow mathematical ideas although it may have required genius to invent them. There is a great difference between breaking a trail through an uncharted wilderness and riding through it on a graded and well-paved road after it has been conquered. To create new mathematics of value often requires the highest order of imagination and intuition, not wild and untrammeled but subject to the final test of reason. (Thus new discoveries are not always the result of logical analysis alone but are often due to insight, vision, experience and the happy "accident" of hitting upon the appropriate path. However, it should be noted that these "accidents," as a great mathematician once remarked, seem to happen only to deserving people.) But to follow an explanation requires only close attention, the requisite background, and a normal ability to reason. In this book we shall demand little of your background. The rest is up to you.

2

Logic, Mathematics, and Science

3. INTRODUCTION

You have recalled that the geometry of the ancient Greeks which you studied in high school was not merely a collection of unconnected assertions, but that all of them after the first few were deduced logically from those first few which, in turn, were assumed without proof. If one characteristic of mathematics were to be singled out as being of outstanding importance, it would certainly be the insistence on logical proof. Since logic plays so important a part, let us turn our attention to logic itself.

Logical thought is neither as common nor as easy as may be supposed. We all know that we believe many things without ever having satisfied ourselves logically about them. For example, the principal reason that most of us have for believing that the earth rotates about its axis and revolves about the sun is that people whose opinions we respect, like our scientists and teachers, tell us it is so. But at one time, nearly everybody believed the earth to be motionless and fixed at the center of the universe, for the same inadequate reason. This state of affairs is largely inevitable simply because life is too short for us to examine critically everything we believe. Even so, it could do us no harm to be aware of what we are accepting uncritically on someone's authority. However, while most of us admit freely that we *do not* always think logically, many people are of the opinion that they are *capable* of thinking logically quite automatically or instinctively and without effort, care, concentration, or study. This opinion is much more prevalent among freshmen than among mathematicians who have really attempted to think logically at least part of the time. Mathematicians are painfully aware of the effort required for the task even when the material is written in the comparatively transparent style of mathematical works where one's

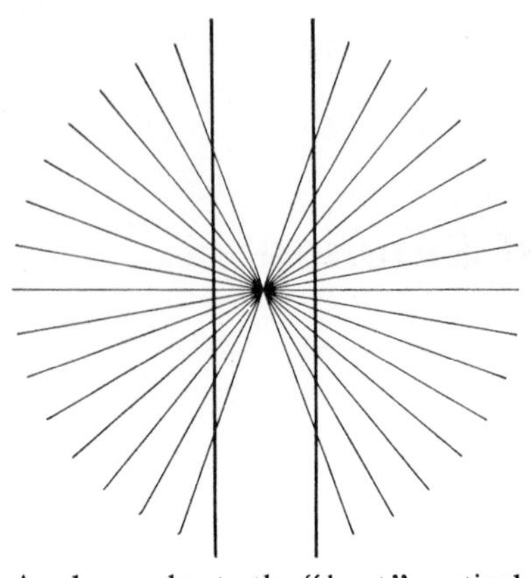

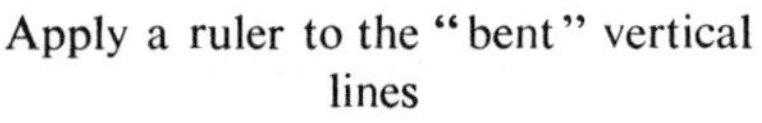

Apply a ruler to the "bent" vertical lines

FIG. 1

attention is deliberately directed to the logical structure of the argument. Surely it is much more difficult to reason logically in subjects where the reasoning, far from being openly exhibited in its skeletal form, is hidden in elaborate verbiage and where our thoughts are colored by our emotions and prejudices.

The fact is that most of us, including professional mathematicians in their unguarded moments, seem to derive an almost athletic exhilaration from the popular sport of jumping to conclusions. There are even some extremists who claim that intuition is a good substitute for reason. Now intuition has an important role in science, especially as a "suggestor," but it certainly does not take the place of reason. The creative mathematician uses imagination and intuition to conjecture new results and new methods of research, but he does not assert that his guesses are correct until he has succeeded in proving them logically. Even a confirmed mystic would hesitate before driving his car over a bridge constructed exclusively by intuition. In fact, simple things like optical illusions teach us not to draw hasty conclusions from the evidence of our senses (Fig. 1).

The results of logical reasoning in the investigation of natural phenomena have amply justified the importance given it in mathematics and science in general. None of the alternatives to logic (authority, intuition, or mysticism) has a record of achievement in these fields as enviable as that of logical reasoning. In the remainder of this chapter, we shall, therefore, examine more closely the nature and importance of logical reasoning and its connection with mathematics and science in general.

Exercises

Answer the following questions intuitively; then check your answers by calculation if you can. These exercises are intended only to show that intuition unaided by reason sometimes lets you down.

1. A square sheet of copper one foot on each side costs 20 cents. What will be the cost of a square sheet of copper one and one half feet on each side?

2. Each bacterium in a culture splits into two bacteria once a minute. If there are 100 billion billlion bacteria present at the end of an hour, when were there exactly 50 billion billion present?

3. A car travels 10 miles at 30 miles per hour and the next 10 miles at 60 miles per hour. Would the trip take more, less, or the same time if it travelled all 20 miles at the steady rate of 45 miles per hour?

4. A man sells 60 pieces of candy at 3 for 1 cent and another 60 pieces at 2 for 1 cent. Would his income be more, less, or the same if he sold 120 pieces at 5 for 2 cents?

5. Two civil service jobs have the same starting salary of $1800 per year and the same maximum salary of $3000 per year. One gets an annual raise of $200; the other gets a semi-annual raise of $50. Which is better?

6. If A can do a job in 6 days and B can do it in 10 days, how long will it take them to do it together?

4. DEDUCTIVE LOGIC. TRUTH AND VALIDITY

In what follows, we shall often encounter statements of the forms "All A's are B's," "No A's are B's," and "Some A's are B's"; for example,

(*a*) All fish are swimmers.
(*b*) No cats are felines.
(*c*) Some college students are clever people.

These statements assert relationships between various classes of objects. Thus (*a*) asserts that the class of fish is contained within the class of swimmers; in other words, that every fish is also a swimmer, or, equivalently, if x is a fish then x is a swimmer. It does *not* assert that every swimmer is also a fish, or that if x is a swimmer then x is a fish. If all A's are B's *and* all B's are A's, then the class of A's is identical with the class of B's. Statement (*a*) is presumably true.

Statement (*b*) asserts that the class of cats and the class of felines have no member in common. Statement (*b*) is certainly false.

Statement (*c*) means that there exists at least one college student who is a clever person. It does *not* assert that some college students are not clever people. The statement some A's are B's is non-committal as to the existence or non-existence of A's which are not B's. This meaning of "some" is different from its everyday usage where it usually means "some but not all." The non-committal usage is universally adopted in logical and mathematical writing. Statement (*c*) is probably true.

A convenient way to picture these relationships between classes is by diagrams like the following. Represent each class by a set of points inside a closed boundary line. Then (*a*) is pictured by placing the class of fish entirely within the class of swimmers (Fig. 2(a)). Statement (*b*) is pictured by placing the two classes entirely outside each other (Fig. 2(b)). Statement (*c*) is pictured by making the two classes overlap and shading the portion they have in common; only the existence of members of the shaded region is asserted, and no inference should be made concerning the existence or non-existence of members of the unshaded regions.

We shall make no attempt here to discuss the philosophical questions "What is truth?" and "How can we determine whether or not a given statement is true?" In fact, it is exceedingly doubtful whether either question can be

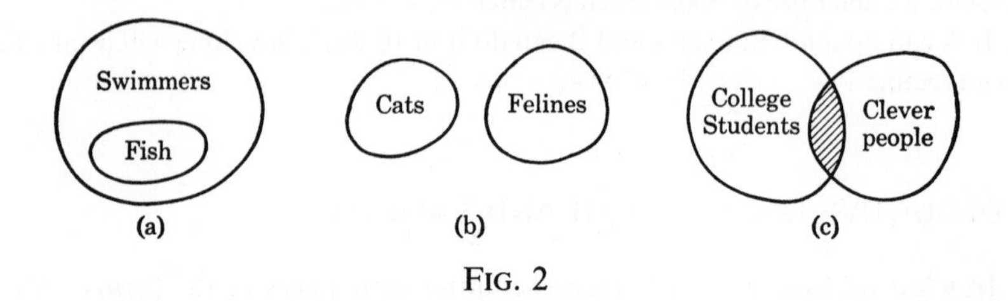

FIG. 2

answered with anything like finality. We shall suppose that we can determine somehow, in some cases, whether given statements are true or false; or at least we will be willing to agree or grant (tentatively perhaps), or simply to assume, that some statements are true and others false. We shall be principally concerned with the problem of getting new truths from old. That is, granting that certain statements are true, what can be said about the truth of certain other statements? This is the problem of logic which we shall now study.

If two statements are so related that the second *must* be true *if* the first is true, then we say that the second **follows from** the first, or the second is a **logical consequence** of the first, or the first **implies** the second. The first statement is called the **hypothesis** and the second is called the **conclusion.**

Example 1.
Hypothesis. (*a*) All freshmen are undergraduates.
(*b*) All undergraduates are geniuses.
Conclusion. All freshmen are geniuses.

Here the hypothesis implies the conclusion, since it is clear that *if* the hypothesis is true *then* the conclusion *must* be. Notice that there may be some doubt about the truth of the conclusion and of part (*b*) of the hypothesis.

If the conclusion of an argument really follows from the hypothesis, the argument is called **valid.** The process of drawing valid conclusions from given hypotheses is called **deduction** or **deductive reasoning.** We must distinguish carefully between the actual *truth* of the statements involved and the correctness or *validity* of the argument. A good way to test the validity of an argument such as the above example is to use diagrams such as those of Fig. 2, as follows.

Represent the class of all freshmen by a set of points inside a closed boundary line. Do likewise with the class of all undergraduates and the class of all geniuses. Part (*a*) of the hypothesis demands that the class of freshmen be entirely contained within the class of all undergraduates. Part (*b*) of the hypothesis demands that the class of undergraduates be entirely contained within the class of geniuses.

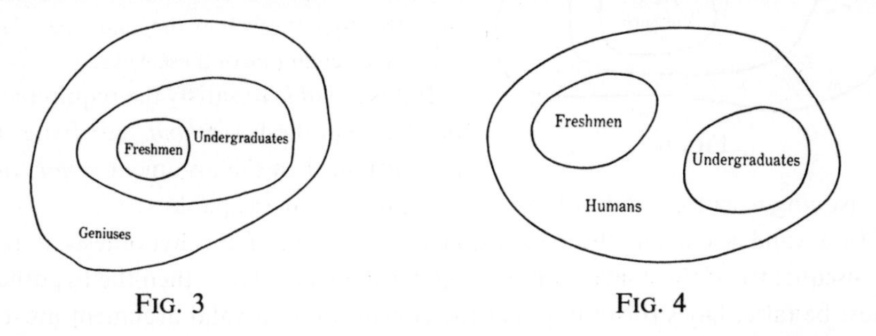

FIG. 3

FIG. 4

Thus the various sets of points representing these classes of people must be placed in the relative positions pictured in Fig. 3. Clearly, the requirements of the hypothesis have *forced* us to place the class of freshmen entirely within the class of geniuses, which is exactly what is asserted in the conclusion. Hence the argument of example 1 is valid, regardless of the actual truth or falsity of the statements involved.

Valid reasoning tells us that *if* the hypothesis *were* true, then the conclusion *would have to be* true. Therefore it is often called "*if* . . . *then* . . ." reasoning.

Example 2.

Hypothesis. (*a*) All freshmen are human.

(*b*) All undergraduates are human.

Conclusion. All freshmen are undergraduates.

There is no disagreement as to the truth of all these statements. But the reasoning is *not* valid, because the hypothesis does not *force* you to place the class of freshmen

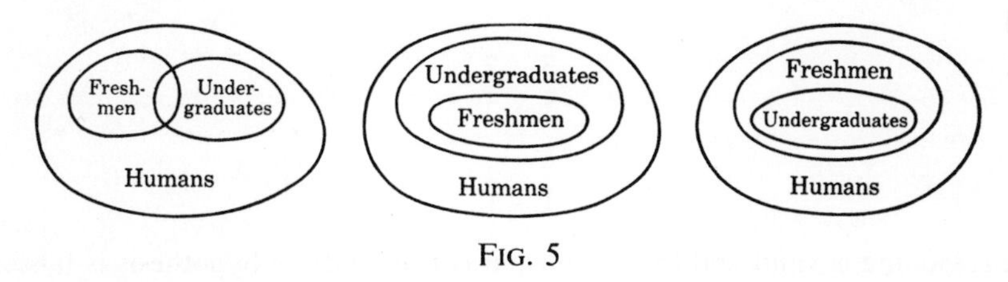

FIG. 5

entirely within the class of undergraduates. You are forced *only* to place the class of freshmen within the class of humans, as in Fig. 4. Therefore the argument is not valid.

Of course it *may* happen that all freshmen are undergraduates. But we are here concerned with the question whether it *must* happen because of our hypothesis. It is important to grasp the distinction between *may* and *must*. The three classes in example 2 *may* be related as in Fig. 4 or as in any of the figures in Fig. 5 as far as we can tell from the hypothesis. But we are unable to conclude from this hypothesis that they *must* be related in any particular one of these ways.

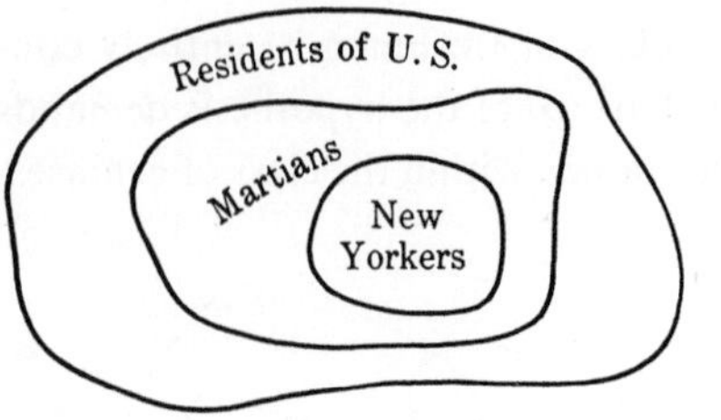

Residents of U. S.
Martians
New Yorkers

FIG. 6

If it is *possible* to satisfy the requirements of the hypothesis *without* satisfying the conclusion, then the argument is *not valid*. Reasoning is called valid only if the conclusion is inescapable.

In a valid argument the conclusion must be true if the hypothesis is true. Consequently, if the conclusion of a valid argument is false, then the hypothesis must be false. Does this imply that the conclusion of a valid argument must be false if the hypothesis is false? Consider the following example.

Example 3.
Hypothesis. (*a*) All New Yorkers are Martians.
(*b*) All Martians are residents of the United States.
Conclusion. All New Yorkers are residents of the United States.

Here the reasoning is valid, the hypothesis is false, but the conclusion is true. See Fig. 6.

As another example, consider the proposition "if $3 = 7$ then $1 = 1$." Granting that if equals are divided by equals the results are equal, we can deduce the conclusion as follows:

if
$$3 = 7,$$
then
$$3 = 7,$$
and
$$\frac{3}{3} = \frac{7}{7},$$
or
$$1 = 1.$$

The reasoning is valid and the conclusion is true, but the hypothesis is false.

Thus a false hypothesis *may* yield a true conclusion. *The truth of the conclusion does not imply the truth of the hypothesis.* This is an important though elementary point to which we shall refer later. That is, *if statement A* (*the hypothesis*) *implies statement B (the conclusion) and B is known to be true, then we have no right to make any inference as to whether A is true or not;* that is, the truth of A is not guaranteed by the truth of B.

The **converse** of the statement "A implies B" (or "if A then B") is the statement "B implies A" (or "if B then A"); that is, *the converse is formed by interchanging hypothesis and conclusion.* If we knew that "B implies A" was valid and B were known to be true, then A would have to be true. But the converse of a valid argument may well fail to be valid, and the converse of a true statement may well be false. For example, a valid argument is the following: "if $x = 2$ and $y = 5$, then $x + y = 7$." The converse "if $x + y = 7$, then $x = 2$ and $y = 5$" is clearly not valid for we might have $x = 3$ and $y = 4$ or some other combination. "If an animal is a dog, it is a quadruped," is true; the converse, "if an animal is a quadruped, it is a dog" is false, as all the donkeys in the world attest. Only statements of the "if . . . then . . ." type have converses. "This apple is red" has no converse. The statement "all a's are b's" has the converse "all b's are a's"; note that "all a's are b's" means that "if anything is an a, then it is a b" and is therefore of the "if . . . then . . ." type.

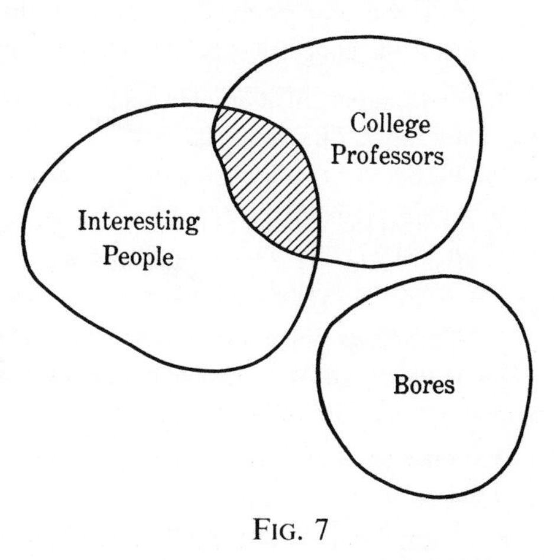

FIG. 7

Example 4.

Hypothesis. (*a*) No interesting people are bores.
(*b*) Some interesting people are college professors.

Conclusion. Some college professors are not bores.

This is a valid argument, regardless of anyone's opinion as to the truth of the statements involved (Fig. 7).

A detailed study of the logic of arguments of the type of most of the examples in this section was made by Aristotle (fourth century B.C.). The diagrams used here are ascribed to the eighteenth century Swiss mathematician L. Euler. These diagrams, while convenient, are not essential to the reasoning. They are merely used to picture the relationships among various classes of objects, such as the relationship "class A is included within class B." The study of logic did not progress materially beyond the state in which Aristotle left it until modern times when mathematicians became interested in it.

Exercises

1. Assuming that the conclusion follows from the hypothesis by valid reasoning, complete each of the following sentences with one of the phrases "must be true," "must be false," "may be true or false":

(*a*) If the hypothesis is true, then the conclusion . . . .
(*b*) If the hypothesis is false, then the conclusion . . . .
(*c*) If the conclusion is true, then the hypothesis . . . .
(*d*) If the conclusion is false, then the hypothesis . . . .

2. (*a*) If statement A implies statement B, and statement B implies statement C, must A imply C? Explain.

(*b*) If statement A implies statement B, must B imply A? Explain.

3. (*a*) Test the validity of the following argument by using diagrams:

Hypothesis. (1) All murders are immoral acts.
(2) Some murders are justifiable.
Conclusion. Some immoral acts are justifiable.

(*b*) If part (1) of the above hypothesis is true and the conclusion is false, what can be said about the truth or falsity of part (2) of the hypothesis? Explain.

4. Make up four true statements of the "if . . . then . . ." type which have false converses.

5. Test the validity of the following arguments in (*a*) and (*b*); and then answer (*c*).

(*a*) *Hypothesis.* (1) No college students are maniacs.
(2) All freshmen are college students.
Conclusion. No freshmen are maniacs.

(*b*) *Hypothesis.* (1) All maniacs are college students.
(2) No freshmen are college students.
Conclusion. No freshmen are maniacs.

(*c*) If a person reasons correctly and obtains a conclusion with which you agree, are you logically forced to agree with his hypothesis? Explain.

In exercises 6 through 18, (a) test the validity of the following arguments for each proposed conclusion by using diagrams, and (b) give your opinion as to the truth of the various statements involved.

6. *Hypothesis.* (1) All dogs are cats.
(2) All cats are mammals.
Conclusion. All dogs are mammals.

7. *Hypothesis.* (1) All men are mortal.
(2) Socrates is a man.
Conclusion. Socrates is mortal.

8. *Hypothesis.* (1) All humane men are kind to animals.
(2) Hitler is kind to animals.
Conclusion. Hitler is a humane man.

9. The same as exercise 8, except that the name Hitler is to be replaced by the name Lincoln.

10. *Hypothesis.* (1) Some college students are clever.
(2) All freshmen are college students.
Conclusion. Some freshmen are clever.

11. *Hypothesis.* (1) All college students are clever.
(2) All freshmen are clever.
Conclusions. (1) All freshmen are college students.
(2) No freshmen are college students.
(3) Some freshmen are college students.
(4) Some freshmen are not college students.
(5) Some college students are freshmen.
(6) Some college students are not freshmen.

12. *Hypothesis.* (1) No conceited people have a sense of humor.
(2) Some teachers do not have a sense of humor.
Conclusion. Some teachers are conceited.

13. *Hypothesis.* (1) All fools are conceited.
(2) All pompous people are conceited.
(3) Some fools are talkative.
Conclusions. (1) All pompous people are fools.
(2) Some conceited people are talkative.
(3) No pompous people are fools.
(4) Some pompous people are fools.
(5) Some pompous people are not fools.

14. *Hypothesis.* (1) All mumbos are jumbos.
(2) All jumbos are boojums.
(3) All boojums are snarks.
Conclusion. All mumbos are snarks.

15. *Hypothesis.* (1) All communists are atheists.
(2) Strzhniewsczki is an atheist.
Conclusion. Strzhniewsczki is a communist.

16. *Hypothesis.* (1) All timid creatures are bunnies.
(2) Some timid creatures are dumb.
(3) Some freshmen are timid creatures.
Conclusions. (1) Some bunnies are dumb.
(2) Some freshmen are bunnies.
(3) Some freshmen are dumb bunnies.

17. *Hypothesis.* (1) All men are mortal.
(2) All wolves are mortal.
(3) Some men are carnivorous.
Conclusions. (1) Some mortals are carnivorous.
(2) Some wolves are carnivorous.
(3) All men are wolves.
(4) Some men are wolves.
(5) No men are wolves.
(6) Some men are not wolves.

18. *Hypothesis.* (1) Poverty improves the character.
(2) Whatever improves the character promotes happiness.
(3) Whatever promotes happiness is good.
Conclusion. Poverty is good.

19. Test the validity of the following argument by using diagrams. Do not give your opinion as to the truth of the statements involved.
Hypothesis. (1) All mathematics instructors are absent-minded people.
(2) All absent-minded people are at least slightly crazy.
Conclusion. All mathematics instructors are at least slightly crazy.

20. (Adapted from Lewis Carroll.) Decide whether or not each proposed conclusion follows from the hypotheses by a valid argument:
Hypotheses. (1) If an exercise in logic is easy, then I can understand it.
(2) I cannot understand an exercise in logic if the hypotheses are not arranged in a familiar pattern.
(3) The hypotheses of this exercise in logic are not arranged in a familiar pattern.
Conclusions. (*a*) I cannot understand this exercise in logic.
(*b*) This exercise in logic is not easy.
(*c*) If I can understand an exercise in logic, then it is easy.

5. THE FORMAL CHARACTER OF DEDUCTIVE LOGIC

We have seen that the validity of an argument does not depend on the actual truth of its statements. More than that, validity depends only on the *form* of the statements and not on their meaning. Some or all of the statements of a valid argument may be false or they may have no meaning at all. For instance, the arguments of example 1, section 4, and of exercises 6 and 19, section 4, all have the following abstract form.

Example 1.
Hypothesis. (*a*) All x's are y's.
(*b*) All y's are z's.
Conclusion. All x's are z's.

This abstract form of argument is *valid* regardless of what concrete meanings you give to x, y, z. To speak of the truth of its statements is clearly absurd since its statements do not have any meaning until we assign to (or substitute for) the undefined terms x, y, z some definite meanings. Reasoning with such meaningless forms is called **formal logic** or **abstract logic.**

Some philosophers have scoffed at this so-called "thoughtless thinking." But it is precisely the fact that abstract logic is independent of any particular subject matter that makes it so valuable. For it can be applied equally well to any subject matter. If you substitute for x, y, and z, in example 1, any meanings which convert the hypotheses into true statements, then you know automatically that the conclusion is also converted into a true statement. This applies equally well to a simple argument or to a long, complicated chain of such arguments. In formal or abstract logic we have the additional practical advantage of being able to decide whether or not reasoning is valid without being disturbed or influenced psychologically or emotionally by the meaning of the statements, since they have no specific meaning and may be given many different meanings. It is much easier to tell good reasoning from bad when the argument is openly exhibited in its skeleton form than when it is surrounded by sonorous rhetoric and deceptive verbiage and when the meanings of the statements are apt to color our thoughts.

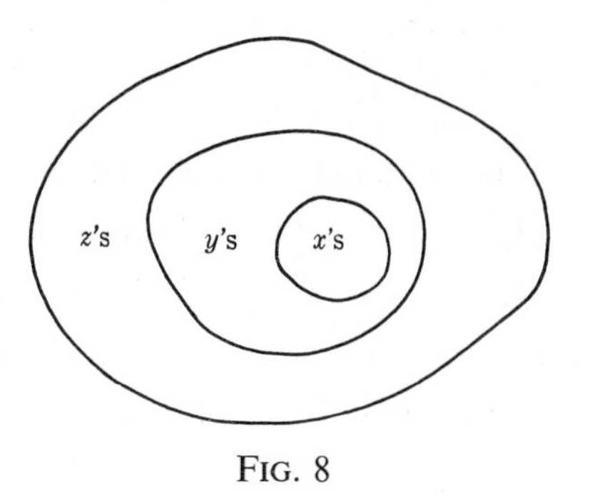

FIG. 8

Statements like

(1) "All x's are y's,"

or

(2) "x was the first President of the United States,"

cannot be considered assertions at all until meanings have been assigned to the undefined terms x and y; when meanings *have* been assigned, the resulting statements may be true or false or merely nonsense. Thus, if we substitute $x =$ "Abraham Lincoln" in (2) we get a false statement; if we substitute $x =$ "George Washington" in (2) we get a true statement; if we substitute $x =$ "imperceptibility" in (2) we get nonsense. The distinction between a false statement and a nonsensical one is not always easy to make. A symbol like x, y, or z, which may take on more than one meaning is called a **variable.** The set of all objects which a variable x may represent is called the **domain** of the variable x. Statements like (1) and (2) which contain undefined terms or variables are often called **propositional functions**; they become **propositions** only when we have substituted meanings for the undefined terms which make the resulting sentences either true or false. A nonsensical statement is not considered a proposition at all. Formal logic is really concerned with propositional functions and with the validity of arguments involving them. When we speak of truth or falsity we are referring to propositions. The sentences on an application form which contain blank spaces are purely formal; that is, they are propositional functions in which the blanks are the variables. When we substitute meanings for these variables (fill in the blanks), these sentences become propositions.

It is important not to be deceived by the similarity of the statements:

(3) If A is true, then B is true;

(4) If B is true, then A is true;

(5) If A is not true, then B is not true.

The unwary often confuse these three. *But* (3) *does not imply* (4), *and* (3) *does not imply* (5). *Likewise* (5) *does not imply* (3), *and* (4) *does not imply* (3). The statements (3) and (4) are *converses* of each other. Statements (5) and (4) are called **contrapositives** of each other. Two statements A and B are called **equivalent** if A implies B *and* B implies A. Hence if (3) and (4), or (3) and (5), are both correct, then A and B are equivalent. Statement (3) is often written in the form "A is true **only if** B is true." Thus, the statement "A is true **if and only if** B is true" means that "A and B are equivalent"; it is a compact way of stating (3) and its converse (4) together. Statement (3) is also written as "A is a **sufficient condition** for B." Statement (4) is also written as "A is a **necessary condition** for B." Hence the statements "A and B are equivalent" or "A is true if and only if B is true" are also written as "A is a necessary and sufficient condition for B."

Example. Consider the following statements. (1) If a person is reading this book, then he is alive. (2) If a person is alive, then he is reading this book. (3) If a person is not reading this book, then he is not alive.

If P represents a statement, then the **contradictory** or **negation** of this statement is symbolized by not-P. For example, if P stands for "It is raining," then not-P stands for "It is not raining." If P is true, then not-P must be false, and if P is false, then not-P must be true.

"All x's are y's" does not imply "Some x's are y's," since the latter implies the existence of at least one x while the former permits the set of x's to be empty. For example, "all witches over 30 feet tall have long noses" is true, while "some witches over 30 feet tall have long noses" is false since there exists no witch over 30 feet tall.

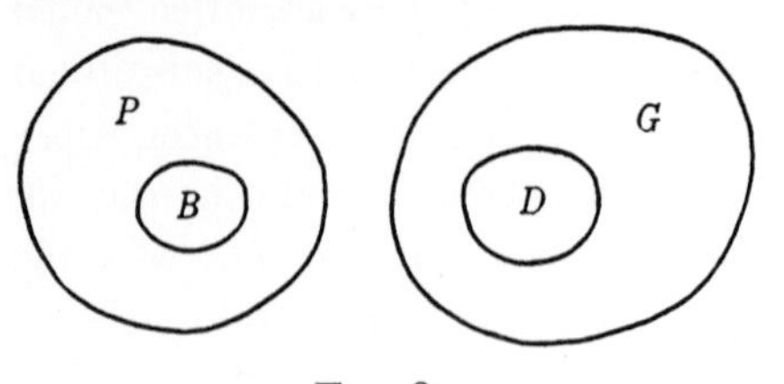

FIG. 9

Many arguments found in print are either absolutely incorrect, or, at best, can be made valid only by the addition of further hypotheses, not stated by the author. Such situations can often be detected by substituting symbols like x, y, and z for the terms in the argument and putting the argument into a form which exhibits its logical structure.

Example. Consider the following argument. "Brown has publicly asserted that he believes in democracy. Therefore he is a good citizen because all who believe in democracy are good citizens." Putting this argument into a form which exhibits its logical structure, we have:

Hypothesis. (*a*) Brown has publicly asserted that he believes in democracy.
(*b*) All who believe in democracy are good citizens.
Conclusion. Brown is a good citizen.

This is certainly *not* valid as it stands. To see this clearly let us introduce symbols as follows. Let B represent Brown; let P be the class of all those who have publicly asserted that they believe in democracy; let G be the class of all good citizens; and let D be the class of those who believe in democracy. Note that P and D are different classes. Our argument becomes (see Fig. 9):

Hypothesis. (*a*) B is in P.
(*b*) D is contained in G.
Conclusion. B is in G.

However, this invalid argument will be changed into a valid one *if* we make the further hypothesis that all who publicly assert that they believe in democracy do believe in it; that is, that P is contained within D (Fig. 10).

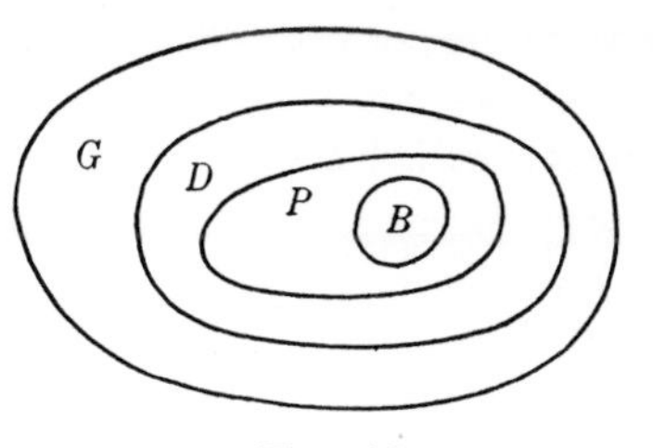

FIG. 10

Exercises

Decide whether or not each proposed conclusion follows from the hypothesis by a valid argument.

1. *Hypothesis.* (1) All x's are z's.
(2) All y's are z's.
Conclusions. (*a*) Some x's are y's.
(*b*) Some x's are not y's.
(*c*) No x's are y's.

2. *Hypothesis.* (1) Some x's are y's.
(2) All x's are z's.

Conclusions. (*a*) Some z's are y's.
(*b*) Some z's are not y's.

3. *Hypothesis.* (1) All x's are y's.
(2) Some z's are y's.
(3) Some t's are not y's.

Conclusions. (*a*) Some t's are z's.
(*b*) Some t's are y's.
(*c*) No t's are x's.
(*d*) Some t's are not x's.
(*e*) Some y's are not x's.

4. *Hypothesis.* All B's are A's.
Some B's are C's.
All B's are D's.

Conclusions. (1) Some D's are C's.
(2) Some A's are C's.
(3) Some A's are D's.
(4) Some C's are not D's.
(5) Some D's are not A's.
(6) Some A's are not D's.
(7) Some D's are not C's.

5. *Hypothesis.* Some A's are B's.
No C's are B's.
Some D's are C's.

Conclusions. (1) No A's are C's.
(2) Some A's are not C's.
(3) Some C's are not A's.
(4) Some A's are not D's.

6. *Hypothesis.* All A's are B's.
Some C's are D's.
No B's are C's.

Conclusions. (1) All B's are A's.
(2) Some D's are B's.
(3) No C's are B's.
(4) No B's are D's.
(5) Some C's are A's.

7. (*a*) Assuming that statement (1) below is true, which of the other numbered statements must be true?
(*b*) Which statement is the converse of (1)?
(*c*) Which statement is the converse of (4)?

(1) If John is intelligent, then he can pass mathematics.
(2) If John is not intelligent, then he cannot pass mathematics.
(3) If John can pass mathematics, then he is intelligent.
(4) If John cannot pass mathematics, then he is not intelligent.
(5) John can pass mathematics if he is intelligent.

8. Consider the five statements:

(1) All x's are y's.

(2) No x's are y's.

(3) Some x's are y's.

(4) Some x's are not y's.

(5) All y's are x's.

(*a*) If P stands for statement (1), which one does not-P represent?

(*b*) If P stands for statement (2), which one does not-P represent?

(*c*) If P stands for statement (3), which one does not-P represent?

(*d*) If P stands for statement (4), which one does not-P represent?

(*e*) Which one is the converse of (1)?

(*f*) Write the contradictory of the converse of (1).

Put each of the following arguments into a form which will exhibit its logical structure, and decide whether or not it is valid as it stands. If not, see if you can make a valid argument out of it by assuming additional hypotheses not stated here.

9. Helping the poor is always good. Therefore giving alms to beggars is always good.

10. Brown's program is unworthy of support. Jones' policies are worthy of support because he is unalterably opposed to Brown's program.

11. A classical education is worthless because we make no practical use of Latin and Greek after graduation.

12. This is an evil theory for we find it supported by some evil men.

13. People with inferiority complexes are always pompous. Professor Blucester is always pompous. Therefore, he has an inferiority complex.

14. Assuming that the statement "If Smith is a college student, then he is more than 12 years old" is true, which of the following statements is necessarily true?

(*a*) If Smith is more than 12 years old, he is a college student.

(*b*) If Smith is not a college student, he is not more than 12 years old.

(*c*) If Smith is not more than 12 years old, he is not a college student.

15. Is "$x=3$ and $y=4$" a necessary or a sufficient condition for "$x+y=7$"? Is it both necessary and sufficient?

16. Is $x^2=9$ a necessary or sufficient condition for $x=3$? Is it both necessary and sufficient?

17. Is "triangle ABC is equiangular" a necessary or sufficient condition for "triangle ABC is equilateral"? Is it both necessary and sufficient?

18. Find some examples of invalid arguments in your outside reading.

6. INDUCTIVE LOGIC AND EXPERIMENTAL SCIENCE

Inductive logic is the name which is given to the process of coming to a *probable* conclusion on the basis of (many) particular instances. It is thus an important weapon of experimental or empirical science and is used unconsciously in everyday life. None the less its conclusions are never certain but only more or less probable. For example, if a man performs repeatedly the simple experiment of throwing a pair of dice and he throws a total of seven 5 times in succession, we are only mildly surprised. But if he throws a total of seven 20 times in succession we form the tentative conclusion that these particular dice will always turn up with a total of seven; that is, they are loaded. However, this conclusion is not really certain, but only probable. It seems to become more probable if it happens 50 times in succession, so probable that many of us would act on the assumption of the truth of our conclusion. Nevertheless, it *may* not be true and we may merely have witnessed an unusual run of luck; there is nothing in the theory of probability that prevents it. We shall return to this topic in Chapter 13. Despite the importance of inductive logic in experimental science we shall refer to it seldom. Of central importance for mathematics is deductive logic with which we shall be principally concerned hereafter.

A **general statement** is one referring to *all* the members of some class of things; a **particular statement** refers only to *some* of the members of some class of things. It is commonly said that deductive reasoning obtains particular statements from universal or general statements while inductive reasoning obtains general statements from particular statements. Neither of these descriptions is appropriate, according to our definition of deductive reasoning. In deduction, one's conclusion may be general or particular. Furthermore, to deduce the particular conclusion "Socrates is mortal" from the general hypothesis "All men are mortal" one must have the additional particular hypothesis "Socrates is a man." Similarly, consider the so-called inductive argument in which we seem to get a general conclusion from a particular hypothesis:

Hypothesis. (*a*) In the 500 cases we tried, treatment *T* cured disease *D*.
Conclusion. Treatment *T* will always cure disease *D*.

This can be made valid by adding the general hypothesis (*b*) that whatever cured our 500 cases will be a cure for all cases of disease *D*. With this additional hypothesis, the argument becomes deductive and the conclusion is inescapable. Now this additional hypothesis is seldom asserted because it is seldom believed to be true. In fact, what many people refer to as induction is the assertion of this additional hypothesis. But if we are to distinguish between the logical question of whether our conclusion really follows from our hypothesis (*a*) and the psychological question of what is likely to convince the average mind, then we must emphasize that our conclusion is not valid unless we know that our 500 cases are really representative of all cases. Since this is seldom known, we usually say that our conclusion is more or less probable. What this means will be discussed further in Chapter 13. More complete discussions of these considerations will be found in the references at the end of the present chapter.

Instead of trying to distinguish between deductive and inductive logic according to whether the conclusion is general or particular, it is better to distinguish between them according to whether the conclusion is necessary or merely probable on the basis of the hypothesis. *The conclusion of an inductive argument is never more than probable. The conclusion of a deductive argument is inescapable if the hypothesis is granted.*

7. GEOMETRY

The first interest in geometry probably arose because of the social need for measurement of tracts of real estate, the problems of architecture, and the agricultural need for a calendar, which involves a knowledge of astronomy. We do not know with certainty how far back the beginnings of geometry go, but the Babylonians and Egyptians, from perhaps 3000 B.C. to about 500 B.C., certainly possessed some geometric knowledge and a remarkably good calendar. It is sometimes said that the river Nile is responsible for the beginnings of geometry. Certainly, the Nile overflowed periodically, and changed its shoreline. The Greek historian Herodotus (fifth century B.C.) conjectured that geometry originated because taxes on real estate in Egypt were paid in proportion to area, and, when the Nile's floods altered the shoreline, the neighboring estates had to be surveyed anew. In any case, while the Egyptian and Babylonian civilizations, long before the Greeks, had some information about geometry, they probably did not have the idea of logical proof. Their geometric theorems were largely unconnected assertions, each established by empirical observation, at least approximately.* During the seventh and sixth centuries B.C. commercial intercourse sprang up between Egypt and Greece, and with it came an interchange of ideas. Greek scholars, visiting Egypt, learned what the Egyptians knew and made important improvements. The statements of geometry were not regarded by the Greeks as unconnected propositions; rather, their purpose was to derive complex statements from simple ones and ultimately to derive all of them logically from the first few simple ones.

How did this important idea come into being? Let us try to blame this on the Nile as well. Imagine that the flooded Nile has erased the boundary lines between neighboring farms and that Brown and Jones are two

* Some of their formulas were erroneous. Much of our knowledge of Egyptian mathematics comes from the Rhind papyrus written by Ahmes some time before 1700 B.C. and having the somewhat ambitious title: "Directions for obtaining the Knowledge of all Dark Things."

Egyptian farmers who, since human nature was probably not very different then, are arguing about the boundary line between the farms. There is a rock at A on the river bank and the boundary is supposed to be at right angles to the bank at A. Brown claims AB is the boundary and Jones holds out for AC. How are they to resolve the dispute? A first method would be for one to kill the other and occupy both farms. This method, while fashionable among great nations, does not seem fair when applied to individuals. A second method would be to apply to the King or the High Priest for an arbitrary ruling. (This method resembles an attempt once said to have been made in the legislature of one of the states in the U.S.A. to make the value of π exactly 3 in that state.) Both of these methods doubtless enjoyed great prestige in the past and to a slightly lower degree still do today, but they do not satisfy a reflective person. Therefore, Brown and Jones try to come to some common agreement as to where the perpendicular goes.

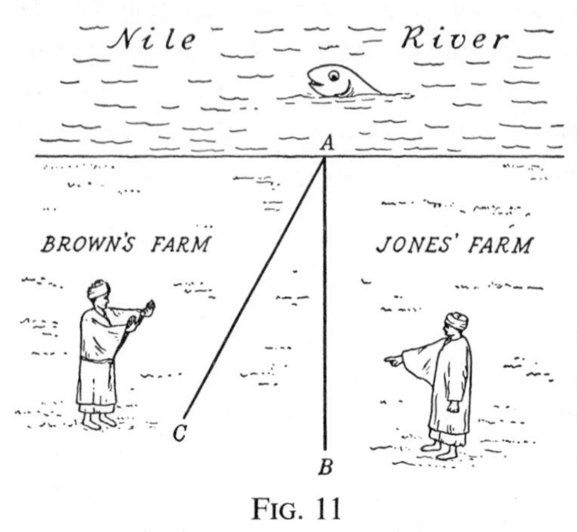

FIG. 11

Jones' argument runs something like this: "The boundary is AC because I well remember that in the middle of that lake of mud, exactly at C, there used to be a bush beside which my favorite dog used to sleep, and I am ten years older than you, and, even if you did go to school in Alexandria, I've never yet admitted that anyone's judgment was as good as mine, and I'm not going to begin at my time of life, by Isis!"

Brown's argument is that if you take a rope with knots at equal intervals, and stretch it taut about three stakes so that the opposite sides contain 3, 4, and 5 intervals, respectively, then the angle opposite the longest side has to be a right angle (this was probably known to the Egyptian surveyors, who were called "rope-stretchers"); and he had done this and found the boundary to be AB.

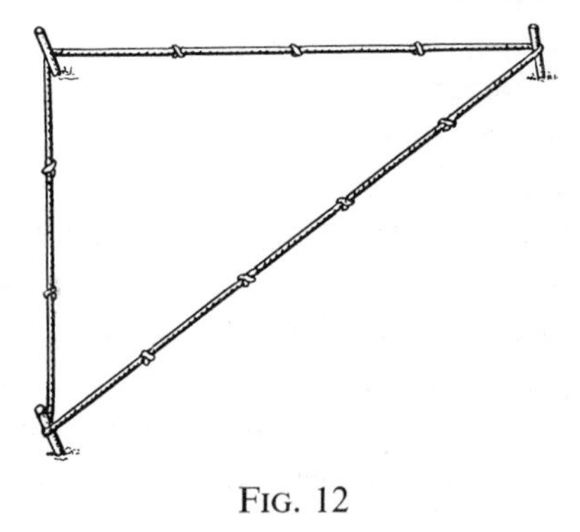
FIG. 12

The following dialogue then takes place.

Jones: I don't believe that 3–4–5 hocus-pocus.

Brown: Do you believe that *if the lengths x, y, and z of the three sides of a triangle satisfy the equation* $x^2 + y^2 = z^2$, *then the angle opposite side z is a right angle*?*

Jones: If that were true, your 3–4–5 rope trick would be correct, since $3^2 + 4^2 = 5^2$, and you would win the argument; so I don't believe it.

Brown: Do you believe (*the Pythagorean theorem*)† that *if x, y, z are the lengths of the sides of a right triangle, z being opposite the right angle, then* $x^2 + y^2 = z^2$?

Jones: That sounds too much like the previous statement. I don't believe it.

Brown: Do you believe that *if two triangles are similar,*‡ *then their sides are in proportion*?

Jones: If it gives you that land, I don't believe it!

Brown, seeing what he has to contend with, takes a breath and begins again.

Brown: Do you believe that through two points, one and only one line can be drawn?

Jones: Certainly, but what has that to do with the case?

Brown: Do you believe that if equals are added to equals, the results are equal?

Jones: Of course. But keep to the subject of this boundary—I'm a busy man.

However, Brown continues asking Jones whether he believes certain simple statements which happen to be axioms or postulates on page 1 of the geometry book which Brown had studied. Jones, impatient, and still failing to see any way in which those statements can cause him to lose the argument, admits that he believes them all. Thereupon, Brown proceeds to prove, step by step, on the basis of these axioms, and with inexorable logic, that the converse of the Pythagorean theorem is valid and therefore that the rope-stretching trick is legitimate, and the disputed land is his.

Now, this tall story is not accurate history, but it illustrates how the notion of proving a large body of statements on the basis of a few admitted statements might have arisen from the necessity for common agreement in very mundane, practical problems. On the other hand, it might be due chiefly to the unusually logical bent of the Greek philosophers.§ This important idea of deducing large

* This is the converse of the Pythagorean theorem which you learned in school. You probably never proved this one yourself, but it can be deduced from the Pythagorean theorem as follows. Construct a right triangle the lengths of whose legs are x and y. Then its hypotenuse is equal to z by the Pythagorean theorem. Hence the second triangle is congruent to the given one since 3 sides of one are equal respectively to 3 sides of the other. Therefore the given triangle is also a right triangle.

† The Pythagorean theorem should be memorized. It is one of the most important theorems in elementary geometry.

‡ Two triangles are called *similar* if the angles of one are respectively equal to the angles of the other.

§ Recent historical researches, especially of O. Neugebauer, indicate that the predecessors of the Greeks in Egypt and Babylon knew more than was hitherto suspected. Cf. O. Neugebauer, *Vorgriechische Mathematik*, Springer, Berlin, 1934.

numbers of statements from a few simple assumptions probably grew slowly in the consciousness of the human race; it seems unlikely that it could have sprung full-grown from the brain of one man, although Thales (seventh–sixth centuries B.C.), one of the first of the great Greek mathematicians, is sometimes given credit for it. The earliest great written example extant of such extensively organized deductive thought is Euclid's *Elements* (about 300 B.C.), the work on which your high school geometry text was based. Euclid's *Elements* has long been regarded as representative of one of the outstanding achievements of the human mind, Greek geometry; but its full significance was probably not grasped until the nineteenth century. Euclid's chief contribution did not consist of the discovery of new theorems but in showing that all known theorems were logical consequences of a few assumptions.

Several practical advantages are derived from the deductive organization of geometry. For example, one might stare at right triangles for ages without perceiving the relation $x^2 + y^2 = z^2$ of the Pythagorean theorem; it is hardly self-evident. But having deduced it from simple assumptions one sees without effort that if the assumptions are true, so is the Pythagorean theorem. Thus instead of having to question the truth of hundreds of theorems separately, the question of their truth is made to depend on the truth of a few simple assumptions. In the other direction, one can deduce from theorems already in existence new, unsuspected theorems which might never have been found out by experimental observation. It is worth noting that Greek geometry, which aimed at understanding the logical interdependence of its statements, proved to be far more useful than, say, Egyptian geometry which aimed at being useful and nothing more.

8. PURE AND APPLIED MATHEMATICS

In this section we shall discuss two of the most basic terms in the entire book, namely *abstract mathematical science* and *concrete interpretation* or *application*. In terms of these two concepts we shall define *pure mathematics* and *applied mathematics*.

Notice that when logical structure is introduced into geometry, it is necessary to allow some of the statements to remain unproved (that is, not deduced from other statements), in order to have something to start with. Thus theorem 20 may be proved by showing that it follows logically from theorem 19; you then know that theorem 20 is true if theorem 19 is true. Similarly, you may deduce theorem 19 from theorem 18, and so on. Sooner or later you must stop and take some statements without proof, because we do not live forever. If you try to prove all your statements, you will necessarily commit the unpardonable sin of "circularity." That is, if you say that statement A is true because it follows from B and B is true, and then you assert that B is true because it follows from A and A is true, you are using circular reasoning. Putting your two steps together, you have said in effect that A is true because A is true. This is the mode of reasoning used by children who stamp their feet and shriek "It's so because it's so." If the truth of A is to be established by showing that A follows from B, then we cannot also establish the truth of B by showing that it follows from A. Hence, the entire structure of geometry must rest on some *unproved statements* called **axioms, assumptions,** or **postulates.**

Example. A king issues a proclamation saying that he is infallible. When asked to justify the truth of this statement, he answers that whatever he says must be true since the proclamation says that he is infallible. This reasoning is circular.

Now, the statements of geometry involve certain terms, such as "triangle." If we ask what this term means, we might define "triangle" in terms of other terms; thus we might say that a "triangle" is the set of all points lying on the line-segments joining three points which are not on the same (straight) line. This defines "triangle" in terms of the terms "point," "line-segment," etc. If we ask what these other terms mean, we might define them, in turn, in terms of still other terms; thus we might say that a "line-segment" is the set of all points lying between two given points. This defines "line-segment" in terms of "point," "between," etc. Sooner or later, this process of definition, like the process of proof, must stop. Clearly, we cannot define *all* our terms unless we fall into the trap of "circularity." We must use some terms without definitions, while all other terms may be defined ultimately in terms of these **undefined terms.** That is, all our definitions must involve some terms which are taken without definition.

Remark 1. The dictionary apparently defines all words. But it must therefore use circular definitions. For example, if you look up the word "insane", it might say that "insane" means "crazy"; but if you look up "crazy," you might find that "crazy" is defined to mean "insane." Together these definitions inform you that "insane" means "insane." This situation is inevitable, as we have seen above, if you try to define all your terms.

For example, to define what we mean by saying that two rods "have the same length," we might say that this is so if one can be moved so as to coincide with the other. But if they were made of rubber, they could be made to coincide in any case. Hence we might go further and say that the two rods have the same length if one can be "moved rigidly" so as to coincide with the other. But how shall we define "moved rigidly"? We usually say that a rod is "moved rigidly" if it is moved in such a way that its "length" remains unchanged. We are saying, in effect, that two rods have the same length if one can be moved so as to coincide with the other in such a way that it has the same length at all times during the motion. This is clearly a circular definition.

Remark 2. A definition, in mathematical usage, is simply an agreement to regard one expression (symbol or set of symbols such as a word or a phrase) as being *equivalent* to another (usually more complicated) expression. The expression defined can always be substituted for its definition, and vice versa, in any context whatever without introducing any distortion or vagueness of meaning (although it may well introduce grammatical awkwardness). A definition, in this sense, should be distinguished from a (partial) description. Many dictionary "definitions" are merely descriptions. For example, we have *defined* a triangle above. But the statement, "a triangle is a figure extensively studied by mathematicians" is a *description.*

Bertrand Russell once* described mathematics as "the subject in which we never know what we are talking about nor whether what we are saying is true." Many students heartily agree with this, in a mood of personal confession. But it is correct literally. We never know what we are talking about since all our definitions rest ultimately on some undefined terms; we never know whether what we are saying is true because all our proofs rest ultimately on some meaningless unproved statements or assumptions involving these undefined terms. Moreover, this situation must come about if you take any subject and try to give it a logical structure. Suppose you assert any proposition in economics, say, and you are asked to prove it. You may prove it by deducing it from other propositions. If these are challenged in turn, you may prove them on the basis of still other statements. Ultimately, however, you are forced to stop and base the whole thing on some unproved propositions or postulates. Similarly, if you are asked what a word means, you will ultimately be driven to rest all your definitions on some undefined terms. When you have done both these things you have made an *abstract mathematical science*, or *deductive science*, or *abstract logical system*, of your subject. That is, an **abstract mathematical science** is a collection of statements beginning with some unproved statements or postulates (hypotheses) involving some undefined terms (basic terms), in which all further statements follow logically from the postulates and all new terms are defined in terms of the undefined ones. Reasoning from postulates in this way is sometimes called **postulational thinking**.

You may ask, "How can we reason about undefined terms? What do we know about them if they have no meaning?" The answer is simple and important. *We know about these undefined terms exactly what we have assumed about them in our postulates, or unproved statements, no more and no less.* In fact we

* *International Monthly*, Vol. 4, 1901, p. 84.

must be careful not to use subconsciously anything that we have not explicitly stated in our postulates. That we can reason about such things is not strange at all. We have already done it in example 1, section 5, which may be considered as a miniature abstract mathematical science, as follows.

Example 1. Let the undefined terms be x, y, z. Let us assume two postulates.

Postulate 1. *All x's are y's.*

Postulate 2. *All y's are z's.*

Theorem 1. *All x's are z's.*

We have here an abstract mathematical science with three undefined terms, two postulates, and one theorem.

Example 2. Let the undefined terms be x, y, z, and w.

Postulate 1. *All x's are y's.*

Postulate 2. *Some x's are z's.*

Postulate 3. *All y's are w's.*

Theorem 1. *Some y's are z's.*

Definition 1. *Any y which is also a z will be called a "v."*

Theorem 2. *Some w's are v's.*

This is an abstract mathematical science with four undefined terms, three postulates, one definition, and two theorems. It is decidedly a miniature abstract mathematical science, but it exhibits all the characteristics of an abstract mathematical science. It begins with undefined terms and unproved postulates; but, thereafter, all new statements are logical consequences of previous statements and all new terms, like the term "v," are defined in terms of previously used terms.

In plane geometry "point," "line," and others, are often taken as undefined terms, and statements like the following are often taken as unproved statements or postulates.

Postulate 1. *Given any two distinct points, there is at least one line containing them.*

Postulate 2. *Given any two distinct points, there is at most one line containing them.*

These two postulates are usually stated together, in high school texts on geometry, as follows: given two distinct points, there is exactly one line containing them, or, two points determine a line.

Definition. *If two lines in the same plane have no point in common they are called* ***parallel.***

Postulate 3. *Given a line l and a point P not on l, there exists one and only one line l' containing P and parallel to l.*

This is called the *Euclidean parallel postulate.**

Many other postulates and undefined terms, which we shall not list here, are taken at the start of geometry. On the basis of these postulates we can deduce all the theorems of geometry by pure deductive logic.

Geometry consists of the logical consequences of a set of unproved statements involving certain undefined terms. Since we are using "point" and "line" as undefined terms, we might have changed the words "point" and "line" to "mumbo" and "jumbo" respectively, and written postulate 1 as: "given any two distinct mumbos, there is at least one jumbo containing them." Or we might have written "point" and "line" as x and y, respectively; then postulate 1 would become "given any two distinct x's, there is at least one y containing them." This cannot affect the validity of the reasoning in our proofs. Geometry, like any other abstract mathematical science, is an example of abstract reasoning, where we reason about undefined terms on the basis of unproved statements. The postulates now constitute our hypothesis and all the theorems constitute our conclusion.

You may fairly ask, "In what sense can this meaningless game, this thoughtless thinking, this mumbo-jumbo, be true? How can it have any bearing on the real world?" The answer, honest and simple, is that such an abstract mathematical science can never tell you that your conclusions are *true* but asserts only that certain logical arguments are *valid.* It says merely that the theorems are logical consequences of the postulates or assumptions. Every mathematical statement is of the form "A implies B." This means that *if* A is true, *then* B must also be true. If we can find *meanings* or *concrete interpretations* for the undefined terms which will make the assumptions become *true* when these

* Postulate 3 was not literally the parallel postulate made by Euclid but is known to be an equivalent replacement for it.

meanings are substituted for the undefined terms, then all the rest of the theorems must automatically become true statements about these meanings. For example, if we could find objects in the real world which have the properties demanded of "points" and "lines" (or mumbos and jumbos) in our postulates for geometry, we would then know that all our theorems are true statements about these objects.

When meanings are given to the undefined terms of an abstract mathematical science, we have a **concrete interpretation** or **application** or **realization** of the abstract science. The meanings assigned to the undefined terms may be understood intuitively or by means of partial descriptions, etc. If the meanings assigned to the undefined terms are such that the postulates become true statements when these meanings are substituted for the undefined terms, then all the theorems become true statements about these meanings, automatically, since the theorems are logical consequences of the postulates. The abstract mathematical science remains valid, however, whether such a concrete interpretation can be found for it or not.

Example 3. In example 1, page 27, we may convert our abstract science into a concrete interpretation by assigning the following concrete meanings to our undefined terms: let $x =$ man, $y =$ mortal, $z =$ fool.

Remark 3. An abstract mathematical science is a body of logically connected propositional functions, while a concrete interpretation is a body of logically connected propositions (see section 5). We may speak of the validity of an abstract mathematical science but not of its truth. The question of truth arises only in connection with concrete interpretations or applications.

Exercise. Can there be different concrete interpretations or applications of the same abstract mathematical science? Illustrate using (a) example 1, page 27; (b) example 2, page 27.

The totality of all abstract mathematical sciences is called **pure mathematics.** The totality of their concrete interpretations or applications is called **applied mathematics. Mathematics** comprises both pure and applied mathematics.

We must distinguish,* for example, between geometry as a branch of pure mathematics and geometry as a branch of applied mathematics, applied to the "real world." It is in this latter sense that you have probably thought of geometry up to now. You have thought of points and lines, for example, as being the dots and streaks you draw on paper, and you may have thought of

* This distinction was not clearly grasped by the ancient Greeks who seem to have perceived the need for unproved postulates but not for undefined terms.

the axioms of geometry as self-evident truths. In geometry, as an abstract mathematical science, point and line are undefined terms. If we think of these terms as having the concrete meanings "dot" and "streak," we are dealing with a concrete interpretation of this abstract mathematical science. With this interpretation, our postulates are certainly not satisfied except approximately. For no matter how small you make the dots or how thin you make the streaks, they are very large smudges viewed under a magnifying glass, and, for example, many streaks can be drawn through two dots, contrary to postulate 2 (Fig. 13). It is only in an approximate sense that you can imagine that the postulates seem to be satisfied. Of course, for practical work, a good approximation is all that is needed because no measurement can ever be exact, since our senses and measuring instruments yield only approximate measurements. This concrete interpretation does seem to work well for our practical sciences, and as long as it does we may make use of it. However, as pure mathematicians, we do not say that our postulates are self-evident truths (although this was said until the nineteenth century). We say only that if the postulates *were* satisfied, that is, converted into true statements, by any interpretation of the undefined terms, the theorems *would be true*, too.

FIG. 13

In any concrete interpretation of an abstract mathematical science, we hope that the assumptions are true. We may indeed verify their truth approximately by observation, or we may feel that they are probably true, for one reason or another, but certainty concerning their absolute truth is often an unattainable ideal so far as science is concerned.

As for the view that our postulates are self-evident truths one may well ask, "Self-evident to whom?" It is notorious that what seems self-evidently true to one person may seem doubtful or false to another. If one says that we mean self-evident to a sufficiently large jury of competent people, we have only to reply that history is strewn with abandoned ideas which were once considered self-evident for intuitive or other reasons. For example: "the earth is flat"; "the heavenly bodies travel around the earth"; "the orbits of the planets around the sun are circles"; "every surface has two sides" (Fig. 14); "a heavier body will fall faster than a lighter one." This last statement was asserted by Aristotle (fourth century B.C.) and therefore believed by everyone until, according to some historians, Galileo (1564–1642) cast doubt upon it by actually dropping two bodies from a tower. They fell simultaneously.

In fact, even in ancient times *one* of the postulates of geometry (our postulate 3, the so-called Euclidean parallel postulate) was not considered as self-evident as the others. This fortunate circumstance led to the invention of non-Euclidean

(a)

TWO-SIDED SURFACE

The spider cannot reach the fly without crossing the boundary. The surface has two sides and two edges.

ONE-SIDED SURFACE

The fly is not safe on this surface, which has only one side and one boundary edge.

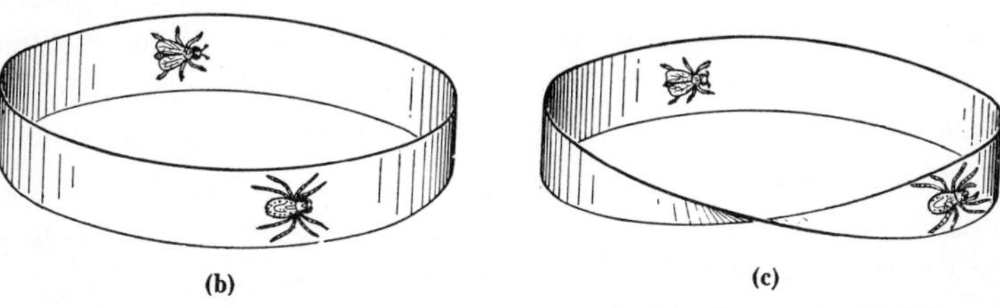

(b) (c)

The surface (b) is made from the rectangular strip (a) of paper *ACDF* by matching *A* with *F*, *B* with *E*, and *C* with *D*, and pasting. The surface (c) is made by twisting one end of the strip (a) through one half-revolution (180°) and matching *A* with *D*, *B* with *E*, and *C* with *F*, and pasting. The line *BE* is to be midway between *CD* and *AF*.

After the surface (c) has been made, try cutting it along the middle line *BE*. Then cut the resulting surface again along a line midway between *its* edges. Anyone who can guess what the resulting surface will look like has a far better intuition than most. Try it again, from the beginning, this time cutting along a line 1/3 of the width away from the edge.

FIG. 14

geometries (in the nineteenth century) whose study contributed greatly to the understanding of the nature of pure mathematics and its application to the real world. We shall return to this subject in Chapter 17.

The notion of mathematics as the totality of all abstract mathematical sciences and their concrete interpretations or applications is a broad conception, far transcending the old definition of mathematics as the science of space and quantity. In fact, it includes all subjects in which we reason logically and amply justifies the assertion that mathematics is basic to all sciences. You may be reluctant to accept this strange meaning of the word "mathematics." In fact, mathematicians accepted it with reluctance only toward the end of the nineteenth century when the development of modern mathematics forced this view on them.

We have seen that to construct an abstract mathematical science you have only to take a few undefined terms, assume a few compatible statements involving them, perhaps also define other terms in terms of them, and deduce all the logical consequences we can. But what undefined terms and assumptions shall we choose to start with, and, having chosen them, to which of the many possible logical consequences shall we give our attention, and what new terms shall we define? And even if we do decide all this, how, you may ask, can grown men waste their time on such empty games? You are partly right. Mathematicians are not much interested in an abstract mathematical science, except perhaps as a mental exercise, unless it shows promise of having interesting concrete interpretations or applications. By and large, we choose to work with certain postulates, definitions, etc., instead of others, because of the concrete interpretations or applications we have in mind for them. *The assumptions and terms we choose to work with and the theorems we try to prove are often suggested by experience.* For example, they might be probable conclusions obtained by induction or they might seem to be self-evident facts. Or, their invention may be due to creative imagination, insight, or intuition. However, censorship should not be too strict. It would be a great mistake to restrict scientific research to those things for which we can find an immediate use. History has shown us many times that pure mathematics, worked out originally for its own sake, has found unsuspected applications many years later. For example, Riemann's ideas on geometry, developed early in the nineteenth century for their own sake, were applied to the physical theory of relativity by Einstein in the twentieth century. Similarly, group theory, a branch of algebra developed largely in the nineteenth century with no thought of physical applications, is now used extensively in quantum physics. To cite an extreme case, certain curves, called conic sections, were studied by the ancient Greeks with no thought of application; they became of central importance in physical science about 1800 years later.

To summarize, an abstract mathematical science is constructed by selecting some undefined terms, some unproved postulates or assumptions involving these terms, and then defining new terms and proving new statements or theorems. If we give concrete meanings to the undefined terms, we obtain a concrete interpretation or application of the abstract science. If we knew that, for these meanings, the postulates become true statements then we would know automatically that the theorems must also be true for this interpretation. But usually we are uncertain as to the truth of our postulates when they are interpreted concretely. For example, the notion that the postulates of geometry, interpreted concretely, are self-evident truths has been seen to be untenable. Reasoning from postulates is called postulational thinking. The totality of all abstract mathematical sciences is called pure mathematics, and the totality of all concrete interpretations is called applied mathematics. Together they constitute mathematics. We have seen that, in this broad sense, mathematics includes every subject in which you try to be logical. For if you wish to prove a statement in any subject, you prove it by deducing it from other statements, and these in turn are either assumed or deduced from still other statements, and so on. Ultimately, if we are to avoid circular reasoning, the entire subject must be rested on some unproved statements or postulates. Similarly, if we define a word it is defined in terms of other terms, and so on. Ultimately, all our terms are expressible in terms of some which are left undefined, unless we fall into the trap of circular definition. When all this is done our subject has become a part of mathematics, according to our definition of mathematics.

We shall return to the ideas of abstract mathematical science and concrete interpretation many times in the remainder of the book and shall see many illustrations of these ideas, especially in Chapter 18.

9. POSTULATIONAL THINKING AND SCIENTIFIC THEORIES. MODELS

We can now touch briefly on some aspects of the nature of scientific theories which often puzzle the layman. For example, how does it happen that Newton's theory of gravitation is discarded after being regarded as "true" for over 200 years? Newton's theory of gravitation can be regarded as an abstract logical system or abstract mathematical science, one of whose postulates, for example, is the so-called first law* of motion: "Every body continues in its state of rest or of uniform motion in a straight line unless it is compelled to change that state by a force impressed upon it." From these postulates one may deduce logically a number of theorems which, when the undefined terms are interpreted in an obvious way, state how baseballs, bombs, planets, and pendulums should move. It may then be possible to verify some of these theorems (approximately) by empirical or experimental observation within the limits of reasonable error. But the postulates themselves usually cannot be verified by direct observation and are thus not self-evident.† For instance, heavenly bodies which are really at rest or in uniform motion in a straight line with respect to each other are entirely outside our experience. The chair on which you are sitting, for example, is undergoing a complicated motion, relative to the sun, resulting from the rotation of the earth on its axis, the revolution of the earth about the sun, etc. Hence we have the logical situation "A implies B and B is true," A being the postulates and B the experimentally verified theorems. But as we saw in section 4,

* The word "law" is often used indiscriminately, in scientific writing, to refer to a postulate, theorem, definition, or a probable truth obtained experimentally.

† Even if they could be regarded as approximately verifiable truths for small billiard balls on a table, it would still be quite a jump to assume that they therefore hold for planets, etc.

this does not mean that A is necessarily true. It is, however, a good working hypothesis and may be used as long as it produces correct predictions.

In fact, we might well get the same theorems from different assumptions. Thus it should not surprise us to find two or more theories which "explain" observed phenomena equally well; for example, there were for some time two rival theories of light, the corpuscular and the wave theories. Nobody had ever seen a light corpuscle or a light wave directly. But assuming that one of the other of these things exists and has certain properties, one can deduce the experimentally verifiable behavior of light. As long as both systems continued to fit the facts equally well, one theory was as good an "explanation" as the other.

However, should an observable phenomenon occur which contradicts one of our deduced theorems, we then have the logical situation A implies B and B is false; hence A must be false. Therefore, we must abandon or modify our abstract system by changing the postulates. If we do this well and arrive at a new abstract logical system which fits not only the old observed facts but the new troublesome facts as well, then we say that we have a better theory than before. This is what happened at the beginning of the twentieth century, for example, when observed facts turned up which did not fit Newton's theory of gravitation. The orbit of the planet Mercury* did not behave as predicted by Newton's theory; and the discrepancy was greater than could be attributed to observational error. There was little use in attempting to persuade the planet Mercury to get back to its course. Although Newton's theory had fitted all the facts for over 200 years, there was nothing to do but change it since we cannot change or ignore the facts. This was done in a remarkable way by Einstein whose new theory fitted the new facts as well as the old.† If new facts were to turn up which did not fit into Einstein's theory, it, too, would have to be abandoned or changed. Similarly, "models" of the interior of an atom are hypotheses which are abandoned as soon as their logical consequences no longer fit the facts.

A striking explanation of the postulational nature of scientific theories is given in the following quotation from *The Evolution of Physics* by A. Einstein and L. Infeld: "In our endeavor to understand reality we are somewhat like a man trying to understand the mechanism of a closed watch. He sees the face and the moving hands, even hears its ticking, but he has no way of opening the case. If he is ingenious he may form some picture of a mechanism which could be responsible for all the things he observes, but he may never be quite sure his picture is the only one which could explain his observations."

* Among other things.

† The discrepancies between Newton's theory and Einstein's are too small to be observed except in connection with extremely large distances or speeds or with atomic phenomena. Hence, for the moderate magnitudes commonly used, we still prefer the simpler theory of Newton.

But neither the question of whether the mechanism, which he has supposed hypothetically to be inside the case, is *really* there, nor even the interesting philosophical question of whether he may be sure that there is anything at all inside the case, need trouble the practical scientist as long as he has a theory which enables him to predict successfully the phenomena which can be observed.

Remark 1. We have said that our hypotheses or postulates are usually suggested by observation. Some people are fond of saying that observed facts are *all* that matter and they use the word "theory" in a derogatory sense, saying, "Oh, that's only a theory." It is worth remarking that observation or empirical science cannot be wholly free from "theoretical" hypotheses. Experiment is always guided by theory. For even in collecting facts, we must have some hypothesis as to which facts are relevant to the investigation in hand, since we can hardly amass all the facts in the universe. In fact, we often do not trust our direct observations but rather correct them because of theoretical considerations. As Poincaré said, "A collection of facts is no more a science than a heap of stones is a house." The facts must be organized into a logical structure before they constitute a science.

We shall return to these ideas again when we have more mathematical background. Let us emphasize once more that postulational thinking is available for and indeed essential to a completely logical study of any subject matter. However, many books, which pretend to be logical, outside of the so-called mathematical sciences, will not bear critical examination from the point of view of postulational thinking. For instance, in reading a book on some social question, it would be a great comfort to know what underlying assumptions the author wants you to take for granted. There must be some, if he intends to prove anything logically. But he seldom tells you the basis for his "reasoning." In fact, if you try to imagine what his assumptions might be, in order to justify his conclusions, you are likely to find that one set of assumptions is needed on one page and an entirely different set on the next. Likewise, the meanings of his terms are likely to change from page to page.

Of course when we say that any logically organized subject "begins" with postulates and undefined terms, we mean "begins" in the logical, not the chronological, sense. Historically, every science has begun somewhere in its logical middle. It usually begins with observations pertaining to some limited aspects of reality. Then it is noticed that some of these observed statements are logical consequences of others. After attempts to organize these statements deductively, someone conjectures hypotheses which would imply conclusions corresponding to these observations. The resulting logically organized body of statements is an abstract mathematical science which is often called a **mathematical model** of the portion of reality with which this particular science is concerned. It may happen that these hypotheses imply other conclusions that may be checked against observation. If some of these do not check, then we must abandon or modify our hypotheses; that is, we try to imagine a new set of postulates whose implications will check with experience when interpreted in some concrete way. Thus empirical science poses problems to pure mathematical science. On the other hand, pure mathematical science deduces theorems logically which have to be tested experimentally by empirical science. That is, deduction may suggest crucial experiments to be performed in the laboratory; and laboratory observations may suggest programs of deductive thought involving the formation and study of various mathematical models. The two play mutually helpful and complementary roles.

Complete* logical organization, such as has been achieved in geometry, for example, is the final stage in the development of a science. If you say that it is extremely difficult to apply such standards of logical rigor to, say, the social sciences, because they are more complex than elementary mathematics, we must agree that it is difficult. It was also difficult to introduce successful logical theories into the apparent chaos of astronomy but it has been done with remarkable success in the course of many years of concentrated and painstaking effort. Today, chemistry and biology are beginning to emerge from their early stages of development and are taking shape as genuine logical systems. Small beginnings are being made in this direction in such subjects as psychology and economics, which are, compared to physics and mathematics, in their early infancy.

Briefly, the goal of science is to find assumptions, the fewer and simpler the better, whose logical consequences correspond with experience. Thus the first attempts to "explain" physical phenomena were mythologies. If each observed phenomenon is "explained" by saying that it is due to the whim of spirits, there is no way to disprove this theory. But it is a useless theory since it does not enable you to predict future phenomena. It should also be noted that the goal of finding a few simple assumptions whose logical consequences account for *all* experience of reality is very far from attainable in the foreseeable future, since reality appears to be far too complicated. In practice, the mathematical models actually found useful by scientists are of limited scope and applicability, and a model or abstract mathematical science useful for one purpose may not be useful for another. Thus, for the purpose of predicting the motions of the earth around the sun, it is useful to replace the actual earth by a particle, or single point, having the mass of the earth concentrated in it. This model of the earth as a particle, or

* According to present standards. This should be understood whenever the expression "completely logical" is used.

mass-point, would be, of course, ludicrously useless for the purpose of navigating ships on the ocean. For the latter purpose, we use a model in which the earth is replaced by a perfect sphere. This model in turn would be a poor one for land or air travel since it ignores such irregularities in the surface of the earth as mountain ranges. However, a model taking account of such details would be too complicated for the first purpose of calculating the motions of the earth around the sun. Thus we use different models, isolating and abstracting from various aspects of reality, for different purposes. Even if a model does not encompass all truth, it is valuable if it provides useful predictions for some limited aspects of reality. Since reality appears to be too complicated to be dealt with in its entirety, science has become useful only by studying such limited models.

Remark 2. In making a concrete interpretation or application to the real world, it seems highly desirable to ascribe meaning to an undefined term by a complete description of the operations used to determine it in practice. Thus, to define distance as applied to the distance across your back yard, you might describe the operations involved in stretching and reading a tape measure. But clearly, these operations cannot be used to define distance from the Earth to a star. Thus, distance across your back yard and distance from the Earth to a star do not have the same operational meaning. Concentration on the operational meanings of terms used in applied science can be illuminating. It is especially important not to indulge too lightly in the use of terms having no operational meanings. For an excellent and extensive discussion of this point of view, see P. W. Bridgman, *The Logic of Modern Physics*.

It must not be supposed that anything said here detracts from the great achievements of science. On the contrary, it should help you to appreciate the remarkable success of scientists in finding postulates whose logical consequences correspond with the varied observations of experience in so many diverse directions; that is, in finding abstract mathematical sciences or mathematical models whose concrete interpretations correspond closely with observation. If little has been said here about the details of these scientific achievements, it is partly because of lack of space and partly because it is assumed that you are at least vaguely familiar with them. Therefore we have concentrated on explaining the postulational nature of science, which you may never have understood.

In any case, an understanding of the nature of abstract postulational thinking and its concrete applications, and of truth and validity, should help us in being critical of our beliefs and in finding out the assumptions and reasoning on which our beliefs rest. It should make us less dogmatic and more tolerant, since it destroys the assurance, that some of us have, that we know with certainty the true answers and the only true answers to all questions.

10. GENERALITY AND ABSTRACTNESS

In arithmetic one begins by counting apples or oranges. The importance of the abstract "number" comes into play when one realizes that three apples, three oranges, or three objects of any nature whatever have some abstract property in common, the number three. Thus instead of making the particular statement that two apples plus one apple make three apples, one prefers the general abstract statement $2 + 1 = 3$.

Later on, one observes that $9 - 4 = 5 \cdot 1$ or $3^2 - 2^2 = (3 + 2)(3 - 2)$, and $16 - 4 = 6 \cdot 2$ or $4^2 - 2^2 = (4 + 2)(4 - 2)$, and $25 - 4 = 7 \cdot 3$ or $5^2 - 2^2 = (5 + 2)(5 - 2)$. The mathematician naturally prefers the general statement $x^2 - 4 = (x + 2)(x - 2)$ which holds for *all* numbers x, instead of the particular statements about individual numbers made above. As a matter of fact, one prefers still more the general statement $x^2 - y^2 = (x + y)(x - y)$ which holds for *all* numbers x and *all* numbers y.

Similarly, in geometry one prefers the general statement that "the area of every rectangle is equal to its base multiplied by its altitude," instead of any particular statement such as "the area of a rectangle whose base is 2 inches and altitude 3 inches is 6 square inches."

At a much higher level, whole abstract theories containing hundreds of complicated theorems frequently may be made to apply bodily to several different concrete subject matters by merely re-interpreting the undefined terms in different concrete ways. Thus in discovering one new theorem in the abstract science, one obtains simultaneously new results in all the different concrete interpretations of it. This great economy of thought is one of the reasons for the importance of abstract or pure mathematics.

In fact, this is characteristic of science in general. The scientist does not want to have to invent a separate explanation for each individual phenomenon. He much prefers to find a general law that will explain all of a large class of phenomena. No two phenomena can ever be exactly alike since they differ at least in time or place. Hence generality can be obtained only by abstracting from the phenomena some characteristics which they have in common, ignoring other characteristics. Similarly, in the beginnings of arithmetic one learns to ignore the color, taste, etc., of the three apples or three oranges and to consider only the common characteristic of number. The same situation arises in logic when one ignores the content of the statements in an argument and considers only their form (see section 5). Perceptiveness in the recognition of patterns of common features is needed for the discovery of scientific generalizations which are often discovered or suggested by observation or inductive reasoning.

Note carefully that in mathematics the word "generality" does not connote vagueness, as it sometimes does in everyday usage. Nor does "abstractness" imply having one's feet firmly planted on a cloud. A general result, in mathematics, always includes within it all the special results that may have suggested it. And an abstract statement yields, upon appropriate application to specific subject matter, all the concrete statements of which it is the prototype. It may help the student to understand the development and importance of mathematics if he grasps the significance of generality and abstractness. The desire to arrive at general statements about all of some class of things often actuates the mathematician and gives direction to his research.

Exercises

1. Explain the nature of (*a*) inductive logic; (*b*) deductive logic.

2. Is the conclusion of a valid argument always true? Explain the distinction between truth and validity.

3. Explain the nature of postulational thinking. What is an abstract mathematical science? a concrete interpretation? Define and discuss the relationship between pure and applied mathematics.

4. Explain the bearing of your answers to parts (*c*) and (*d*) of exercise 1, section 4, on the acceptance or rejection of scientific theories or hypotheses.

5. Make up examples of different hypotheses which imply the same conclusion.

11. THE LANGUAGE OF SETS

In the next two sections, we shall discuss some concepts and symbolic notations which will permeate the rest of the book and which are basic to much of modern mathematics.

The word **set** will be understood intuitively as a synonym for collection, assemblage, or class of objects. The objects of which a set is composed are called its **elements** or **members**.

Let us begin by considering any definite *collection* or *set* or *class* of objects. For example, (1) a class of four people: Smith, Jones, Brown, and Robinson; or, (2) the set of all people in New York City; or, (3) the set of all points on a given page; or, (4) a set of chessmen.

*Whatever set we choose to consider, let that be the basic set from here on.** The basic set is also called the **universal set** or **universe of discourse**.

We consider hereafter only sets of objects chosen from the basic collection.

* The diagrams will be most easily interpreted as referring to the basic collection (3) of all points on a given page.

Thus if the first example above is our basic set, a class consisting of Smith and Robinson is a set; the class consisting of Jones and Smith is a different set. If the second example above is our basic set, the set of people in New York 21 years of age is a set; the set of people in New York with blue eyes is a different set. If we take the third example as our basic set, the class of points within the curve in Fig. 15 is a set; the class of points outside the curve is a different set.

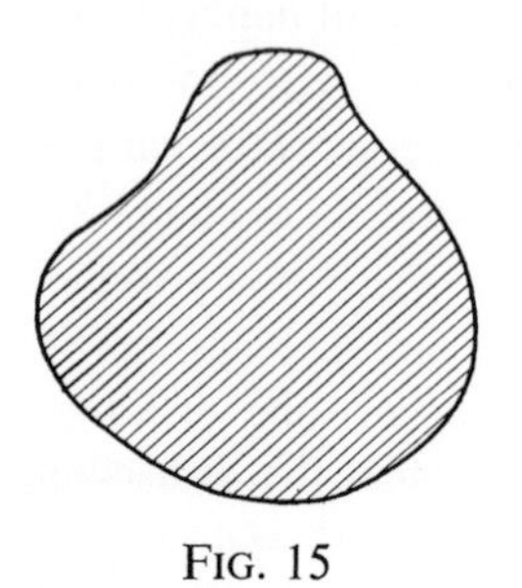

FIG. 15

It will be convenient to denote the universal set by the symbol I. This symbol is not to be confused with the number one—it simply means the entire basic collection of objects we are considering. It will also be convenient to consider the set which has no elements in it. For example, the set of people in New York who are more than 30 feet tall is a set with no elements. *This set is called the* **empty set** *and is denoted by the symbol* $\varnothing$. We conceive of just one empty set; it is a matter of indifference to us whether a set has no people in it or no dogs.

Sets will usually be denoted by capital letters, and their elements by small letters. If A is a set and x is one of its elements, we write $x \in A$, read "x is an element of A," or "x belongs to A," or "x is in A." Thus if A is the set (1) above and x stands for Smith, then $x \in A$.

Two sets A and B are called **equal** if and only if they have exactly the same elements or members; that is, if every element of A is an element of B and every element of B is an element of A.

By the **union** (sometimes, **logical sum**) of two sets we shall mean simply the set composed of all the elements belonging to one or the other or both of these two sets. For example, the union of the set consisting of Smith and Robinson and the set consisting of Jones and Smith will be the set consisting of Smith, Robinson, and Jones. If we denote sets by letters A, B, $\cdots$, we shall denote the union of two sets A and B by $A \cup B$. If A and B are the sets of points on the page (Fig. 16) which are shaded horizontally and vertically, respectively, then the set $A \cup B$ is the whole set of points shaded in any way.

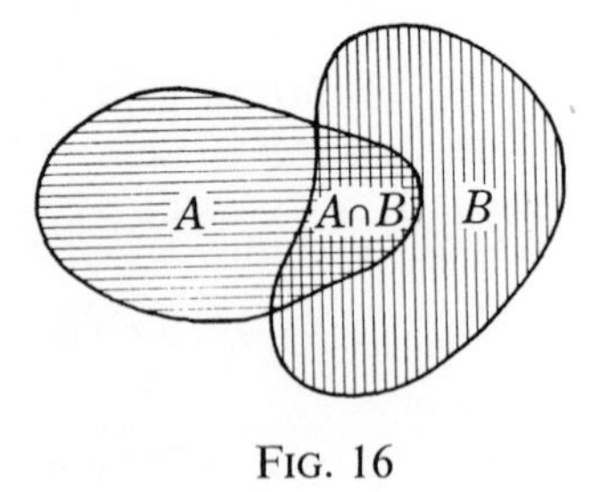

FIG. 16

By the **intersection** (sometimes, **logical product**) of two sets we shall mean the set composed of those elements which belong simultaneously to both of the given sets—that is, their common part. For example, the intersection of the set consisting of Smith and Jones and the set consisting of Smith and Robinson is the set consisting of Smith alone. If A and B are the horizontally and vertically shaded sets of points in Fig. 16, respectively, the intersection, denoted by $A \cap B$, will be the set which is shaded crosswise. The symbols $\cup$ and $\cap$ are called "cup" and "cap," respectively.

For example, suppose in our first illustrative basic set we denote by A the set consisting of Smith and Jones and by B the set consisting of Brown and Robinson. Then we may write $A \cup B = I$ because the union of these two sets is the entire basic set. We may also write $A \cap B = \varnothing$ because these two sets have no elements in common; that is, their intersection or common part is the empty set.

If every element of one set A is also an element of another set B, then A is said to **be contained within** B; we write $A \subset B$, or $B \supset A$ (read "A is contained in B" or "B contains A"), and A is said to be a **subset** of B and B is called a **superset** of A. In particular, every set A is a subset of itself, and the empty set $\varnothing$ is considered a subset of every set. For example, the set consisting of Smith and Jones is contained within the set consisting of Smith, Jones, and Brown. The assertion $A = B$ is equivalent to the pair of assertions $A \subset B$ and $B \subset A$.

If A is a subset of B and A is not equal to B then A is said to be a **proper** subset of B.

Two sets A and B are called **disjoint** if $A \cap B = \varnothing$, that is, if they have no common element.

Sometimes a set may be designated by listing its elements or members within braces, as $\{a, b, c\}$ for the set consisting of the letters a, b, c, or {Smith, Jones, Brown, Robinson} for the set (1) above.

By an **ordered pair** (a,b) we mean the pair of objects a, b in the stated order; the ordered pair (b,a) is regarded as different from the ordered pair (a,b) except in the special case where a and b represent the same object. If A and B are two sets, the class of all ordered pairs (a,b) of which the first member belongs to set A and the second member belongs to set B is called the **Cartesian* product** of the two sets, and it is denoted by $A \times B$. For example, if A is the set whose members are a, b, c and B is the set whose members are p, q, r, s, then $A \times B$ is the set of ordered pairs

$$\begin{array}{c} (a,p), (a,q), (a,r), (a,s) \\ (b,p), (b,q), (b,r), (b,s) \\ (c,p), (c,q), (c,r), (c,s). \end{array}$$

The set of objects which convert a propositional function into a true proposition is called the **truth-set** of the propositional function. For example, the truth-set of the propositional function "x is the first president of the U.S." is the set consisting of one element: {George Washington}. The truth-set of the propositional function "$x^2 = 9$" is the set consisting of two elements: $\{3, -3\}$.

* After René Descartes, whose Latinized name was Cartesius, a French mathematician and philosopher of the 17th century.

Exercises

1. If A is the set of letters $\{x, y, z, w\}$ and B is the set of letters $\{x, v, w, r,\}$, write each of the following sets: (*a*) $A \cup B$; (*b*) $A \cap B$.

2. If A is the set of letters $\{x, y, z\}$ and B is the set of letters $\{m, n\}$, write each of the following sets: (*a*) $A \times B$, (*b*) $B \times A$, (*c*) $A \times A$, (*d*) $B \times B$.

3. If I is the set of chessmen, A is the set of black chessmen, and B is the set of four knights, describe each of the following: (*a*) $A \cup B$; (*b*) $A \cap B$.

4. If A is a set of two sandwiches, egg (e) and ham (h), and B is a set of three beverages: coffee (c), tea (t), and milk (m), describe the set $A \times B$.

5. (*a*) List all the subsets of the set $A = \{a, b, c\}$.

(*b*) List all the proper subsets of the set $A = \{a, b, c\}$.

(*c*) Write all the elements of the set $A \times A$.

6. (*a*) If P, Q, R, S are four points occurring in that order on a straight line I, and if A represents the set of points on the line-segment PR and B represents the set of points on the line-segment QS, (endpoints included on the given line segments), describe the sets: (1) $A \cup B$; (2) $A \cap B$.

(*b*) The same as (*a*) if endpoints are not included in the given line-segments PR and QS.

7. If p and q are propositional functions in x, and if P is the truth-set of p and Q is the truth-set of q, what is the truth-set of the compound propositional functions (*a*) either p or q (or both), (*b*) both p and q.

8. Find the truth set of each of the following propositional functions:

(*a*) $p : x$ is a number such that $x^2 = 4$.

(*b*) $q : x$ is a number such that $x^2 - 5x + 6 = 0$.

(*c*) either p or q.

(*d*) both p and q.

9. If I is the set of numbers $\{1, 2, 3, 4, 5, 6, 7, 8, 9\}$, E is the set of numbers $\{2, 4, 6, 8, 10\}$, and T is the set of numbers $\{3, 6, 9\}$, (*a*) write the set $E \cup T$; (*b*) write the set $E \cap T$; (*c*) Is $E \cap T$ a subset of $E \cup T$? (*d*) Is $E \cap T$ a proper subset of $E \cup T$?

12. BINARY RELATIONS

The idea of "binary or dyadic relation" is an easy one to grasp. We shall indicate the meaning of the word by some illustrative examples: "being father of," "being an ancestor of," "being taller than," "being equal to," "being greater than," are *relations* in which things of various kinds may stand to one another. The first three relations mentioned above may hold between people, while the last two may hold between numbers. We shall list three important properties that relations sometimes have.

Consider an arbitrary relation R and let x, y, z, etc., represent things which may stand in this relation to each other. If x has the relation R to y we may write $x \; R \; y$.

It *may* happen that for any object x it *must* be true that x has the relation R to itself. If this is the case, the relation R is called **reflexive.** For example, the relation "is equal to," for numbers, is a reflexive relation, since $a = a$. But "is the father of," for people, is definitely not reflexive since no person x is the father of himself.

It *may* happen that whenever x has the relation R to y, then y *must* also have the relation R to x. If this is the case, the relation R is called **symmetric.** Thus "is equal to," for numbers, is a symmetric relation since if $a = b$, then $b = a$. But "is the father of," for people, is not symmetric since if x is the father of y, it is not true that y is the father of x.

It *may* happen that if x has the relation R to y and y has the relation R to z, then x *must* have the relation R to z. If this is the case, the relation R is called **transitive.** The relation "is equal to," for numbers, is transitive, since if $a = b$ and $b = c$, then $a = c$. But "is the father of," for people, is not transitive, since if x is the father of y and y is the father of z, it is not true that x is the father of z.

Example 1. Consider the relation "implies," which may hold between propositions p, q, r, etc. This relation is clearly reflexive since p implies p; that is, if p is true, then p is true. It is not symmetric, since p implies q may be correct while q implies p is not; that is, a proposition may be correct while its converse is not. It is transitive since if p implies q and q implies r, then p implies r; in fact, this is an important principle of logic which we use continually in our proofs.

Example 2. Consider the relation "was born in the same country as," which may hold among people. This is reflexive, symmetric, and transitive.

A binary relation R may be thought of as the truth-set of a propositional function with two variables. Thus the relation "father of" is the set of all ordered pairs of people (x, y) for which the propositional function "x is the father of y" is true. Hence a **binary relation** R is a subset of the cartesian product $S \times T$, where S is the set of objects which the first variable x may represent, and T is the set of objects which the second variable y may represent. In our example $S = T$ may be the set of all people. If John is the father of Mary, then the pair (John, Mary) is "in" the relation "father of." In general if $x\ R\ y$ then the ordered pair $(x, y) \in R$ where $R \subset S \times T$ is the truth-set of the propositional function $x\ R\ y$. A more precise term would be binary relation R from S to T, since the sets S and T enter into the definition of R. The sets S and T may be the same or may overlap in any manner or may be disjoint. *Whenever $S = T$ we shall speak of a relation R defined for elements of S instead of a relation R from S to S.* For example, if $S = T = \{a, b, c\}$, then $S \times T$ is the set $\{(a,a), (a,b), (a,c), (b,a), (b,b), (b,c), (c,a), (c,b), (c,c)\}$ with nine elements each of which is an ordered pair of letters chosen from the set $\{a, b, c\}$. The relation R described by the propositional function "x precedes y alphabetically" is the subset $\{(a,b), (a,c), (b,c)\}$; that is, this subset is the truth-set of the propositional function in quotation marks.

If a relation is reflexive, symmetric, and transitive, it is termed an **equivalence relation.** For example, equality for numbers is an equivalence relation.

Theorem. *If an equivalence relation R is defined for elements of a set S, then R determines a decomposition of S into mutually disjoint non-empty subsets, called* **equivalence classes**, *each equivalence class consisting of mutually equivalent elements, elements of different equivalence classes being non-equivalent.*

Proof. If x is any element of S, denote by C_x the set of all elements of S which have the relation R to x. Since R is reflexive, we must have $x \in C_x$. C_x is called the equivalence class to which x belongs. Thus, every x in S belongs to some equivalence class.

If $y \in C_x$ and $z \in C_x$ then $y\ R\ x$ and $z\ R\ x$. Since R is symmetric, $y\ R\ x$ and $x\ R\ z$. Since R is transitive, $y\ R\ x$. Thus, all elements of C_x are equivalent to each other. Further, every element z equivalent to any element y of C_x is in C_x itself, since $z\ R\ y$ and $y\ R\ x$ implies $z\ R\ x$.

On the other hand, if w is not in C_x, then w is not equivalent to any element y of C_x, since $y\ R\ x$ and $w\ R\ y$ would imply $w\ R\ x$. Furthermore, no element v of C_w is equivalent to x; for if $v\ R\ w$ and $x\ R\ v$, then $x\ R\ w$. Hence, $C_x \cap C_w = \varnothing$; that is, C_x and C_w are disjoint if and only if $x\ R\ w$ is false, and otherwise C_x and C_w are equal sets.

Example 1. If S is the set of numbers $\{1, 2, 3, 4, 5, 6, 7, 8, 9, 10\}$ and aRb means that $a - b$ is an integral multiple of 3, then R is an equivalence relation. S is decomposed by this relation into the disjoint equivalence classes $\{1, 4, 7, 10\}$, $\{2, 5, 8\}$, $\{3, 6, 9\}$. The equivalence class $\{2, 5, 8\}$ may be denoted by either C_2, C_5 or C_8.

Example 2. Congruence is an equivalence relation for triangles in a plane. All 3—4—5 triangles constitute one of the many equivalence classes for this relation.

Exercises

Which of the adjectives "reflexive," "symmetric," "transitive" is applicable to the following relations?

1. "Is the mother of," for people.
2. "Is an ancester of," for people.
3. "Is the spouse of," for people.
4. "Is in love with," for people.
5. "Is taller than," for people.

6. "Is less than," for numbers.

7. "Is the husband of," for people.

8. "Is west of," for places in America.

9. "Is west of," for places anywhere on earth except the poles.

10. "Has the same length as," for line-segments.

11. "Is perpendicular to," for lines in a plane.

12. "Is not equal to," for numbers.

13. "Is congruent to," for triangles.

14. "Is similar to," for triangles.

15. "Lives within a mile of," for people.

16. "Has the same number of elements as," for sets.

17. "Is equivalent to," for propositions.

18. "Were graduated in the same calendar year from a given college," for graduates of this college.

19. What are the equivalence classes for the equivalence relation in exercise 18 usually called?

20. Prove that if S is decomposed into the union $S = S_1 \cup S_2 \cup S_3 \cup \dots$ of disjoint subsets $S_1, S_2, S_3, \dots$, then the relation R defined as $x\ R\ y$ if and only if x and y belong to the same subset S_i is an equivalence relation.

***21.** Prove that the relation defined in example 1 of section 12 above is an equivalence relation. (Hint: zero is an integral multiple of 3 since $0 = 3 \cdot 0$.)

13. A SIMPLE ABSTRACT MATHEMATICAL SCIENCE

Neither algebra nor geometry provides a *simple* example of an abstract mathematical science since each rests on a large number of postulates. On the other hand, the examples 1 and 2 of section 8 are simple but trivial. The following is a good example of an abstract mathematical science with several different concrete interpretations; it is neither complicated nor unimportant.

Consider a collection of objects, of unspecified nature, and an undefined relation, of unspecified nature, which may hold between pairs of these objects. The objects in the collection will be denoted by small letters, like a, b, c, and we shall write $a\ R\ b$ to mean that a has the relation (mentioned above) to b. Assume the following postulates.

Postulate 1. *If $a\ R\ b$, then a is different from b.*

Postulate 2. *If $a\ R\ b$ and if $b\ R\ c$, then $a\ R\ c$.*

From these postulates we deduce the following theorem.

Theorem 1. *If $a\ R\ b$ is true, then $b\ R\ a$ is false.*

Proof. By hypothesis, $a \; R \; b$ is true. Suppose that $b \; R \; a$ were also true. Then from postulate 2, we would have $a \; R \; a$, because $a \; R \; b$ and $b \; R \; a$ would imply $a \; R \; a$, But by postulate 1, $a \; R \; a$ implies that a is different from a, which is absurd. Hence the supposition that $b \; R \; a$ is true must be false since it leads to a false conclusion. That is, $b \; R \; a$ is false.

We now introduce a defined term.

Definition. *If a R b and b R c, then b is said to be* ***between*** *a and c.*

Theorem 2. *If b is between a and c and if c is between b and d, then c is between a and d.*

Proof. The hypothesis "b is between a and c" means that $a \; R \; b$ and $b \; R \; c$. By postulate 2, this implies that $a \; R \; c$. The hypothesis "c is between b and d" implies that $b \; R \; c$ and $c \; R \; d$. But $a \; R \; c$ and $c \; R \; d$ means, by definition, that c is between a and d.

Here we have the beginnings of an abstract mathematical science with undefined terms, postulates, defined terms, and theorems. This abstract mathematical science has many important concrete interpretations, some of which we shall now list.

First interpretation. Let the "objects" be whole numbers, and let $a \; R \; b$ mean "a is less than b."

Second interpretation. Let the "objects" be whole numbers, and let $a \; R \; b$ mean "a is greater than b."

Third interpretation. Let the "objects" be points on a line, and let $a \; R \; b$ mean "a is to the left of b."

Fourth interpretation. Let the "objects" be instants of time, and let $a \; R \; b$ mean "a is before b."

Fifth interpretation. Let the "objects" be people, and let $a \; R \; b$ mean "a is an ancestor of b."

Sixth interpretation. Let the "objects" be people, and let $a \; R \; b$ mean "a is taller than b."

Seventh interpretation. Let the "objects" be states of affairs or things, and let $a\,R\,b$ mean "a is preferred to b." This interpretation will be elaborated in section 194.

Eighth interpretation. Let the objects be all the subsets of the set $I = \{a, b, c\}$, and let the relation R be "is a proper subset of."

It is clear that the study of relations of various sorts may have applications in many fields. In particular, we shall indicate briefly in section 194 that careful logical study of the implications of various assumptions about relations may serve to throw light on and stimulate inquiry into the social sciences.

Exercise. Verify intuitively that each of these concrete interpretations converts our postulates into true statements and therefore converts our theorems into true statements as well. Restate postulates, definitions, and theorems in terms of each interpretation, in succession.

References

Numbers refer to the bibliography at the back of the book.

Bell 18, 19, 20, 21
Bennett and Baylis 23
Braithwaite 36, 37
Bridgman 39
Cohen and Nagel 55
Courtant and Robbins 58
Einstein and Infeld 68
Galileo Galilei 82
Keyser 109, 110, 111, 112, 113
Kline 117
Lieber and Lieber 122
Littlewood 123
Nagel 138
Newman 140
Poincaré 148
Russell 163, 164, 165, 166
Sawyer 171
Stabler 184
Stoll 187
Tarski 190
Whitehead 206, 207
Wilder 210

3

*The Simplest Numbers**†

14. INTRODUCTION

We did not attempt in section 8 to give a complete set of postulates for Euclidean geometry and to deduce the familiar theorems from them. Such a task involves considerable technical difficulty. Neither your high school text in geometry nor Euclid's original work, *The Elements* (about 300 B.C.), succeeded in presenting a completely logical deduction of the theorems from the postulates according to present standards. In fact, such a treatment could not be given without a more complete set of postulates and was not given until the latter part of the nineteenth century. However, the treatment of geometry in your secondary school course, though incomplete, did make clear that the subject may be considered as an example of postulational thinking in the light of our discussion in section 8. We may now turn to algebra and arithmetic, which we shall treat in greater detail because your secondary school treatment of these subjects was much inferior, from this point of view, to that of your geometric studies. Much of your algebra was probably learned by rote; here, it will be treated logically. While we cannot attempt a complete treatment because of technical difficulties, which would tax the abilities of more advanced students than you, we shall try to do enough to convince you that algebra has a logical structure similar to that of geometry and to acquaint you with its historical growth. Since a completely logical treatment is not feasible here, we shall have

* *Note to the student:* This chapter should be read slowly since the idea of logical proof in connection with numbers is strange to you. After completing this chapter, the work of Chapters 4, and, especially, 5 will be found to be much easier.

† *Note to the instructor:* If it is felt that fewer proofs than are given here will suffice to enable the student to grasp the idea of logical proof, then the remaining proofs may be omitted and the facts assumed or discussed informally without disturbing the continuity of the book. We have tried to include as much rigor as anyone would want since it is more convenient for the instructor to omit than to insert such details.

to ask you to adopt a kind of split personality. Sometimes we shall address you as if you were children or barbarians and we shall build up with careful logic even the most elementary of subjects. At other times we shall ask you to recall some simple things with which you have long been familiar, such as the addition and multiplication tables.

The system of numbers, with which you became acquainted in your previous study of algebra, did not come into being full-grown. It developed very slowly, beginning in prehistoric times and reaching its present state only recently. The so-called natural numbers, 1, 2, 3, 4, and so on, certainly prehistoric in origin, were doubtless the only numbers known to the human race for a long time. Fractions, like 3/5, 7/2, 1012/357, etc., were probably invented in order to facilitate the handling of problems of measurement concerning the division of things (like real estate or harvests) into equal parts. In their study of geometric magnitudes the Greeks discovered that some lengths could not be represented even by fractions (see section 30). Considerations of this sort led to the invention of irrational numbers like $\sqrt{2}$. When it became convenient, for various purposes, to be able to subtract a larger number from a smaller one, negative numbers were invented. If one wishes to take the square root of a negative number, one is led to invent the so-called imaginary numbers like $\sqrt{-2}$. Finally, there was evolved the system of so-called complex numbers, like $2 + 3\sqrt{-7}$, with which you became acquainted in school. In the present chapter we shall discuss only the simplest numbers, namely, the natural numbers and fractions, in some detail. In Chapter 4, we shall continue our discussion of the gradual evolution of the number system. Since our purpose is not merely historical but also to develop the subject from a modern, logical point of view, we shall depart somewhat from the chronological order of development, for pedagogical reasons. It would be foolish to retrace here all the blunderings of the human race in its efforts to create a satisfactory number system.

In later chapters, we shall indicate the logic underlying the familiar manipulations of algebra. However, as remarked in Chapter 2, our choice of postulates is usually suggested by some sort of experience. *It is the purpose of Chapters* 3 *and* 4 *to acquaint you with experiences of the human race which lead up to the formulation of the postulates used in our number system, and, at the same time, to introduce you gradually to the use of logical proofs and strict definitions in connection with numbers. Chapters* 3 *and* 4 *do not themselves constitute an abstract mathematical science*, since the basic term *natural number* will not be regarded here as an undefined term devoid of meaning but will rather have a concrete meaning, understood intuitively, to be indicated at the beginning of the next section.*

*A deeper analysis of these concepts will be found in Chapters 15 and 16. These chapters could be interpolated at this point, if desired.

Many of the things we shall write down may seem trivial to you but you must recall that, as far as possible, you are to remember nothing of your high school algebra, that we want to write down everything that we take for granted, and that we must use nothing in our proofs except what is explicitly assumed or previously proved.

15. NATURAL NUMBERS. ADDITION AND EQUALITY

Let us begin by imagining ourselves to be young children or primitive savages who know nothing of numbers. Our earliest mathematical discovery would probably be that two apples, two fingers, two people, two dogs, etc., have something in common. Thus, the first numbers to be invented would probably be one and two. Some primitive races are said to find it too much of a strain to enter into further refinements and have in their language only three words of number—one, two, and many. Since none of us can grasp intuitively large numbers of objects, such as the number of blades of grass on a lawn or the number of people in an auditorium, it is likely that our ancestors would not have progressed much further than this were it not for the invention of counting. However, having invented the process of counting objects in succession (that is, "counting by ones"), our ancestors, early in prehistoric times, surely developed the numbers 1, 2, 3, 4, and so on, which are used in counting. These are called the **natural numbers**. From our experience with counting objects we develop next the idea of the sum of two numbers. For example, if we have three apples and we add two more apples we have five apples; this fact and others like it lead to the statement $3 + 2 = 5$. We then find it convenient to record and memorize the resulting tables of addition

$$\begin{array}{cccc} 1+1=2 & 2+1=3 & 3+1=4 & \cdots \\ 1+2=3 & 2+2=4 & 3+2=5 & \cdots \\ 1+3=4 & 2+3=5 & 3+3=6 & \cdots \\ \vdots & \vdots & \vdots & \end{array}$$

which we can use in calculating sums. Devices other than tables, such as the abacus (Fig. 17) or various forms of finger-reckoning, were once used universally for addition and are still used today among various people. We shall now assume that you are familiar with the usual way of writing and naming the natural numbers and that you can add. We also assume that you are familiar with the use of letters to represent unspecified numbers.

The intuitive fact that any two natural numbers can be added to obtain another natural number may be formulated as a postulate or assumption as follows.

A_1. *Given any pair of natural numbers, a and b, in the stated order, there exists one and only one natural number, denoted by* $a + b$, *called the* **sum** *of a and b.* (This is called the **postulate of closure for addition of natural numbers.**) *The numbers a and b are called* **terms** *of the sum.*

CHINESE ABACUS OR SWAN-PAN
FIG. 17

The significance of the word closure is that the set of all natural numbers form a "closed system" under addition in the sense that the result of adding two numbers in the set always remains in the set. It is as though all natural numbers filled a fenced-in enclosure, and performing the operation of addition never takes us outside the enclosure. This may be made clearer by considering the following examples of systems not closed under addition.

Example 1. Consider the set of all natural numbers from 1 up to 10, inclusive. This is not a closed system under addition for it would not be correct to say that given any two numbers in the set there is a number in the set called their sum. For instance, 4 and 7 are in the set but their sum is not.

Example 2. Consider the set of all odd numbers; that is, 1, 3, 5, 7, $\cdots$.* This is not a closed system under addition since the sum of two odd numbers is even. On the other hand, the set of all even numbers (2, 4, 6, $\cdots$) is a closed system under addition, for the sum of two even numbers is always even. (These statements are not being proved here; we are merely taking these illustrations intuitively.)

If we add two pebbles to a collection of three pebbles we get the same number of pebbles as if we had added three pebbles to a collection of two pebbles. Thus $3 + 2 = 2 + 3$. This, and similar experience, suggests formulating the following property of natural numbers as a postulate.

A_2. *If a and b are any natural numbers,* $a + b = b + a$. (This is called the **commutative law for addition of natural numbers.**)

That is, we may commute or interchange the order of the terms in the sum $a + b$.

* Wherever three dots occur, the first dot means "and," the second dot means "so," and the third dot means "on."

Let us recall that parentheses are used to group together what is in them. This is merely a rule or agreement in the grammar of our written language of algebra. Thus, $2 + (3 + 4)$ means that we add 3 and 4 first, obtaining 7, and then find $2 + 7$, obtaining 9. Similarly, $(2 + 3) + 4$ means $5 + 4$, or 9. The fact that we get the same result from both expressions, although the operations performed are different, leads us to formulate the following property of natural numbers as a postulate.

A_3. *If a, b, c are any natural numbers, $(a + b) + c = a + (b + c)$.* (This is called the **associative law for addition of natural numbers.**)

This says that we get the same result whether we add the sum of a and b to c, or a to the sum of b and c. That is, the parentheses may be put around the first or the second pair of natural numbers, at will.

To say that $a = b$ means that a and b are different symbols representing the same natural number; that is, they are different names for the same thing. *If $a = b$, then, in any statement involving a, we may replace a by b and vice versa.* This is a fundamental principle of our underlying logic, called the **principle of substitution.** For example, postulate A_3 tells us that when we see the expression $(a + b) + c$ we may replace it by the expression $a + (b + c)$. Similarly, A_2 tells us that we may substitute $b + a$ for $a + b$. The principle of substitution is related to the following postulates concerning equality, which we shall use, often without explicit mention.

E_1. *If a is a natural number, $a = a$.*

E_2. *If a and b are any natural numbers and $a = b$, then $b = a$.*

E_3. *If a, b, c are natural numbers, and if $a = b$ and $b = c$, then $a = c$. (Things equal to the same thing are equal to each other.)*

E_4. *If $a = b$ and $c = d$, all letters representing natural numbers, then $a + c = b + d$. (If equals are added to equals, the results are equal.)*

Postulates E_1, E_2, and E_3 state that the relation of equality for natural numbers is reflexive, symmetric, and transitive, respectively. Together, they state that this relation is an equivalence relation.

As a consequence of E_3 (or substitution) we may use long chains of equalities; thus if $a = b$, $b = c$, $c = d$, $d = e$, $e = f$, we may conclude that $a = f$, and we may write $a = b = c = d = e = f$.

A statement of equality is called an **equation**; the expressions on either side of the equals sign are referred to as the **left member** and **right member** of the equation, respectively.

We can now prove some simple theorems like the following.

Theorem 1. *If* x, y, *and* z *are any natural numbers, then* $(x + y) + z = (z + x) + y$.

Proof. By hypothesis x and y are natural numbers. Hence, by the postulate of closure for addition of natural numbers (A_1) it follows that $x + y$ is a natural number. That is, $x + y$ is a long name for a certain natural number. By hypothesis z is a natural number. By the commutative law for addition of natural numbers (A_2), applied to the natural numbers $(x + y)$ and z, we have

$$(1) \qquad (x + y) + z = z + (x + y).$$

By the associative law for addition of natural numbers (A_3), applied to the right member of (1), we have

$$(2) \qquad z + (x + y) = (z + x) + y.$$

By closure for addition (A_1), $(z + x)$, $(x + y) + z$, $z + (x + y)$, and $(z + x) + y$ are natural numbers. From (1) and (2) we obtain by substitution, or by E_3, the result

$$(x + y) + z = (z + x) + y$$

which is what we had to prove.

Note that before we applied A_2 to the symbols $(x + y)$ and z, we had to be sure that they both represented natural numbers, since A_2 applies only to natural numbers. That $(x + y)$ was a natural number was established by using A_1.

Remark 1. The sum of three or more terms has not been determined by A_1. Nor does the addition table tell you the sum of more than two terms. Thus a symbol like $a + b + c$ has no meaning at present. But $(a + b) + c$ has a meaning and so has $a + (b + c)$ since each indicated step in either expression is addition of two terms which is possible by A_1. Furthermore by A_3, both of these expressions are equal. Hence we *define* $a + b + c$ to mean the number obtained by inserting parentheses in either way: $a + (b + c)$ or $(a + b) + c$. As for sums involving four terms, we observe that $([3 + 4] + 6) + 5 = (7 + 6) + 5 = 13 + 5 = 18$ while $[3 + 4] + (6 + 5) = 7 + 11 = 18$. This suggests that we can now prove theorems like the following on the basis of our postulates.

Theorem 2. *If* a, b, c, *and* d *are any natural numbers then*

$$([a + b] + c) + d = [a + b] + (c + d).$$

Proof. By hypothesis, a and b are natural numbers. Hence, the postulate of closure for addition of natural numbers (A_1) tells us that $[a + b]$ is a natural number. Since $[a + b]$, c, and d are now known to be natural numbers, the associative law for addition of natural numbers (A_3) tells us that $([a + b] + c) + d = [a + b] + (c + d)$. This is what we had to prove.

Similarly, we could show that all expressions obtained by inserting parentheses in the various permissible ways must yield the same result. Thus, $[a + (b + c)] + d = a + [(b + c) + d]$, and so on. Hence, we define the expression $a + b + c + d$ to mean the number arrived at by pairing off the terms by inserting parentheses in any way that makes sense, since all such ways yield the same result. In general, the sum of any number of terms $a + b + c + \cdots + k$ may be defined, and we can write such sums without parentheses, or we may group the terms in any way by putting in parentheses at will (as long as we are only adding). This could be proved rigorously* but we will not go into details here. *We shall say that such insertion or removal of parentheses in sums is justified by the* **generalized associative law for addition of natural numbers.**

Remark 2. The commutative and associative laws may seem trivial, but there are in fact many operations which do not obey them. To anticipate, subtraction obeys neither. For $2 - 7$ is not the same as $7 - 2$; and $(8 - 4) - 2$ is not the same as $8 - (4 - 2)$, since the first expression means $4 - 2$ or 2 and the second means $8 - 2$ or 6. Similar grouping symbols are sometimes needed in ordinary language to avoid ambiguity, as in the phrase "high school building" which may mean "high (school building)" or "(high school) building." Similarly, the operation of doing one thing after another is not commutative, for the order in which you do two things may well matter; for example, shelling an egg and beating it up; or undressing and bathing. Chemistry students all know that one may safely pour sulphuric acid into water, while it is dangerous to pour water into sulphuric acid.

Remark 3. The student should memorize the names of these laws, not their numbers, although for the sake of brevity we shall often use the numbers for cross references. When quoting a postulate as justification for a step in a proof, the student should either write out the postulate in full, or use abbreviations like Comm. Add. Nat. Nos. for the commutative law for addition of natural numbers.

Remark 4. The commutative and associative laws are implicitly used when we say that we can add a column of figures either up or down. Thus adding the column

$$\begin{array}{r} 7 \\ 4 \\ 6 \\ \hline 17 \end{array}$$

* With the help of further postulates not stated here. In particular, the postulate of mathematical induction, discussed in Chapter 15 is needed.

up means $(6 + 4) + 7$ while adding it down means $(7 + 4) + 6$. The results are the same.

Exercises

1. Name the postulate which justifies each of the following statements, all letters representing natural numbers:

(*a*) $5 + 7 = 7 + 5$.
(*b*) $(5 + 7) + 2 = 5 + (7 + 2)$.
(*c*) $x + y = y + x$.
(*d*) $(m + x) + r = m + (x + r)$.
(*e*) $a + b$ is a natural number.

2. Prove the following, justifying each step by means of one of our postulates, all letters representing natural numbers. Do not use the generalized associative law discussed in remark 1.

(*a*) $[a + (b + c)] + d$ is a natural number. (Hint: use A_1 several times.)
(*b*) $a + [(b + c) + d]$ is a natural number.
(*c*) $[a + (b + c)] + d = a + [(b + c) + d]$.
(*d*) $(x + y) + z = x + (z + y)$. (Hint: use A_3 and A_2.)
(*e*) $(x + y) + z = y + (x + z)$.
(*f*) $(a + b) + c = c + (a + b)$. (Hint: use A_1 and A_2.)
(*g*) $(a + b) + (c + d) = (c + d) + (a + b)$.
(*h*) $[a + (b + c)] + d = a + [d + (b + c)]$. (Hint: use A_1, A_3, and A_2.)
(*i*) $[a + (b + c)] + d = (a + b) + (c + d)$.
(*j*) $(x + y) + z = (x + z) + y$.

16. MULTIPLICATION OF NATURAL NUMBERS

Early in this history of the human race it must have been noticed that repeated additions of the same natural number can be abbreviated by the invention of multiplication. Thus, a herdsman counting cattle passing through a gate three abreast might have observed that he could "count by threes" more quickly than by "ones," and he might then have decided to remember that four threes add up to twelve, and similar facts. Hence we might define "4 times 3" to mean $3 + 3 + 3 + 3$. This leads us to the following definition.

Definition 1. *If a and b are natural numbers, the* ***product*** *of a and b shall mean the number $b + b + b + \cdots + b$ where there are a terms in the sum. In symbols, $ab = b + b + \cdots + b$ (a terms on the right of the equals sign). The numbers a and b are called the* ***factors*** *of the product. The product of a and b will be written* as ab or $a \cdot b$. In particular $1 \cdot b = b$.*

* The dot is always used when specific numbers are multiplied. For example, 4 times 3 is written $4 \cdot 3$, not 43.

For example, $4 \cdot 3 = 3 + 3 + 3 + 3$. Note that our definition of product involves only terms (like "sum") which have already been introduced. Since the sum of any number of natural numbers is a natural number, it is natural to assume the following postulate.

M_1. *If a and b are any two natural numbers, given in the stated order, there exists one and only one natural number denoted by ab or $a \cdot b$, called the product of a and b.* (This is called the **postulate of closure for multiplication of natural numbers.**)

This could have been proved* but we shall assume it here. An example of a system of numbers not closed under multiplication is the system of all natural numbers between 1 and 10 inclusive; for the numbers 3 and 4 are in this system but their product is not. Postulate M_1 asserts that the system of *all* natural numbers *is* closed under multiplication.

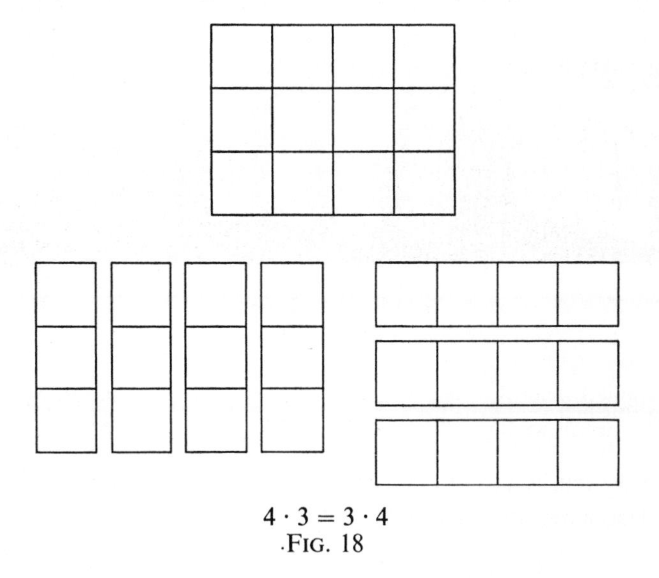

$4 \cdot 3 = 3 \cdot 4$
FIG. 18

According to definition 1, $4 \cdot 3 = 3 + 3 + 3 + 3$ while $3 \cdot 4 = 4 + 4 + 4$. These expressions represent different operations but the result is the same in both cases. Our experience suggests that we should always get the same result even if the order of our factors is reversed. Therefore we assume the following postulate.

* See footnote, page 55. We make no attempt in this book to use a minimum set of postulates. Nor do we always give a completely sufficient set for the subject at hand. To do either of these things would tax the abilities of advanced students. In particular, by assuming more than we need we are able to get by with fewer difficult proofs. Obviously, if we assumed less, for example a minimal set of postulates, then we would have to prove more.

M_2. *If a and b are any natural numbers, then ab = ba.* (This is called the **commutative law for multiplication of natural numbers.**)

Similarly our experience tells us that although $(4 \cdot 3) \cdot 2 = 12 \cdot 2$ and $4 \cdot (3 \cdot 2) = 4 \cdot 6$ represent different operations, they yield the same result. Therefore it is natural to make the following postulate.

M_3. *If a, b, c, are any natural numbers, then* $(ab)c = a(bc)$. (This is called the **associative law for the multiplication of natural numbers.**)

From these postulates we can deduce some simple theorems like the following.

Theorem *If x, y, z are any natural numbers, then* $x(yz) = z(xy)$.

Proof. By M_3, $x(yz) = (xy)z$. By M_1, (xy) is a natural number. Hence we may apply M_2 to the natural numbers (xy) and z, obtaining $(xy)z = z(xy)$.

$4 \cdot (3 \cdot 2) = 2 \cdot (4 \cdot 3)$
FIG. 19

By M_1, applied several times, $x(yz)$, $(xy)z$, and $z(xy)$ are natural numbers. By E_3 or substitution we have $x(yz) = z(xy)$ which was to be proved.

We now assume you to be familiar with the tables of multiplication which can be derived from definition 1 and the tables of addition:

$$\begin{array}{llll}
1 \cdot 1 = 1 & 2 \cdot 1 = 2 & 3 \cdot 1 = 3 & \cdots \\
1 \cdot 2 = 2 & 2 \cdot 2 = 4 & 3 \cdot 2 = 6 & \cdots \\
1 \cdot 3 = 3 & 2 \cdot 3 = 6 & 3 \cdot 3 = 9 & \cdots \\
\vdots & \vdots & \vdots &
\end{array}$$

Remark. The product of three terms is not defined yet. But M_3 enables us to define and use symbols like abc or $abcd$. *We shall insert or remove parentheses in a product of any number of factors freely, saying that this is justified by the* ***generalized associative law for multiplication.*** Compare what we said in connection with addition in remark 1, section 15.

We recall the convention of notation (a rule of grammar in the written language of algebra) that *in a chain of additions and multiplications the multiplications are to be done first except where otherwise indicated by parentheses.* This convention enables us to omit cumbersome parentheses around products. For example, $2 + (3\cdot 4)$ can be written simply as $2 + 3\cdot 4$. Note that $2 + 3\cdot 4$ means $2 + 12$ or 14 while $(2 + 3)\cdot 4$ means $5\cdot 4$ or 20. Similarly, $2\cdot 3 + 4 = 6 + 4 = 10$ while $2\cdot(3 + 4) = 2\cdot 7 = 14$. However, we observe that $2\cdot(3 + 4) = 2\cdot 3 + 2\cdot 4$ since the left member is $2\cdot 7$ while the right is $6 + 8$. In fact, $2\cdot(3 + 4) = (3 + 4) + (3 + 4)$ by definition of product. But, using the associative

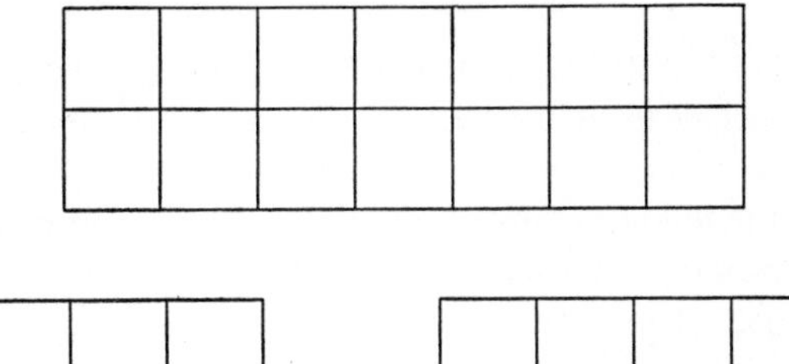

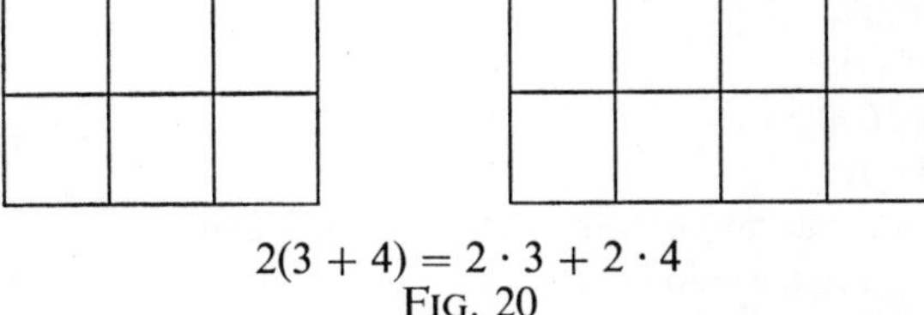

$2(3 + 4) = 2 \cdot 3 + 2 \cdot 4$
FIG. 20

and commutative laws, we have $(3 + 4) + (3 + 4) = 3 + 4 + 3 + 4 = 3 + 3 + 4 + 4 = (3 + 3) + (4 + 4) = 2\cdot 3 + 2\cdot 4$. This suggests the following general postulate.

D. If a, b, c are natural numbers, then $a(b + c) = ab + ac$. (This is called the **distributive law for natural numbers.**)

The effect of the multiplier a is distributed between the terms b and c. This is the first postulate we have made which connects addition and multiplication. In high school this law was referred to as "removing parentheses" if read from left to right, and as "taking out a common factor" if read from right to left.

We also assume the following postulate of equality.

E_5. *If* $a = b$ *and* $c = d$, *all letters representing natural numbers, then* $ac = bd$. (*If equals are multiplied by equals, the results are equal.*)

Exercises

1. Name the postulate or postulates which justify each of the following statements, all letters representing natural numbers:

(*a*) $3\cdot 5 = 5\cdot 3$. (*b*) $(3\cdot 5)\cdot 4 = 3\cdot(5\cdot 4)$.
(*c*) $3(5+4) = 3\cdot 5 + 3\cdot 4$. (*d*) $5\cdot 2 + 5\cdot 3 = 5(2+3)$.
(*e*) $xy = yx$. (*f*) $(xy)z = x(yz)$.
(*g*) $x(y+z) = xy + xz$. (*h*) $mp + mq = m(p+q)$.

2. According to the definition of multiplication what is the meaning of $3\cdot 5$? of $5\cdot 3$? of $5a$?

3. Find the value of each of the following:

(*a*) $4+3\cdot 2$. (*b*) $(4+3)\cdot 2$. (*c*) $4\cdot 3+5$.
(*d*) $4\cdot(3+2)$. (*e*) $4+3\cdot 2+6$. (*f*) $(4+3)\cdot 2+6$.
(*g*) $(4+3)\cdot(2+6)$. (*h*) $4+3\cdot(2+6)$. (*i*) $4+3\cdot(2+6[7+5])$.

4. Notice that $2+3\cdot 4 = 2+12 = 14$, and $2\cdot(3+4) = 2\cdot 7 = 14$. Hence $2+3\cdot 4 = 2\cdot(3+4)$. May we conclude from this that $a + b\cdot c = a\cdot(b+c)$ for all natural numbers a, b, and c?

5. Prove each of the following, justifying each step by means of one of our postulates, all letters representing natural numbers.

(*a*) $(xy)z = x(zy)$. (Hint: use M_3 and M_2.)
(*b*) $(xy)z = y(xz)$.
(*c*) $(xy)(zu) = (zu)(xy)$. (Hint: use M_1 and M_2.)
(*d*) $(xy)z = (xz)y$.
(*e*) $xy + xz$ is a natural number. (Hint: use M_1 and A_1.)
(*f*) $x(y+z)$ is a natural number.

17. SOME THEOREMS ABOUT NATURAL NUMBERS

We are now in a position to prove some theorems about natural numbers on the basis of our postulates. The student's chief difficulty here will be the necessity for confining himself to steps which are justified by the postulates. It will be necessary to refrain consciously from performing manipulations, made familiar by habitual use, which are not assumed and have not yet been proved to be permissible here. We give two illustrations.

Theorem 1. *If x, y, z are any natural numbers, then $(y+z)x = yx + zx$.*

Note that this is not the distributive law as we assumed it, since the number outside the parentheses here is on the right instead of the left of the parentheses. It will be advisable to restate all theorems indicating hypothesis and conclusion clearly, as follows.

Hypothesis. x, y, and z are natural numbers.

Conclusion. $(y + z)x = yz + zx$.

Proof. By the postulate of closure for addition of natural numbers (A_1), $y + z$ is a natural number. Now x is a natural number by hypothesis. Hence, applying the commutative law for multiplication of natural numbers (M_2) to the natural numbers $(y + z)$ and x, we have

$$(y + z)x = x(y + z).$$

But, by the distributive law (D),

$$x(y + z) = xy + xz.$$

Now, by the commutative law for multiplication (M_2),

$$xy = yx \quad \text{and} \quad xz = zx.$$

By closure for multiplication (M_1), xy, yx, xz, and zx are natural numbers. Hence,

$$xy + xz = yx + zx \qquad \text{(by } E_4\text{)}.$$

Finally,

$$(y + z)x = yx + zx \qquad \text{(by } E_3 \text{ or substitution)}.$$

This is what we had to prove.

Remark. Instead of recognizing that $y + z$ may be regarded as a long name for a natural number, the student may substitute a short name for it if he wishes. Thus we might have said: let $y + z = a$. Then $(y + z)x = ax$ by substitution. Now $ax = xa$ by M_2. Hence $(y + z)x = x(y + z)$ by substitution. The rest of the proof would proceed as before. However, this substitution is unnecessary. Note that the step "let $y + z = a$" is not a step of reasoning but merely a matter of name-calling. Logic should not be confused with name-calling even in a political campaign.

Theorem 2. *If a, b, c, d are natural numbers, then $a(b + c + d) = ab + ac + ad$.*

Hypothesis. a, b, c, d are natural numbers.

Conclusion. $a(b + c + d) = ab + ac + ad$.

Proof. By the associative law for addition of natural numbers (see remark 1, section 15), $b + c + d$ can be written as $[b + c] + d$. By A_1, $[b + c]$ is a natural number. Then

$$a(b + c + d) = a([b + c] + d) \qquad \text{(by substitution)}.$$

Now,

$$a([b + c] + d) = a[b + c] + ad \qquad \text{(by } D\text{)}.$$

But,

$$a[b + c] = ab + ac \quad \text{(by } D\text{)}.$$

Thus,

$$a[b + c] + ad = ab + ac + ad \quad \text{(by substitution)}.$$

Finally,

$$a(b + c + d) = ab + ac + ad \quad \text{(by } E_3 \text{ or substitution)}.$$

Notice that the steps in these proofs are things that you would have done in secondary school without stopping to think at all. Our purpose is not to "get the answer" quickly, but rather to deduce our results from the postulates or assumptions we set down, being careful to justify each step on that basis. The extreme care we have employed in justifying each minute step logically is doubtless new to you. All of mathematics, from these small beginnings to the most advanced branches, can be built up in this way with each step justified by a logically rigorous argument.

While you will have had little difficulty in following the proofs given above, you may be at a loss as to how to proceed in the original exercises below. When the proof is given, you can see that each step is logically justified. But when you have to invent your own proof you may be puzzled as to which of the many possible justifiable steps you ought to take. The best counsel that the author can think of in this connection is the advice given to Alice by the Cheshire Cat in *Alice in Wonderland** by C. L. Dodgson (Lewis Carroll). Alice asks the Cat:

" 'Would you tell me, please, which way ought I go from here?'

" 'That depends a good deal on where you want to get to,' said the Cat.

" 'I don't much care where—,' said Alice.

" 'Then it doesn't matter which way you go,' said the Cat."

Similarly, it is usually easier to see what to do next if you know what goal you are driving at. Thus when you are trying to determine which of many possible logically justifiable steps you should take, think of what you are trying to prove and select some justifiable step which will bring you nearer to that goal.

As an illustration, let us analyze theorem 1 so as to discover naturally how the proof should go. We have to prove that $(y + z)x = yx + zx$. There is only one postulate which deals with both addition and multiplication together, namely, the distributive law. But we cannot apply the distributive law since x is on the wrong side of the parentheses. Therefore we would like to put the x on the left side of the parentheses. This could be done by the commutative law for multiplication provided the parenthesis represented a natural number. But

* This book and *Through the Looking Glass*, by the same author, make good reading for adults. The Reverend Charles L. Dodgson was a teacher of mathematics, and his tales contain many sly allusions of mathematical and philosophical character.

it does by the law of closure for addition. Therefore we begin our proof by saying that $y + z$ is a natural number by A_1. Then by M_2, we get $(y + z)x = x(y + z)$. By D, $x(y + z) = xy + xz$. Now we have attained our first objective of removing the parentheses. But the right member of the last step is not yet what we have to obtain. However, it is easily made so by the commutative law for multiplication. Having thus analyzed the proof, we then write it down in good order as above.

Theorems 1 and 2 and exercises 11 and 12 below are all instances of what may be called the **generalized distributive law**. That is,

$$a(b + c + d + \cdots + k) = ab + ac + ad + \cdots + ak$$

and

$$(b + c + d + \cdots + k)a = ba + ca + da + \cdots + ka$$

no matter how many terms are within the parentheses. We shall not prove this generalized distributive law here but we shall use it in later sections. Do not use it in the following exercises.

In applying any postulate or theorem to any expression, or in using "substition," always be sure you know what you are substituting for what. Write out all "reasons" in full. If you are doubtful about whether a certain postulate applies to the situation in hand, it is a good idea to write out the postulate and then substitute in it the expressions which are to play the parts of the symbols in the postulate. For example, in the above analysis of theorem 1 we want at one stage to use M_2 which says: if a and b are natural numbers, then $ab = ba$. Applying this to the situation in hand, we write: if $(y + z)$ and x are natural numbers then $(y + z)x = x(y + z)$. This will be all right provided $(y + z)$ *is* a natural number. And so on.

The student should note that every step in our proofs, no matter how small, is carefully justified. However, if this practice were continued throughout the book, the proofs would become intolerably long. Therefore, **as a matter of expedience, as soon as we have become sufficiently familiar with the justification of tiny steps such as those involving the commutative and associative laws, we shall begin to slur them; that is, we shall begin to do several of them simultaneously and finally shall do them mentally without explicit mention.** However, the student should not relax his standard of proof in this way until he has become thoroughly familiar with the task of proving things in full, justifying even the smallest steps. He should be *capable* of putting in *every* step if it is desired.

Exercises

(a) Prove the following, all letters being understood to represent natural numbers, justifying each step by means of a postulate or a previously proved theorem. (b) Also illustrate each formula by replacing the letters by particular numbers.

1. $m(p+q) = qm + mp$. **2.** $x(y+z) = zx + yx$.
3. $(a+b)c = ca + cb$. **4.** $(m+n)t = tn + mt$.
5. $2(x+4) = 2x + 8$. **6.** $(x+3)\cdot 3 = 3x + 9$.
7. $(x+2)(y+4) = xy + 2y + 4x + 8$.
8. $(a+5)(b+3) = ab + 5b + 3a + 15$.
9. $(a+b)(c+d) = ac + bc + ad + bd$.
10. $a(b+c) + bd = ac + b(d+a)$.
11. $a(b+c+d+e) = ab + ac + ad + ae$. (Hint: write $b+c+d+e = [b+c]+[d+e]$ and proceed as in theorem 2.)
12. $a(b+c+d+e+f) = ab + ac + ad + ae + af$. (Hint: write $b+c+d+e+f = [b+c]+[d+e]+f$ and apply theorem 2.)
13. $(2x+1)(2y+1) = 4xy + 2x + 2y + 1$.
14. $a(bc+d) = ad + abc$.
15. $ad(b+c) = bad + cad$.

18. SUBTRACTION AND DIVISION OF NATURAL NUMBERS

"My friend has more marbles than I have; how many more?" This question occurs early in a child's life just as it must have occurred early in the history of the human race. It leads to the concept of subtraction. Children are often taught to subtract 2 from 5 by asking, "What must be added to 2 in order to get 5?" Formalizing this question, we make the following definition.

Definition 1 (*a*). *If a and b are natural numbers then the symbol $a - b$ means a natural number x such that $b + x = a$, provided such a number x exists. The natural number $a - b$ is called the **difference** a minus b.*

This is not unnatural since the number of marbles which must be added to 2 in order to get 5 is clearly the same as the number of marbles left when 2 are taken away from 5. This is exhibited in the fact that there are two schools of thought among shopkeepers in regard to making change from a five-dollar bill. Some will figure out what is left when the purchase price is taken away from \$5.00; but most will start with the purchase price and calculate what must be added to it to obtain \$5.00.

Definition 1 (*b*). *If there exists a natural number x such that $b + x = a$, then a is said to be **greater than** b or b is said to be **less than** a; in symbols, $a > b$ or $b < a$.*

Note that, as always, we define new terms in terms of old ones. Thus "$a - b$" and "$a > b$" are defined in terms of addition.

Notice that while sums and products of two natural numbers a and b always exist (among the natural numbers), the difference may not. For example, $5 - 2$ means a number x such that $2 + x = 5$; or $x = 3$ since we discover from the addition table that $2 + 3 = 5$. But $2 - 5$ means a number x such that $5 + x = 2$, and no such number exists among the natural numbers. Hence $2 - 5$ is at present a meaningless symbol. Our definition 1(a) is like the requirements for a degree or title. If a number x satisfies the requirement $b + x = a$, then x is entitled to be called $a - b$. But it may be that no number x satisfies the requirements, as in the case $2 - 5$. The set of natural numbers is not a closed system under the operation of subtraction.

Similarly, children often are taught to divide 6 by 2 by asking "By what must we multiply 2 in order to get 6?" Formalizing this question, we get the following definition.

Definition 2 (a). *If a and b are natural numbers, then the symbol $a \div b$ means a natural number x such that $bx = a$, provided such a number x exists. The natural number $a \div b$ is called the* ***quotient*** *a divided by b.*

Definition 2 (b). *If there exists a natural number x such that $bx = a$, we say that a is a* ***multiple of*** *b, or a is* ***divisible by*** *b, or b is a* ***factor of*** *a.*

Example. 6 is a multiple of 2 and 2 is a factor of 6 since $2 \cdot 3 = 6$.

Note that we define the new terms "$a \div b$" and "a is a multiple of b" in terms of the old term "multiplication."

The quotient of two natural numbers need not exist. Thus $6 \div 2$ means a natural number x such that $2x = 6$; or $x = 3$, since we discover from the multiplication table that $2 \cdot 3 = 6$. Similarly, $5 \div 2$ means a natural number x such that $2x = 5$; but no such natural number exists. Hence $5 \div 2$ is at present a meaningless symbol. The set of natural numbers is not a closed system under the operation of division.

We shall often use the following postulates of equality.

E_6. *If $a = b$ and $c = d$, all letters representing natural numbers, then $a - c = b - d$, provided these differences exist. (If equals are subtracted from equals, the results are equal.)*

E_7. *If $a = b$ and $c = d$, all letters representing natural numbers, then $a \div c = b \div d$, provided these quotients exist. (If equals are divided by equals, the results are equal.)*

We might raise the natural question: if there is a number x satisfying the requirements of definition 1, may there not be more than one such number? That is, is $a - b$ a uniquely determined number? There are many instances of symbols whose meanings are not uniquely determined. For example, if A and B are a husband and wife, the symbol "son of A and B" may not have a uniquely determined meaning for there may be more than one person satisfying the requirements of the definition of this symbol. That the numbers $a - b$ and $a \div b$ *are* uniquely determined, if they exist at all, follows at once from the postulates E_6 and E_7, respectively. Therefore the use of the definite article "the" in the expressions "the difference" and "the quotient" is justified.

Only a novice would calculate the value of the expression $(675 + 348) - 675$ by actually adding the numbers in the parentheses and then subtracting, although this is what the expression seems to call for. That this labor is needless is shown by the following theorem.

Theorem 1. *If p and q are any natural numbers, then $(p + q) - p = q$.*

Hypothesis. p and q are natural numbers.

Conclusion. $(p + q) - p = q$.

Proof. By A_1, $p + q$ is a natural number. To prove that one natural number $(p + q)$ minus a second (p) equals a third (q), we have only to prove that the second plus the third equals the first, by definition 1(a). But $p + q = (p + q)$ by identity. This completes the proof.

Theorem 2. *If p and q are any natural numbers, then $(pq) \div p = q$.*

Hypothesis. p and q are natural numbers.

Conclusion. $(pq) \div p = q$.

Proof. By M_1, (pq) is a natural number. To prove that one natural number (pq) divided by a second (p) equals a third (q), we have only to prove that the second multiplied by the third equals the first, by definition 2(a). But $pq = (pq)$ by identity. This completes the proof.

Subtraction is called the *inverse* of addition and division is called the *inverse* of multiplication, for obvious reasons. Theorems 1 and 2 show that subtraction of x undoes addition of x and division by x undoes multiplication by x.

Note that in proving theorems 1 and 2 we have made use, essentially, only of definitions 1 and 2. One must guard against the temptation to say, in proving theorem 1, for example, that

$$(p+q)-p=p+q-p=p-p+q=0+q=q.$$

For we have no number zero at our command, since the only numbers we know about at present are the natural numbers, and we have never assumed any "commutative law" justifying the second step above. In proving theorems about subtraction, division, greater than, etc., we must not use any intuitive notions, since these terms are defined, not undefined. *We must prove any theorem about a defined term in the light of its definition.*

The existence of the distributive law connecting multiplication with addition suggests that we might have a similar law with subtraction. This is provided by the following theorem.

Theorem 3. *If a, p, and q are natural numbers, and if $p-q$ exists, then $a(p-q)=ap-aq$.*

Hypothesis. a, p, *and* q are natural numbers; $p-q$ exists.

Conclusion. $a(p-q)=ap-aq$.

Proof. Since $p-q$ exists by hypothesis, we may let $x=p-q$. By definition $1(a)$, this means that

(1) $$q+x=p.$$

This statement involves p and q as individual terms. What we want to prove involves aq and ap. Hence it is natural to think of multiplying both sides of (1) by a. Now

(2) $$a=a$$

by identity. Hence, applying E_5 to (1) and (2), we obtain

$$a(q+x)=ap.$$

Now

$$aq+ax=ap \qquad \text{(by } D \text{ and substitution).}$$

This means, by definition $1(a)$, that

(3) $$ax=ap-aq.$$

But $x=p-q$. Hence, substituting in (3),

$$a(p-q)=ap-aq \qquad \text{(by substitution).}$$

This completes the proof.

Theorem 3 is an instance of what we shall refer to as the **generalized distributive law** which we shall not prove here but which we shall use in later sections. We shall write*

$$a(b + c - d - e + \cdots + k) = ab + ac - ad - ae + \cdots + ak$$

or

$$(b + c - d - e + \cdots + k)a = ba + ca - da - ea + \cdots + ka$$

whenever these expressions have a meaning. Do not use this generalized distributive law in the exercises immediately below.

Exercises

All letters represent natural numbers.

1. Explain what is meant by the statement $10 \div 2 = 5$ in terms of definition 2(*a*).

2. Explain what is meant by the statement $10 - 2 = 8$ in terms of definition 1(*a*).

3. Which of the following expressions are meaningless? Explain. (*a*) $8 \div 2$. (*b*) $3 \div 2$. (*c*) $3 - 7$. (*d*) $2 \div 3$. (*e*) $2 \div 8$. (*f*) $7 - 3$.

4. Do the following expressions *always* represent a natural number? (*a*) $a + b$. (*b*) $a - b$. (*c*) ab. (*d*) $a \div b$.

5. If your answer to parts of exercise 4 is negative, what can be said of a and b when these expressions do represent natural numbers?

★6. Prove the following, justifying each step by means of a postulate, definition, or previously proved theorem.

(*a*) $(m + n) - n = m$.
(*b*) $(mn) \div n = m$.
(*c*) If $m - n$ exists, then $n + (m - n) = m$.
(*d*) If $m \div n$ exists, then $(m \div n) \cdot n = m$. (Hint: use definition 2(*a*).)
(*e*) $m \div m = 1$. (Hint: use definition 2(*a*).)
(*f*) If $p - q$ exists, then $(p - q)a = pa - qa$. (Hint: see theorem 3.)
(*g*) $(ab + ac) \div a = b + c$. (Hint: use definition 2(*a*).)
(*h*) $(a + b) \cdot (b + c) \div (a + b) = b + c$. (Hint: use definition 2(*a*).)
(*i*) If a is a multiple of b and b is a multiple of c, then a is a multiple of c. (Hint: use definition 2(*b*).)
(*j*) If $a > b$ and $b > c$, then $a > c$.
(*k*) If a is a factor of b and b is a factor of c, then a is a factor of c.
(*l*) If $a < b$, then $a + c < b + c$.
(*m*) If $a < b$ and $c < d$, then $a + c < b + d$.
(*n*) If $a < b$ then $ca < cb$, and conversely.

* In an expression like $b + c - d - e + \cdots + k$ it is understood that the operations indicated are to be performed in the given order, reading from left to right.

19. FRACTIONS, RATIONAL NUMBERS, EQUALITY

Early in history, practical problems of measurement, involving the division of things (such as real estate or quantities of grain) into equal parts, must have led to the invention of fractions. As long as we have only natural numbers at our disposal, division of 4 by 6 is impossible, for there exists no natural number x such that $6x = 4$. In order to make division of one natural number by another always possible without restriction, we invent fractions. To be entirely naive about it, let us notice that when we write a fraction, like $\frac{2}{3}$, we are merely writing down a symbol consisting of two natural numbers: 2 and 3. Hence we make the following definition.

Definition 1. *A **fraction** is a symbol* $\dfrac{a}{b}$ *(or a/b) where a and b are natural numbers (read "a over b"). We call a the **numerator** and b the **denominator**.*

For example, $\frac{4}{6}$ and $\frac{6}{4}$ are fractions. We wish to apply the symbol $\frac{4}{6}$ to represent four of six equal parts of something. Notice that $\frac{4}{6}$ does not have anything to do with division at present; it is merely a symbol composed of two natural numbers. We might equally well have used some other symbol, like (a, b), for example; thus $\frac{4}{6}$ would be written $(4, 6)$. We shall retain the familiar symbolism to avoid confusion. Be careful, however, to read $\frac{4}{6}$ as "four over six," not "four divided by six." Notice that we have defined the new term "fraction" in terms of the old term "natural number."

The fractions $\frac{4}{6}$, $\frac{2}{3}$, $\frac{6}{9}$, $\frac{8}{12}$ are all different; that is, they are different symbols. But because we have in mind the division of things into equal parts as the application for our abstract fractions, we would like the different fractions $\frac{4}{6}$, $\frac{2}{3}$, $\frac{6}{9}$, $\frac{8}{12}$ to be regarded as equivalent (Fig. 21). Notice that

$$\frac{4}{6} = \frac{2 \cdot 2}{3 \cdot 2}, \quad \frac{6}{9} = \frac{2 \cdot 3}{3 \cdot 3}, \quad \frac{8}{12} = \frac{2 \cdot 4}{3 \cdot 4}.$$

Of course, since fractions are merely symbols created by us, we are free to decide what we shall mean by "equivalent" fractions. Our practical application to division into equal parts suggests the following provisional definition.

Definition 2(*a*). *If a, b, and x are any natural numbers, then*

$$\frac{ax}{bx} \approx \frac{a}{b}.$$

where the symbol $\approx$ is to be read as "is equivalent to."

This means that we may multiply numerator and denominator of a fraction by the same natural number x and obtain an equivalent fraction. Multiplying numerator and denominator of $\frac{2}{3}$ by 2 to get $\frac{4}{6}$ simply means concretely that we

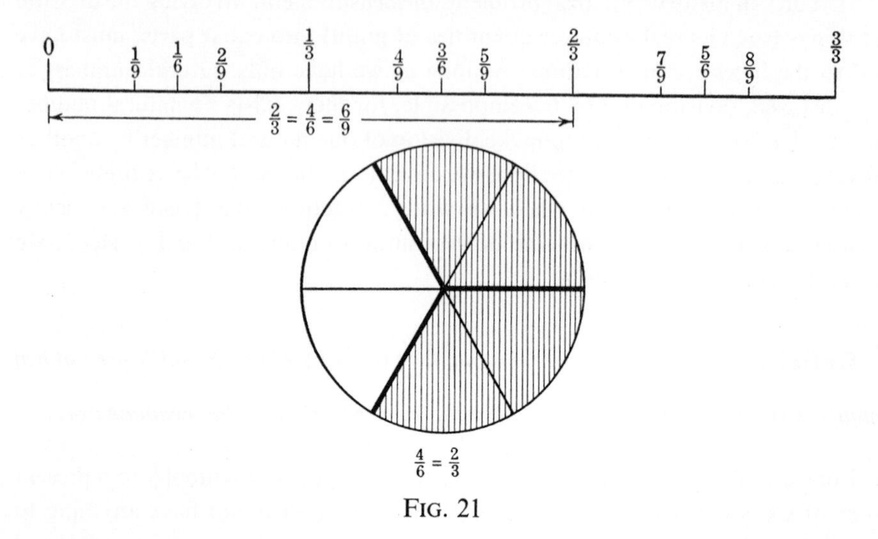

FIG. 21

split each of our 3 equal parts (Fig. 21) into halves and take twice as many of the new parts. Conversely, definition 2(a) means that we may remove a common factor from the numerator and denominator of a fraction, and obtain thereby an equivalent fraction. This is sometimes called "canceling."* Thus

$$\frac{4}{6} = \frac{2 \cdot 2}{3 \cdot 2} \approx \frac{2}{3}.$$

Note that the first two fractions are equal, that is, the same ordered pair of natural numbers, while the second two are only equivalent.

By M_2, it follows from definition 2(a) that we may also write

$$\frac{xa}{xb} \approx \frac{a}{b}. \tag{1}$$

The word denominator is analogous to the word denomination, used in connection with money. For example, two quarters of a dollar may be expressed by the fraction $\frac{2}{4}$, the denominator telling the kind of part of the dollar (denomination of the coin) we are talking about while the numerator tells the number of such parts we are considering. To find out whether or not 2 quarters ($\frac{2}{4}$) is equivalent to 5 dimes ($\frac{5}{10}$) we first express each amount in a common

* It may surprise some students to learn that "cancellation" is not a license to strike out any symbol in both places whenever it appears twice on the same paper or blackboard.

denomination. Thus 2 quarters may be expressed as 50 cents and 5 dimes may be expressed as 50 cents. We want to regard $\frac{2}{4}$ as equivalent to $\frac{5}{10}$ since

$$\frac{2}{4} \approx \frac{2 \cdot 25}{4 \cdot 25} = \frac{50}{100} \qquad \text{(by definition 2(}a\text{))}$$

and

$$\frac{5}{10} \approx \frac{5 \cdot 10}{10 \cdot 10} = \frac{50}{100} \qquad \text{(by definition 2(}a\text{))}$$

and we would of course like to have the statement "things equivalent to the same thing are equivalent to each other" be valid for fractions. But the statement $\frac{2}{4} \approx \frac{5}{10}$ cannot be obtained from definition 2(a) since there is no natural number x such that $2x = 5$ and $4x = 10$. Nevertheless we want to be able to say that $\frac{2}{4} \approx \frac{5}{10}$. This suggests the following definition.

Definition 2(b). *Two fractions shall be **equivalent** if and only if, when they are converted to equivalent fractions with the same denominator (by means of definition 2(a), if necessary), they then have the same numerator.*

Applying this definition to two arbitrary fractions a/b and c/d we see that

$$\frac{a}{b} \approx \frac{ad}{bd} \qquad \text{(by definition 2(}a\text{))}$$

and

$$\frac{c}{d} \approx \frac{bc}{bd} \qquad \text{(by equation (1))}$$

and hence that our two fractions are equivalent if and only if the numerators ad and bc are equal. This proves the following theorem.

Theorem 1. *Two fractions a/b and c/d are equivalent if and only if $ad = bc$.*

We might have adopted the statement of theorem 1 as our definition of equivalent fractions. But we prefer to think in terms of definition 2(b) because it is more natural. For example, to decide whether or not $\frac{20}{24}$ and $\frac{30}{36}$ are equal we have only to express them with a common denominator and then compare the numerators. Thus, $\frac{20}{24} \approx \frac{20 \cdot 3}{24 \cdot 3} = \frac{60}{72}$, while $\frac{30}{36} \approx \frac{30 \cdot 2}{36 \cdot 2} = \frac{60}{72}$. Hence, our two given fractions are equivalent. Note also that $20 \cdot 36 = 24 \cdot 30$ (see theorem 1).

Theorem 2. *The relation of equivalence ($\approx$) for fractions is an equivalence relation; that is, it is reflexive, symmetric and transitive.*

Proof. *Reflexive.* Using theorem 1, we see that $a/b \approx a/b$, since $ab = ba$.

Symmetric. We must prove that if $a/b \approx c/d$ then $c/d \approx a/b$. The hypothesis implies that $ad = bc$ by theorem 1. Hence $cb = da$, which, in turn, implies $c/d \approx a/b$ by theorem 1.

Transitive. We must prove that if $a/b \approx c/d$ and $c/d \approx e/f$, then $a/b \approx e/f$. The two hypotheses imply, that

$$ad = bc$$

and

$$cf = de.$$

Multiplying the left members of these two equations and the right members, we obtain

$$adcf = bcde.$$

Dividing both members of this equation by cd, we get

$$af = be$$

which implies, by theorem 1, that $a/b \approx e/f$.

From section 12, we know that this equivalence relation decomposes the set of all fractions into mutually disjoint equivalence classes. Thus, the equivalence class to which $\frac{2}{3}$ belongs consists of all fractions equivalent to $\frac{2}{3}$, such as $\frac{4}{6}$, $\frac{6}{9}$, $\frac{20}{30}$, and others. We shall call this equivalence class the "rational number" $\frac{2}{3}$. It is also possible to call it the "rational number" $\frac{4}{6}$, and so on, since the same equivalence class may be identified by naming any of its members arbitrarily. Thus, while the fraction $\frac{2}{3}$ is not "equal" to the fraction $\frac{4}{6}$, since they are different ordered pairs of natural numbers, the rational numbers $\frac{2}{3}$ and $\frac{4}{6}$ are equal in the sense of equality of sets. That is, the extensive set of all fractions equivalent to the fraction $\frac{2}{3}$ is exactly the same set as the set of all fractions equivalent to $\frac{4}{6}$. In general, we make the following definition.

Definition 3. *The set of all fractions equivalent to a given fraction a/b is called the* ***rational number*** *a/b.*

Any fraction belonging to a given rational number may be used as a representative or name for that rational number. For example $\frac{2}{3}$, $\frac{4}{6}$, $\frac{20}{30}$, etc. may be used interchangeably as names for the same rational number to which all of them belong.

Since two rational numbers a/b and c/d are equal (sets) if and only if the fractions a/b and c/d are equivalent, we have the following theorem.

Theorem 3. *Two rational numbers a/b and c/d are equal if and only if $ad = bc$.*

Proof. By definition 3 and theorem 1.

We could now prove, on the basis of our definitions, that statements* analogous to postulates E_1, E_2, E_3 for natural numbers hold for rational numbers as well. We shall not do this here. In particular, for any rational number we may substitute an equal rational number, in any true equation or statement.

When all common factors, other than 1, have been removed from numerator and denominator of a fraction, we say that the corresponding rational number has been **reduced to lowest terms** or expressed in its **simplest form.** That is, a rational number is in lowest terms when its numerator and denominator are as small as possible. It could be proved† that each rational number can be reduced to a unique simplest form. For example, $\frac{4}{6}$ and $\frac{6}{9}$ both have the simplest form $\frac{2}{3}$. It could also be proved that two rational numbers are equal if and only if they have the same simplest form. We shall not prove these statements here.

Definitions 2(*a*) and 2(*b*) are motivated by the practical application we have in mind for fractions, namely, the division of things into equal parts. If we were going to use the symbol a/b to denote the length and width of a rug it would be foolish to use these definitions; for a rug whose length was 4 and width 6 would be represented by $\frac{4}{6}$ while $\frac{2}{3}$ would represent a rug whose length is 2 and width 3, and it would be silly to regard $\frac{4}{6}$ as equal to $\frac{2}{3}$. But these fractions (symbols) were created by us for our own use, and we make definitions and postulates suitable for the use we have in mind for the symbols.

As is customary, we deliberately use the same symbol for a fraction and the rational number to which it belongs. We may also follow customary usage and sometimes refer to a rational number as a fraction, but this should be recognized as an abuse of language.

Exercises

1. Decide whether or not each of the following pairs of fractions are equivalent

* This could have not been done for fractions. For example, one should be able to substitute an equal for an equal in any context whatever. But if in the true statement "4 is the numerator of 4/6" we substitute the "equal fraction" 2/3 for 4/6, we obtain the false statement "4 is the numerator of 2/3." Of course, these fractions are not equal but only equivalent. The rational numbers, which are equal sets of equivalent fractions, do not have numerators; only individual fractions do.

† With the help of further postulates not stated here. A similar remark applies to many of our statements beginning with "It can be proved that. . . ." Our set of postulates is neither complete nor irreducible.

(that is, elements of the same equivalence class or rational number):

(*a*) $\frac{3}{5}, \frac{6}{10}$ (*b*) $\frac{6}{10}, \frac{9}{15}$
(*c*) $\frac{4}{7}, \frac{12}{21}$ (*d*) $\frac{12}{21}, \frac{20}{35}$
(*e*) $\frac{12}{18}, \frac{10}{16}$ (*f*) $\frac{21}{27}, \frac{24}{30}$.

2. Decide whether or not the following pairs of rational numbers are equal:

(*a*) $\frac{24}{60}, \frac{8}{22}$ (*b*) $\frac{8}{10}, \frac{10}{12}$
(*c*) $\frac{26}{60}, \frac{39}{90}$ (*d*) $\frac{24}{46}, \frac{36}{69}$.

3. Name three other fractions belonging to the rational number (equivalence class) $\frac{10}{18}$.

4. Write a fraction equivalent to

(*a*) $\frac{2}{3}$ having the denominator 21.
(*b*) $\frac{2}{3}$ having the denominator 18.
(*c*) a/b having the denominator bd.

20. MULTIPLICATION AND DIVISION OF RATIONAL NUMBERS

Our application of fractions to division into equal parts also suggests that $\frac{2}{3}\cdot\frac{4}{5}$ should be $\frac{8}{15}$ since $\frac{2}{3}\cdot\frac{4}{5}$ is interpreted practically to mean two-thirds *of* four-fifths (Fig. 22). This is suggested by various considerations. If an automobile goes at the rate of 2 miles per minute for 3 minutes, it covers 6 miles. This suggests the formula $rt = d$, rate times time equals distance, all these quantities being measured in appropriate units.* If a car goes at the rate of $\frac{1}{2}$ mile per minute for $\frac{1}{3}$ of a minute, it covers half of $\frac{1}{3}$ of a mile or $\frac{1}{6}$ of a mile. Hence if we want the same formula to apply to fractional rates and times we are led to define $\frac{1}{2}\cdot\frac{1}{3}$ to be $\frac{1}{6}$ or half *of* $\frac{1}{3}$. Similarly, if we sell two dozen eggs at 50 cents per dozen the amount is 100 cents. This suggests the formula $pn = a$, price per

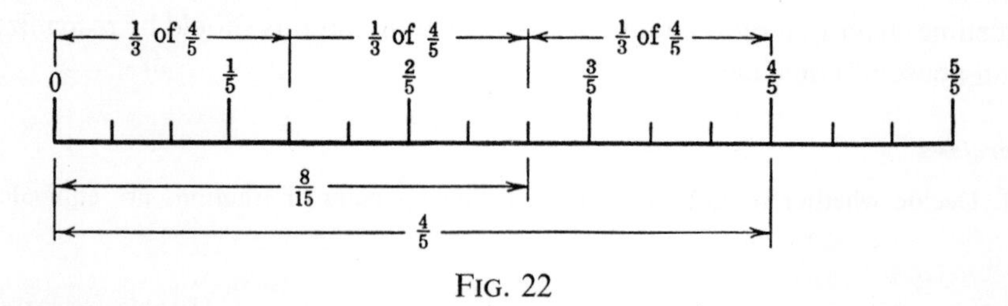

FIG. 22

item times number equals amount, all these quantities being measured in appropriate units. If we want the same formula to hold for fractional numbers

* One cannot "multiply" miles per minute by minutes to get miles. One can only multiply numbers by numbers to get numbers. Hence in any such formula it is understood that each letter represents a number (of units of some kind).

and prices we are led to define $\frac{1}{2}\cdot\frac{1}{3} = \frac{1}{6}$ or half *of* $\frac{1}{3}$ since if we sell $\frac{1}{3}$ of a dozen eggs at the rate of $\frac{1}{2}$ dollar per dozen the amount is $\frac{1}{6}$ of a dollar. This is also suggested by the following illustration. The area of a rectangle of length 5 feet and width 2 feet is 10 square feet (Fig. 23). Similarly the area of a rectangle $ABCD$ of length 1 foot and width 1 foot is 1 square foot (Fig. 24). This suggests the formula $A = lw$ for the area of a rectangle, all these quantities being measured in appropriate units. Now if we want the area of the rectangle $AEFG$ (Fig. 24) to be given by the same formula we want $\frac{1}{2}\cdot\frac{1}{3}$ to be $\frac{1}{6}$. Notice that the area of $AEFG$ is $\frac{1}{2}$ of the area of $AEHB$ which is $\frac{1}{3}$ square foot. Hence we want to interpret $\frac{1}{2}\cdot\frac{1}{3}$ as one-half *of* one-third or $\frac{1}{6}$. Similarly, $\frac{5}{2}\cdot\frac{4}{3}$ could be interpreted as five halves of $\frac{4}{3}$; that is, five times four-sixths or $\frac{20}{6}$. These considerations suggest the following definitions.

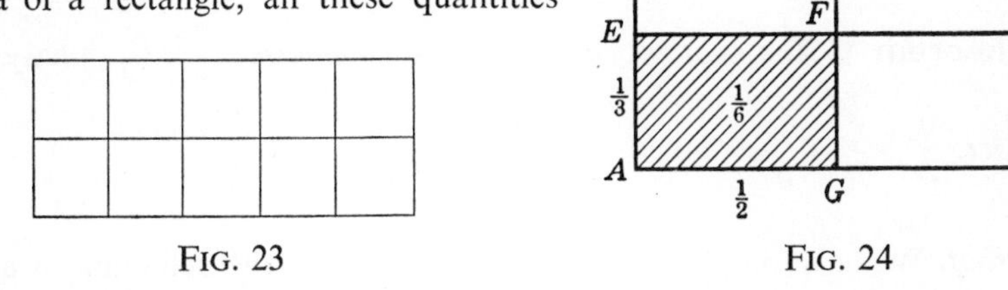

FIG. 23 FIG. 24

Definition 1. *If a/b and c/d are any rational numbers, their* ***product*** $\dfrac{a}{b}\cdot\dfrac{c}{d}$ *shall mean the rational number* $\dfrac{ac}{bd}$.

In effect, the product of two fractions shall be a fraction whose numerator is the product of the two given numerators and whose denominator is the product of the two given denominators.

It can be shown that if a/b or c/d or both are replaced by equivalent fractions, then the resulting product remains equivalent to ac/bd (see exercise 9). Therefore, definition 3 is justified as a definition of product of rational numbers, rather than merely of fractions, since no matter which of many possible representative fractions is chosen for each of the two given rational numbers, the product always represents the same rational number. *A similar remark will hold for the quotient, sum, and difference of two fractions.*

It must be emphasized that the paragraph preceding definition 1 must not be construed as a "proof" that the definition is "so." This paragraph is merely an intuitive explanation of why we *choose* this definition out of all possible definitions.

As in section 18, we may now define division of two rational numbers as the inverse of multiplication.

Definition 2. *The* ***quotient*** *of* $\frac{a}{b} \div \frac{c}{d}$ *shall mean another rational number* $\frac{x}{y}$ *such that* $\frac{c}{d} \cdot \frac{x}{y} = \frac{a}{b}$, *provided such a rational number exists.*

Theorem 1. *The quotient of two rational numbers* $\frac{a}{b} \div \frac{c}{d}$ *always exists; in fact,* $\frac{a}{b} \div \frac{c}{d} = \frac{ad}{bc}$.

Proof. We have only to prove that ad/bc satisfies the definition of quotient. That is, we have to show that $\frac{c}{d} \cdot \frac{ad}{bc} = \frac{a}{b}$. But $\frac{c}{d} \cdot \frac{ad}{bc} = \frac{cad}{dbc}$ by definition 1. By M_2, $\frac{cad}{dbc} = \frac{acd}{bcd}$. By definition 2(*a*) of the preceding section, $\frac{acd}{bcd} = \frac{a}{b}$. Hence, by substitution, $\frac{c}{d} \cdot \frac{ad}{bc} = \frac{a}{b}$. This completes the proof.

This theorem will be recognized as corresponding to the rule learned by rote in school; namely, to divide one fraction by another, "invert" the second and multiply.

We would like to identify the rational number a/b with the quotient $a \div b$, so that division of one natural number by another would always be possible. But if we did that we would have $3 \div 1 = \frac{3}{1}$ and also $3 \div 1 = 3$ by definition 2 of section 18. But the natural number 3 is not the same as the fraction $\frac{3}{1}$ which is a symbol composed of two natural numbers, nor is it the same as the rational number $\frac{3}{1}$ which is the class of all fractions equivalent to the fraction $\frac{3}{1}$. Hence we are led to make the following agreement to prevent such a conflict of meaning. *A rational number which can be represented by a fraction $a/1$ with 1 as denominator shall be written interchangeably with the natural number a.*

This might also have been motivated by our concrete application of fractions to division of things into equal parts. Just as $\frac{3}{4}$ foot may be interpreted as "divide a foot into 4 equal parts and take 3 of these fourths," we would like to interpret $\frac{3}{1}$ foot to mean "divide" a foot into one part (that is, leave it undivided) and take 3 of these "parts." The result of this is of course 3 feet. Hence we would like to regard $\frac{3}{1}$ as equal to 3.

Theorem 2. *If a and b are any two natural numbers, then* $a \div b = \frac{a}{b}$.

Proof. We write $a \div b = \frac{a}{1} \div \frac{b}{1}$. By theorem 1, $\frac{a}{1} \div \frac{b}{1} = \frac{a \cdot 1}{1 \cdot b} = \frac{a}{b}$. This completes the proof.

The fraction line may now be used interchangeably with the division sign, although we shall not prove this completely here. The rational numbers (including the natural numbers which are now identified with rational numbers which are representable by fractions having the denominator 1) have the advantage that *any* two rational numbers may be divided. We could now prove that the statement "if equals are multiplied or divided by equals, the results are equal" is true for rational numbers. (This was assumed only for natural numbers, of course.)

We shall use the symbols E_1, E_2, E_3, etc., freely to refer to analogous statements for fractions as well as for natural numbers.

Example. As an example, we give another proof of theorem 3, of the preceding section, which is really a theorem and its converse.

(*a*) *If* $\frac{a}{b} = \frac{c}{d}$, *then* $ad = bc$.

Proof. By hypothesis, $\frac{a}{b} = \frac{c}{d}$. Multiplying both sides by the common denominator bd, we have

$$bd \cdot \frac{a}{b} = bd \cdot \frac{c}{d} \qquad \text{(by } E_5\text{)}.$$

Or,

$$\frac{bd}{1} \cdot \frac{a}{b} = \frac{bd}{1} \cdot \frac{c}{d}.$$

Hence,

$$\frac{bda}{b} = \frac{bdc}{d} \qquad \text{(by definition 1)}.$$

Therefore,

$$da = bc. \qquad \text{(Reasons?)}$$

Or,

$$ad = bc \qquad \text{(by } M_2\text{)}$$

(*b*) *Conversely, if* $ad = bc$, *then* $\frac{a}{b} = \frac{c}{d}$.

Proof. By hypothesis, $ad = bc$. Dividing both sides by bd, we have

$$\frac{ad}{bd} = \frac{bc}{bd} \qquad \text{(by } E_7\text{)}.$$

Hence,

$$\frac{a}{b} = \frac{c}{d} \qquad \text{(by definition 2(}a\text{) section 19)}.$$

Notice that when we write $\frac{2}{3} = \frac{2 \cdot 2}{3 \cdot 2} = \frac{4}{6}$ we obtain an equal rational number by definition. This is in harmony with the fact that $\frac{2 \cdot 2}{3 \cdot 2} = \frac{2}{3} \cdot \frac{2}{2}$ (by definition of multiplication of rational numbers) and therefore $\frac{2}{3} = \frac{2 \cdot 2}{3 \cdot 2} = \frac{2}{3} \cdot \frac{2}{2} = \frac{2}{3} \cdot 1 = \frac{2}{3}$ since any number a times 1 should yield a as the product.

Exercises

All letters represent natural numbers. All fractions represent rational numbers unless otherwise indicated.

1. Apply our definitions or theorems to calculate the indicated products and quotients and reduce to simplest form:

(*a*) $\frac{2}{3} \cdot \frac{4}{7}$. (*b*) $\frac{2}{3} \div \frac{4}{7}$. (*c*) $\frac{2}{5} \cdot \frac{10}{4}$. (*d*) $\frac{3}{4} \div \frac{9}{12}$.

(*e*) $\frac{2}{3} \div \frac{4}{12}$. (*f*) $\frac{3}{4} \div \frac{9}{4}$. (*g*) $\left(\frac{2}{3} \cdot \frac{5}{4}\right) \div \frac{5}{6}$. (*h*) $\frac{2}{3} \cdot \left(\frac{5}{4} \div \frac{5}{6}\right)$.

2. Prove, justifying each step by means of our definitions, theorems, and postulates:

(*a*) $\frac{ab}{cd} \div \frac{b}{d} = \frac{a}{c}$. (*b*) $\frac{2a}{3b} \div \frac{1}{bc} = \frac{2\,ac}{3}$. (*c*) $\frac{ab + ac}{a} = b + c$.

(*d*) $\frac{ab + ac}{df} \cdot \frac{d}{a} = \frac{b + c}{f}$. (*e*) $\frac{mx + my}{ad} \div \frac{m}{ad} = x + y$.

(*f*) $\frac{ax + ay}{bc + bd} \div \frac{x + y}{c + d} = \frac{a}{b}$.

3. Prove that if $\frac{a}{b} = \frac{c}{d}$, then $\frac{a}{c} = \frac{b}{d}$.

4. Prove that if $\frac{a}{b} = \frac{c}{d}$, then $\frac{b}{a} = \frac{d}{c}$.

5. Prove that if $\frac{a}{b} = \frac{a + c}{b + d}$, then $\frac{a}{b} = \frac{c}{d}$.

6. State and prove the converse of exercise 5.

7. Prove that if $\frac{a}{b} = \frac{c}{d}$, then $\frac{a+b}{b} = \frac{c+d}{d}$.

8. State and prove the converse of exercise 7.

9. Prove that if the fraction $\frac{a}{b} \approx \frac{a'}{b'}$ and the fraction $\frac{c}{d} \approx \frac{c'}{d'}$, then the fraction $\frac{ac}{bd} \approx \frac{a'c'}{b'd'}$. (Hint: use theorem 1 of section 19.)

10. Prove that if the fraction $\frac{a}{b} \approx \frac{a'}{b'}$ and the fraction $\frac{c}{d} \approx \frac{c'}{d'}$, then the fraction $\frac{a}{b} \div \frac{c}{d} \approx \frac{a'}{b'} \div \frac{c'}{d'}$.

21. ADDITION AND SUBTRACTION OF RATIONAL NUMBERS

Since rational numbers were created by us, it is up to us to decide what we shall mean by the sum of two rational numbers. Here again our choice of definition will be motivated by the practical application we have in mind, namely, the division of things into equal parts.

To add coins of the same denomination we merely add the numbers of coins; for example, two quarters plus one quarter yields three quarters. If two fractions have the same denominator we would naturally like their sum to be a fraction with the same denominator whose numerator is the sum of the two given numerators. For example, we would like $\frac{3}{6} + \frac{2}{6}$ to be $\frac{5}{6}$. This suggests the following definition for addition of rational numbers represented by fractions with the same denominator.

Definition 1(a). $\frac{a}{b} + \frac{c}{b} = \frac{a + c}{b}$.

To add coins of different denominations we first express them in a common denomination and then add as before. For example, two quarters and three dimes may be added by saying that two quarters is equivalent to 50 cents and three dimes is equivalent to 30 cents; hence the sum is 80 cents. Analogously, it is natural, bearing our applications in mind (Fig. 25), to add $\frac{1}{2}$ and $\frac{1}{3}$ as follows. By definition 2(a), section 19, $\frac{1}{2} = \frac{1 \cdot 3}{2 \cdot 3} = \frac{3}{6}$ and $\frac{1}{3} = \frac{1 \cdot 2}{3 \cdot 2} = \frac{2}{6}$; hence $\frac{1}{2} + \frac{1}{3} = \frac{3}{6} + \frac{2}{6} = \frac{5}{6}$. This leads us to make the following definition.

Definition 1(b). *The* ***sum*** *of two rational numbers represented by fractions with different denominators shall be the rational number obtained by replacing* *these fractions by equivalent fractions having a common denominator (by definition* 2(a), *section* 19) *and then adding according to definition* 1(a).

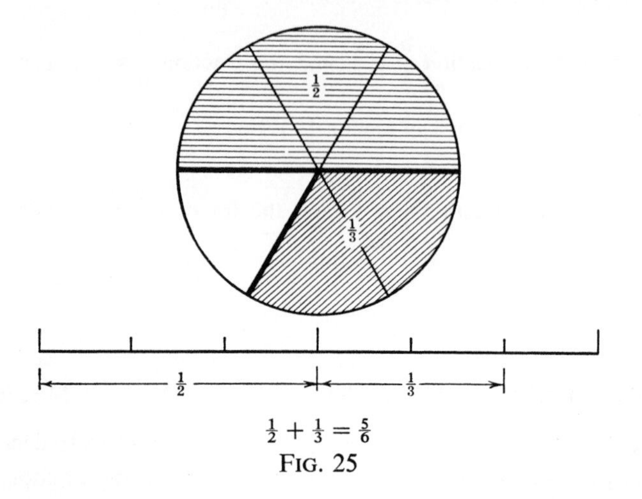

$\frac{1}{2} + \frac{1}{3} = \frac{5}{6}$

FIG. 25

It can be proved that the same rational number is obtained no matter what common denominator is chosen, and no matter what fractions are chosen to represent the given rational numbers. See exercise 8 below. One commonly uses the least common denominator.

Example. If $\frac{a}{b}$ and $\frac{c}{d}$ are any two rational numbers, we have

$$\frac{a}{b} + \frac{c}{d} = \frac{ad}{bd} + \frac{bc}{bd} \qquad \text{(by definition 2(}a\text{), section 19).}$$

Hence,

$$\text{(1)} \qquad \frac{a}{b} + \frac{c}{d} = \frac{ad + bc}{bd} \qquad \text{(by definition 1(}a\text{)).}$$

Instead of going through this process every time we want to add fractions, we might have dispensed with the definitions 1(a) and 1(b) altogether and adopted (1) as a general definition. However, it is more natural and, in practice, it is often more convenient to use our definitions instead of the general definition (1). For example, if we add $\frac{1}{2} + \frac{3}{8}$ by definition (1) we obtain $\frac{1 \cdot 8 + 2 \cdot 3}{2 \cdot 8} = \frac{14}{16}$ which has to be reduced to $\frac{7}{8}$. But if we add $\frac{1}{2} + \frac{3}{8}$ by our definitions we say $\frac{1}{2} + \frac{3}{8} = \frac{1 \cdot 4}{2 \cdot 4} + \frac{3}{8}$, by definition 2($a$) section 19, and then $\frac{4}{8} + \frac{3}{8} = \frac{7}{8}$, by definition 1($a$), which doesn't need to be reduced to lowest terms.

We now define subtraction of rational numbers as the inverse of addition.

Definition 2. *If* $\frac{a}{b}$ *and* $\frac{c}{d}$ *are any two rational numbers, the* ***difference*** $\frac{a}{b} - \frac{c}{d}$ *shall mean the rational number* $\frac{x}{y}$ *such that* $\frac{c}{d} + \frac{x}{y} = \frac{a}{b}$*, provided such a rational number exists. If such a rational number does exist, we shall say that* $\frac{a}{b} > \frac{c}{d}$ or $\frac{c}{d} < \frac{a}{b}$.

Representing the given rational numbers $\frac{a}{b}$ and $\frac{c}{d}$ by fractions with a common denominator, we have $\frac{ad}{bd}$ and $\frac{bc}{bd}$. It would seem natural to subtract one from the other by subtracting numerators and retaining the common denominator, just as one would do with coins of the same denomination. For example, three quarters minus one quarter is two quarters. This would yield the fraction $\frac{ad - bc}{bd}$ as the difference $\frac{ad}{bd} - \frac{bc}{bd}$ provided bc can be subtracted from ad, that is, if $ad > bc$. This result is established by the following theorem.

Theorem 1. *If* $ad > bc$, *then* $\frac{a}{b} - \frac{c}{d} = \frac{ad - bc}{bd}$.

Proof. Note that if ad were not greater than bc, then $ad - bc$ would not be a natural number and $\frac{ad - bc}{bd}$ would not be a fraction at all. We have to prove that $\frac{ad - bc}{bd}$ satisfies definition 2; that is, that $\frac{c}{d} + \frac{ad - bc}{bd} = \frac{a}{b}$. Now

$$\frac{c}{d} + \frac{ad - bc}{bd} = \frac{bc}{bd} + \frac{ad - bc}{bd} \qquad \text{(definition 2(}a\text{), section 19)}$$

$$= \frac{bc + (ad - bc)}{bd} \qquad \text{(definition 1(}a\text{))}$$

$$= \frac{ad}{bd} \qquad \text{(exercise 6(}c\text{), section 18)}$$

$$= \frac{a}{b} \qquad \text{(definition 2(}a\text{), section 19).}$$

This completes the proof.

The converse of this theorem can also be proved; in fact, it can be proved that the three statements "$\frac{a}{b} - \frac{c}{d}$ exists," "$\frac{a}{b} > \frac{c}{d}$," and "$ad > bc$" are equivalent. (We shall not prove this here.) This last statement means that *one rational number is greater than another if and only if its numerator is greater than the numerator of the other when they have both been represented by fractions with a common denominator.* Thus to decide whether or not $\frac{21}{24}$ is greater than $\frac{31}{36}$ we may write $\frac{21}{24} = \frac{21 \cdot 3}{24 \cdot 3} = \frac{63}{72}$ and $\frac{31}{36} = \frac{31 \cdot 2}{36 \cdot 2} = \frac{62}{72}$; hence $\frac{21}{24} > \frac{31}{36}$. We might also have decided this from the fact that $21 \cdot 36 = 756 > 744 = 24 \cdot 31$ since $\frac{21}{24} = \frac{21 \cdot 36}{24 \cdot 36} = \frac{756}{864}$ while $\frac{31}{36} = \frac{31 \cdot 24}{36 \cdot 24} = \frac{744}{864}$. In general $\frac{a}{b} = \frac{ad}{bd}$ while $\frac{c}{d} = \frac{bc}{bd}$; hence we can verify that $\frac{a}{b} > \frac{c}{d}$ by merely observing that $ad > bc$.

In practice, it is unnecessary to memorize theorem 1. To subtract rational numbers, simply express them as fractions with a common denominator and subtract the numerators, as follows: $\frac{1}{2} - \frac{1}{3} = \frac{3}{6} - \frac{2}{6} = \frac{3-2}{6} = \frac{1}{6}$.

We could now prove easily that the statement "if equals are added to, or subtracted from, equals, the results are equal" is true for rational numbers, but we shall not do so here. (These statements were assumed only for natural numbers.) We shall use freely the symbols E_6 and E_7 to refer to these analogous statements for rational numbers as well as for natural numbers.

Note that if we express natural numbers a and c as rational numbers $a/1$, $c/1$, respectively, then the operations defined for rational numbers yield the same results as the former operations for natural numbers, wherever the latter have a sense. For example, $\frac{a}{1} \cdot \frac{c}{1} = \frac{ac}{1}$ and $\frac{a}{1} + \frac{c}{1} = \frac{a+c}{1}$ which is what we would get from our operations for the natural numbers a and c if we did not write them as rational numbers. This is essentially why "identifying" a with $a/1$ causes no trouble.

It can be shown that if a and b are any two unequal rational numbers, either $a < b$ or $a > b$, but not both.

Exercises

1. Apply our definitions, theorems and postulates to calculate the indicated sums and differences, wherever possible, and reduce to lowest terms:

(*a*) $\frac{3}{4} + \frac{4}{3}$. (*b*) $\frac{4}{3} - \frac{3}{4}$. (*c*) $\frac{5}{6} - \frac{6}{5}$. (*d*) $\frac{5}{6} - \frac{5}{6}$.

(*e*) $\left(\frac{2}{3} + \frac{3}{4}\right) + \frac{5}{6}$. (*f*) $\frac{2}{3} + \left(\frac{3}{4} + \frac{5}{6}\right)$.

2. If a and b are any two rational numbers, does there always exist a rational number

(*a*) $a+b$; (*b*) $a-b$; (*c*) ab; (*d*) $a \div b$;

and, if not, what can be said of a and b when it does exist?

3. Prove, justifying each step by a definition, postulate, or theorem, all letters representing natural numbers:

(*a*) $\frac{1}{x}+\frac{1}{2}=\frac{2+x}{2x}$. (*b*) $\frac{y}{2x}+\frac{1}{2}=\frac{y+x}{2x}$. (*c*) $x+\frac{1}{y}=\frac{xy+1}{y}$.

(*d*) $\left(\frac{a}{b}+3\right) \div \left(\frac{a}{bc}+\frac{3}{c}\right)=c$. (*e*) $\left(\frac{1}{a}+\frac{1}{b}\right) \div \left(\frac{2}{a}+\frac{2}{b}\right)=\frac{1}{2}$.

(*f*) $\left(\frac{ad}{bx}+\frac{2d}{x}\right) \div \left(\frac{a}{bc}+\frac{2}{c}\right)=\frac{cd}{x}$.

(*g*) $\left(\frac{1}{a}+\frac{1}{b}\right) \div \left(\frac{1}{a}-\frac{1}{b}\right)=\frac{b+a}{b-a}$, assuming $a<b$.

(*h*) $\left(\frac{x}{y}+\frac{u}{v}\right)+\frac{m}{n}=\frac{xvn+yun+yvm}{yvn}$.

(*i*) $\frac{x}{y}+\left(\frac{u}{v}+\frac{m}{n}\right)=\frac{xvn+yun+yvm}{yvn}$.

(*j*) $\frac{x}{y}\left(\frac{u}{v}+\frac{m}{n}\right)=\frac{xun+xvm}{yvn}$.

(*k*) $\frac{x}{y}\cdot\frac{u}{v}+\frac{x}{y}\cdot\frac{m}{n}=\frac{xun+xvm}{yvn}$.

4. Is $\frac{34}{51}$ equal to, greater than, or less than $\frac{38}{57}$?

5. Is $\frac{34}{51}$ equal to, greater than, or less than $\frac{48}{69}$?

6. Arrange in order of increasing magnitude: $\frac{192}{208}$, $\frac{190}{247}$, $\frac{187}{221}$.

★**7.** Prove that if $x>y$ then $\frac{x}{y}>1$, and conversely.

★**8.** Prove that if the fraction $\frac{a}{b} \approx \frac{a'}{b'}$ and the fraction $\frac{c}{d} \approx \frac{c'}{d'}$ then the fractions $\frac{ad+bc}{bd} \approx \frac{a'd'+b'c'}{b'd'}$. (*Hint*: use theorem 1, section 19.)

★**9.** Prove that if the fraction $\frac{a}{b} \approx \frac{a'}{b'}$ and the fraction $\frac{c}{d} \approx \frac{c'}{d'}$ and if $ad>bc$, then $a'd'>b'c'$ and $\frac{ad-bc}{bd} \approx \frac{a'd'-b'c'}{b'd'}$.

22. SOME PROPERTIES OF RATIONAL NUMBERS

We have seen in connection with natural numbers that many of the familiar manipulations can be justified by the associative, commutative, and distributive laws. These laws were assumed for natural numbers only. We shall now *prove* that rational numbers obey them. As a result we shall be able to manipulate rational numbers in the usual ways.

Theorem 1. (*Compare* A_1.) *Given any pair of rational numbers* a/b *and* c/d, *in the stated order, there is a third rational number called their sum.* **(Law of closure for addition of rational numbers.)**

Proof. By definition 1, section 21.

Theorem 2. (*Compare* A_2.) *If* x/y *and* u/v *are any rational numbers, then*

$$\frac{x}{y}+\frac{u}{v}=\frac{u}{v}+\frac{x}{y}.$$

(Commutative law for addition of rational numbers.)

Proof. By definition 1, section 21, $\frac{x}{y}+\frac{u}{v}=\frac{xv}{yv}+\frac{yu}{yv}=\frac{xv+yu}{yv}$ and $\frac{u}{v}+\frac{x}{y}=\frac{uy}{vy}+\frac{vx}{vy}=\frac{uy+vx}{vy}$. Now $yv=vy$, $xv=vx$ and $yu=uy$ by M_2. Thus $xv+yu=vx+uy$. Finally, $vx+uy=uy+vx$ by A_2. The theorem follows by E_3.

Theorem 3. (*Compare* A_3.) *If* x/y, u/v, m/n *are any rational numbers,*

$$\left(\frac{x}{y}+\frac{u}{v}\right)+\frac{m}{n}=\frac{x}{y}+\left(\frac{u}{v}+\frac{m}{n}\right).$$

(Associative law for addition of rational numbers.)

Proof. Use the results of exercises 3(*h*) and 3(*i*) of section 21.

Theorem 4. (*Compare* M_1.) *If* a/b *and* c/d *are any rational numbers, given in the stated order, there exists a third rational number called their product.* **(Law of closure for multiplication of rational numbers.)**

Proof. By definition 1, section 20.

Theorem 5. (*Compare* M_2.) *If* x/y *and* u/v *are any rational numbers,*

$$\frac{x}{y}\cdot\frac{u}{v}=\frac{u}{v}\cdot\frac{x}{y}.$$

(Commutative law for the multiplication of rational numbers.)

Proof. Left to the reader.

Theorem 6. (*Compare* M_3.) *If* x/y, u/v, m/n *are any rational numbers*

$$\left(\frac{x}{y}\cdot\frac{u}{v}\right)\frac{m}{n} = \frac{x}{y}\left(\frac{u}{v}\cdot\frac{m}{n}\right).$$

(Associative law for the multiplication of rational numbers.)

Proof. Left to the reader.

Theorem 7. (*Compare D.*) *If* x/y, u/v, m/n *are any rational numbers, then*

$$\frac{x}{y}\left(\frac{u}{v}+\frac{m}{n}\right) = \frac{x}{y}\cdot\frac{u}{v}+\frac{x}{y}\cdot\frac{m}{n}.$$

(Distributive law for rational numbers.)

Proof. Use exercises 3(j) and 3(k) of section 21.

We may use these theorems to good advantage in simplifying expressions involving rational numbers.

Example. Prove that $\frac{x}{y}\left(\frac{cy}{x}+\frac{my}{nx}\right) = \frac{m}{n}+c$. By the distributive law for rational numbers,

$$\frac{x}{y}\left(\frac{cy}{x}+\frac{my}{nx}\right) = \frac{x}{y}\cdot\frac{cy}{x}+\frac{x}{y}\cdot\frac{my}{nx}$$

$$= \frac{xcy}{yx}+\frac{xmy}{ynx} \qquad \text{(definition 1, section 20)}$$

$$= \frac{c}{1}+\frac{m}{n} \qquad \text{(definition 2(}a\text{), section 19)}$$

$$= \frac{m}{n}+\frac{c}{1} \qquad \text{(commutative law for addition of rational numbers)}$$

$$= \frac{m}{n}+c.$$

The ancient Greeks were acquainted with fractions but regarded a fraction as a relation between two numbers. From the modern point of view, a rational number is considered as a single number *because it does have many important properties in common with the natural numbers, such as the associative, commutative, and distributive laws.*

We have proved that rational numbers have the properties enunciated for natural numbers in postulates A_1, A_2, A_3, M_1, M_2, M_3, and D. An important consequence of this is that rational numbers must therefore have the properties enunciated for natural numbers in all the theorems which follow from these postulates alone. That is, any theorem about natural numbers whose proof depends only on the seven postulates mentioned can be converted into a correct theorem about rational numbers by merely changing the term "natural number" into the term "rational number." This is so because, since the postulates are true of rational numbers, all their consequences must be, too. Another way to put this is that if we based an abstract mathematical science on the seven postulates mentioned, writing mumbo instead of natural number, then interpreting the undefined term mumbo as meaning natural number would yield a concrete interpretation of this mathematical science; while interpreting the undefined term mumbo as meaning rational number would yield a different concrete interpretation of the same abstract mathematical science.

By this time the student is beginning to see how a great many of the manipulations of symbols which he learned by rote in school are really logical consequences of a few simple postulates and definitions which in turn are suggested by experience. It goes without saying that mechanical manipulations are quicker for the technician who does not wish to waste time, and there is no harm in using short cuts and trick devices provided their use is preceded by a clear understanding of the reasoning behind them. However, if mechanical devices *replace* reasoning, the purposes and ideals of mathematics are forgotten and we are merely learning a trade by memory, much as some sea captains navigate without understanding trigonometry, upon which navigation is based. In any case, *our* purpose is not technical facility but rather understanding of the logical structure of algebra.

Exercises

1. Simplify, justifying each step by means of a definition, theorem, or postulate, all letters representing natural numbers.

(*a*) $5\left(\frac{1}{5} + 5\right)$. (*b*) $\frac{1}{3} \cdot \frac{5}{7} + \frac{1}{3} \cdot \frac{16}{7}$. (*c*) $\frac{3 + 9x}{3}$. (*d*) $\frac{2 + 3}{2 + 9}$.

(*e*) $\dfrac{\frac{1}{2} + \frac{1}{3}}{\frac{1}{2} - \frac{1}{3}}$. (*f*) $\dfrac{\frac{a}{b} + \frac{c}{d}}{\frac{a}{b} - \frac{c}{d}}$, assuming that $ad > bc$. (*g*) $\dfrac{\frac{2}{3} - \frac{2}{5}}{1 + \frac{2}{3} \cdot \frac{2}{5}}$.

(*h*) $\dfrac{\frac{1}{a} + \frac{1}{b}}{1 - \frac{1}{a} \cdot \frac{1}{b}}$ if $ab > 1$.

$$(i)\ \frac{\dfrac{r}{s}-\dfrac{u}{v}}{1+\dfrac{r}{s}\cdot\dfrac{u}{v}} \qquad \text{if } rv > su.$$

2. Prove, justifying each step by means of a definition, theorem, or postulate, all letters representing natural numbers:

$(a)\ \left(\frac{p}{q}+\frac{m}{n}\right)\frac{a}{b}=\frac{am}{bn}+\frac{ap}{bq}.$ $\qquad (b)\ \frac{a}{b}\left(\frac{bc}{ad}+\frac{be}{a}\right)=\frac{c}{d}+e.$

$(e)\ \frac{6}{5b}\left(\frac{10bc}{3}+\frac{db}{a}\right)=4c+\frac{6d}{5a}.$ $\qquad (d)\ \frac{1}{x}\left(\frac{x}{y}+x\right)=\frac{1}{y}+1.$

$(e)\ \frac{x}{y}\left[\frac{cy}{x}+\left(\frac{m}{n}\div\frac{x}{y}\right)\right]=\frac{m}{n}+c.$

$(f)\ \frac{a}{b}\left(\frac{bc}{a}+\frac{bd}{a}\right)=c+d.$

(*g*) Theorem 3.
(*h*) Theorem 5.
(*i*) Theorem 6.
(*j*) Theorem 7.

3. Prove, using definition 2 of section 21, and theorems of the present section:

if $\frac{a}{b}>\frac{c}{d}$ and $\frac{c}{d}>\frac{e}{f}$, then $\frac{a}{b}>\frac{e}{f}$.

4. Prove that if $\frac{a}{b}>\frac{c}{d}$, then $\frac{a}{b}+\frac{x}{y}>\frac{c}{d}+\frac{x}{y}$.

References

Numbers refer to the bibliography at the back of the book.

Archibald 4
Ball 12
Bell 20
Cajori 46, 47
Cogan 52
Cohen and Ehrlich 53
Dantzig 62
Dresden 65
Eves 70
Eves and Newsom 71
Fine 74, 75
Smith 181
Whitehead 206
Young 215

4

Further Evolution of the Number System

23. INTRODUCTION

In the last chapter we discussed in considerable detail the logical development of the simplest numbers, that is, the natural numbers and the rational numbers. These numbers satisfied the practical needs of man for many thousands of years and were the only ones dealt with until comparatively modern times. In this chapter we shall discuss still other types of numbers such as negative, irrational, and imaginary numbers. We shall make no attempt to carry through many strictly logical proofs in connection with these more sophisticated kinds of numbers, since such a task would be too difficult. We shall, however, indicate why it was natural for these numbers to be invented, and we shall try to dispel some of the misconceptions which you may have about them.

24. DIRECTED NUMBERS

Among the rational numbers, it is possible to add, multiply, and divide freely, since the sum, product, and quotient of any two fractions exist within the system of rational numbers (that is, are rational numbers). But it is still impossible to subtract a larger rational number from a smaller one, or even a rational number from itself. In other words, the system of rational numbers is closed under the operations of addition, multiplication, and division, but not under subtraction. We shall remedy this situation by extending the idea of number in a fundamental way. Corresponding to each number already in existence, such as 3, we invent two new symbols or marks, such as $+3$ and -3. Corresponding to the number $\frac{1}{2}$ we invent two new symbols $+\frac{1}{2}$ and $-\frac{1}{2}$. The symbols preceded by a plus sign are called **positive numbers** and those preceded by a minus sign are called **negative numbers**. We also invent a new symbol 0, called **zero**. The symbols 0, $+1$, $+2$, $+3$, and so on, and -1, -2, -3, and so on, are called **integers**, or **whole numbers**. (The Latin word *integer* means whole.) We speak of positive and negative integers, and of positive and negative rational numbers. Zero is neither positive nor negative.

All these new symbols are called **directed numbers** or **signed numbers**. They are so-called because they may be interpreted geometrically in terms of direction. This is done by choosing a line, a suitable unit of length, and a starting point on the line which we shall call the origin. To the origin we attach the number zero. Marking off equal intervals in both directions (Fig. 26), we attach positive integers to marked points in one direction and negative integers in the other.

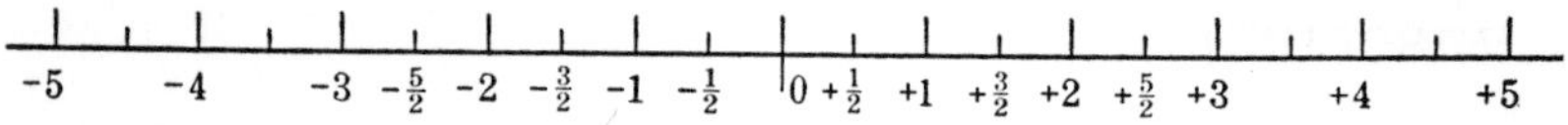

$-5 \quad -4 \quad -3 \quad -\frac{5}{2} \quad -2 \quad -\frac{3}{2} \quad -1 \quad -\frac{1}{2} \quad 0 \quad +\frac{1}{2} \quad +1 \quad +\frac{3}{2} \quad +2 \quad +\frac{5}{2} \quad +3 \quad +4 \quad +5$

FIG. 26

The other positive and negative rational numbers are also attached to points on the line in the obvious way. It is customary to use the right-hand side of the line for the positive numbers.

Notice that the plus and minus signs in the symbols $+3$ and -3 are not intended to indicate the operations of addition and subtraction, but are merely marks to distinguish one direction from another. We might well have denoted $+3$ and -3 by ${}_R3$ and ${}_L3$, respectively, to indicate the right-hand 3 and the left-hand 3. Or we might have used black and red ink. However, we shall adhere to the usual notation to avoid confusing you. The numbers studied in the preceding chapter will be called **unsigned numbers** to distinguish them from our new signed or directed numbers.

The idea of a negative number struggled for recognition for centuries and was received with great reluctance as late as the early years of the seventeenth century, even by mathematicians. Negative numbers were often called false or fictitious numbers. Now it is true that no one ever saw -3 books on a table. But the whole point is that directed numbers are no longer to be interpreted as quantity or magnitude alone. One way of interpreting them is as quantity or magnitude together with direction. To try to think of -3 as referring to taking away 3 books from an empty table is to miss the point completely. But since these new things involve a new idea, namely, direction, why do we call them numbers? Simply because, when we have made the appropriate definitions of addition and multiplication, they will have many of the characteristics of our former numbers, such as the commutative, associative, and distributive laws. In fact, we will be careful to make our definitions of addition and multiplication in such a way as to insure the validity of these laws. As for applications, they are convenient for such things as east and west, up and down, profit and loss, past and future, temperature above and below zero, a push in one direction and a push in the opposite direction, etc.

In fact, to question whether a word, like "number," *can be permitted* to have a certain meaning is foolish, because the meaning of any word or symbol is merely a matter of agreement. All that one may reasonably demand is that the writer inform us what he *intends* a given symbol or word to mean.* This point was encountered by Alice in Lewis Carroll's *Through the Looking Glass* when Humpty Dumpty said:

"'When *I* use a word, it means just what I choose it to mean—neither more nor less.'

"'The question is,' said Alice, 'whether you *can* make words mean so many different things.'

"'The question is,' said Humpty Dumpty, 'which is to be the master—that's all.'"

Since these directed numbers were created by us, it is up to us to decide what we shall mean by the sum, product, etc., of two directed numbers. Our definition of the sum of two directed numbers will be motivated by Fig. 26.

Suppose we stand at the origin facing the positive direction and interpret each successive directed number as a marching order. The directed number $+2$ will mean "march forward (that is, to the right) 2 units," while the directed number -2 will mean "march backward (that is, to the left) 2 units." The plus sign for addition will mean "and then." Zero will be interpreted as "do not march at all." The number attached to the point at which we arrive at the end is called the *sum* of the given directed numbers.

Example 1. $(+3) + (+2)$ means walk forward 3 units and then walk forward two units. We arrive at the point marked $+5$. Hence $(+3) + (+2) = +5$. Note that the plus signs within the parentheses on the left indicate positive numbers while the plus sign between the two sets of parentheses indicates the operation of addition. It would be preferable to avoid this ambiguity by reserving the plus sign for the operation of addition and to write ${}_R3 + {}_R2 = {}_R5$, but we shall not do this because of the weight of habit and tradition.

Example 2. $(+5) + (-2)$ means walk 5 units forward and then 2 units backward, arriving at the point marked $+3$. Hence, $(+5) + (-2) = +3$, or ${}_R5 + {}_L2 = {}_R3$.

* In discussions of social problems, this is, unfortunately, seldom done. The futility of many debates is due to the *undeclared* use of different meanings for the same word.

Example 3. $(+2)+(-5)$ means walk forward 2 units and then 5 units backward. Hence $(+2)+(-5)=-3$, or ${}_R2+{}_L5={}_L3$.

Example 4. $(+3)+(-3)$ means walk forward 3 units and then backward 3 units. Hence $(+3)+(-3)=0$, or ${}_R3+{}_L3=0$.

Example 5. $(-3)+(-2)$ means walk backward 3 units and then backward 2 units. Hence $(-3)+(-2)=-5$, or ${}_L3+{}_L2={}_L5$.

Example 6. Clearly, any number plus zero will be the given number again, since zero means "do not march at all."

This intuitive idea of walking back and forth on the line of Fig. 26 is expressed formally in the following definition of addition of directed numbers. The formal definition seems complicated only because of the necessity for treating exhaustively all possible cases so that the definition of the new term "sum of two directed numbers" is given in terms of old terms, namely, operations on unsigned numbers. For example, we would like $(+5)+(-2)$ to be $+3$; this can be written formally as $(+5)+(-2)=+(5-2)$ where the $5-2$ in the parentheses on the right means subtraction of the *unsigned* numbers 5 and 2. This subtraction has a sense since $5>2$. But we could not write $(+2)+(-5)$ as $+(2-5)$ because the difference $2-5$ of the *unsigned* numbers 2 and 5 does not exist since $2<5$. Hence in this case we write $(+2)+(-5)=-(5-2)$ or -3 since the difference $5-2$ of the unsigned numbers 5 and 2 does have a present meaning. The several cases in the following definition are numbered so as to correspond to the numbered examples above. *There is no need to memorize this formal definition; the intuitive idea of walking up and down on the line of Fig. 26 suffices for working numerical examples.*

Definition 1. *If a and b are unsigned numbers, then:*

Case 1. $(+a)+(+b)=+(a+b)$;

Case 2. $(+a)+(-b)=(-b)+(+a)=+(a-b)$ if $a>b$;

Case 3. $(+a)+(-b)=(-b)+(+a)=-(b-a)$ if $a<b$;

Case 4. $(+a)+(-b)=(-b)+(+a)=0$ if $a=b$;

Case 5. $(-a)+(-b)=-(a+b)$;

Case 6. $(+a) + 0 = 0 + (+a) = +a,$
$(-a) + 0 = 0 + (-a) = -a,$
$0 + 0 = 0.$

Exercise. Substitute particular numbers in each case of definition 1 and verify that it yields the expected results. Interpret each illustration on a diagram like that of Fig. 26.

It is convenient to identify our positive (signed) numbers with our previous unsigned numbers. We shall do this from here on. Hence we shall write 3 and +3 interchangeably.

Our definition of multiplication of directed numbers will be motivated by our desire to have directed numbers behave as much like our former (unsigned) numbers as possible. For example, we would like them to obey the commutative and distributive laws.

Definition 1, section 16, tells us that $3 \cdot 2$ means $2 + 2 + 2$. Therefore we would like $3 \cdot (-2)$ to mean $(-2) + (-2) + (-2)$ or -6; that is, $3 \cdot (-2)$ means what you get by counting out three -2's and adding them up. However, we cannot similarly let $(-2) \cdot 3$ mean what you get by counting out -2 threes and adding them up. But, since we want the commutative law to remain in force, we would like $(-2) \cdot 3$ to be the same as $3 \cdot (-2)$, that is, -6. Similarly, we want $3 \cdot 0$ to mean $0 + 0 + 0$ or 0; because we want to keep the commutative law, we want $0 \cdot 3$ to be 0 as well.

As for the mysterious case $(-3)(-2) = +6$ we may motivate it by referring to the distributive law. Consider the expression $(-3)[(-2) + 2]$. We want the distributive law to hold so that

$$(-3)[(-2) + 2] = (-3)(-2) + (-3) \cdot 2.$$

But the left member is $(-3) \cdot 0$ which we should like to be zero. Hence the right member $(-3)(-2) + (-3) \cdot 2 = 0$. The second term, as we have already decided, should be -6. Hence $(-3)(-2) + (-6) = 0$. For this to be true, $(-3)(-2)$ should be 6. Notice that we have not *proved* that $(-3)(-2) = 6$. We have only shown that if we want the distributive law and other former rules to remain valid we have to *define* $(-3)(-2) = 6$.

Another consideration that suggests this definition is the following. We would certainly like $(-3)(-2)$ to be either $+6$ or -6. Now $(-6) = (-3) \cdot 2$ by previous agreement. If we took $(-3)(-2) = -6$ and *if* we wanted the axiom that "if equals are divided by equals, the results are equal" to hold, then $(-3)(-2) = (-3) \cdot 2$ would yield $(-2) = 2$ (dividing both sides by -3). This is undesirable.

Since we find it convenient to have our rules operate without exception we make the following definition of multiplication of directed numbers.

Definition 2. *If a and b are unsigned numbers,*

Case 1. $(+a)(+b) = +(ab)$,

Case 2. $(-a)(-b) = +(ab)$,

Case 3. $(+a)(-b) = (-b)(+a) = -(ab)$,

Case 4. $\begin{cases} (+a)\cdot 0 = 0(+a) = 0, \\ (-a)\cdot 0 = 0\cdot(-a) = 0, \\ 0\cdot 0 = 0. \end{cases}$

This is sometimes called the "rule of signs." Briefly, it states that the product of two numbers with like signs is positive; with unlike signs, negative.

Note that $2\cdot 3 = 6$ is 3 less than $3\cdot 3 = 9$, and $1\cdot 3 = 3$ is 3 less than $2\cdot 3 = 6$. Hence we would like $0\cdot 3$ to be 3 less than $1\cdot 3 = 3$, or 0; and we would like $(-1)3$ to be 3 less than $0\cdot 3 = 0$, or -3; and we would like $(-2)3$ to be 3 less than $(-1)3 = -3$, or -6. Similarly, we note that $1(-3) = -3$ is 3 more than $2(-3) = -6$. Hence we would like $0(-3)$ to be 3 more than $1(-3) = -3$, or 0; and we would like $(-1)(-3)$ to be 3 more than $0(-3) = 0$, or $+3$; and we would like $(-2)(-3)$ to be 3 more than $(-1)(-3) = +3$, or $+6$. These desires for uniform behavior are satisfied by our definition 2.

Subtraction and division of directed numbers will be defined as the inverses of addition and multiplication, respectively, as before.

Definition 3. *If a and b are any directed numbers, then $a - b$ shall mean a directed number x such that $b + x = a$, if such a number exists.*

For example $(-2)-(-3)$ means a number x such that $(-3)+x = -2$; thus $x = 1$, since $(-3)+1 = -2$; hence $(-2)-(-3) = 1$. Similarly, $2-(-3)$ means a number x such that $(-3)+x = 2$; thus $x = 5$, since $(-3)+5 = 2$; hence $2-(-3) = 5$. The results obtained here from our definition 3 are exactly what would be obtained from the familiar rule, learned by rote in high school: to subtract a second quantity from a first, change the sign of the second and add.

Note that the minus sign is being used in two different ways: to indicate negative numbers and to indicate the operation of subtraction. It might be preferable to use $_L2$ instead of -2 for the negative number "minus two" and reserve the minus sign for the operation of subtraction. Then $2-(-3) = 5$

would be written $2 -_L 3 = 5$. However, we shall adhere to the customary notation.

It is intuitively evident and it can be proved that the difference between any two directed numbers *always exists* and is unique.

Definition 4. *If a and b are any directed numbers, $a \div b$ shall mean the unique directed number x such that $bx = a$, if such a number exists.*

It can be shown that, except for the case where $b = 0$, to be discussed in the next section, the quotient $a \div b$ of any two directed numbers exists and is unique.

Examples. $(-6) \div 2$ means a directed number x such that $2x = -6$; thus $x = -3$, since $2(-3) = -6$; hence $(-6) \div 2 = -3$. Similarly, $6 \div (-2)$ means a number x such that $(-2)x = 6$; thus $x = -3$, since $(-2)(-3) = 6$; hence $6 \div (-2) = -3$. Finally, $(-6) \div (-2)$ means a number x such that $(-2)x = -6$; thus $x = 3$, since $(-2)3 = -6$; hence $(-6) \div (-2) = 3$.

This suggests the familiar "rule of signs" for division: the quotient of two numbers of like sign is positive, the quotient of two numbers of unlike sign is negative.

Exercises

Calculate, using the appropriate definitions:

1. $5 + (-2)$. **2.** $5 - (-2)$. **3.** $(-5) + 2$. **4.** $(-5) + (-2)$.
5. $(-5) - (-2)$. **6.** $(-5) - 2$. **7.** $(-5) \cdot 2$. **8.** $5 \cdot (-2)$.
9. $(-5) \cdot (-2)$. **10.** $(-8) \div 2$. **11.** $(-8) \div (-2)$. **12.** $8 \div (-2)$.

25. THE NEGATIVE OF A DIRECTED NUMBER

Definition. *The **negative** of a directed number x is a directed number having the property that when it is added to x the sum is zero. The negative of a directed number x is denoted by $-x$. In other words, $-x$ stands for the number $0 - x$.*

Example. The negative of $(+3)$ is (-3) since $(+3) + (-3) = 0$. Similarly, the negative of (-3) is $(+3)$ since $(-3) + (+3) = 0$. Hence $-(+3) = -3$ and $-(-3) = +3$. That is, $+3$ and -3 are negatives of each other.

In general, x and $-x$ are negatives of each other; thus $-(-x) = x$.

That is, if a directed number x is interpreted as a marching order, starting from 0, then $-x$ shall signify what you must do to get back to 0 after obeying the order "x." Thus, the order "$-x$" undoes the order "x."

This is still a third meaning for the minus sign. It can be shown that no trouble arises from this triple use of the minus sign. For example, it is easy to prove that $-a = (-1)a$ for any signed number a.

We could now prove that the associative, commutative, and distributive laws hold for directed numbers; we shall not do so here. All the rules for manipulating fractions carry over to directed numbers in an obvious way. For example,

$$\frac{ax}{bx} = \frac{a}{b},$$

where a, b, x are any directed numbers (b and $x \neq 0$). The fraction line is used interchangeably with the $\div$ sign. In short, *our definitions enable you to manipulate directed numbers as you have been taught to do it in secondary school.* While we shall not establish all this in detail here, we prove the following theorems as illustrations; each of them justifies a manipulation long familiar to the student.

Theorem 1. *If a and b are any directed numbers, then $a - b = a + (-b)$.*

Proof. Note that the minus sign on the left indicates the operation of subtraction, while the one on the right indicates the negative of b (definition above). By definition 3 of section 24, we have only to show that b plus the right member equals a. But

$$\begin{aligned} b + [a + (-b)] &= [a + (-b)] + b && \text{(commutative law for addition)} \\ &= a + [(-b) + b] && \text{(associative law for addition)} \\ &= a + 0 && \text{(definition above)} \\ &= a && \text{(definition 1, section 24).} \end{aligned}$$

This completes the proof.

Theorem 1 says that subtraction of b is equivalent to addition of $-b$. To apply the commutative law for addition, say, to $a - b$, it is understood that we are to write the expression as a sum first; thus, $a - b = a + (-b) = (-b) + a$.

Theorem 2. *If a and b are any directed numbers, then $a - (-b) = a + b$.*

Proof. By theorem 1, a minus $(-b)$ is equal to a plus the negative of $(-b)$. But the negative of $(-b)$ is b. Hence, $a - (-b) = a + b$.

Theorem 3. *If a and b are any directed numbers, then $a(-b) = -(ab)$.*

Proof. By definition above and definition 2 of section 24,

$$a[b + (-b)] = a \cdot 0 = 0.$$

By the distributive law,

$$a[b + (-b)] = ab + a(-b).$$

Hence,

$$ab + a(-b) = 0.$$

By definition above, this means that $a(-b)$ is the negative of ab. This completes the proof.

Theorem 4. *If a and b are any directed numbers, then* $(-a)(-b) = ab$.

Proof. By theorem 3, $(-a)(-b)$ equals the negative of $(-a)b$. But $(-a)b = -(ab)$ by theorem 3 and the commutative law for multiplication. Hence the negative of $(-a)b$ equals the negative of $-(ab)$, that is, ab. Hence, $(-a)(-b) = ab$.

It can also be proved that $\frac{-a}{b} = \frac{a}{-b} = -\frac{a}{b}$ and $\frac{-a}{-b} = \frac{a}{b}$, where a and b are any signed numbers, $b \neq 0$.

We shall use these rules for manipulating directed numbers in the remainder of the book without explicit mention.

Our rules for manipulating directed numbers fit in well with applications such as the following.

Example 1. Consider the rectangles in Fig. 27. The area of the unshaded rectangle is $(a - c)(b - d)$, or $[a + (-c)][b + (-d)]$. Applying the distributive law to this expression we get $[a + (-c)]\, b + [a + (-c)]\, (-d) = ab + (-c)b + a(-d) + (-c)(-d)$. Now using our definitions for multiplying directed numbers, we get $ab - cb - ad + cd$ as the area of the unshaded rectangle. This is in agreement with the geometry of the situation, for ab is the area of the entire large rectangle, cb is the area of the shaded horizontal rectangle, ad is the area of the shaded vertical rectangle, and cd is the area of the cross-shaded rectangle. Our result is in agreement with the geometric interpretation of each term, because in subtracting cb and ad from ab we have subtracted the cross-shaded area twice and therefore have to put it back once by adding the term cd. However, this *does not prove* that the definition $(-c)(-d) = cd$ *must* be adopted. It merely shows that *if* we want our multiplication of directed numbers to be applicable

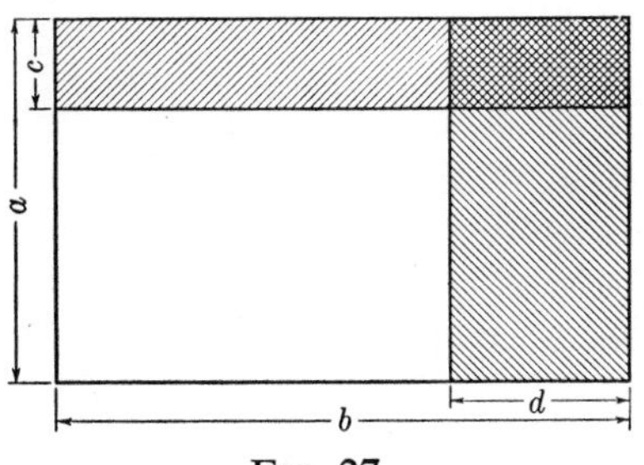

FIG. 27

to the geometrical situation above and *if* we want the distributive law to hold for directed numbers, *then* we should make the *definition* $(-c)(-d) = cd$.

Example 2. If the water level in a tank is rising at the steady rate of 2 inches per minute, and we want to know how much higher it will be in 3 minutes from now, the answer is $3 \cdot 2$ or 6 inches. The usual rule is $rt = a$ (rate times time equals amount). Suppose we interpret negative time as referring to the past and negative rate as meaning that the water level is sinking. We can say that if the water level is rising at the rate of 2 inches per minute, then 3 minutes ago it was $2(-3) = -6$ inches "higher" or 6 inches lower. If the water level is sinking at the rate of 2 inches per minute, we might say it is rising at the rate of -2 inches per minute. Then 3 minutes from now it will have risen $(-2) \cdot 3 = -6$ inches; that is, it will have sunk 6 inches. Similarly, 3 minutes ago (that is, -3 minutes from now), it would be $(-2)(-3) = +6$ inches higher. Our rules for directed numbers evidently fit this practical situation. But we have *not proved* here that our rules are correct. We have only shown that *if* we want our rules for negative numbers to fit this application and *if* we want the formula $rt = a$ to apply in all cases, *then* we should *define* $(-2)(-3) = 6$.

Exercises

1. Does $-a$ always represent a negative number? Illustrate.

Calculate and simplify each of the following:

2. $\frac{1}{3} + \frac{-2}{3}$. **3.** $\frac{-1}{3} + \frac{-2}{3}$. **4.** $\frac{-1}{3} + \frac{3}{2}$. **5.** $\frac{1}{3} - \frac{3}{2}$.

6. $-\frac{1}{3} - \frac{3}{2}$. **7.** $\left(-\frac{1}{3}\right)\left(\frac{2}{3}\right)$. **8.** $\left(-\frac{1}{3}\right)\left(-\frac{2}{3}\right)$.

9. $\left(-\frac{1}{3}\right) \div \left(\frac{2}{3}\right)$. **10.** $\frac{1}{3} \div \left(-\frac{2}{3}\right)$. **11.** $\left(-\frac{1}{3}\right) \div \left(-\frac{2}{3}\right)$.

12. $[3 + (-2)] + (-4)$. **13.** $3 + [(-2) + (-4)]$.

14. $(-3)[5 + (-2)]$. **15.** $(-3)5 + (-3)(-2)$.

16. $\frac{2 - (-2)(-3)}{(-4)(+3) - (-2)}$. **17.** $3 + (-1)(-2)\left(-\frac{5}{6}\right) - (-4) \div (-8)$.

18. Prove that:

(*a*) $\frac{-6}{3} = -2$; (*b*) $\frac{6}{-3} = -2$; (*c*) $-\frac{6}{3} = -2$; (*d*) $\frac{-6}{-3} = 2$.

★**19.** Prove that $-a = (-1)a$.

★**20.** Prove that if a and b are any signed numbers, $b \neq 0$, then

(*a*) $\frac{-a}{b} = \frac{a}{-b}$; (*b*) $\frac{-a}{b} = -\frac{a}{b}$; (*c*) $\frac{-a}{-b} = \frac{a}{b}$.

★**21.** By means of the generalized distributive law, simplify:
(*a*) $(-1)(a-b)$; (*b*) $(-1)(-a+b)$.

★**22.** Prove, by means of the definition above, that:
(*a*) $-(a-b) = -a+b$; (*b*) $-(-a+b) = a-b$.

26. THE SYSTEM OF RATIONAL NUMBERS

All the numbers introduced so far, namely zero, the positive and negative integers, and the positive and negative rational numbers (and no others), are called **rational numbers**. The word "rational" does not mean reasonable. It comes from the word ratio; every rational number can be expressed as a quotient or ratio of two integers.

When we had natural numbers only, the sum and product of two natural numbers was always a natural number, but we could not say as much about quotients and differences. With unsigned rational numbers we could say that the sum, product, or quotient of any two unsigned rational numbers was always an unsigned rational number, but we could not say as much for differences. But the system of all rational numbers is closed under addition, subtraction, multiplication, and division save for one exceptional case. That is, it can now be proved that the sum, difference, product, and quotient of any two rational numbers exist within the system of rational numbers, with the single exception that *division by zero must be excluded.* Why we must make this exception will be seen at once from the definition of division:

The quotient $a \div b$ is the unique number x such that $bx = a$, if such a number exists.

Let us attempt to apply this definition with $b = 0$. Now either $a \neq 0$ or $a = 0$.

Case 1. Let $a \neq 0$. Then $a \div 0$ means a number x such that $0 \cdot x = a$. But $0 \cdot x = 0$ no matter what number x is and $a \neq 0$. Hence the definition cannot be satisfied. For example, $3/0$ means a number x such that $0 \cdot x = 3$, provided such a number x exists. But clearly no such number can exist since $0 \cdot x = 0$ and not 3 no matter what x is.

Case 2. If $a = 0$, $a \div 0$ or $0 \div 0$ means a number x such that $0 \cdot x = 0$; but this equation is satisfied by any number x whatever and hence is quite useless.

Therefore division by zero is excluded in all cases.

This is analogous to the following situation. Suppose the only requirement for admission to the college were that one must be more than 30 feet tall. Then no one could satisfy the requirement. This is analogous to case 1 where no number can satisfy the requirement of the definition. Case 2 is analogous to the situation we would find if the only entrance requirement were that one must be less than 30 feet tall. Then the requirement excludes no candidate. Neither arrangement is a usable requirement.

On the other hand, $0 \div b$ does have a definite value if $b \neq 0$. By definition $0 \div b$ means a number x such that $bx = 0$. There is such a number x, namely zero. *Thus* $0 \div b = 0$ *if* $b \neq 0$. For example, $0 \div 3$ means a number x such that $3x = 0$; hence $x = 0$. That is, $0 \div 3 = 0$.

Note that $0/1 = 0$ while $1/0$ is a meaningless symbol, since there exists no number satisfying the definition of $1/0$. To say that a symbol has no meaning is not the same as to say it has the meaning "zero." A student who is not registered for this course receives no mark in it; a student must register for the course before he can aspire to the mark of zero.

Amusing results can be obtained if division by zero is overlooked. (We assume for the moment that the student recalls some secondary school algebra.) For example, let Alice be a years old and Betty be b years old. Suppose the two girls are of the same age. Then $b = a$. Multiplying both sides of this equation by a, we obtain $ab = a^2$. Subtracting b^2 from both sides of the equation, we obtain $ab - b^2 = a^2 - b^2$. Factoring, we have $b(a - b) = (a + b)(a - b)$. Dividing both sides by $(a - b)$ we have $b = a + b$, or $b = a + a$, or $b = 2a$. Thus Betty discovers to her dismay that she is twice as old as Alice. The trouble is, of course, that we have divided by $a - b$ which is zero since $a = b$ by hypothesis, and division by zero has been excluded. If division by zero were permissible we could obtain a somewhat oversimplified system of arithmetic which might well appeal to some students although it would not be very practical. For, from the result $b = 2a$ just obtained above, we get $a = 2a$ and hence, dividing by a, we obtain $1 = 2$. Then $3 = 2 + 1 = 1 + 1 = 2 = 1$, and $4 = 3 + 1 = 1 + 1 = 2 = 1$, and so on. Hence all numbers would be equal to each other and there would be no such thing as a wrong answer.

As remarked above, the quotient of any two rational numbers exists except when the divisor is zero. In particular, $1/a$ exists if $a \neq 0$.

Definition 1. *If* $a \neq 0$, *the number* $1/a$ *is called the* ***reciprocal*** of a.

Note that division by $a(\neq 0)$ is equivalent to multiplication by $1/a$.

The number zero has another important property, which will be useful later, as follows.

Theorem 1. *If* $ab = 0$ *and* $a \neq 0$, *then* b *must be* 0.

Proof. Since $a \neq 0$, there is a rational number $1/a$. By hypothesis, $ab = 0$. Multiplying both sides by $1/a$, we have

$$\frac{1}{a}\cdot ab = \frac{1}{a}\cdot 0. \tag{1}$$

By our now familiar processes of algebra, the left member becomes $\frac{ab}{a}$ or b and the right member becomes 0. Hence (1) becomes $b = 0$, which is what we had to prove.

This theorem may be stated in other ways, as follows: *the product of two non-zero numbers cannot be zero; if the product of two numbers is zero, at least one of the factors is itself zero; the product of two numbers can be zero only when one or the other (or both) of the factors is zero.*

We may characterize rational numbers by means of the following theorem, which we shall not prove here.

*A number is **rational** if and only if it can be expressed as the quotient a/b of two integers a and b, with $b \neq 0$.*

Thus $\frac{-7}{2}$ and $\frac{3}{-21}$ are rational numbers.

We can classify rational numbers as follows:

Rational Numbers
- *Integers* (rational numbers which can be expressed as fractions with denominators = 1)
  - *Negative integers*
  - *Zero*
  - *Positive integers or Natural Numbers.*

Exercises

1. If a and b are any two rational numbers, which of the following expressions must also represent a rational number:

(*a*) $a + b$; (*b*) $a - b$; (*c*) $a \cdot b$; (*d*) $a \div b$?

2. If a and b are any two integers, which of the expressions in exercise 1 must also represent an integer?

3. Which of the following systems are closed under addition? (*a*) the system of all even numbers; (*b*) the system of all odd integers; (*c*) the system of all integral multiples of 3; (*d*) the system consisting of the numbers 0 and 1 alone; (*e*) the system consisting of $-1, 0, 1$ alone.

4. Which of the systems of exercise 3 are closed under multiplication? subtraction? division, except for division by zero?

27. POWERS AND ROOTS

The following definition is no more than an abbreviation.

Definition 1. *If n is a natural number, x^n means $x \cdot x \cdots x$ with n factors.*

For example, $x^3 = xxx$. The **exponent** n is merely the number of factors. We say that x^n is the ***n*th power** *of* x. We term x^2 the **square** of x, and x^3 the **cube** of x.

Definition 2. *If there exists a number x such that $x^n = a$, n being a natural number, then x is called an* ***n*th root** *of a. In particular if $x^2 = a$, x is called a* ***square root*** *of a, and if $x^3 = a$, x is called a* ***cube root*** *of a.*

For example, 3 is a square root of 9 since $3^2 = 9$. Similarly, (-3) is a square root of 9 since $(-3)^2 = 9$. Both 2 and -2 are fourth roots of 16 since $2^4 = 16$ and $(-2)^4 = 16$. A cube root of 8 is 2.

If a is a positive number, we shall use the radical sign $\sqrt[n]{a}$ to denote the positive nth root of a, provided such a positive nth root exists. The number n written above the radical sign is called the **index** of the root. In the case of square roots it is customary to omit the index 2. Thus $\sqrt{9}$ stands for 3, but not for -3. If we wish to indicate -3 we shall write $-\sqrt{9}$. This agreement is made in order to avoid the confusion that would arise if we allowed the symbol $\sqrt{9}$ to stand for either 3 or -3 ambiguously. Similarly, although both 2 and -2 are fourth roots of 16, the symbol $\sqrt[4]{16}$ will mean 2 alone. We shall be almost always concerned with positive nth roots of positive numbers, only; these are unique whenever they exist.

We make the linguistic agreement that *powers shall take precedence over multiplication and division, except where parentheses indicate otherwise.* For example, $5 \cdot 2^3 = 5 \cdot 8 = 40$ while $(5 \cdot 2)^3 = 10^3 = 1000$. *The radical sign, however, acts as parentheses; all indicated operations under the radical sign are to be done before extracting the root.* For example, $\sqrt{9 + 16}$ means $\sqrt{(9 + 16)} = \sqrt{25} = 5$.

It may be conjectured that our radical sign (from the Latin word *radix* meaning "root") comes from the letter r and the *vinculum* $\overline{}$ (a Latin word meaning "bond") which was often used as we use parentheses. For example, older books might write $a \cdot \overline{b + c} = ab + ac$ for our distributive law. Hence $\sqrt{x + y}$ means $\sqrt{(x + y)}$.

Theorem 1. *If n is any positive integer, then $(xy)^n = x^n y^n$.*

Proof. $(xy)^n = (xy)(xy)\cdots(xy)$ where there are n parentheses. By the generalized associative law for multiplication we have

$$\begin{aligned}(xy)^n &= xyxy \cdots xy \\ &= xx \cdots xyy \cdots y && \text{(commutative law for multiplication)} \\ &= x^n y^n && \text{(by definition 1).}\end{aligned}$$

For example, $(xy)^3 = (xy)(xy)(xy) = xxxyyy = x^3y^3$.

Theorem 2. *If n is any positive integer, then $\sqrt[n]{a}\cdot\sqrt[n]{b} = \sqrt[n]{ab}$, provided that all these nth roots exist, a and b being positive.*

Proof. Let $x = \sqrt[n]{a}$; then $x^n = a$ by definition 2. Let $y = \sqrt[n]{b}$; then $y^n = b$. By theorem 1, $(xy)^n = x^n y^n = ab$. Hence $xy = \sqrt[n]{ab}$ by definition 2. By substitution we have $\sqrt[n]{a}\cdot\sqrt[n]{b} = \sqrt[n]{ab}$.

For example, $\sqrt{4}\cdot\sqrt{9} = \sqrt{4\cdot 9} = \sqrt{36}$.

Exercises

1. Find *(a)* $\sqrt[3]{27}$; *(b)* $\sqrt[4]{16}$; *(c)* $\sqrt{49}$; *(d)* $\sqrt[5]{32}$; *(e)* $\sqrt[6]{64}$; *(f)* $\sqrt[4]{81}$.

2. Is it true that $\sqrt{a^2 + b^2} = a + b$? Illustrate with particular numbers replacing a and b.

3. Of what is $a + b$ a square root? (We assume some previous knowledge of algebra here.)

4. Is it true that $\sqrt{a^2 - b^2} = a - b$? Illustrate with particular numbers replacing a and b.

5. Of what is $a - b$ a square root? (We assume some previous knowledge of algebra here.)

6. Is it true that $\sqrt{x + y} = \sqrt{x} + \sqrt{y}$? Illustrate with particular numbers replacing x and y.

7. Is it true that $\sqrt{x - y} = \sqrt{x} - \sqrt{y}$? Illustrate with particular numbers replacing x and y.

Simplify each of the following, assuming all indicated numbers exist and all letters represent positive numbers:

8. $(\sqrt{5})^2$. **9.** $\sqrt{\dfrac{1 - \frac{1}{2}}{2}}$ **10.** $\sqrt{36 + 64}$.

11. $\sqrt{1 - \left(\dfrac{\sqrt{3}}{2}\right)^2}$. **12.** $(\sqrt[3]{a})^3$. **13.** $(\sqrt[5]{x^2})^5$.

14. $(\sqrt[p]{x})^p$. **15.** $2\cdot 3^2$. **16.** $(2\cdot 3)^2$.

17. $2 + 2\cdot 3^2$. **18.** $(2 + 2)\cdot 3^2$. **19.** $2 + (2\cdot 3)^2$.

20. $(2 + 2\cdot 3)^2$. **21.** $([2 + 2]3)^2$. **22.** $\sqrt{16x^2}$.
23. $\sqrt{2x}\,\sqrt{32x}$. **24.** $\sqrt{2xy}\,\sqrt{18xy}$. **25.** $(\sqrt{5x})^2$.

★**26.** Prove that if n is any positive integer, then $\sqrt[n]{\dfrac{a}{b}} = \dfrac{\sqrt[n]{a}}{\sqrt[n]{b}}$, provided that all these nth roots exist, a and b being positive.

28. INEQUALITIES

For signed or directed numbers, we define inequality as follows.

Definition. *If a and b are any signed numbers, we say that a* ***is greater than*** *b, or b* ***is less than*** *a, in symbols $a > b$, or $b < a$, if and only if $a - b$ is positive.*

In other words, $a > b$ if and only if there exists a *positive* number x such that $b + x = a$. The symbol $a \geqq b$, or $b \leqq a$, means that a is greater than or equal to b. On the line of Fig. 26, $a > b$ means that a lies to the right of b. Thus $5 > 2$, $2 > -3$, $-3 > -5$. The statement x is positive is equivalent to $x > 0$; x is negative is equivalent to $x < 0$. If a and b are any signed numbers, one and only one of the three relations $a > b$, $a = b$, $a < b$ holds. Statements of the form $a > b$, $a \geqq b$, $a < b$, or $a \leqq b$ are termed **inequalities**.

Theorem 1. *If $a > b$ and $b > c$, then $a > c$.*

Proof. By definition, $a - b = x$ and $b - c = y$ where x and y are positive. Adding left members and right members of these equations we get $(a - b) + (b - c) = x + y$. (Reason?) Thus $a - c = x + y$. But $x + y$ is positive. Hence $a > c$.

Theorem 2. *If $a > b$, then $a + c > b + c$ where c is any number.*

Proof. By hypothesis, $a = b + x$ where x is positive. Adding c to both sides we have $a + c = (b + c) + x$. Hence $a + c > b + c$.

Two inequalities are said to have the **same sense** if their symbols for inequality point in the same direction; they are said to have **opposite senses** if their symbols for inequality point in opposite directions.

Theorem 3. *If $a > b$ and c is positive, then $ac > bc$. That is, the sense of an inequality is not changed if both sides are multiplied by the same positive number.*

Proof. By hypothesis, $a = b + x$ where x is positive. Multiplying both sides by c, we get $ac = bc + xc$. But xc is positive by the rule of signs. Hence $ac > bc$.

Theorem 4. *If $a > b$ and c is negative, then $ac < bc$. That is, the sense of an inequality is reversed if both sides are multiplied by the same negative number.*

Proof. By hypothesis, $a = b + x$ where x is positive. Hence $ac = bc + xc$ and xc is negative. Subtracting ac and xc from both sides, we have $-xc = bc - ac$. But $-xc$ is positive. Hence $bc > ac$.

Corollary *If $a > b$, then $-a < -b$.*

Proof. Take $c = -1$ in theorem 4.

Theorem 5. *If $a > b$ and if $ab > 0$, then $\frac{1}{a} < \frac{1}{b}$.*

Proof. Case 1. Suppose a and b are both positive. By hypothesis, $a = b + x$ where x is positive. Multiplying both sides by $\frac{1}{ab}$ we get $\frac{1}{b} = \frac{1}{a} + \frac{x}{ab}$. But $\frac{x}{ab}$ is positive. Hence $\frac{1}{b} > \frac{1}{a}$.

Case 2. Suppose a and b are both negative. The proof in this case is left as an exercise.

The proofs of theorems 6, 7, and 8 are left as exercises.

Theorem 6. *If $a > b$ and $c > d$, then $a + c > b + d$. That is, if unequals are added to unequals in the same sense, then the results are unequal in the same sense.*

Theorem 7. *If a, b, c, d are positive and if $a > b$ and $c > d$, then $ac > bd$.*

Theorem 8. *If a and b are positive and $a > b$, then $a^n > b^n$ where n is any positive integer.*

Theorem 9. *If a and b are positive and $a > b$ and the numbers $\sqrt[n]{a}$ and $\sqrt[n]{b}$ exist, where n is a positive integer, then $\sqrt[n]{a} > \sqrt[n]{b}$.*

Proof. Let $x = \sqrt[n]{a}$ and $y = \sqrt[n]{b}$. Then one and only one of the relations $x < y$ or $x = y$ or $x > y$ holds. If $x < y$ held, then $x^n < y^n$, by theorem 8, or

$a < b$ contrary to hypothesis. If $x = y$ held, then $x^n = y^n$, or $a = b$ contrary to hypothesis. Hence neither of these two relations can hold. But one of the three relations $x < y$, $x = y$, or $x > y$ must hold. Therefore $x > y$, or $\sqrt[n]{a} > \sqrt[n]{b}$.

Remark 1. We have just used the so-called **indirect method** of proof, or ***reductio ad absurdum*** which the student first met in geometry. It consists in showing that a supposition A leads logically to a false conclusion B, so that A must be false. (Compare section 4, exercise 1.) If all but one of various alternatives are thus shown to be false, and one of them must be true, then the remaining one must be true.

Remark 2. Whether $x > 0$, $x = 0$, or $x < 0$, we must have $x^2 \geqq 0$, by the rule of signs for multiplication.

Exercises

1. Illustrate each of Theorems 1 through 9 by means of a numerical example, and draw a diagram for each example.

Prove each of the following:

2. If $2x - 6 < 0$, then $x < 3$, and conversely.
3. If $4x - 3 < x + 9$, then $x < 4$, and conversely.
4. If $x^2 < 9$, then $-3 < x < 3$, and conversely.
5. If $x^2 > 4$, then $x > 2$ or $x < -2$, and conversely.
6. Theorem 6.
7. Theorem 7.
8. Theorem 8 for the case $n = 2$.
9. Theorem 8 for the case $n = 3$.
10. If $2x + 4y < 8$, then $x < 4 - 2y$.
11. If $3x - 2y < 4$, then $y > (3x/2) - 2$.
12. If $4x + 2y < 3$, then $y < -2x + \frac{3}{2}$.
13. If $4x - 2y < 5$, then $y > 2x - \frac{5}{2}$.
14. If $x - 3y > 6$, then $y < \frac{1}{3}x - 2$.

★**15.** If $x < y$, then $x < \dfrac{x + y}{2} < y$.

★**16.** If $x_1 \leqq x_2$, $w_1 \geqq 0$ and $w_2 \geqq 0$, and not both w_1 and w_2 are zero, then

$$x_1 \leqq \frac{w_1 x_1 + w_2 x_2}{w_1 + w_2} \leqq x_2.$$

★**17.** If x_1, x_2, x_3 are any three numbers and x_1 is the smallest and x_3 the largest, then

$$x_1 \leqq \frac{x_1 + x_2 + x_3}{3} \leqq x_3.$$

★**18.** If x_1, x_2, x_3 are any three numbers and x_1 is the smallest and x_3 is the largest and $w_1 \geqq 0$, $w_2 \geqq 0$, $w_3 \geqq 0$, and not all three of w_1, w_2, w_3 are zero, then

$$x_1 \leqq \frac{w_1x_1 + w_2x_2 + w_3x_3}{w_1 + w_2 + w_3} \leqq x_3.$$

★19. If $x_1, x_2, \cdots, x_n$ are any n numbers and x_1 is the smallest and x_n the largest, then

$$x_1 \leqq \frac{x_1 + x_2 + \cdots + x_n}{n} \leqq x_n.$$

★20. If in addition to the hypothesis of exercise 19, we have $w_1 \geqq 0$, $w_2 \geqq 0, \cdots$, $w_n \geqq 0$ and not all the numbers $w_1, w_2, \cdots, w_n$ are zero, then

$$x_1 \leqq \frac{w_1x_1 + w_2x_2 + \cdots + w_nx_n}{w_1 + w_2 + \cdots + w_n} \leqq x_n.$$

21. Prove that if $0 \leqq r \leqq r' < d$, then $0 \leqq r' - r < d$.

29. DIVISION WITH REMAINDER

It is a somewhat unpleasant fact that the word "division" is used in two different senses in connection with the system of integers. In the sense already taken up, to divide an integer n by a non-zero integer d means to find an integer q, called the *quotient*, such that $n = dq$. This quotient q may not exist in the system of integers, although it always does in the system of rational numbers. Thus, $14 \div 3 = \frac{14}{3}$ in the system of rational numbers, since $3 \cdot \frac{14}{3} = 14$, but there is no integer q such that $3q = 14$. If the integral quotient q exists, then n is said to be *divisible* by d in the system of integers, or n is an *integral multiple* of d. Since 14 is not divisible by 3, it must lie between two successive integral multiples of 3 (Fig. 28), namely 12 and 15, and hence is equal to $3 \cdot 4$ plus 2. We say that on

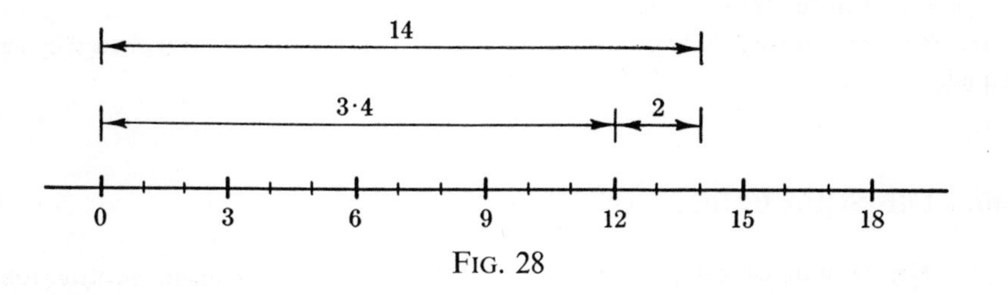

FIG. 28

dividing 14 by 3 we get a quotient of 4 and a remainder of 2. Clearly, any integer n is equal to a multiple of 3 plus either 0, 1, or 2. In general we make the following definition.

Definition. *To **divide** an integer n, the **dividend**, by a positive integer d, the **divisor**, means to find an integer q, the **quotient**, and a non-negative integer r, the **remainder**, such that*

(a) $$n = dq + r,$$

(b) $$0 \leqq r < d.$$

For example, $14 = 3 \cdot 4 + 2$, $13 = 3 \cdot 4 + 1$, and $12 = 3 \cdot 4 + 0$. Division in this sense is called **division with remainder** and is always possible in the system of integers. It can be proved that the quotient q and remainder r satisfying the definition not only always exist in the system of integers, but are in fact uniquely determined by n and d.

This sense of "division" is also a reversal of multiplication. For, multiplication by a positive integer is repeated addition, while division with remainder amounts to repeated subtraction as far as it can be done so as to leave a non-negative remainder less than d. Thus, we can subtract four 3's from 14 leaving the non-negative remainder 2, but we could not subtract five 3's since the "remainder" would then be negative (namely -1), and subtracting three 3's would leave a remainder larger than 3 (namely 4).

Exercises

Find the quotient and remainder in each of the following divisions:

1. $7 \div 2$. **2.** $18 \div 4$. **3.** $18 \div 5$. **4.** $18 \div 3$.
5. $17 \div 3$. **6.** $16 \div 3$. **7.** $15 \div 3$. **8.** $440 \div 21$.
9. $-7 \div 3$. **10.** $-14 \div 3$. **11.** $-13 \div 3$. **12.** $-20 \div 3$.

13. Prove that the q and r determined by the above definition are unique. That is, show that if $n = dq + r$, $0 \leqq r < d$, and if also $n = dq' + r'$, $0 \leqq r' < d$, then $q = q'$ and $r = r'$. (Hint: use exercise 21 of section 28.)

14. Prove that if any two of the three integers a, b, c are divisible by d, and if $c = a + b$, then the third is also divisible by d.

15. Prove that if each of two positive integers is divisible by the other then they are equal.

30. THE SQUARE ROOT OF TWO

The system of rational numbers is closed under addition, subtraction, multiplication, and division save for the unavoidable exception that division by zero is excluded. Nevertheless, we shall see that this system of rational numbers remains insufficient for our needs. We shall prove the following surprising theorem.

Theorem 1. *No rational number can be a square root of 2.*

Before proving this theorem, let us see why it is surprising. A rational number is one which can be expressed as a quotient a/b of two integers ($b \neq 0$). If we arrange the positive rational numbers according to the following scheme

$$\begin{array}{ccccc}
\frac{1}{1} & \frac{2}{1} & \frac{3}{1} & \frac{4}{1} & \frac{5}{1} \cdots \\[2ex]
\frac{1}{2} & \frac{2}{2} & \frac{3}{2} & \frac{4}{2} & \frac{5}{2} \cdots \\[2ex]
\frac{1}{3} & \frac{2}{3} & \frac{3}{3} & \frac{4}{3} & \frac{5}{3} \cdots \\[2ex]
\frac{1}{4} & \frac{2}{4} & \frac{3}{4} & \frac{4}{4} & \frac{5}{4} \cdots \\
\vdots & \vdots & \vdots & \vdots & \vdots
\end{array}$$

we see at once that every positive rational number is represented somewhere in this endless array. For example, the number 273/565 is to be found in the 273rd column and 565th row. Let us imagine the points corresponding to these numbers marked off on a line one row at a time, the number attached to each point representing its distance from the zero-point or origin. At each stage (Fig. 29) the marked points are more and more thickly strewn ("densely

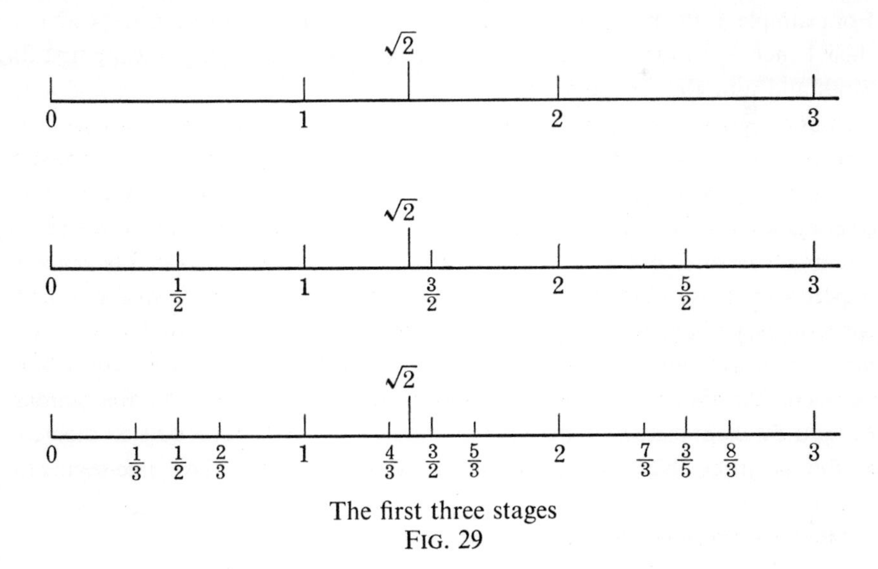

The first three stages
FIG. 29

distributed" is a technical term for this) on the line. Although it cannot* be accomplished in practice, since the number of rational numbers is unlimited, we can imagine all the rational numbers marked off on the line. You might think that they fill up the entire line. But if our theorem is correct, this is not so; despite the density of the marked points on the line there are points which are not marked. One such point can be constructed by taking an isosceles right triangle whose side is 1 unit in length. Its hypotenuse then must be $\sqrt{1^2 + 1^2} = \sqrt{2}$ by the Pythagorean theorem. The length of this hypotenuse can then be laid off on the line from the origin and the other end cannot be a marked point, if our theorem is correct. For all marked points have rational numbers corresponding to them, while our theorem asserts that $\sqrt{2}$, whatever it may be, is not a rational number. If you recall that we have assumed that *all* rational numbers, including all fractions with denominators equal to a million, a billion, a trillion, etc., have been marked off, it may seem remarkable that there is still a "gap," that is, an unmarked point, left.

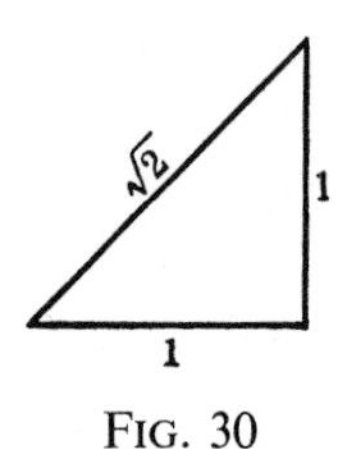

FIG. 30

The density of the rational numbers may be seen from the fact that between any two rational numbers a and b, no matter how close together, there must be another rational number; in fact, $(a + b)/2$ is such a rational number. It is not hard to see intuitively that $(a + b)/2$ is exactly midway between a and b.

Let us now look at theorem 1 from a somewhat different point of view. Consider two line-segments. A length is said to be a **common measure** of these two line-segments if it goes into *each* of them *exactly* a *whole* number of times. For example, if the two given line-segments are 1 yard and $1\frac{1}{4}$ foot, respectively, then 1 inch is a common measure for them, since 1 inch goes into the first 36 times and into the second 15 times. Similarly, a 1 foot line-segment and a $5\frac{3}{4}$ inch line-segment have $\frac{1}{4}$ inch as a common measure, since $\frac{1}{4}$ inch goes into the first 48 times and into the second 23 times. If two line-segments have a common measure they are called **commensurable**. It would seem intuitively that any two line-segments would be commensurable if only we try a small enough length as common measure. But if theorem 1 is correct, this is not the case. The leg and hypotenuse of the right triangle in Fig. 30 can have no common measure. For, suppose they could have a common measure. Then it would go into the unit leg q times and into the hypotenuse p times, where q and p are both whole numbers. But then the common measure would be represented by the number $1/q$ and the hypotenuse by the *rational* number p/q. But, according to theorem 1, this is impossible since $\sqrt{2}$ is not a rational number. Two line-segments

* However, any particular fraction can be marked off.

which have no common measure are called **incommensurable**. The existence of incommensurable lengths was probably known to Pythagoras (about the sixth century B.C.) and is said to have disturbed him so much that he tried to suppress the information lest it discredit mathematicians in the eyes of the general public.

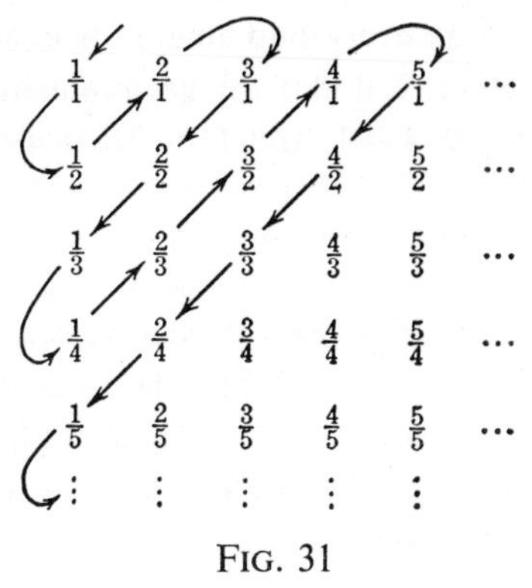

FIG. 31

Still another way to understand what our theorem asserts is to imagine all the rational numbers enumerated in some order. If we tried to enumerate them one row at a time we would never get to the second row since we could never finish the first row. Hence we enumerate them in the diagonal order indicated in Fig. 31 by the arrows, starting with 1/1. That is, we write them in the following order:

$$(A)\quad \frac{1}{1},\quad \frac{1}{2},\quad \frac{2}{1},\quad \frac{3}{1},\quad \frac{2}{2},\quad \frac{1}{3},\quad \frac{1}{4},\quad \frac{2}{3},\quad \frac{3}{2},\quad \frac{4}{1},\ \ldots .$$

In this way we must reach any given positive rational number if we proceed along the sequence (A) far enough. Our theorem asserts that none of them will yield exactly 2 when squared. This cannot be proved by trying them in succession, because life is short and there is no end to the sequence (A) of positive rational numbers. If there were only a limited number of rational numbers we could prove the theorem by testing each number. But the number of rational numbers is unlimited. If we squared the first thousand (or first billion) positive rational numbers in the sequence (A) without getting 2 as the result, we could not be sure that we might not get 2 at some later trial. It might be that we simply hadn't found the right one yet.

How then *can* we prove that no rational number can yield exactly 2 when squared? We shall need a few preliminaries.

Definition 1. *An integer is called* ***even*** *if and only if it can be expressed as $2x$ where x is some integer.*

In other words, an integer is even if it is divisible by 2, or has 2 as a factor. For example, 10 is even since $10 = 2 \cdot 5$.

Remark. Notice the necessary restriction that x be an integer. The number 3 can be expressed as $2 \cdot (3/2)$ but we would not call 3 even.

An integer which is not even is called **odd.** By the preceding section *an integer is odd if and only if it can be expressed as* $2x + 1$ *where* x *is an integer.* In other words every odd integer is exactly *one* more than some even integer. Or, an integer is odd if you get a remainder of one when you divide it by 2. For example, $7 = 2 \cdot 3 + 1$, and $11 = 2 \cdot 5 + 1$ are odd.

***Theorem A.** *If a is even, a^2 is even.*

Proof. Since a is even we can write $a = 2x$ where x is an integer, by definition 1. Thus $a^2 = (2x)^2 = 4x^2 = 2(2x^2)$. Now since x is an integer so is x^2, because the product of two integers is an integer, and hence so is $2x^2$ for the same reason. Hence a^2 has been expressed as 2 times the *integer* $2x^2$. Thus a^2 is even, by definition 1.

Theorem B. *If a is odd, a^2 is odd.*

Proof. Since a is odd we can write $a = 2x + 1$ where x is an integer. Thus $a^2 = (2x + 1)^2 = 4x^2 + 4x + 1 = 2(2x^2 + 2x) + 1$. (We assumed in this step that the student remembers how to multiply $2x + 1$ by itself. This will be taken up again in Chapter 5. Compare exercise 13, section 14.) Now since x is an integer and since the sum and product of two integers is again an integer, $2x^2 + 2x$ is an integer. Hence a^2 has been expressed as twice the *integer* $(2x^2 + 2x)$ plus 1 and is therefore odd.

Theorem C. *If n is an integer and n^2 is even, then n is even.*

Proof. Since n is an integer it is either even or odd. If n were odd, then n^2 would have to be odd by theorem B. Since n^2 is even, by hypothesis, this cannot be so. Hence the only possibility is that n is even, which is what we had to prove.

We are now ready for the proof of theorem 1.

Proof of theorem 1. Either there is a rational number $= \sqrt{2}$ or there is not. Suppose there were such a rational number; it could be reduced to lowest terms, and hence expressed as p/q where p and q are integers having no factor in common except ± 1 $(q \neq 0)$. Then,

$$p/q = \sqrt{2}.$$

If this were so, then

$$p^2/q^2 = 2. \qquad \text{(Reason?)}$$

* Theorem A is not needed, but is included to emphasize the distinction between it and theorems B and C.

Hence

$$p^2 = 2q^2. \qquad (1) \qquad \text{(Reason?)}$$

Now q is an integer; therefore q^2 is an integer. Hence (1) says that p^2 is an even integer since it is twice the integer q^2. By theorem C it follows that p is an even integer. Since p and q have no factor in common *q must be odd*, for if q were also even, p and q would have a common factor 2. Since p is even, we can write $p = 2x$ where x is an integer. Substituting this in (1) we get

$$(2x)^2 = 2q^2$$

or,

$$4x^2 = 2q^2$$

or,

$$q^2 = 2x^2. \qquad \text{(Reason?)}$$

But this says that q^2 is even since it is twice the integer x^2. By theorem C it follows that *q is even*. But the italicized statements contradict each other since q cannot be *both* even *and* odd; hence the supposition that $p/q = \sqrt{2}$ is absurd because it leads to a false conclusion. The only remaining possibility is that no rational number can be $= \sqrt{2}$, which is what we had to prove.

A simpler proof using more powerful methods is found in section 80.

Remark. In this section we used the so-called *indirect proof* or *reductio ad absurdum* again. See remark 1, section 28. That is, we show that since supposition A leads logically to a false (or, self-contradictory) conclusion B then A must be false. Hence the contrary of A must be true since one of the two, A or not-A, must be true.

Exercises

1. Prove that if a is even, then a^3 is even. (Hint: imitate as far as possible the proof of theorem A.)

2. (*a*) Prove that if a is odd, then a^3 is odd. (Hint: imitate as far as possible the proof of theorem B.)

(*b*) Prove that if n is an integer and n^3 is even, then n is even. (Hint: imitate as far as possible the proof of theorem C. Use the theorem of exercise 2(*a*).)

(*c*) Prove that no rational number is equal to $\sqrt[3]{2}$. (Hint: using exercise 2(*b*), imitate as far as possible the proof of theorem 1.)

3. Prove that if a is divisible by 3, then a^2 is divisible by 3. (Hint: by definition, an integer is divisible by 3 if and only if it can be expressed as $3x$ where x is some integer.)

4. (*a*) Prove that if a is not divisible by 3, then a^2 is not divisible by 3. (Hint: if an integer is not divisible by 3 it can be expressed as either $3x + 1$ or $3x + 2$ where x is an integer; that is, if you divide any integer by 3, you get a remainder of 0, 1, or 2. For example, $15 = 3 \cdot 5$, $16 = 3 \cdot 5 + 1$, $17 = 3 \cdot 5 + 2$, $18 = 3 \cdot 6$, ... Imitate the proof of theorem B as far as possible. There will be two cases.)

(*b*) Prove that if n is an integer and n^2 is divisible by 3, then n is divisible by 3. (Hint: imitate as far as possible the proof of theorem C. Use exercise 4(*a*).)

(*c*) Prove that no rational number is equal to $\sqrt{3}$. (Hint: using exercise 4(*b*), imitate as far as possible the proof of theorem 1.)

5. Prove that no rational number is equal to $\sqrt[4]{2}$.

★**6.** Prove that no rational number is equal to $\sqrt{5}$.

★**7.** Prove that no rational number is equal to $\sqrt[3]{3}$.

8. Prove that the sum of two even numbers is even.

9. Prove that the product of two odd numbers is odd.

10. Prove that the product of any natural number and an even number is even.

★**11.** Prove that no rational number is equal to $\sqrt{6}$. (Hint: use exercise 9.)

31. IRRATIONAL NUMBERS. DECIMAL NOTATION

The fact that no rational number is exactly equal to $\sqrt{2}$ means that our system of rational numbers contains no number which can represent the length of the hypotenuse of an isosceles right triangle whose leg is of unit length. This is regarded as an inadequacy in the rational number system. We are therefore led to invent *irrational numbers*. The word "irrational" must not be taken to mean "unreasonable"; it means not expressible as a ratio of two integers. We shall give no accurate definition of irrational number here because of the technical difficulties involved. In fact, as we remarked above, the strange story of $\sqrt{2}$ was probably known to Pythagoras (about the sixth century B.C.) but the difficulties involved were not straightened out with complete logical rigor until about 1870 when G. Cantor and R. Dedekind, two German mathematicians, did it independently of each other. However, we can point out some of the essential characteristics of irrational numbers.

Notice that the usual decimal notation for numbers, which you learned as children, is based on powers of 10. For example, 2347.568 *means*

$$2 \cdot 10^3 + 3 \cdot 10^2 + 4 \cdot 10 + 7 + \frac{5}{10} + \frac{6}{10^2} + \frac{8}{10^3}.$$

Recall the peculiar process you once memorized for extracting the square root of a number as a decimal. (Your knowledge of this weird process is a splendid example of sheer memorization without the slightest understanding. In fact, it will be unnecessary to recall the process as far as this book is concerned, for, as we shall see soon, the same results can be obtained in a more straightforward, although slower, way.) Applying this process to the task of extracting the square root of 2, we get 1.4 as a first result, but there is a remainder. If we go further we get 1.41, then 1.414, then 1.4142, and so on. At each stage the process produces a remainder and hence fails to give an exact square root of 2. In fact,

$$(1.4)^2 = 1.96 < 2 < (1.5)^2 = 2.25,$$
$$(1.41)^2 = 1.9881 < 2 < (1.42)^2 = 2.0164,$$
$$(1.414)^2 = 1.999396 < 2 < (1.415)^2 = 2.002225,$$

and so on. Hence, if $\sqrt{2}$ is to exist at all, we deduce from theorem 9 of section 28 that

$$1.4 < \sqrt{2} < 1.5,$$
$$1.41 < \sqrt{2} < 1.42,$$
$$1.414 < \sqrt{2} < 1.415,$$

and so on. Thus the decimal expression for $\sqrt{2}$ does not seem to stop. We cannot prove that it does not stop by continuing the process until we are exhausted, for if it had not stopped by the 1000th place, we could still not be sure that it would not stop at the 2000th. But we *can* in fact prove that the process *never* stops. For if it did stop we would have a terminated decimal expression for $\sqrt{2}$. Now **if a decimal terminates, then it represents a rational number**; that is, the quotient of two integers. For example, 2.315 means $\frac{2315}{1000}$. But $\sqrt{2}$ is not a rational number, by section 30. Hence its decimal expression cannot stop. However, each of the successive stages of the process gives a rational number whose square becomes closer and closer to 2. That is, *$\sqrt{2}$ is approximated by rational numbers and can be so approximated as closely as we wish* (that is, to the nearest thousandth, or millionth, etc.) by carrying the process far enough. *This is one essential characteristic of irrational numbers.*

The converse of the theorem in heavy type above would say that if a number is rational, then its decimal expression terminates. *This is not so*, as can be seen from the rational numbers

$$\tfrac{1}{3} = .3333333 \cdots$$

and

$$\tfrac{1}{7} = .142857142857142857 \cdots$$

whose decimal expressions do not terminate, as you can see from the process of obtaining them by division. Notice that both of these decimals "repeat in blocks"; in technical language they are *periodic*. In the case of $\frac{1}{7}$, notice that when you divide 1 by 7, the only remainders which can occur in the process of long division are the numbers 0, 1, 2, 3, 4, 5, 6. If 0 occurred, the process would terminate. If 0 does not occur, the only possible remainders are 1, 2, 3, 4, 5, 6. After enough steps (seven or fewer) are made in the process of long division, we must therefore get one of these remainders back again for the second time, whereupon the whole process repeats itself exactly, thus producing a periodic decimal.

Exercise. Perform the long division of 1 by 7 long enough to observe the described phenomenon.

In the same way it can be proved that if the decimal expression for any rational number p/q does not terminate, then it is necessarily periodic. It can also be proved that every periodic decimal represents a rational number. It follows that the decimal expression for $\sqrt{2}$ can neither terminate nor be periodic. Every irrational number has a decimal expression which neither terminates nor is periodic.

We shall assume that the irrational numbers fill up all the "gaps" left in the line (Fig. 29), so that every point on the line has a number attached to it, rational or irrational. These numbers are called **real**. In particular, we now have a number to represent each length, such as, for example, the hypotenuse of Fig. 30. Every real number can be expressed as a decimal, either terminating or not, and conversely. The processes of addition, subtraction, multiplication, and division can be defined for real numbers so that the sum, difference, product, and quotient of any two real numbers is again a real number, except that division by 0 remains excluded. The new numbers can be shown to satisfy the familiar laws, such as the associative, commutative, and distributive laws, and we are therefore content to call them numbers. We shall be unable to prove these statements here because we have not given a clear-cut definition of real number. The system of real numbers is subdivided into irrational and rational numbers.

You might think that irrational numbers are rare because we have pointed out only a few. But it can be shown that the square root of any positive integer which is not the square of an integer is irrational. In general, the nth root of any positive integer which is not the nth power of an integer is irrational. There are many more irrational numbers which cannot be expressed as roots at all such as $\pi = 3.14159265 \cdots$, a number you met in your geometry course. It is not hard to prove the following exercises by means of the indirect method or *reductio ad absurdum*.

Exercise A. Prove that if you add any rational number r to an irrational one, s, the sum t must be irrational. (Hint: the sum is either rational or not. Suppose it is rational and show that this leads to a contradiction.)

Exercise B. Prove that if you multiply any rational number $r(\neq 0)$ by an irrational one, s, the product t is irrational.

Hence there are at least as many irrational numbers as rational numbers such as $2\sqrt{2}$, $3\sqrt{2}$, $\frac{1}{2}\sqrt{2}$, $\cdots$ and $1 + \sqrt{2}$, $2 + \sqrt{2}$, $\frac{1}{2} + \sqrt{2}$, $\cdots$. It can be proved that between every pair of rational numbers, no matter how close together, there is an irrational one and between every pair of irrational numbers there is a rational one.

Whether a real number is rational or not does not matter to the practical engineer since measurements are never more than approximate and an irrational number can be approximated as closely as we please by rational numbers. But the idea of irrational numbers is essential to any careful theory of geometric magnitudes and to the logical derivation of the theorems of calculus, upon which much practical work is based. *All real numbers are either positive, negative, or zero, according to where they lie on the line* (Fig. 26); that is, a real number is positive or negative according as it lies to the right or the left of the origin or zero point.

Note that it is not necessary to remember the complicated process for extracting square roots. One can proceed as follows. By multiplication we find that $1^2 = 1$; $2^2 = 4$; and hence $1^2 < 2 < 2^2$, or, by theorem 9 of section 28, $1 < \sqrt{2} < 2$. Then by trying successive tenths, $(1.1)^2$, $(1.2)^2$, and so on, we find, as above, that $(1.4)^2 < 2 < (1.5)^2$ or $1.4 < \sqrt{2} < 1.5$. Then by trying successive

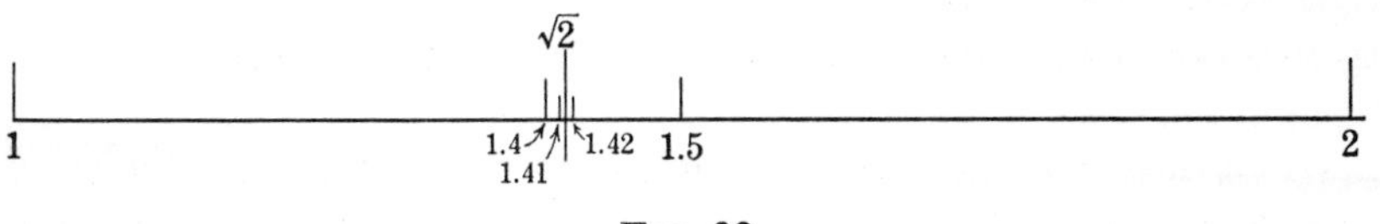

FIG. 32

hundredths we find that $(1.41)^2 < 2 < (1.42)^2$ or $1.41 < \sqrt{2} < 1.42$, and so on. This simple straightforward method of successive approximations can be applied equally well to cube roots, fourth roots, etc. It resembles the process of running down a base-runner between first and second base in a baseball game, except that while we continue to pinch the irrational number between narrower and narrower limits, we never tag it.

Remark. The word "fraction" is often used for any indicated quotient as $\sqrt{2}/3$ which is not a fraction in the sense of section 19. To avoid confusion we might now refer to the "fractions" of section 19 as "positive rational fractions."

Exercises

(*a*) *Approximate as far as three decimal places; that is, locate between successive thousandths:*

(*b*) *Write the answer correct to the nearest hundredth:*

1. $\sqrt{3}$. **2.** $\sqrt{5}$. **3.** $\sqrt[3]{2}$. **4.** $\sqrt[3]{3}$. **5.** $\sqrt[3]{5}$.

Show that each of the following numbers is irrational. (*Hint: assume it to be rational and show that this leads to a contradiction.*)

6. $1 + \sqrt{2}$. **7.** $3\sqrt{2}$. **8.** $\dfrac{\sqrt{2}}{3}$. **9.** $\dfrac{1 + \sqrt{2}}{4}$. **10.** $\dfrac{1 - \sqrt{2}}{4}$.

11. Let $a = \frac{53}{17}$, $b = \frac{58}{19}$, $c = \frac{5}{8} + \frac{31}{16} - (-\frac{23}{32}) - \frac{1}{4}$, $d = \sqrt[3]{33}$. Arrange the letters, a, b, c, d in order of increasing magnitude.

12. Let $a = \sqrt[3]{30}$, $b = \sqrt{10}$, $c = \frac{22}{7}$. Arrange the letters a, b, c in order of increasing magnitude.

32. THE SYSTEM OF REAL NUMBERS

Although it is possible to define real numbers in terms of rational numbers in a logically satisfactory way (in fact, in several ways), we shall not do so here because of technical difficulties. The interested reader is referred to more advanced books* for the details. When an adequate definition of real numbers is given it can be proved that they have the following properties:

I. *To every pair of numbers a and b, in that order, there is a unique third number denoted by* $a + b$, *called the sum of a and b.* **(Law of closure for addition.)**

II. $a + b = b + a$. **(Commutative law for addition.)**

III. $(a + b) + c = a + (b + c)$. **(Associative law for addition.)**

IV. *To every pair of numbers a and b, in that order, there is a unique third number denoted by* ab *or* $a \cdot b$, *called the product of a and b.* **(Law of closure for multiplication.)**

V. $ab = ba$. **(Commutative law for multiplication.)**

VI. $a(bc) = (ab)c$. **(Associative law for multiplication.)**

VII. $a(b + c) = ab + ac$. **(Distributive law.)**

* See McCoy [130] or Birkhoff and MacLane [28] for a method due to Dedekind, and Cohen and Ehrlich [53] or Cogan [52] for a method due to Cantor.

VIII. *There is a unique number 0, called "zero," such that*

(*a*) $0 + a = a$, *for any number* a;

(*b*) $0 \cdot a = 0$, *for any number* a;

(*c*) *if* $a \neq 0$ *and* $b \neq 0$ *then* $ab \neq 0$.

IX. *There is a unique number* 1, *different from zero, called "one," such that* $1 \cdot a = a$, *for any number* a.

X. *If* a *and* b *are any numbers, there exists a unique number* x *such that* $b + x = a$.

Definition. *This number* x *is called* $a - b$. *The number* $0 - b$ *is denoted by* $-b$.

XI. *If* a *and* b *are any numbers* ($b \neq 0$), *there exists a unique number* x *such that* $bx = a$.

Definition. *This number* x *is called* a/b.

XII. $a = a$.

XIII. *If* $a = b$, *then* $b = a$.

XIV. *If* $a = b$ *and* $b = c$, *then* $a = c$. (*Things equal to the same thing are equal to each other.*)

XV. *If equals are* (*a*) *added to,* (*b*) *subtracted from,* (*c*) *multiplied by,* (*d*) *divided by equals, the results are equal.*

XVI. *If* a *and* b *are any two numbers, then one and only one of the relations* $a < b$, $a = b$, *or* $b < a$ *holds.*

Definition. *If* $b < a$, *we also write* $a > b$.
If a number $x > 0$, *it is called* ***positive.***
If a number $x < 0$, *it is called* ***negative.***

XVII. *If* $a < b$ *and* $b < c$, *then* $a < c$.

XVIII. *If* $a < b$ *and* $c > 0$, *then* $ac < bc$.

XIX. *If* $a < b$ *and* $c < 0$, *then* $ac > bc$.

XX. *If* $a < b$ *and* c *is any number, then* $a + c < b + c$.

XXI. (*a*) *If* $a > 0$ *and* $b > 0$, *then* $ab > 0$.
(*b*) *If* $a < 0$ *and* $b > 0$, *then* $ab < 0$. **(Rule of signs.)**
(*c*) *If* $a < 0$ *and* $b < 0$, *then* $ab > 0$.

A twenty-second property, termed the *completeness property* will be discussed in Chapter 11.

If real number, sum, product, less than, are taken as undefined terms this set of twenty-two properties may be taken as postulates and serve to characterize the real number system completely. That is, all theorems about the behavior of real numbers are logical consequences of this set of postulates, although we shall not attempt to carry out this program here.

For example, from the distributive law, and others, we may deduce immediately, as in Chapter 3, such results as

$$a(b + c - d - e + f + \cdots + k) = ab + ac - ad - ae + af + \cdots + ak$$

and

$$(b + c - d - e + f + \cdots + k)a = ba + ca - da - ea + fa + \cdots + ka$$

which we shall use freely and call the **generalized distributive law.** Also, as in Chapter 3, we shall use the right to insert or remove parentheses in a sum of terms (or a product of factors), calling the justification for this the **generalized associative law for addition** (or **multiplication**).

Note that in our present abstract mathematical science, "real number," "sum," "product" are completely undefined terms. Thus counting and measuring and all the preceding work of Chapters 3 and 4 may be regarded as concrete interpretations or applications of our present abstract mathematical science. For example, we need not assume the tables of addition on the basis of experience here (as we did in Chapter 3) because we can deduce them logically from our postulates. Let us indicate briefly how this may be done. By postulate IX, there is a number 1. By postulate I, there is a number $1 + 1$; call it 2. By postulate I, there is a number $2 + 1$; call it 3. By postulate I, there is a number $3 + 1$; call it 4; and so on. We can now prove the following important theorems.

Theorem 1. $2 + 2 = 4$.

Proof. By definition, $2 = 1 + 1$ and $4 = 3 + 1 = (2 + 1) + 1$. We have to prove that $2 + 2 = 4$ or,

$$2 + (1 + 1) = (2 + 1) + 1.$$

But this follows immediately from the associative law for addition.

Theorem 2. $2 \cdot 2 = 4$.

Proof. By definition, $2 = 1 + 1$. Hence we have to prove that $2(1 + 1) = 4$. But by the distributive law, $2(1 + 1) = 2 \cdot 1 + 2 \cdot 1$. By the commutative law for multiplication and postulate IX, $2 \cdot 1 = 1 \cdot 2 = 2$. Thus $2(1 + 1) = 2 + 2$ which is 4 by theorem 1. This is what we had to prove.

In a similar fashion we could deduce the rest of the tables of addition and multiplication.

Thus the arithmetic and the algebra of real numbers can be considered as an abstract mathematical science which has no logically necessary connection with counting and measuring, but which does have counting and measuring among its applications or concrete interpretations.

Exercises

Defining 5 as $4 + 1$, 6 as $5 + 1$, and so on, prove, by means of our postulates, that:

1. $2 + 3 = 5$. **2.** $2 + 4 = 6$. (Hint: use exercise 1.)
3. $3 + 3 = 6$. (Hint: use exercise 2.) **4.** $3 \cdot 2 = 6$. (Hint: use exercise 3.)
5. $6 + 2 = 8$. **6.** $5 + 3 = 8$. **7.** $4 + 4 = 8$. **8.** $2 \cdot 4 = 8$.

33. COMPLEX NUMBERS

Our original motive for the introduction of irrational numbers was our desire to have a number to represent each length or to have a number to attach to every point on a line (Fig. 29). This implied, in particular, that we wanted some number to be the square root of 2. While our number system consisted of only rational numbers, it contained no number exactly equal to $\sqrt{2}$, so we enlarged the number system again to include irrational numbers.

Suppose we now consider any negative number, say -4. A square root of -4 would be a number x such that $x^2 = -4$. We shall now prove that such a number x cannot be found even in our larger system of real numbers. For any real number x is either positive, zero, or negative. If x is positive, x^2 is also positive and cannot be -4. If $x = 0$, then $x^2 = 0$ and not -4. Finally, if x is negative, x^2 is positive and not -4. We have exhausted all the possibilities for a real number. This argument clearly applies to any negative number. Hence negative numbers have no square roots among the real numbers. In order to remedy this situation we define complex numbers as follows.

Definition 1. *A **complex number** is an ordered pair of real numbers (a,b). Two complex numbers (a,b) and (a',b') are equal if and only if $a = a'$ and $b = b'$.*

Definition 2. *The **sum** of two complex numbers (a,b) and (a',b') is the complex number $(a + a', b + b')$.*

Definition 3. *The **product** of two complex numbers (a,b) and (a',b') is the complex number $(aa' - bb', ab' + ba')$.*

Note that if $b = b' = 0$, definitions 2 and 3 yield $(a,0) + (a',0) = (a + a',0)$ and $(a,0)\cdot(a',0) = (aa',0)$, respectively, so that the numbers $(x,0)$ behave just like the real numbers x with respect to addition and multiplication. *We therefore agree to write $(x,0)$ simply as x, and identify it with the real number x. The number $(0,1)$ is designated by i.* Note that, by definition 3, i is a square root of -1 since

$$i^2 = (0,1)\cdot(0,1) = (0\cdot 0 - 1\cdot 1, 0\cdot 1 + 1\cdot 0) = (-1,0) = -1.$$

And, in accordance with the italicized convention above, if a and b are real we may write

$$\begin{aligned} a + bi &= (a,0) + (b,0)(0,1) = (a,0) + (b\cdot 0 - 0\cdot 1, b\cdot 1 + 0\cdot 0) && \text{(by def. 3)} \\ &= (a,0) + (0,b) = (a,b) && \text{(by def. 2)} \end{aligned}$$

so that *every complex number (a,b) can be written in the form $a + bi$, where a and b are real and $i = (0,1)$ is a square root of -1.* Now, it is easily verified that -4 has square roots, namely $2i = (0,2)$ and $-2i = (0,-2)$. It is also easily verified that complex numbers satisfy properties I–XV of the preceding section, and therefore that they can be manipulated in the usual manner except that i^2 must be replaced by -1. For example,

$$(2 + 3i)(1 + 2i) = 2 + 3i + 4i + 6i^2 = 2 + 7i - 6 = -4 + 7i.$$

We call a the **real component** of the complex number $a + bi = (a,b)$ and b is called its **imaginary component.**

*Any symbol of the form bi, where b stands for a real number ($\neq 0$) and i for $(0,1)$, will be called a **pure imaginary** number.*

The **complex numbers** $a + bi$ (a and b being real and i being $(0,1)$) *include* all the previous kinds of numbers as special cases. If $b \neq 0$ the complex number $a + bi$ is called **imaginary**. For example, $3 + 5i$ is imaginary. If $a = 0$ and $b \neq 0$ we have a *pure imaginary* number as $5i$. If $b = 0$ we have a *real* number. Thus 3 can be written as $3 + 0i$ and $3i$ as $0 + 3i$. We may summarize the entire number system as it now stands:

Complex Numbers $(a + bi)$
  Imaginary $(b \neq 0)$
    Pure Imaginary $(a = 0, b \neq 0)$
  Real $(b = 0)$
    Irrational
    Rational
      Integers
        Negative integers
        Zero
        Positive integers or Natural Numbers.

Do not think that the word "imaginary" means that these numbers are mystical or fictitious or "unreal" in the everyday sense of the word, or that "complex" means complicated. It is true that pure imaginary and complex numbers did meet with opposition on some such grounds in the sixteenth and seventeenth centuries, but so did negative numbers and with as little justice. Imaginary numbers have very "real" applications in many branches of physical science, into which we cannot go here, and may be given concrete interpretations. There is no room for the imaginary numbers on the line of Fig. 29, for the real numbers already account for every point on the line. To represent imaginary numbers graphically we use a whole plane. We shall not go into this here, nor shall we stop to explain our motivation for the curious definition 3 of multiplication of complex numbers, since we shall not use imaginary numbers very much. As far as we are concerned, we are content to call them numbers for the usual reason that the familiar operations can be defined for them and that they can be shown to satisfy the familiar laws like the associative, commutative, and distributive laws. It is impossible to introduce a usable "less than" relation among all the complex numbers. Thus $<$ and $>$, and hence "positive" and "negative" are used only in connection with real numbers.

Exercises

1. Calculate: (*a*) $(2 + 3i) + (4 - 5i)$.
(*b*) $(3 - 5i) - (5 - 2i)$.
(*c*) $2i(3 + 4i)$.
(*d*) $(1 + i)(2 + 3i)$.

(*e*) $\dfrac{1}{2 + 3i}$. (*f*) $\dfrac{2 + i}{3 - 4i}$.

2. Calculate: (*a*) i^3. (*b*) i^4. (*c*) i^5.
(*d*) i^6. (*e*) i^7. (*f*) i^8.

Using the definitions given above, show each of the following:

3. $2i = (0, 2)$ is a square root of -4.

4. $-2i = (0, -2)$ is a square root of -4.

5. $-i = (0, -1)$ is a square root of -1.

6. $-\frac{1}{2} + \frac{\sqrt{3}}{2} i$ is a cube root of 1.

7. $-\frac{1}{2} - \frac{\sqrt{3}}{2} i$ is a cube root of 1.

8. $\frac{1}{2} + \frac{\sqrt{3}}{2} i$ is a cube root of -1.

9. $2i$ is a fourth root of 16.

10. $\frac{1}{2} - \frac{\sqrt{3}}{2} i$ is a cube root of -1.

11. $-2i$ is a fourth root of 16.

12. What was our original motive in introducing
(*a*) unsigned rational numbers; (*b*) negative numbers; (*c*) irrational numbers; (*d*) pure imaginary numbers; (*e*) complex numbers?

13. List all the adjectives "complex, imaginary, pure imaginary, real, irrational, rational, integral, positive, negative, zero, natural" which apply to each number:

(*a*) $2 + 3\sqrt{-4}$. (*b*) $3\sqrt{4}$. (*c*) $3\sqrt{-4}$. (*d*) $3\sqrt{5}$.

(*e*) $\frac{\sqrt{2}}{3}$. (*f*) $-\frac{2}{3}$. (*g*) $(1 + \sqrt{3})/2$. (*h*) $(1 + \sqrt{9})/2$.

14. State some properties which the systems of rational, real, and complex numbers have in common.

15. If (a, b) is different from $0 = (0, 0)$, then

$$(a, b)\left(\frac{a}{a^2 + b^2}, \frac{-b}{a^2 + b^2}\right) = (1, 0) = 1.$$

Hence,

$$\frac{1}{a + bi} = \frac{a}{a^2 + b^2} - \frac{bi}{a^2 + b^2} \qquad \text{if } a + bi \neq 0.$$

★**16.** Prove that complex numbers satisfy the associative law for multiplication.

★**17.** Prove that complex numbers satisfy the commutative law for multiplication.

★**18.** Prove that complex numbers satisfy the distributive law.

★**19.** Prove that if $a + bi$ and $c + di$ are two complex numbers whose product is zero and if $a + bi$ is not zero, then $c + di = 0$.

34. CONCLUSION

We have come a long way from the natural numbers we started with. The system of complex numbers did not spring into being full-grown. Natural numbers satisfied the needs of primitive man for an indeterminate length of time. The unsigned rational numbers became necessary when people began to share real estate or harvests of grain. These numbers arose in answer to the needs of everyday life. The others, like negative, irrational, and imaginary numbers, arose in answer to the more sophisticated needs of mathematicians. But at each stage we introduced new kinds of numbers because of some inadequacy in the system of numbers already at hand.

Recall that a system of numbers is called closed under a given operation if performing that operation on numbers in the system always yields as a result a number in the system, that is, never takes us outside the system. The system of natural numbers is closed under addition and multiplication since the sum or product of two natural numbers is again a natural number. But the system of natural numbers is not closed under division. We would like our system of numbers to be closed under all our operations, so that we may freely perform the operations and always be sure that the result is in our number system. Therefore we invented the unsigned rational numbers. The system of unsigned rational numbers is closed under addition, multiplication, and division, but not under subtraction. Therefore we invented the negative rational numbers and zero. The entire system of rational numbers is closed under addition, subtraction, multiplication, and division except that division by zero is excluded. But the system of rational numbers is not closed under the operation of taking nth roots. The irrational numbers were introduced because the rational numbers did not provide a number to attach to every point on a line, so that, in particular, not every positive rational number had a square root among the rational numbers. The system of real numbers is still not closed under the operation of taking nth roots since negative numbers have no square roots among the real numbers. Hence we invented the system of complex numbers.

The reader may now be in a state of mortal terror lest we have to extend the number system still further if we look at cube roots or some other operation. However, this will not be necessary. The complex number system is not going to be extended any further. There are several reasons for this. One reason is that the complex number system is closed under all the operations to be studied in this book. This will be discussed from a slightly different point of view in the next chapter (section 43). Another reason is that the complex numbers are sufficient for most practical applications. However, there are other number systems, some of which are called hypercomplex number systems, which are studied for various reasons in higher mathematics and which include the complex number system as a special case, much as the complex number system includes the real number system which, in turn, includes the rational number system.

The natural numbers can be considered as the basis for all the numerical portions of mathematics. All the different kinds of numbers introduced can be rigorously defined in terms of the natural numbers, although we have not done this here completely. For example, a fraction was defined as a symbol consisting of an ordered pair of natural numbers, and a rational number as a class of equivalent fractions. L. Kronecker (1823–1891) is said to have remarked that "the whole number was created by God, everything else is man's handiwork." The fundamental character of the natural numbers, alluded to by Kronecker, has led not only to the extensive study of their arithmetical properties (the theory of numbers,* one of the oldest branches of mathematics) but also, frequently, to

Leopold Kronecker
1823–1891, German

the long common practice of attributing to them mystical and supernatural properties (numerology, one of the oldest branches of balderdash). In fact, the practice of ascribing mystic properties to numbers is not confined to commercial frauds

* Many arithmetical tricks and amusements depend on the theory of numbers. See the chapter on the Theory of Numbers in J. W. A. Young, *Monographs on Topics of Modern Mathematics*, Longmans, Green, N. Y. 1932, W. W. R. Ball, *Mathematical Recreations and Essays*, Macmillan, London, 1939, and text-books on the theory of numbers.

who give marital and financial advice based on numbers assigned to your name, and so on, but has been indulged in by scientists, ancient and modern. Pythagoras, for instance, seems to have been mystically inspired by his discovery that the ratio of the frequencies of harmonious sounds is always expressible in terms of small numbers. For example, if two sounds form an octave, their frequencies are in the ratio of 2/1; if a fifth, their frequencies are in the ratio of 3/2; a fourth, 4/3; a third, 5/4; a minor third, 6/5.* The entire group of Pythagorean disciples mixed mysticism with their science. They felt, for various reasons, that in the whole numbers lay the key to the universe. It may have been this belief that caused them to be so upset about the fact that $\sqrt{2}$ is not expressible as the ratio of two whole numbers that they decided to suppress the information. The human tendency toward mysticism is seen not only in the simultaneous and often intertwined development of the mathematical theory of numbers and mystical numerology but also in the simultaneous and often intertwined development of astronomy and astrology. When we are depressed about the various forms of stupidity abroad in the world today, it may be some small comfort to reflect that only three centuries ago as great a man as Kepler wrote with equal seriousness about both astronomy and astrology.

Numerology has been taken with the utmost seriousness by some people at all times in human history. For example, according to the New Testament,† the number of the beast is 666. This statement was for many years a choice weapon of numerological theologians who would prove a man to be a heretic by attaching the number 666 to his name. This was usually done by assigning numbers to some or all of the letters in some form of his name in some language and showing that these numbers added up to 666. In the middle ages it was no laughing matter to have this done to you. Much the same kind of scheme is used today by the commerical variety of numerologists.

References

Numbers refer to the bibliography at the end of the book.

Bell 17
Birkhoff and MacLane 28
Cogan 52
Cohen and Ehrlich 53
Jeans 99
McCoy 130
All references at the end of chapter 3.

* J. H. Jeans, *Science and Music*, Macmillan, London, 1938, p. 154.
† Revelation 13:18.

5

The Logic of Algebra

The principal objective of this chapter will be to explain the logical justification of many more of the familiar manipulations of algebra which you have learned by rote in secondary school. In particular, we shall see that many results of algebra are merely logical consequences of properties I–XXI of section 32. There is no need for the student to memorize all these properties since we shall not use many of them formally.

Having justified many of the familiar elementary manipulations in Chapters 3, 4, and 5, we shall use them freely in the remainder of the book without explicit mention.

35. ALGEBRAIC EXPRESSIONS

A letter which may represent different numbers during the same discussion is called a **variable**. A symbol which is permitted to represent only one certain number throughout a discussion is called a **constant** even if we do not specify what number it represents. It is customary to use the later letters of the alphabet for variables and the earlier ones for constants. For example, x, y, z will usually represent variables and a, b, c, d will represent constants; of course, specified numbers like 2, $-3/2$, or $3 + 2\sqrt{-4}$ are constants.

The operations of addition, subtraction, multiplication, and division are called **rational operations**. The rational operations together with the operation of taking nth roots, where n is any integer >1, are called **algebraic operations**. An expression which can be built up from the variable x and any constants by means of a finite (limited) number of algebraic operations is called an **algebraic**

expression in x. For example,

$$(2x + \sqrt{3})\sqrt[3]{3x - 1} + \frac{a}{x^4}$$

is an algebraic expression in x. Note that x^4 is built up by means of multiplication alone; that is, $x^4 = xxxx$.

Remark. As an example of a non-algebraic expression we might mention the "exponential" expression 2^x. This is not algebraic because the exponent x is a variable. On the other hand, the expression x^2 is algebraic since $x^2 = xx$.

An expression which can be built up from the variable x and any constants whatever by means of a finite number of rational operations alone is called a **rational expression in x**. Thus

$$\frac{1}{x}, \frac{2x^2 - 3x + 5}{3x - 7}, \frac{1/2}{x - 2} + \frac{x}{x + 3}, \frac{2x^2 + ax - \sqrt{-1}}{\sqrt{3} + x}$$

are rational expressions in x. Note that radicals may occur in a rational expression; the essential thing is that the expression can be built up in such a way that x does not occur under a radical. The last example *is* a rational expression since it may be built up from x and the constants 2, a, $\sqrt{-1}$, $\sqrt{3}$ by rational operations alone. An algebraic expression in x which is not a rational expression (that is, which necessarily involves an nth root of some expression involving x) is called an **irrational expression in** x. Thus $1 + \sqrt{x}$ is an irrational expression in x. A rational expression in x which can be built up from the letter x and any constants by means of the operations of addition, subtraction, and multiplication alone (but not division) is called a **polynomial in** x. For example, x, $2x^2 - 7$ and

$$ax^3 + \frac{\sqrt{3}}{2}x^2 - \frac{3}{5}x + (4 + 2\sqrt{-3}) \tag{1}$$

are polynomials in x. Note that the last example is a polynomial in x even though divisions occur; the essential thing is that the expression can be built up in such a way that we do not divide by any expression involving x. For example, (1) can be built up from the letter x and the constants a, $\sqrt{3}/2$, $3/5$, and $4 + 2\sqrt{-3}$ by means of the operations of addition, subtraction, and multiplication alone and is therefore a polynomial in x. On the other hand, the rational expression $1/x$ is not a polynomial. Polynomials are a special kind of rational expression, and rational expressions are a special kind of algebraic expression.

Note that the three terms "rational number," "rational operation," and "rational expression" have entirely different meanings.

Every rational expression in x can be reduced to a quotient of two polynomials in x, by performing the indicated operations. For example, the rational expression $\frac{1}{x} + \frac{5}{x-3}$ can be reduced to $\frac{6x-3}{x^2-3x}$, by addition of fractions.

By carrying out all indicated operations as far as possible, every polynomial in x can be expressed as a sum of expressions, called its **terms**, of the form cx^n, where c is some constant and n is a natural number, or possibly a constant alone. The constant factor in a term is called its **coefficient**. For example, the polynomial $(x+1)(x-3)$ can be expressed as $x^2 - 2x - 3$ which has three terms, namely x^2, $-2x$, and -3, having the coefficients 1, -2, -3 respectively. A term of form cx^n is said to have the **degree** n; a constant term c is said to have the degree zero. A polynomial in x is said to have the same **degree** as that of its term of highest degree.

Example (1), above, is a polynomial of degree 3. The coefficients in (1) are a, $\sqrt{3}/2$, $-3/5$, and $4 + 2\sqrt{-3}$. The polynomial $(x+1)(x+2) - x^2$ is a polynomial of degree 1 since it reduces to $3x + 2$. Polynomials of degrees 1, 2, 3 are called **linear, quadratic**, and **cubic**, respectively. For example, $2x - 3$, $3x^2 + 4x - 1$, and $2x^3 - 5$ are linear, quadratic, and cubic polynomials, respectively.

Similarly, we have algebraic expressions, rational and irrational expressions, and polynomials in several variables. For example, $3x^2y^3 + 4x^2y - 3y + x - 3$ is a polynomial in x and y. A **term** in a polynomial of two variables x and y, for example, is an expression of the form cx^my^n, where c is a constant and m and n are natural numbers, or of form cx^m or cy^n, or c alone. The **degree of a term involving more than one variable** is defined to mean the sum of the exponents attached to these variables. The **degree of a polynomial in more than one variable** is defined to mean the highest of the degrees of its terms, after all indicated operations have been carried out as far as possible. The degree of the polynomial in the last example is 5.

Algebraic expressions do not represent definite numbers because of the presence of variables. If, however, we replace the variable by a definite number, the expression is either undefined or takes on a definite value. For example, the rational expression $(12 - x)/x$ has the value 5 if we let $x = 2$, the value 3 if we let $x = 3$, the value $7/5$ if we let $x = 5$, the value 0 if we let $x = 12$, and no value at all if we let $x = 0$ because division by zero is excluded. Note that to say an expression has no value at all is not the same as to say it has the value zero.

Exercises

In exercises 1–12, (a) list all the terms "algebraic expression," "irrational expression," "rational expression," "polynomial" which apply to each of the following: (b) find the value of each expression when $x = 3, y = 2$:

1. $\sqrt{3x+7}$. **2.** $6/x$. **3.** $\frac{1}{2}x^2+\sqrt{3}$. **4.** $\dfrac{5x^2-7x+1}{3-x^3}$.

5. x. **6.** $x+3y$. **7.** $\dfrac{2x-3}{x+7}$. **8.** $\dfrac{\sqrt{x}-2}{2x+1}$.

9. $2x^3+4x-7$. **10.** $\sqrt{x^2+16}$. **11.** $\dfrac{1}{(x+3y)}$. **12.** $2x^3y+3xy+7$.

13. If rational numbers are substituted for the variables in a rational expression whose coefficients are rational numbers, what kind of number must the resulting value of the expression be? Explain and illustrate.

14. If integers are substituted for the variables in a polynomial whose coefficients are integers, what kind of number must be the resulting value of the expression be? Explain and illustrate.

15. Will the value of an irrational expression for any value of the variable always be an irrational number? Explain and illustrate.

36. POLYNOMIALS. ADDITION AND MULTIPLICATION

To add two polynomials, for example, $2x^2+3x+5$ and $3x^2+4x-3$, you have learned to write "like powers" beneath each other and proceed as follows:

$$\begin{array}{r} 2x^2+3x+5 \\ 3x^2+4x-3 \\ \hline 5x^2+7x+2. \end{array}$$

Let us see how this result follows logically from our postulates. We are asked for the sum of the two expressions

$$(2x^2+3x+5)+(3x^2+4x-3).$$

For any value of x, the individual terms may be regarded as single numbers, because of the law of closure for multiplication. By the generalized associative law for addition we may remove the parentheses. Then by the commutative law for addition we may rearrange the order of the terms, obtaining

$$2x^2+3x^2+3x+4x+5-3.$$

By the generalized associative law for addition we may regroup the terms like this:

$$(2x^2+3x^2)+(3x+4x)+(5-3).$$

By the generalized distributive law $2x^2 + 3x^2 = (2 + 3)x^2$ and $3x + 4x = (3 + 4)x$. Thus we obtain

$$5x^2 + 7x + 2,$$

by substitution.

Let us recall the fact that $x^2 \cdot x^3 = x^5$. This follows from the definition of exponent. For $x^2 = xx$ and $x^3 = xxx$. Hence $x^2x^3 = (xx)(xxx) = xxxxx = x^5$. In general, we have the following theorem.

Theorem 1. *If m and n are any positive integers,* $x^m \cdot x^n = x^{m+n}$.

Proof. By definition $x^m = xx \cdots x$(m factors) and $x^n = xx \cdots x$ (n factors). Hence

$$x^m \cdot x^n = \overbrace{(xx \cdots x)}^{m \text{ factors}} \cdot \overbrace{(xx \cdots x)}^{n \text{ factors}} = xx \cdots x(m + n \text{ factors}).$$

Hence $x^m \cdot x^n = x^{m+n}$.

We can now recall the process you learned for multiplying polynomials, for example, $2x + 3$ and $3x + 4$:

$$\begin{array}{r} 2x + 3 \\ 3x + 4 \\ \hline 8x + 12 \\ 6x^2 + 9x \\ \hline 6x^2 + 17x + 12. \end{array}$$

How can this result be justified on the basis of our postulates? We want the product $(2x + 3)(3x + 4)$. By the laws of closure for addition and multiplication, $2x + 3$ is a single number for any particular value of x. Hence, treating the first parenthesis as a single quantity with a long name, the distributive law enables us to write

$$(2x + 3)(3x + 4) = (2x + 3)3x + (2x + 3)4.$$

(This line already gives clear instructions for carrying out the usual short scheme above; that is, it tells us to multiply the top line by 4, and to multiply the top line by $3x$, and to add these two products.)

Using the generalized distributive law on each of the terms of the right member, we get

$$2x \cdot 3x + 3 \cdot 3x + 2x \cdot 4 + 3 \cdot 4.$$

By the commutative law for multiplication, we obtain

$$2 \cdot 3 \cdot x \cdot x + 3 \cdot 3 \cdot x + 2 \cdot 4 \cdot x + 3 \cdot 4.$$

By the generalized associative law for multiplication, we get

$$(2\cdot 3)(x\cdot x) + (3\cdot 3)x + (2\cdot 4)\cdot x + 3\cdot 4$$

or

$$6x^2 + 9x + 8x + 12.$$

By the generalized associative law for addition this may be written

$$6x^2 + (9x + 8x) + 12.$$

But $(9x + 8x) = (9 + 8)x = 17x$ by the generalized distributive law. Hence we obtain, finally, $6x^2 + 17x + 12$.

Of course the short arrangement of the work you learned in school is far quicker than what we have done, and no one in his right mind would prefer what we have done *if his purpose were to obtain the right answer quickly*. But our purpose is not technical facility but the logical deduction of our results from our postulates or assumptions. We have thus indicated that the queer processes of addition and multiplication of polynomials, which you learned by memory in school, may be justified on the basis of our postulates. We shall not stop to show how more complicated processes like division or extraction of square roots may be justified similarly on the basis of our postulates.*

Exercises

Perform the indicated operations by means of the usual short scheme, and then derive the same result from our postulates, justifying each step:

1. $(2x^2 + 5x + 3) + (5x^2 + 4x + 2)$.
2. $(3x + 2)\cdot(4x + 5)$.
3. $(3x^3 + 2x + 6) + (x^3 + 4x^2 + 5x + 1)$.
4. $(x^2 + 2x + 3)\cdot(2x + 4)$.
5. $(x + y)(x + y)$.
6. $(x + y)(x - y)$.
7. $(x - y)(x - y)$.
8. $(2ax + b)(2ax + b)$.
9. $\left[x + \frac{b}{2a}\right]\left[x + \frac{b}{2a}\right]$.
10. $(7x + 3)\cdot(2x - 1)$.
11. $(2x + 5xy + y^2) + (3x - xy - 4y^2)$.
12. $(x - y)\cdot(x^2 + xy + y^2)$
13. $(x + y)(x^2 - xy + y^2)$.
14. $(x^2 - 5x - 3) - (3x^2 - x + 2)$.

* See M. Richardson, *College Algebra*, Third edition, Prentice-Hall, Englewood Cliffs N. J., 1966, sections 41 and 18, for explanations of these processes.

37. FACTORING

We have just multiplied two polynomials to obtain their product. Frequently it is convenient to be able to begin with the product and tell what factors were multiplied to obtain it. This is called **factoring.** It is usually much harder to factor or "unmultiply" than it is to multiply, just as it is much harder to unscramble eggs than it is to scramble them. In fact we shall not take up any systematic method of factoring, but will consider only the simplest special cases.

Case 1. *Taking out a common factor.* For example, $3x^2 + 6xy + 9x^2y = 3x(x + 2y + 3xy)$. This, we have already observed, is merely an application of the (generalized) distributive law.

Case 2. *Difference of two squares.* We observe and remember that $(a + b)(a - b) = a^2 - b^2$ by direct multiplication. Hence we factor $x^2 - y^2 = (x + y)(x - y)$.

Case 3. *Quadratic trinomials.* These are factored by trial and error. For example, to factor $x^2 - 5x + 6$, we see that, if it can be factored, it must be the product of two linear factors of the form $(x - ?)(x - ?)$. We experiment with various values in place of the question marks until we arrive at $(x - 3)(x - 2)$.

In short, *we factor essentially by remembering our experiences in multiplying.* To check the correctness of our factoring, we have only to multiply our factors together and see if we get back the original expression. Whether a polynomial can be factored or not is not a simple question. It depends (among other things) on what kind of numbers you are willing to allow as coefficients in the factors. For example, $x^2 - 2$ is not factorable if you insist on rational coefficients in the factors, but it can be factored into $(x + \sqrt{2})\ (x - \sqrt{2})$ if you allow irrational coefficients. Similarly, $x^2 + 1$ cannot be factored if you insist on real coefficients in the factors, but it can be factored into $(x + \sqrt{-1})(x - \sqrt{-1})$ if you allow imaginary coefficients.

Exercises

Factor and check:

1. $4x^3 + 2xy + 2xy^2$.
2. $6x^2y - 4xy^2 + 8x^3y^3$.
3. $x^2 - 16$.
4. $9x^2 - 4a^2b^2$.
5. $x^2 - 7x + 12$.
6. $2x^2 + 5x - 12$.
7. $4x^2 - 5x - 6$.
8. $3x^2 - 2x - 8$.

9. $2x^3 + 5x^2 - 3x$.
10. $2x^4 - x^3 - 15x^2$.
11. $y^2 + 2ky + k^2$.
12. $y^2 - 2ky + k^2$.
13. $4a^2x^2 + 4abx + b^2$.
14. $x^2 + \frac{b}{a}x + \frac{b^2}{4a^2}$.
15. $(x + 2)^2 - (y - 1)^2$.
16. $(x - 3)^2 - (y + 2)^2$.
17. $(x + 3)^2 + 5(x + 3) + 6$.
18. $(x - 2)^2 - (x - 2) - 12$.
19. $(x + y)^2 - 4(x + y) - 12$.
20. $(x + y)^2 - 11(x + y) - 12$.

38. EQUATIONS

The equation

$$2(x + 3) = 2x + 6 \tag{1}$$

seems to say that two different expressions are "equal." But an algebraic expression has no definite value unless we first assign a numerical value to the variable x. What, then, does it mean to say that these expressions are "equal"? In this example, it means that no matter what number x represents, the resulting values of the two expressions will be equal. Thus, if $x = 1$, the statement (1) asserts that $2(1 + 3) = 2 \cdot 1 + 6$ or $2 \cdot 4 = 2 + 6$; if $x = 2$, it says that $2(2 + 3) = 2 \cdot 2 + 6$ or $2 \cdot 5 = 4 + 6$, and so on.

Definition 1. *If an equation becomes a true statement for every value of x for which each expression involved has a value, it is called an* ***identical equation*** *or an* ***identity***.

Thus (1) is an identity. Also,

$$\frac{1}{x - 2} + \frac{1}{x - 1} = \frac{2x - 3}{(x - 2)(x - 1)}$$

is an identity; it has no sense for the values $x = 1$ and $x = 2$ since division by zero is meaningless, but for all other values of x it is true, as we may verify by adding the two fractional expressions on the left. Similarly, $\frac{1}{x} = \frac{3}{3x}$ is an identity since it is true for all values of x except $x = 0$ for which value the expressions involved have no meaning.

Consider, however, the equation

$$2x + 3 = x + 6. \tag{2}$$

This is clearly not an identity, because for $x = 1$ it says that $5 = 7$ which is notoriously false. In fact, an equation cannot be considered an assertion (that is, a proposition) at all until a value has been assigned to x; and when values or meanings have been assigned to the variable x, the resulting statement may be true or false, or simply nonsense. Such statements which contain variables are often called "propositional functions"; they become "propositions" only when we have substituted meanings or values for the variables which make the resulting statements either true or false (see section 5). For example, $x + y = 5$ is a propositional function, while $2 + 3 = 5$ is a true proposition and $2 + 4 = 5$ is a false proposition. Similarly, equation (2), which is a sentence with the verb "is equal to," is a propositional function. If we substitute $x = 1$ in it, we get the false proposition $5 = 7$. If we substitute $x = 3$ in it, we get the true proposition $9 = 9$. We say $x = 3$ *satisfies the equation* $2x + 3 = x + 6$, or *makes it true*; 3 is called a *root* of the equation. If an equation is not an identity, it is called *conditional.* That is, we make the following definition.

Definition 2. *If an equation becomes a false statement for some value of the unknown, it is called a* **conditional equation** *or simply an* **equation.** *A value of x which does satisfy the equation, that is, a value of x for which the equation becomes a true statement, is called a* **root** *of the equation. To* **solve** *an equation means to find its roots.*

In other words, the roots of an equation are the members of the truth-set of the propositional function which the equation expresses. This truth-set may be the empty set. That is, a conditional equation may have no root; for example, $1/x = 0$, or $x = x + 3$. These are propositional functions which are true for no value of the unknown. Similarly, "x is a man more than 30 feet tall" is a propositional function which is false no matter what meaning or value we substitute for x.

For example, let us prove that

$$x(x + 3) + 6 = x^2 + 3(x + 2)$$

is an identity. To prove this we try to reduce the statement to something which we recognize as an identity. Using the distributive law we obtain

$$x^2 + 3x + 6 = x^2 + 3x + 6$$

which is clearly true by identity. But what have we really proved? Our reasoning has been: if the first line is true, then the second line must be true; and the second line is true. Does it follow that the first line is therefore true? Certainly not! From "A implies B and B is true" it does not follow that A is true (see section 4).

What we really need is the converse proposition "if the second line is true, then the first must be true," because "B implies A and B is true" *does* imply that A is true. Since the converse proposition does not follow automatically (a valid proposition may have an invalid converse), we must prove it independently. This can be done by simply starting from the bottom and working up to the original statement, *provided* each step we made on the way down is *reversible.* In the above example this is so. In fact, *if the only steps taken are merely substitutions then, clearly, the argument can be reversed.* For if a step was made by replacing a by its equal b, the reverse step can be made by replacing b by its equal a.

But one must guard against non-reversible steps. For instance, assuming that

$$3 = 7,$$

we can write

$$7 = 3,$$

and, therefore, adding both sides of these equations, we obtain

$$10 = 10$$

because if equals are added to equals the results are equal. We cannot conclude from the truth of our conclusion that our hypothesis was true. Similarly the proposition "if $a = b$, then $a^2 = b^2$" is true because if equals are multiplied by equals the results are equal. But the converse "if $a^2 = b^2$, then $a = b$" is false. For instance, from the assumption $-3 = +3$ we can conclude that $9 = 9$ since $(-3)^2 = 3^2$; but from the truth of the latter statement we cannot infer the truth of the former. However, it is true that "if $a^2 = b^2$, then $a = +b$ or $a = -b$." Similarly, from the assumption $3 = 7$ and the fact that $0 = 0$, we get, by multiplication, the result $0 = 0$ since if equals are multiplied by equals the results are equal. But we cannot infer from the truth of the conclusion that the hypothesis was true. All of these examples exhibit non-reversible steps.

A method for verifying identities which does not involve us with the question of reversible steps is to leave one member of the equation untouched and to substitute various equivalent expressions for the other until it becomes identical in appearance with the first member. This establishes the identity by virtue of the axiom "things equal to the same thing are equal to each other." This procedure is often convenient.

We shall be concerned principally with polynomial equations, that is, equations of which both members are polynomials. Thus,

$$3x^2 + 5x - 6 = x^2 + x - 1$$

is a polynomial equation. Since if equals are subtracted from equals the results are equal, we may subtract the right member from both sides, obtaining

$$3x^2 + 5x - 6 - (x^2 + x - 1) = x^2 + x - 1 - (x^2 + x - 1),$$

or, using the associative, commutative, and distributive laws and the rule of signs,

$$2x^2 + 4x - 5 = 0.$$

The process of subtacting the right member from both sides was known to you in school as "transposing." Similarly, *every polynomial equation can be written with a polynomial on the left and zero on the right of the equals sign.* When this is done, the degree of the polynomial on the left is called the **degree of the equation.** Equations of degrees 1, 2, 3 are called **linear**, **quadratic**, and **cubic**, respectively. Every linear equation can be written in the form $ax + b = 0$ where a and b are constants ($a \neq 0$). Every quadratic equation can be written in the form $ax^2 + bx + c = 0$ ($a \neq 0$). Every cubic equation can be written in the form $ax^3 + bx^2 + cx + d = 0$ ($a \neq 0$), and so on.

Many elementary practical problems in geometry, surveying, commerce, etc., lead to the necessity for solving equations. Some easy ones are given in section 47. In Europe these problems began to demand attention in the thirteenth century, when algebra, as we know it, began its slow development. We shall now study the problem of solving or finding the roots of equations.

Exercises

Verify the identities:

1. $x^2 + 2(x - 3) = x(x + 2) - 6.$

2. $\dfrac{2}{x - 1} + \dfrac{1}{x} = \dfrac{3x - 1}{x^2 - x}.$

3. $\dfrac{1}{x} + \dfrac{2}{x - 3} = \dfrac{3x - 3}{x^2 - 3x}.$

4. $\dfrac{2x}{3x - 1} + \dfrac{2}{x - 2} = \dfrac{2(x^2 + x - 1)}{(3x - 1)(x - 2)}.$

5. $2(3x + [x + 1] + 2[x + 3\{x - 1\}]) = 24x - 10.$

6. $\dfrac{x + 2}{x} + \dfrac{x + 3}{3x} = \dfrac{4x + 9}{3x}.$

7. $\dfrac{\dfrac{x}{y} - \dfrac{y}{z}}{\dfrac{x}{y} + \dfrac{y}{z}} = \dfrac{xz - y^2}{xz + y^2}.$

8. $\dfrac{5x}{x - 2} - \dfrac{3}{2} = \dfrac{7x + 6}{2(x - 2)}.$

Find the degree of each of the following equations:

9. $3x^4 + 2x^3 - x^2 + 3 = 3x^4 - x^3 + 2x - 1.$

10. $x^3 - x + 1 = x^3 - 3x + 4$.

11. $2x^4 + 3x^3 - x^2 + 2 = 2x^4 + 3x^3 - 3x^2 - x - 5$.

Decide whether each of the following equations is an identity or a conditional equation:

12. $3(x - 2) = 3x - 6$.

13. $5(x - \frac{1}{15}) = 5x - 3$.

14. $\frac{1}{x} + \frac{2}{2x} = \frac{3}{3x}$.

15. $\sqrt{x^2 + 9} = x + 3$.

16. $5 - 2x = 3x$.

17. $\frac{5x}{3} - \frac{2x}{3} = x$.

18. $x^3 - y^3 = (x - y)(x^2 + xy + y^2)$.

19. $x^3 + y^3 = (x + y)(x^2 - xy + y^2)$.

20. $(x - a)(x - b) = x^2 - (a + b)x + ab$.

39. LINEAR EQUATIONS

The procedure which some students employ to solve an equation like $3x + 5 = x + 11$ is something like this. They first "transpose" the 5 and the x, being careful to change the signs of transposed terms (because they were taught to do so), obtaining $3x - x = 11 - 5$ or $2x = 6$. Then they "bring the 2 across to the other side" and place it under the 6, being careful *not* to change the sign of the 2 (because they were taught to do this), obtaining $x = \frac{6}{2}$ or $x = 3$. After the 3 they write "answer" as a kind of solemn "amen" to the entire ritual.

Let us examine carefully the logic of this process. We wish to find a root of the equation, provided it has any roots—which is something we do not know in advance. Suppose x is a root, that is, a number which satisfies the equation

$$3x + 5 = x + 11. \tag{1}$$

We would like to obtain an equation with no x's in the right member and no constant term in the left. This suggests subtracting x from both sides to remove the x from the right member of (1) and subtracting 5 from both sides to remove the 5 from the left side of (1). Therefore we reason as follows. If the number x satisfies (1), then it also satisfies

$$3x + 5 - (x + 5) = x + 11 - (x + 5)$$

since we may subtract $(x + 5)$ from both sides by virtue of the axiom "if equals are subtracted from equals, the results are equal." By means of the associative, commutative, and distributive laws, we obtain

$$2x = 6. \tag{2}$$

But if x is a number such that $2x = 6$, we may divide both sides of (2) by 2 by virtue of the axiom "if equals are divided by equals, the results are equal." Thus we obtain the conclusion $x = 3$. But what have we proved as a result of this chain of reasoning? Clearly, we have proved the proposition "*if* x is a number satisfying $3x + 5 = x + 11$, *then* $x = 3$." Can we then assert that 3 *does* satisfy the original equation? Clearly not! For to say this is to assert the proposition "*if* $x = 3$, *then* x satisfies the equation $3x + 5 = x + 11$." This is, however, the *converse* of what we proved and we know that a proposition may well be valid without having a valid converse. All we have really proved is that if x is a root of the original equation, then x cannot be anything else but 3. That is, 3 is the only possible candidate eligible for the position of root. But, so far as we know, the equation may have no root at all! What can we do to see if 3 is a root or not? One procedure would be to substitute 3 for x in the equation $3x + 5 = x + 11$ and verify directly whether or not it satisfies the equation. Another satisfactory procedure would be to prove the converse proposition by reasoning backwards from the last step to the first, which can be done provided all the steps taken originally are reversible steps. This is so in the case of linear equations because all we use is property XV, section 32, and if to get from one step to the next we add the same thing to both sides we can get back again by simply subtracting the same thing from both sides, and so on. If we never multiply by zero we will have no trouble with division by zero. This is why there is no need to worry about the converse proposition in the case of linear equations. The following example, which is not itself linear, but which leads to a linear equation, shows that we cannot always be so carefree.

Example. Solve the equation

$$\frac{2}{x} + \frac{x+2}{x(x-2)} = \frac{4}{x(x-2)}.$$

The equation has no sense for $x = 0$ and $x = 2$. (Why?) We may multiply both sides of the equation by the common denominator $x(x - 2)$, since if equals are multiplied by equals, the results are equal, obtaining

$$x(x-2)\left[\frac{2}{x} + \frac{x+2}{x(x-2)}\right] = \frac{4}{x(x-2)} \cdot x(x-2).$$

Using the distributive law in the left member, we get

$$x(x-2) \cdot \frac{2}{x} + x(x-2) \cdot \frac{(x+2)}{x(x-2)} = \frac{4}{x(x-2)} \cdot x(x-2).$$

Simplifying the fractions, this becomes

$$2(x-2) + (x+2) = 4,$$

except, perhaps, for $x = 0$ or $x = 2$, in which cases the cancellation is not valid. (Why?)

Applying the generalized distributive law, we have

$$2x - 4 + x + 2 = 4.$$

By the commutative, associative, and distributive, laws, etc., this becomes

$$3x - 2 = 4.$$

Or,

$$3x = 6. \qquad \text{(Reason ?)}$$

Or,

$$x = 2. \qquad \text{(Reason ?)}$$

But $x = 2$ is not a root of the original equation, since substituting $x = 2$ causes the term $4/[x(x - 2)]$ to become 4/0 which is meaningless. All that our reasoning above established was that *if* the original equation had a root it would have to be 2. But 2 does *not* satisfy the equation. Hence this equation has no root. This equation is a propositional function whose truth-set is empty. *This indicates the necessity for establishing the converse proposition (most easily done by direct substitution in the original equation) before asserting that your "answer" is really a root of the equation.*

Exercises

Solve, justifying each step on the basis of our postulates:

1. $3x - 8 = 7x + 8.$

2. $7 - 6x = 3x - 11.$

3. $3x - 1 = x + 6.$

4. $5 - 4x = 3x - 7.$

5. $7x - 3 = 2(x + 3) - 4.$

6. $6x - 2(x - 3) = x + 8.$

7. $\dfrac{1}{x} + \dfrac{3}{x} = \dfrac{1}{3}.$

8. $\dfrac{1}{6} + \dfrac{1}{10} = \dfrac{1}{x}.$

9. $\dfrac{4}{3(x - 1)} + \dfrac{1}{2(x - 1)} = \dfrac{1}{2(x + 1)} + \dfrac{1}{x^2 - 1}.$

10. $\dfrac{2}{(2x - 1)(x - 3)} = \dfrac{5}{(5x - 2)(x - 3)}.$

40. SOLUTION OF QUADRATIC EQUATIONS BY FACTORING

Some students learn in school to solve the equation

$$x^2 - 5x + 6 = 0 \tag{1}$$

as follows. They factor the left side, obtaining

$$(x - 2)(x - 3) = 0. \tag{2}$$

Then they draw a ⊤ and tear the equation in half, making two equations out of it, completing the ritual thus:

$x - 2 = 0$	$x - 3 = 0$
$x = 2$	$x = 3$
ans.	ans.

What is the reasoning behind this mysterious procedure? In particular, what logical justification is there for ruthlessly splitting the equation into two equations? We say, as before, *if* x is a number such that (1) is true (assuming there *are* any such numbers), then x must make (2) true as well, since the left members of (1) and (2) are equal *identically* (that is, for all values of x). But by postulate VIII (c) of section 32, **the product of two quantities can be 0 only when one or the other (or both) of the two quantities is itself zero.** (See also theorem 1, section 26.) But the first parenthesis is zero only when $x = 2$, and the second is zero only when $x = 3$. We have proved that "*if* x is a number such that $x^2 - 5x + 6 = 0$, *then* x can only be either 2 or 3. " That is, 2 and 3 are the only eligible candidates for the rootship. Before we can say that they are really roots, we need the converse propositions, "*if* $x = 2$, *then* x satisfies the equation $x^2 - 5x + 6 = 0$," and "*if* $x = 3$, *then* x satisfies the equation $x^2 - 5x + 6 = 0$." As in the last section, this can be proved either by direct substitution in (1) or by proceeding from the bottom line to the top by reversing each step of reasoning. We leave this to the reader as an exercise.

Note that the following "solution" is *incorrect*:

$$x^2 - 5x + 6 = 12$$

$$(x - 2)(x - 3) = 12$$

$x - 2 = 12$	$x - 3 = 12$
$x = 14$	$x = 15.$

The third line is erroneous because we cannot make for the number 12 a statement such as the statement in heavy type above for the number 0. That is, it is not true that the product of two quantities can be 12 only when one or the other (or both) of the quantities is itself 12. Zero is the only number with this property.

Exercises

Solve, justifying each step:

1. $x^2 + x - 12 = 0.$
2. $x^2 - 5x + 6 = 30.$
3. $(x - 3)(x - 2) = 20.$
4. $3x^2 - 11x - 20 = 0.$
5. $(x + 3)(2x - 1) = 15.$
6. $(x - 4)(x - 1) = -2.$
7. $x^2 - 16 = 0.$
8. $9x^2 - 25 = 0.$
9. $4x^2 - 1 = 0.$
10. $12x^2 + x - 6 = 0.$
11. $\dfrac{x^2}{(x - 2)(x - 3)} = \dfrac{2}{x - 2} + \dfrac{6}{(x - 2)(x - 3)}.$
12. $1 + \dfrac{x}{4 - x} = \dfrac{x - 2}{x - 4}.$

41. IRRATIONAL EQUATIONS

We shall see again that our fussing about the converse proposition in the two preceding sections was not mere academic purism.

Example 1. Solve

$$x - 7 = \sqrt{x - 5}. \tag{1}$$

This is called an **irrational equation** because while both sides are algebraic expressions, at least one of them is not a rational expression. Recall that we have agreed that $\sqrt{\ }$ shall mean the *positive* square root, wherever possible, to avoid amibiguity. To solve (1), we reason as follows. If x is a number satisfying (1) (provided there *are* any such numbers), then, squaring both sides, $x^2 - 14x + 49 = x - 5$, because if $a = b$, then $a^2 = b^2$. Then $x^2 - 15x + 54 = 0$, or $(x - 6)(x - 9) = 0$. Hence $x = 6$ or $x = 9$. We have proved that "*if* x satisfies (1), *then* $x = 6$ or $x = 9$." What about the converse proposition? Do $x = 6$ and $x = 9$ really satisfy (1)? We have only proved so far that they are the only *possible* roots, that is, the only candidates eligible for the position of root. Let us see whether or not they *are* roots by substituting in (1). Substituting $x = 6$, we obtain $6 - 7 = \sqrt{6 - 5}$ or $-1 = 1$. Thus 6 is *not* a root. On the other hand, substituting $x = 9$, we get $9 - 7 = \sqrt{9 - 5}$ or $2 = 2$, so that 9 *is* a root.

Example 2. Solve

$$\sqrt{x - 2} = \sqrt{x} + 2. \tag{2}$$

Squaring both sides we get $x - 2 = x + 4\sqrt{x} + 4$, or $-6 = 4\sqrt{x}$, or $-3 = 2\sqrt{x}$. Squaring again, we get $9 = 4x$, or $x = 9/4$. Therefore 9/4 is the only possible root. Substituting in (2), we get

$$\sqrt{\frac{9}{4} - 2} = \sqrt{\frac{9}{4}} + 2, \text{ or } \sqrt{\frac{1}{4}} = \sqrt{\frac{9}{4}} + 2, \text{ or } \frac{1}{2} = \frac{3}{2} + 2,$$

which is clearly not true. Hence 9/4 is not a root, and our equation has no root at all. It is a propositional function whose truth-set is empty.

The unsuccessful candidates for the position of root, which turn up sometimes in these examples, are often called *extraneous roots*, but this is merely a euphemistic way of saying that they are not roots at all. Of course, not all irrational equations have extraneous roots.

The occurrence of extraneous roots shows clearly that substituting our possible answers in the original equation is more than a mere (superfluous) "check" but is really an essential part of the argument.

Since extraneous roots occur in the above examples, it must be that the converse proposition is not true and hence that not every step in the reasoning on the way down is reversible. Clearly, the non-reversible step is the step of squaring. For although "if $a = b$, then $a^2 = b^2$" is valid, the converse "if $a^2 = b^2$, then $a = b$" is not, as we saw in section 38.

Exercises

Solve:

1. $\sqrt{x+2} = 3$.
2. $\sqrt{x+2} = -3$.
3. $\sqrt{x} = x - 2$.
4. $\sqrt{x} = 2 - x$.
5. $\sqrt{3x+4} = 2 + \sqrt{2x-4}$.
6. $\sqrt{x-4} = 9 - \sqrt{x+5}$.
7. $\sqrt{x-4} = \sqrt{x+5} - 9$.
8. $\sqrt{x+4} + \sqrt{x+11} = 7$.
9. $\sqrt{x-2} = 2 - x$.
10. $\sqrt{x+5} + \sqrt{2x+3} = 3$.
11. $\sqrt{x+2} + \sqrt{2x+5} = 1$.
12. $\sqrt{2x+10} = \sqrt{x+12} - 1$.
13. $\sqrt{2x-1} = 2 + \sqrt{x}$.
14. $\sqrt{3x-1} + \sqrt{3x+6} = 7$.
15. $\sqrt{3-2x} = 3 + \sqrt{2+2x}$.
16. $\sqrt{3x+1} = 1 + \sqrt{2x-1}$.
17. $\sqrt{2x+5} + \sqrt{4x+3} = 3$.
18. $\sqrt{6x-2} + \sqrt{2x-1} = \sqrt{2x}$.
19. $\sqrt{3x+9} = \sqrt{2x+8} + \sqrt{x+5}$.
20. $\dfrac{1}{\sqrt{x-3}} = 2 + \sqrt{\dfrac{2x-5}{x-3}}$.

42. SOLUTION OF QUADRATIC EQUATIONS BY FORMULA

We have seen that every quadratic equation can be written in the form

$$ax^2 + bx + c = 0 \tag{1}$$

where $a \neq 0$. (If $a = 0$, the equation is not really quadratic.) We shall now derive the familiar formula for the roots of any quadratic equation.

The expression $x^2 + 2hx$ can be converted into a perfect square, namely, $(x + h)^2 = x^2 + 2hx + h^2$, by adding the square of half the coefficient of x, that is, h^2. This can be seen directly by considering the areas in Fig. 33; adding the upper right-hand square as in a jig-saw puzzle makes the figure a perfect square. This process is termed **completing the square**.

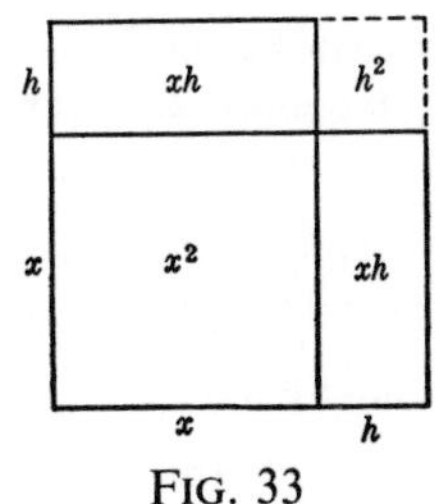

FIG. 33

We now apply this process to solve equation (1). Subtracting c from both sides of (1), and then dividing by a (which is not zero), we obtain

$$x^2 + \frac{b}{a}x = -\frac{c}{a}. \tag{2}$$

Completing the square on the left by adding to both sides the square of half the coefficient of x, that is $\left(\frac{b}{2a}\right)^2 = \frac{b^2}{4a^2}$, we obtain

$$x^2 + \frac{b}{a}x + \left(\frac{b}{2a}\right)^2 = -\frac{c}{a} + \frac{b^2}{4a^2}.$$

Factoring the left side and adding fractions on the right, we get

$$\left(x + \frac{b}{2a}\right)^2 = \frac{b^2 - 4ac}{4a^2}.$$

Hence,

$$x + \frac{b}{2a} = \frac{\pm\sqrt{b^2 - 4ac}}{2a}$$

or

$$x = -\frac{b}{2a} \pm \frac{\sqrt{b^2 - 4ac}}{2a},$$

and finally,

$$x = \frac{-b \pm \sqrt{b^2 - 4ac}}{2a}. \qquad (3)$$

We have proved that if x satisfies equation (1) then x must be given by (3). We leave it to the reader to show that the converse proposition is also true, either by verifying that each step is reversible no matter which of the answers we start with or by substitution.

We can apply our formula to solve any quadratic by merely substituting the values of a, b, and c in (3).

Example 1. Consider the equation $x^2 - 5x + 6 = 0$. Here $a = 1$, $b = -5$, $c = 6$. Hence the roots are

$$\frac{-(-5) \pm \sqrt{(-5)^2 - 4\cdot 1\cdot 6}}{2\cdot 1} = \frac{5 \pm 1}{2} = \begin{cases} 3 \\ 2. \end{cases}$$

Example 2. Consider the equation $x^2 + 2x + 4 = 0$. Here $a = 1$, $b = 2$, $c = 4$. Hence the roots are

$$\frac{-2 \pm \sqrt{2^2 - 4\cdot 1\cdot 4}}{2\cdot 1} = \frac{-2 \pm \sqrt{-12}}{2} = \frac{-2 \pm \sqrt{(-3)4}}{2}$$

$$= \frac{-2 \pm 2\sqrt{-3}}{2} = \frac{2(-1 \pm \sqrt{-3})}{2} = \begin{cases} -1 + \sqrt{-3} = -1 + i\sqrt{3}. \\ -1 - \sqrt{-3} = -1 - i\sqrt{3}. \end{cases}$$

Notice that the roots of a quadratic equation may be imaginary, even though the coefficients are real.

Exercises

Solve by formula and tell whether the roots are imaginary, real, rational, or irrational:

1. $2x^2 - 7x + 6 = 0.$ **2.** $6x^2 - 5x - 4 = 0.$ **3.** $x^2 - 4x + 1 = 0.$
4. $2x^2 - 5x - 3 = 0.$ **5.** $x^2 + 9 = 0.$ **6.** $x^2 + x + 4 = 0.$
7. $3x^2 - 11x = 20.$ **8.** $6x^2 = 3 - 7x.$ **9.** $(x + 5)(x + 1) = 13.$
10. $x^2 + 7x + 2 = 0.$ **11.** $x^2 + \sqrt{5}x + 1 = 0.$ **12.** $x^2 - \sqrt{20}x + 1 = 0.$
13. $x^2 + 4ix - 4 = 0.$ **14.** $x^2 + 2ix - 5 = 0.$ **15.** $2x^2 - \sqrt{8}x + 1 = 0.$

43. THE FUNDAMENTAL THEOREM OF ALGEBRA

Karl Friedrich Gauss
1777–1855, German

We can now review briefly the growth of the number system in the light of the theory of equations and see why we made the statement, at the close of the preceding chapter, that the complex number system need not be enlarged further. Suppose we decide that we want all polynomial equations to have roots. Now let us imagine that we have no numbers in our possession except the natural numbers. Then a simple linear equation like $2x = 3$ has no root. In order to remedy this condition, we invent fractions. But a simple linear equation like $x + 5 = 2$ has no root even among the fractions. Hence we invent negative numbers. A simple quadratic equation like $x^2 = 2$ has no root among all the (positive and negative) rational numbers, as we proved in section 30. Therefore we invent the irrational numbers which together with the rational numbers complete the system of real numbers. However, a simple quadratic equation like $x^2 = -1$ has no root among all the real numbers (section 33). Hence we invent the pure imaginary numbers. But a simple quadratic equation like $x^2 + 2x + 4 = 0$ has no root among either the real or pure imaginary numbers (example 2, section 42). Therefore we invent the complex numbers. Now we might well expect that there might be some equation of degree 3 or higher which has no root even in the entire system of complex numbers. That this is not the case was known to Karl Friedrich Gauss, who proved (in 1799) the following theorem, the truth of which had long been suspected.

Fundamental Theorem of Algebra. *Every polynomial equation, of degree one or more, with coefficients in the complex number system, has a root among the complex numbers.*

For example, an equation like

$$(2+3\sqrt{-5})x^{1941}+\frac{\sqrt{2}}{3}x^{1776}+\frac{1865}{7}x^{1492}+\sqrt{-11}x+13=0$$

is known in advance to have a root among the complex numbers. The proof of this theorem is too difficult to be taken up here. We can see, however, that for the purpose of solving polynomial equations we do not need to extend the number system any further.

44. ALGEBRAIC FORMULAS FOR THE ROOTS

The general linear equation can be written in the form $ax+b=0 (a \neq 0)$. Hence a formula for its roots is $x=(-b)/a$. Every quadratic equation can be written in the form $ax^2+bx+c=0 (a \neq 0)$. Its roots, as we have seen, are given by the formulas $(-b+\sqrt{b^2-4ac})/2a$ and $(-b-\sqrt{b^2-4ac})/2a$. The formulas for the roots of both the general linear equation $ax+b=0$ and the general quadratic equation $ax^2+bx+c=0$ give the roots as algebraic expressions* in the coefficients. The mathematician's desire for general results makes it natural to ask the following question. Can we get similar formulas giving the roots as algebraic expressions in terms of the coefficients for the general equation of any degree? For the general cubic equation $ax^3+bx^2+cx+d=0$, such formulas were substantially obtained by Tartaglia (about 1540), though they are often referred to as Cardan's formulas because they were first published in 1545 by Cardan, who obtained them from Tartaglia under a pledge of secrecy.† For the general equation of degree 4, $ax^4+bx^3+cx^2+dx+e=0$, such formulas were obtained by Ferrari at about the same time. We shall not state the formulas

* Recall the definition of "algebraic expression" (section 35).

† It was customary at that time to withhold new discoveries and to challenge all comers to solve the problem independently.

for the general equations of degrees 3 and 4 here.* The next task was, naturally, to obtain similar formulas for the general equation of degree 5, $ax^5 + bx^4 + cx^3 + dx^2 + ex + f = 0$. Attempts to find such formulas were made from the sixteenth century until early in the nineteenth century without success. The reason for this failure became evident in 1824 when N. H. Abel, a brilliant young Norwegian mathematician, proved, at the age of 22, that it is not possible to write the roots of the general equation of degree higher than four as algebraic expressions in terms of the coefficients.

Niels Henrik Abel
1802–1829, Norwegian

You may be tempted to ask: "How can you boldly assert that it is impossible to find such formulas? Perhaps some day some genius will discover them. All things are possible. Are you sure you don't mean simply that no one has found them yet?" The answer is that we don't merely mean that no one has found them yet; we mean that no one will ever find them because it is impossible for such formulas to exist. If you ask how we can prove something definitely impossible, we reply that you have already done such things yourselves. In section 30, Chapter 4, we showed that it is impossible to find a fraction whose square is exactly 2. We did not say merely that we had examined 10,000 fractions and hadn't yet found one whose square is 2. In fact, we pointed out that such a procedure could not possibly lead to a proof. We actually proved that the existence of a rational number whose square is 2 would lead inevitably to self-contradiction and is, therefore, impossible. All proofs of impossibility are of that general nature. An even simpler example of an impossible task is to find two even numbers whose sum is odd. (See exercise 8, section 30.)

Notice that we have not said the general equation of degree 5 cannot be solved. In fact, it can be solved by other means, but its roots cannot be given as algebraic expressions in the coefficients. However, the roots of some *particular* equations of degree 5 or more can be written as algebraic expressions in terms of the coefficients. For example, if in the fifth degree equation above we restrict ourselves

* See M. Richardson, *College Algebra*, Third Edition, Prentice-Hall, Englewood Cliffs, N. J., 1966, for discussions of these solutions.

to the particular case where $b = c = d = e = 0$, $a \neq 0$, that is, to equations of the form $ax^5 + f = 0$, then we can clearly express one root as $x = \sqrt[5]{-f/a}$ which is an algebraic expression. Therefore a natural question to raise is: given a definite polynomial equation of degree 5 or more, how can we tell whether or not its roots are expressible as algebraic expressions in its coefficients?* This question was settled by Évariste Galois. The work of Galois was quite original in character and was not well understood at the time because of the sketchy expositions which he presented. Galois' ability was not appreciated by his teachers. In fact, because of various circumstances, including manuscripts lying unread on desks, he received no recognition for his work while he lived. However, what is now called the Galois theory of equations is studied everywhere by advanced students.

Évariste Galois
1811–1832, French

Abel was not yet 27 when he died, leaving behind a wealth of highly original work which stimulated mathematical research for many years after. Galois was killed in 1832 in a duel at the age of less than 21.

45. SYSTEMS OF LINEAR EQUATIONS

Consider the linear equation $x + y = 7$. It is satisfied by the values $x = 1$, $y = 6$, and by the values $x = 2$, $y = 5$, and by the values $x = 9$, $y = -2$, and so on. Clearly, if you choose any value for x the equation is satisfied by that value of x and the value $y = 7 - x$; for example, if we take $x = \frac{15}{2}$, then the values $x = \frac{15}{2}$, $y = -\frac{1}{2}$ satisfy the equation. Any pair of values for x and y which satisfies the equation is called a **solution** of the equation. A single linear equation in two variables has infinitely many solutions, one for each value of x. If we

* We have here an instance of advanced research arising from exceedingly natural and elementary questions.

consider a system of two equations like

$$(1) \qquad x + y = 7$$

and

$$(2) \qquad x - y = 1$$

we may fairly ask whether these equations have a **common solution**, that is, whether there exists a pair of values for x and y which satisfies both equations simultaneously. In the language of sets, the truth-set of each equation is an infinite set, but we seek the intersection of these two sets. The technique of solving such a system of equations is to "eliminate" one of the variables. We reason as follows. If (x,y) is a pair of numbers satisfying both equations (provided there is such a pair), then from (1) we have $y = 7 - x$. Substituting this in (2) we have $x - (7 - x) = 1$, an equation in one variable. Hence, $2x - 7 = 1$ or $x = 4$. But $y = 7 - x = 7 - 4 = 3$. We have thus proved that if (x,y) is a pair of numbers satisfying (1) and (2), then x can only be 4 and y can only be 3. To show, conversely, that this pair of numbers really does satisfy both equations we can merely substitute $x = 4$, $y = 3$ in *both* of the equations and verify it directly.*

It can of course happen that a pair of equations has *no* common solution. For example, consider the system

$$(3) \qquad x + y = 5$$

$$(4) \qquad x + y = 6.$$

It is perfectly clear that if x and y are any numbers satisfying (3), they cannot satisfy (4) since their sum cannot be both 5 and 6. Such equations are called **incompatible**, or **inconsistent**. The intersection of their truth-sets is the empty set.

It can also happen that *every* pair of numbers satisfying one equation will also satisfy the other. For example, consider

$$(5) \qquad x + y = 15$$

$$(6) \qquad 2x + 2y = 30.$$

Since $2x + 2y = 2(x + y)$ it is clear that if x and y satisfy (5) (that is, their sum is 15), then $2x + 2y = 30$ automatically. Such equations may be called **equivalent**; their truth-sets are the same.

A graphical or geometric interpretation of the work of this section and the next will be discussed in Chapter 9, section 100.

* The student may recall various tricks for performing the elimination of one of the variables, perhaps slightly more rapid than our procedure. But our method is straightforward and can be applied to more general situations as in the next section.

Exercises

Solve the following systems:

1. $\begin{cases} 3x+2y=13 \\ x-3y=-3. \end{cases}$

2. $\begin{cases} 3x-y=7 \\ 2x+3y=1. \end{cases}$

3. $\begin{cases} y-x=1 \\ 2y-3x=5. \end{cases}$

4. $\begin{cases} 2x-3y=5 \\ 5x+y=2. \end{cases}$

5. $\begin{cases} 3x-y=0 \\ 5x+3y=7. \end{cases}$

6. $\begin{cases} 6x+3y=4 \\ 5x-y=1. \end{cases}$

7. $\begin{cases} 3x-2y=1 \\ 2x+3y=3. \end{cases}$

8. $\begin{cases} 2x+3y=1 \\ 3x-4y=3. \end{cases}$

9. $\begin{cases} 4x-3y=3 \\ 3x+2y=5. \end{cases}$

10. $\begin{cases} 5x+4y=18 \\ 6x+2y=16. \end{cases}$

11. $\begin{cases} 7x+3y=1 \\ 14x+6y=3. \end{cases}$

12. $\begin{cases} 5x-2y=4 \\ 4x-3y=5. \end{cases}$

13. $\begin{cases} ax+by=c \\ dx+ey=f \end{cases}$ if $ae-bd \neq 0$.

46. SYSTEMS OF EQUATIONS OF HIGHER DEGREE

We shall take only the case where one equation is linear and the other quadratic. For example, consider the system of equations

$$x^2+y^2=34 \tag{1}$$

$$x-y=2. \tag{2}$$

We obtain $x=y+2$ from (2) and substitute this expression in (1), obtaining

$$\begin{aligned} (y+2)^2+y^2&=34, \\ y^2+4y+4+y^2&=34, \\ 2y^2+4y-30&=0, \\ y^2+2y-15&=0, \\ (y+5)(y-3)&=0, \\ y=-5 \text{ or } y&=3. \end{aligned}$$

For $y=-5$ we obtain from (2) the value $x=-3$ and for $y=3$ we obtain the value $x=5$. To see whether both the pair $(x=-3,\ y=-5)$ and the pair $(x=5,\ y=3)$ satisfy the system we substitute in (1) and (2).

The problem of solving systems of two equations in x and y of any degree is in general quite difficult. The procedure used above and in the preceding section was to express one variable in terms of the other from one equation and substitute in the other equation, thus eliminating one of the variables and obtaining an equation in the other variable alone which could then be solved. But this was easy because we had, in the above cases, a linear equation from which we could obtain an expression for y in terms of x, or x in terms of y. From equations like $5x^3+x^2y+7xy^2+11x+13y^3=17$ and $x^5+3xy^3-y^4=19$, it would not be so easy to eliminate x or y. The mathematician's tendency to seek general theorems and methods would inevitably lead him to attack the general problem of solving systems of any number of equations of any degree in any number of unknowns. This problem leads to interesting, modern, and difficult researches in higher algebra, called elimination theory. Here again we have an example of advanced mathematics which springs from natural and elementary questions.

Exercises

Solve the following systems:

1. $\begin{cases} x^2 + y^2 = 25 \\ 2x + y = 10. \end{cases}$

2. $\begin{cases} x^2 + y^2 = 1 + 4x \\ 2x - y = 4. \end{cases}$

3. $\begin{cases} x^2 + y^2 = 13 \\ 2x - y = 4. \end{cases}$

4. $\begin{cases} xy = 1 \\ 3y - 5x = 2. \end{cases}$

5. $\begin{cases} 7y^2 - 6xy = 8 \\ 2y - 3x = 5. \end{cases}$

6. $\begin{cases} y^2 = 4x \\ y + 2x = 4. \end{cases}$

7. $\begin{cases} x + y = 7 \\ xy = 12. \end{cases}$

8. $\begin{cases} y^2 = 4x \\ x + y = 3. \end{cases}$

9. $\begin{cases} x^2 + y^2 = 25 \\ 4x - 3y = 0. \end{cases}$

10. $\begin{cases} x^2 + y^2 = 41 \\ x + y = 9. \end{cases}$

11. $\begin{cases} x^2 - y^2 = 5 \\ 3x + y = 11. \end{cases}$

***12.** $\begin{cases} xy = 2 \\ x^2 = y. \end{cases}$

47. PROBLEMS LEADING TO THE SOLUTION OF EQUATIONS

The student is already familiar with verbal problems which lead to the solution of equations. One must read the problem carefully, choose symbols to represent the various quantities involved, and use the given relations among these quantities to set up the equation or equations. The problem is essentially nothing but that of translating from the clumsy language of everyday prose into the much more convenient language of algebra. Hence the student should carefully write down a systematic list or vocabulary of all symbols to be used and express all the quantities to be considered in terms of these symbols.* If you fail to write down what your symbols stand for, you are writing in a secret code.

Example 1. Within a flower garden 6 yards wide and 12 yards long, we want to pave a path of uniform width around the boundary so as to leave an area of 40 square yards for flowers. How wide shall we make the path?

* Various schemes of arrangement of this vocabulary on the page, such as "boxes" or other bookkeeping devices, seem to be popular. They may save a few seconds but are inessential and often serve only to obscure the reasoning.

Let x = width of path, measured in yards. Then the width of the actual flower plot is $6 - 2x$, and its length is $12 - 2x$. The area of this flower plot is therefore $(6 - 2x)(12 - 2x)$. But this area is to be 40 square yards. Hence

(1) $$(6 - 2x)(12 - 2x) = 40.$$

Solving this equation we have

$$72 - 36x + 4x^2 = 40,$$

or,

$$x^2 - 9x + 8 = 0,$$

or,

$$(x - 1)(x - 8) = 0.$$

Hence,

$$x = 1 \text{ or } x = 8.$$

Clearly $x = 1$ satisfies the conditions of the problem for the flower plot then has the dimensions $6 - 2 = 4$ and $12 - 2 = 10$ which yield an area of 40. But the root $x = 8$ clearly does not satisfy the conditions of the problem since you cannot pave a path 8 yards wide in a garden only 6 yards wide. However, 8 is a bona fide root of equation (1). How can this happen? The answer is simply that in setting up the equation (1) we reasoned that *if* x satisfies the conditions of the verbal problem, *then* x will have to satisfy the equation (1). But the *converse* of this proposition need not be so. Thus it should not surprise us if there is a value of x which satisfies the equation without satisfying the problem. In all verbal problems it is therefore essential to check the roots of the equation against the actual verbal problem before accepting them.

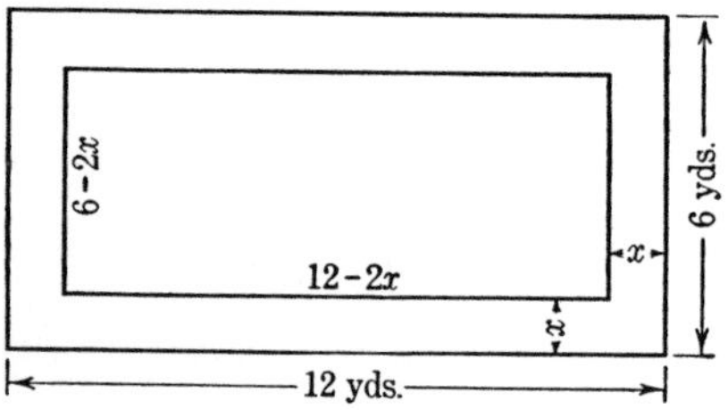

FIG. 34

Example 2. It is found experimentally that if a corpse is dropped from the top of a vertical cliff, it falls $16t^2$ feet in t seconds. (This is known as the falling body problem.) If the cliff is 144 feet high, in how many seconds will the body reach the bottom?

Clearly $16t^2 = 144$ or $t^2 = 9$. Hence $t = \pm 3$. But -3 seconds has no meaning for our problem. Thus 3 seconds is the answer. However, -3 is a root of our equation. Explain this phenomenon.

Example 3. The following was proposed to Leonardo of Pisa, a famous mathematician, about 1200 A.D., as a difficult problem.*

If A gets from B seven denare,† then A's sum is five-fold B's; if B gets from A five denare, then B's sum is seven-fold A's. How much has each?

* F. Cajori, *History of Mathematics*, 2nd Edition, Macmillan, N. Y., 1917, p. 123.
† An ancient coin.

Let x represent A's original sum and let y represent B's original sum. Then clearly,

$$x + 7 = 5(y - 7)$$

and

$$7(x - 5) = y + 5.$$

Solving these equations simultaneously we obtain $x = 7\frac{2}{17}$ denare and $y = 9\frac{14}{17}$ denare.

The fact that this problem was considered difficult indicates the importance of an adequate symbolism. The reader has only to try to solve this problem, or some other problem, without using any symbolic notation to be convinced of this. No convenient algebraic notation was used about 1200 A.D.

Exercises

1. The area of a rectangular garden is 192 square yards. The perimeter is 56 yards. Find the length and width.

2. One-fifth of a man's age 5 years ago equals one-sixth of his age 3 years hence. How old is he now?

3. A student has quiz grades of 68 and 76. What grade must he achieve on a third quiz in order to have an average of 80?

4. A man is 24 years older than his son. Eight years ago he was twice as old as his son was. What are their present ages?

5. A solution of acid is 75% pure. How many grams of acid must be added to 48 grams of this solution in order to make the resulting solution 76% pure?

6. One leg of a right triangle is 2 feet smaller than twice the other leg. The hypotenuse is 34 feet long. Find the legs. (Hint: use the Pythagorean theorem.)

7. A can do a certain job in 6 days and B can do it in 10 days. How long will it take them to do it together?

8. A stone is dropped from a vertical cliff 96 feet high. Using the formula

$$s = 16t^2 \tag{1}$$

for the distance s, measured in feet, through which the body will fall in t seconds, find the number of seconds it takes for the stone to reach bottom.

9. A can do a job in 8 days, and A and B together do it in 4 days. How long would it take B to do it alone?

10. A collection of nickels and quarters contains 30 coins. Their total value is $3.70. How many of each kind of coin are there?

11. A rectangular field is four times as long as it is wide. If it were 5 feet shorter and 2 feet wider its area would be increased by 20 square feet. Find its length and width.

12. An automobile travels 120 miles. A second automobile travels 10 miles per hour faster than the first and makes the same trip in 2 hours less time. Find the speed of each.

13. A and B do a job together in 6 days. A alone can do it in 5 days less than it takes B to do it alone. How long would it take each to do the job alone?

14. The two legs of a right triangle differ by 7 feet. The hypotenuse is 13 feet long. Find the legs.

15. The area of a rectangle is 400 square feet. The perimeter is 100 feet. Find the length and width.

16. A boat, operating uniformly at full power, goes 5 miles downstream in 60 minutes and returns in 90 minutes. What would the speed of the boat be in still water and what is the rate of the current?

17. A freight train, running at the rate of 20 miles per hour, leaves a station three hours before an express which travels in the same direction at the rate of 50 miles per hour. How long after the express leaves will it catch the freight and how far from the station will they be?

18. Achilles races with a Tortoise, giving the Tortoise a handicap of 990 yards. Achilles runs at the rate of 500 yards per minute while the Tortoise runs at the rate of 5 yards per minute. How long will it take Achilles to catch the Tortoise?

19. How many gallons of cotton seed oil must be added to 45 gallons of a solution of olive oil which is 90% olive oil in order to make the resulting solution 80% olive oil?

20. The age of Diophantus, a brilliant Greek mathematician of about 250 A.D., may be calculated from an epitaph which runs as follows: Diophantus passed one-sixth of his life in childhood, one-twelfth in youth, and one-seventh more as a bachelor; five years after his marriage was born a son who died four years before his father, at half his father's final age.

21. If the price of eggs rises 10 cents per dozen, one will be able to get 2 dozen fewer eggs with $6.00 than was possible at the lower price. Find the lower price.

References

Numbers refer to the bibliography at the end of the book.

Bell 16
Birkhoff and MacLane 28
Dresden 65
Fine 74
McCoy 130
Richardson 158

6

Arithmetical Computation and Its Relief

48. INTRODUCTION

The popular notion that mathematicians as a class generally enjoy doing routine arithmetical computations is false. In fact, mathematicians have disliked this irksome necessity so much that they have invented many ways to diminish the time spent on it. Although the pain cannot be entirely cured, it can be considerably relieved. In this chapter, we shall discuss some of these labor-saving devices.

Algebra, as you know it, dates roughly from the thirteenth to the seventeenth centuries, during which time algebraic symbolism passed through many stages of development, although some of it goes back thousands of years. The first symbolic advances over ordinary prose were mere abbreviations. For example, in his *Ars Magna de Rebus Algebraicis* (1545), Cardan wrote *cubus p.* 6. *rebus aequalis* 20 for $x^3 + 6x = 20$. The equal sign $=$ is found for the first time in print in *The Whetstone of Witte* by Robert Recorde, published in 1557. The symbol ℞ (*radix*, root) was often used; thus, ℞ cu. 8 would be written for $\sqrt[3]{8}$. In the early seventeenth century we still find *aaaaa* written for a^5. The ancients had no adequate arithmetical or algebraic symbolism, and it is probable that this greatly handicapped their development of arithmetical and algebraic ideas.

Systems of notation for numbers seem to have been almost universally influenced by the anatomical accident that most of us possess two hands with five fingers on each. There is scarcely any doubt that the human race learned to count on its fingers, just as a child does. In fact, various elaborate schemes of finger-reckoning are still in use today among various people. Thus, the numbers five and (especially) ten have always been important. Some tribes, the Mayas of Central America, for example, gave twenty a special place and used a word for twenty meaning "a whole person," thus indicating that they counted on both fingers and toes. Other indications that twenty was once considered important are found in the English word "score," and in the French *quatre-vingt* (four twenties) for eighty. But ten is more commonly regarded as basic. The Egyptians, for example, used the symbol ∩ for ten and wrote twenty-three as ∩ ∩ | | |. Similarly, the Romans had special symbols for five and ten. For example, they wrote eighteen as XVIII. The notation you learned in school is called the Arabic system (although it was probably developed by the Hindus about 500 A.D.), because it was brought into Europe by the Arabs after they over-ran Spain in the eighth century. The earliest Arabic manuscripts using this system date from the ninth century. However, it was not widely used in Europe until the fifteenth century. The Arabic or Hindu-Arabic notation also shows the influence of the number ten but in an essentially different way. Thus 7346 means $7 \cdot 10^3 + 3 \cdot 10^2 + 4 \cdot 10 + 6$.

If our sole concern with numbers were to record them, as, say, historians record dates, then one system of notation would be pretty much as good as another. But if we are going to add, multiply, and so on, then some systems are clearly superior to others. If anyone doubts it, let him multiply 1748 by 34 as he was taught in school and then try to multiply the same numbers MDCCXLVIII and XXXIV using only the Roman numerals. It is our simple arabic notation which makes it possible for a child of ten to do arithmetical problems which would have taxed the ability of a Roman senator. The ancients, of course, used the abacus, counting boards with pebbles, and other devices. In fact, the word "calculate" comes from the Latin word *calculus* meaning "pebble." Despite its obvious advantages over previous methods, the Arabic system was adopted generally in Europe only after a long struggle against the repressive forces of tradition and resistance to change. In fact, the new notation was adopted by the enlightened merchants long before the "learned" authorities became reconciled to it. It enabled the general public, instead of experts only, to learn arithmetic. Its importance in the operation of our complicated modern industrial and commercial civilization is easy to see.

49. OPERATIONS WITH ARABIC NUMERALS

It would be inconvenient to express large numbers in Roman numerals without inventing more and more symbols such as I, V, X, L, C, D, M, etc. The convenience of the Arabic system is due to the fact that it is a cleverly devised *positional* notation. That is, we need only the ten symbols or digits (notice the word "digit," meaning finger) 0, 1, 2, 3, 4, 5, 6, 7, 8, 9, other numbers being written as combinations of these in which the position of each digit tells us how it is to be interpreted; thus

$$345 = 3 \cdot 10^2 + 4 \cdot 10 + 5$$

while

$$534 = 5 \cdot 10^2 + 3 \cdot 10 + 4.$$

A number expressed in positional notation is essentially a sum of terms, each term being a power of ten multiplied by a coefficient which is one of the digits from 0 to 9 inclusive. The powers of ten occur in descending order. In school, we spoke of the "units place," "tens place," "hundreds place," and so on. Briefly, 345 is the value of the polynomial $3x^2 + 4x + 5$ when $x = 10$, and so is every natural number in Arabic notation a value of a polynomial when $x = 10$, with the understanding that the coefficients, required to be one of the digits from 0 to 9, are the only things actually written. This fact accounts for the convenience of Arabic notation in performing calculations, as we shall now see.

Suppose we add 378 and 145 as we learned to do it in school:

$$\begin{array}{r} 11 \\ 378 \\ \underline{145} \\ 523. \end{array}$$

Let us examine more closely the reasons for the correctness of this scheme and how the trick of "carrying" arises. Adding, we get

$$\begin{array}{rl} 3 \cdot 10^2 + 7 \cdot 10 + 8 & (\text{or } 3x^2 + 7x + 8 \text{ when } x = 10) \\ \underline{1 \cdot 10^2 + 4 \cdot 10 + 5} & \underline{(\text{or } 1x^2 + 4x + 5 \text{ when } x = 10)} \\ 4 \cdot 10^2 + 11 \cdot 10 + 13 & (\text{or } 4x^2 + 11x + 13 \text{ when } x = 10) \end{array}$$

by the usual scheme for adding polynomials which is, of course, justifiable by means of the axioms of algebra as we saw in Chapter 5. But since the coefficients 11 and 13 are larger than 9 we must reduce them before we can say that our answer is in Arabic notation. Thus,

$$\begin{aligned} 4 \cdot 10^2 + 11 \cdot 10 + 13 &= 4 \cdot 10^2 + 11 \cdot 10 + (1 \cdot 10 + 3) \\ &= 4 \cdot 10^2 + (11 \cdot 10 + 1 \cdot 10) + 3 \quad (\text{generalized associative law for addition}) \\ &= 4 \cdot 10^2 + (11 + 1)10 + 3 \quad (\text{distributive law}) \\ &= 4 \cdot 10^2 + 12 \cdot 10 + 3 \\ &= 4 \cdot 10^2 + (1 \cdot 10 + 2)10 + 3 \\ &= 4 \cdot 10^2 + 1 \cdot 10^2 + 2 \cdot 10 + 3 \quad (\text{generalized distributive law}) \\ &= (4 + 1)10^2 + 2 \cdot 10 + 3 \quad (\text{generalized distributive law}) \\ &= 5 \cdot 10^2 + 2 \cdot 10 + 3 = 523. \end{aligned}$$

This shows how carrying is justified by the axioms.

In the same way let us examine the process of multiplication. Consider the following example done by the device you learned by rote as children:

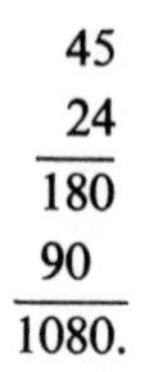

Now let us derive this result from the postulates. We want the product

$$(4 \cdot 10 + 5)(2 \cdot 10 + 4).$$

Regarding the first parenthesis as a single quantity for the moment, the distributive law allows us to write

$$(4 \cdot 10 + 5)2 \cdot 10 + (4 \cdot 10 + 5)4.$$

The right-hand term

$$\begin{aligned} (4 \cdot 10 + 5)4 &= 4 \cdot 10 \cdot 4 + 5 \cdot 4 && \text{(generalized distributive law)} \\ &= 4 \cdot 4 \cdot 10 + 20 && \text{(reason?)} \\ &= 160 + 20 = 180 \end{aligned}$$

which corresponds to the first line of work in the usual scheme above. Similarly, the left-hand term $(4 \cdot 10 + 5)2 \cdot 10$ corresponds to the 900 which appears (with a blank space in place of the last zero) in the second line of the above scheme. The indicated addition is then carried out as explained earlier.

The reader should now have no difficulty in explaining the process of borrowing in the familiar scheme for subtraction as in the example

$$\begin{array}{rrr} & \overset{4}{} & \\ 2 & \not{5} & {}^{1}3 \\ & -2 & 9 \\ \hline 2 & 2 & 4. \end{array}$$

As already defined in section 29, the process of **division with remainder** of one natural number n, called the **dividend**, by another d, called the **divisor**, is to find two non-negative integers q and r, called **quotient** and **remainder**, respectively, such that (1) $n = dq + r$ and (2) $0 \leq r < d$. Thus to divide 9 by 2 means to find the quotient $q = 4$ and remainder $r = 1$; thus $9 = 2 \cdot 4 + 1$. Of course, it is true that 9 is also equal to $2 \cdot 3 + 3$ but the latter 3 is not less than the divisor 2. Thus to divide, in this sense, is merely to subtract as many d's from n as you can until a remainder is left which is too small to allow any more subtractions of d. Thus $n - dq = r$, where $0 \leqq r < d$. The usual scheme of long division is a process of repeated subtraction, as in the example

$$\begin{array}{rl} & 2\ 3\ \ = q = 20 + 3 \\ d = 1\ 5 &)\overline{3\ 5\ 1}\ \ = n \\ & 3\ 0(0) = 20 \cdot d \\ & \overline{\ \ 5\ 1}\ \ = n - 20 \cdot d \\ & \ \ 4\ 5\ \ = 3d \\ & \overline{\ \ \ \ 6}\ \ = r = n - 23d \end{array}$$

where the zero in parentheses is usually not written. Of course, $n = dq + r$ is equivalent to $\frac{n}{d} = q + \frac{r}{d}$. *If the remainder $r = 0$, then d is a factor of n.*

Notice the importance of the rather sophisticated invention of a symbol for zero in positional notation. Without it, we would have difficulty in distinguishing between 1080, 108, 180, 1800, and 18. On an abacus (see Fig. 17) an empty line plays the part of zero. In fact, the abacus contains the essence of positional notation, since one line is used for units, the next for tens, and so on, and in using the abacus one "carries" from one line to the next.

The extraction of square roots might be similarly analyzed but as it is somewhat more complicated we shall not do so here.*

We may treat decimal fractions similarly, recalling that 28.345 means

$$2 \cdot 10 + 8 + \frac{3}{10} + \frac{4}{10^2} + \frac{5}{10^3}.$$

Decimal fractions did not come into use until the late sixteenth or early seventeenth century, and systems of measurement adapted to them were not used until the time of the French Revolution. In America and England systems of measurement are still used which do not accommodate themselves well to decimal fractions.

50. OTHER SCALES OF NOTATION

We have just seen that the convenience in the manipulation of Arabic numerals is due to the positional character of the notation, which makes possible the use of only 10 digits and such devices as carrying. The question arises whether or not one might have such systems of positional notation which are not *decimal*,

* See M. Richardson, *College Algebra*, Third edition, Prentice-Hall, Englewood Cliffs N.J., 1966.

that is, not based on powers of 10. It has been suggested that our system is decimal because of the fact that we have 10 fingers on which we first learned to count. Thus we use the ten digits 0, 1, 2, 3, 4, 5, 6, 7, 8, 9, and we write twenty-four as 24, meaning "two tens and four units." Suppose, however, that we were all born with only one hand with five fingers. Then it is likely that we would write our numbers in powers of five, and twenty-four would be written as 44, meaning "four fives and four units" or $4 \cdot 5 + 4$ instead of 24 or $2 \cdot 10 + 4$. In this system we would have only five digits, 0, 1, 2, 3, 4. That is, we would use a units column, a fives column, a five-squared column, and so on, instead of a units column, a tens column, a ten-squared column, and so on. We would then write:

	one	*two*	*three*	*four*	*five*	*six*	*seven*	*eight*	*nine*	*ten*	*eleven*	*twelve*	
in the ten scale	1	2	3	4	5	6	7	8	9	10	11	12	···
in the five scale	1	2	3	4	10	11	12	13	14	20	21	22	···

The symbols 14 and 22, for example, in the last line should be read as one-four and two-two, respectively, and not fourteen and twenty-two, since they mean "one five and four units" or $1 \cdot 5 + 4$, and "two fives and two units" or $2 \cdot 5 + 2$, respectively.

For example, the number written as 23 in the 10 scale means $2 \cdot 10 + 3$ which is equal to $4 \cdot 5 + 3$ and is therefore written as 43 in the 5 scale.

Example. A number is written as 38 in the ten scale; rewrite it in the five scale. Clearly, the highest power of five which is contained in 38 is 5^2. There are one 5^2, two fives, and three units in thirty-eight. That is, $38 = 1 \cdot 5^2 + 2 \cdot 5 + 3$. Hence, thirty-eight is written as 123 in the five scale. It is the value of the polynomial $1 \cdot x^2 + 2x + 3$ when $x = 5$.

Other scales could be used equally well. In writing a number in the 3 scale, we use the three digits, 0, 1, 2. Hence twenty-four is written in the 3 scale as 220 since $24 = 2 \cdot 3^2 + 2 \cdot 3 + 0$. In the two scale, we use only the two digits 0, 1. Hence twenty-four is written as 11000 in the two scale, since $24 = 1 \cdot 2^4 + 1 \cdot 2^3 + 0 \cdot 2^2 + 0 \cdot 2 + 0$. The same number is written in different ways if we use different scales of notation. In the two scale the first ten numbers are written as 1, 10, 11, 100, 101, 110, 111, 1000, 1001, 1010.

Changing from one scale to another is merely a problem for the packing department. When thirty-eight is written in the ten scale, it is as though thirty-eight objects were packed into 3 boxes of 10 each and 8 boxes of one each

$(38 = 3 \cdot 10 + 8)$. Changing to the five scale amounts to repacking the thirty-eight objects into one box of $25(=5^2)$, 2 boxes of 5 each and 3 boxes of 1 each $(123 = 1 \cdot 5^2 + 2 \cdot 5 + 3)$. In the ten scale we pack by ones, 10's, 10^2's, 10^3's, and so on. In the five scale, we pack by ones, 5's, 5^2's, 5^3's, and so on, always using the largest box that can be filled.

We are merely discussing different ways of writing the same old numbers. That is, we are discussing different systems of notation or different (written) languages. When we say that the number which is written as 24 in our usual decimal language would be written as 44 in the "5 scale" language, we are merely translating from one language to another. In the following table, each horizontal line contains just one number rewritten in several different languages.

10 *scale*	5 *scale*	3 *scale*	2 *scale*	7 *scale*	9 *scale*
24	44	220	11000	33	26
31	111	1011	11111	43	34
8	13	22	1000	11	8

Similarly, the same symbol, say 231, would mean different things according to the system of notation in which it is intended to be interpreted. In the usual 10 scale, the symbol 231 means $2 \cdot 10^2 + 3 \cdot 10 + 1$, or the value of the polynomial $2x^2 + 3x + 1$ when $x = 10$, or two hundred and thirty-one. In the 5 scale, 231 means $2 \cdot 5^2 + 3 \cdot 5 + 1$, or the value of the polynomial $2x^2 + 3x + 1$ when $x = 5$, or the number sixty-six. To avoid possible confusion as to which language or scale a number such as 231 is written in we may either state the scale in words as we have done so far, or we may use a subscript in parentheses such as $231_{(5)}$ to indicate that the 5 scale is being used. Such subscripts will always be written in the familiar 10 scale since that is our "native" language. If no subscript is used nor any explicit remark made, the 10 scale is always understood.

These new notations look strange only because we have been brought up since early childhood to interpret numerals automatically in the 10 scale. The processes of adding and multiplying would be quite as easy in another scale, say the 5 scale, including the device of "carrying"; only we would find it clumsy unless we memorized new tables of addition and multiplication for the other scale as thoroughly as we have memorized those of the 10 scale. In the 5 scale, for example, we have the addition table:

$1 + 1 = 2$	$2 + 1 = 3$	$3 + 1 = 4$	$4 + 1 = 10$
$1 + 2 = 3$	$2 + 2 = 4$	$3 + 2 = 10$	$4 + 2 = 11$
$1 + 3 = 4$	$2 + 3 = 10$	$3 + 3 = 11$	$4 + 3 = 12$
$1 + 4 = 10$	$2 + 4 = 11$	$3 + 4 = 12$	$4 + 4 = 13.$

To add numbers like 34 and 42 (both are written in the 5 scale) we proceed as follows

$$\begin{array}{r} 1 \\ 34 \\ \underline{42} \\ 131. \end{array} \tag{1}$$

That is, 2 + 4 from the above table is 11. We write the right-hand 1 and "carry" the other, which really represents one 5, into the 5's column. Then 4 + 4 = 13. This may be justified by the axioms just as for the 10 scale. The example (1) rewritten in the 10 scale would look like this:

$$\begin{array}{r} 1 \\ 19 \\ \underline{22} \\ 41. \end{array} \tag{2}$$

That is, (1) and (2) *represent exactly the same numerical facts; they are merely written in different languages*. Numbers written in the 10, 5, 3, or 2 scale are often said to be written in the **decimal**, **quinary**, **ternary**, or **binary scale**, respectively.

We can also use scales larger than 10 if we invent new digits. For example, in the 12 scale we would have twelve digits 0, 1, 2, 3, 4, 5, 6, 7, 8, 9, t, e where t and e are digits representing ten and eleven, respectively. In the 12 scale we would write twelve as 10 or $1 \cdot 12 + 0$, thirteen as 11 or $1 \cdot 12 + 1$, one hundred and seventy-one as 123 or $1 \cdot 12^2 + 2 \cdot 12 + 3$, and two hundred and seventy-five as $1te$ or $1 \cdot 12^2 + t \cdot 12 + e$ or one "twelve-squared" plus ten "twelves" plus eleven units (one gross, ten dozen, and eleven units). In fact, the Babylonians, thousands of years ago, used a positional system of notation based on 60.

There is little reason to prefer one of these scales to another except that we are familiar with the 10 scale. In some parts of higher mathematics it is, however, quite convenient to use other scales, notably the ternary and binary scales. Recently, various scales, particularly the 2 scale, have been applied in remarkable new calculating machines, sometimes called mechanical or electronic brains.

For the 2 scale, the tables of addition and multiplication are particularly simple:

$$\begin{array}{ll|ll} \multicolumn{2}{c|}{\textit{Addition}} & \multicolumn{2}{c}{\textit{Multiplication}} \\ 0+0=0 & 1+0=1 & 0 \cdot 0=0 & 1 \cdot 0=0 \\ 0+1=1 & 1+1=10 & 0 \cdot 1=0 & 1 \cdot 1=1. \end{array} \tag{3}$$

Thus to multiply 1101 by 11, both already written in the binary scale, we have

$$
\begin{array}{r}
1\,1\,0\,1 \\
1\,1 \\
\hline
1\,1\,0\,1 \\
1\,1\,0\,1 \\
\hline
1\,0\,0\,1\,1\,1.
\end{array}
\tag{4}
$$

In the ten scale, $1101_{(2)}$ becomes $1 \cdot 2^3 + 1 \cdot 2^2 + 0 \cdot 2 + 1 = 13$, $11_{(2)}$ becomes $1 \cdot 2 + 1 = 3$, and $100111_{(2)}$ becomes $1 \cdot 2^5 + 0 \cdot 2^4 + 0 \cdot 2^3 + 1 \cdot 2^2 + 1 \cdot 2 + 1 = 32 + 4 + 2 + 1 = 39$. Thus (4) is an account in the binary language of the fact that thirteen times three is thirty-nine.

Note that a given number, say 28, written in the ten-scale can be expressed in any other scale, say the 2 scale, by repeated division with remainder. Thus,

(5)

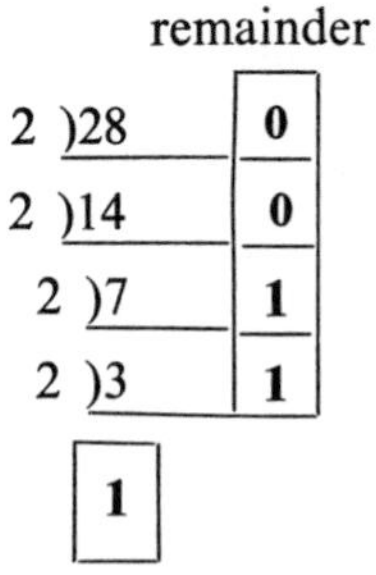

Hence, $28_{(10)} = 11100_{(2)}$. For, the first division means that

$$28 = 2 \cdot 14 + 0. \tag{6}$$

The second means that $14 = 2 \cdot 7 + 0$. Substituting this in (6), we get

$$28 = 2(2 \cdot 7 + 0) + 0 = 2^2 \cdot 7 + 2 \cdot 0 + 0. \tag{7}$$

The third division means that $7 = 2 \cdot 3 + 1$. Substituting in (7), we get

$$28 = 2^2(2 \cdot 3 + 1) + 2 \cdot 0 + 0 = 2^3 \cdot 3 + 2^2 \cdot 1 + 2 \cdot 0 + 0. \tag{8}$$

The last division means that $3 = 2 \cdot 1 + 1$. Substituting in (8), we get

$$
\begin{aligned}
28 &= 2^3(2 \cdot 1 + 1) + 2^2 \cdot 1 + 2 \cdot 0 + 1 \\
&= 1 \cdot 2^4 + 1 \cdot 2^3 + 1 \cdot 2^2 + 0 \cdot 2 + 0.
\end{aligned}
\tag{9}
$$

Thus, in practice, it is sufficient to read off the final quotient and the remainders of the successive divisions in (5), in reverse order, to get the binary expression 11100.

Exercises

In exercises 1—6, write each number in

(*a*) *the 10 scale;*	(*b*) *the 5 scale;*	(*c*) *the 9 scale;*
(*d*) *the 8 scale;*	(*e*) *the 7 scale;*	(*f*) *the 6 scale;*
(*g*) *the 4 scale;*	(*h*) *the 3 scale;*	(*i*) *the 2 scale:*

1. twenty-four. **2.** thirty-six. **3.** thirty-two. **4.** five. **5.** eight. **6.** thirty.

7. What number would be represented by the symbol 222 if the symbol 222 is to be interpreted in (*a*) the 5 scale; (*b*) the 8 scale; (*c*) the 3 scale; (*d*) the 10 scale? Write your answers in the usual 10 scale.

8. If the number 222 is already written in the 4 scale, rewrite it in (*a*) the 8 scale; (*b*) the 2 scale.

9. Rewrite the entire statement "$2 + 5 = 7$" (now written in the 10 scale) to express it in (*a*) the 5 scale; (*b*) the 2 scale; (*c*) the 3 scale; (*d*) the 7 scale; (*e*) the 8 scale.

10. Add 234 and 432 (both already written in the 5 scale) using addition table in text. Translate both numbers and their sum into the 10 scale and check.

11. Make up a table of multiplication for the 5 scale and use it to multiply 23 by 34 (both already written in the 5 scale). Translate both numbers and their product into the 10 scale and check.

12. Make up a table of addition for the 3 scale and use it to add 221 and 102 (both already written in the 3 scale). Translate the whole problem into the 10 scale and check.

13. Make up a table of multiplication for the 3 scale and use it to multiply 102 by 22 (both already written in the 3 scale). Translate both numbers and their product into the 10 scale and check.

14. The following numbers are already written in the twelve scale; rewrite them in the 10 scale:

(*a*) 23; (*b*) *t*1; (*c*) *t*0*e*; (*d*) 2*et*.

15. The following numbers are already written in the 10 scale; rewrite them in the 12 scale:

(*a*) 64; (*b*) 49; (*c*) 120; (*d*) 131; (*e*) 167.

16. The following numbers are already written in the binary or two scale; rewrite them in the ten scale:

(*a*) 1110; (*b*) 1011; (*c*) 11010; (*d*) 10010; (*e*) 100100.

17. The following numbers are already written in the ten scale; rewrite them in the 2 scale:

(*a*) 37; (*b*) 7; (*c*) 15; (*d*) 57; (*e*) 111.

The following numbers are already written in the two scale. Perform the indicated operations, using the tables (3) above, within the two scale and check by translating both numbers and the answer into the ten scale:

18. $\begin{array}{r} 101 \\ +11 \\ \hline \end{array}$ **19.** $\begin{array}{r} 1011 \\ +101 \\ \hline \end{array}$ **20.** $\begin{array}{r} 111 \\ +110 \\ \hline \end{array}$ **21.** $\begin{array}{r} 111 \\ \times 11 \\ \hline \end{array}$

22. $\begin{array}{r} 1011 \\ \times 101 \\ \hline \end{array}$ **23.** $\begin{array}{r} 1101 \\ \times 101 \\ \hline \end{array}$ **24.** $\begin{array}{r} 1001 \\ \times 111 \\ \hline \end{array}$

25. $\begin{array}{r} 1\ 1\ 0\ 1 \\ -\ 1\ 1\ 1 \\ \hline \end{array}$ **26.** $1\ 0\ 1\overline{)1\ 1\ 1\ 1}$ **27.** $1\ 1\ 0\overline{)1\ 1\ 1\ 1\ 0}$.

28. A number is written as 33 in the 8-scale. In what scale would it be written as 43?

29. Two numbers are written in the x-scale as 32 and 24, respectively. The same two numbers are written in the y-scale as 43 and 33, respectively. Find x and y.

30. Two numbers are written in the x-scale as 123 and 31, respectively. The same two numbers are written in the y-scale as 33 and 15, respectively. Find x and y.

31. A number is written as 25 in the x-scale. Twice the number is written as 52 in the x-scale. Find x.

32. The number one hundred and two is written as 123 in the x-scale. Find x algebraically.

51. FURTHER PROGRESS IN ARITHMETIC

We have already seen the great simplifications introduced into arithmetic by the Arabic notation and by the use of decimal fractions. However, in the early years of the seventeenth century, astronomers like Tycho Brahe and Galileo had made extensive observations, and Kepler and others were attempting to reason about heavenly bodies on the basis of these observations. Now in astronomical work the distances involved are very large while the angles are often very small, and the calculations become unbearably tedious. Astronomers found that they were literally wasting years of their lives on computation. In response to the need for still easier methods of computation, two men, Napier (about 1614), a Scotsman and, Bürgi, a Swiss, independently discovered a further great simplification of arithmetic called logarithms. We shall be unable to discuss here the way in which these men actually were led to the idea of logarithms since their methods were too advanced for this book. However, we

John Napier
1550–1617, Scottish

shall introduce logarithms by a method developed later, which is much easier to follow; that is, by way of exponents. First, however, we shall have to extend the notion of exponent, much as we extended the concept of number itself in Chapters 3 and 4, beginning with the positive integers and going on to other kinds of numbers.

52. POSITIVE INTEGRAL EXPONENTS

We already have the following definition of exponent.

Definition 1. *If n is a positive integer, then $x^n = xx \cdots x$ where there are n factors on the right.*

The restriction to positive integers is necessary because only positive integers are used for counting, and we have defined the exponent here as the number of factors. We can now prove the following theorems, *in which p and q are understood to be positive integers.*

Theorem 1. $x^p x^q = x^{p+q}$.

Proof. See section 36.

Theorem 2. (*a*). *If $p > q$, $x^p/x^q = x^{p-q}$ ($x \neq 0$).*

Proof.

$$x^p = (xx \cdots x)(xx \cdots x)$$

where the first parenthesis has $p - q$ factors and the second has q factors. Hence,

$$\frac{x^p}{x^q} = \frac{\overbrace{(x \cdot x \cdots x)}^{(p-q \text{ factors})}\overbrace{(x \cdot x \cdots x)}^{(q \text{ factors})}}{\underbrace{(x \cdot x \cdots x)}_{(q \text{ factors})}} = \overbrace{(x \cdot x \cdots x)}^{(p-q \text{ factors})}$$
$$= x^{p-q}$$

by definition. The restriction $x \neq 0$ must be made because if $x = 0$ the expression x^p/x^q becomes 0/0 which has been excluded.

For example, $\dfrac{x^5}{x^2} = \dfrac{(xxx)(xx)}{(xx)} = xxx = x^3 = x^{5-2}$.

Theorem 2 (*b*). *If $p < q$, $x^p/x^q = 1/x^{q-p}$ ($x \neq 0$).*

Proof. $x^q = (x \cdot x \cdots x)(x \cdot x \cdots x)$ where the first parenthesis has $q - p$ factors and the second has p factors. Hence,

$$\frac{x^p}{x^q} = \frac{\overbrace{(x \cdot x \cdots x)}^{(p \text{ factors})}}{\underbrace{(x \cdot x \cdots x)}_{(q-p \text{ factors})}\underbrace{(x \cdot x \cdots x)}_{(p \text{ factors})}} = \frac{1}{\underbrace{(x \cdot x \cdots x)}_{(q-p \text{ factors})}} = \frac{1}{x^{q-p}}.$$

For example, $\dfrac{x^2}{x^5} = \dfrac{(xx)}{(xxx)(xx)} = \dfrac{1}{(xxx)} = \dfrac{1}{x^3} = \dfrac{1}{x^{5-2}}.$

Theorem 2 (*c*). *If $p = q$, then $x^p/x^q = 1 (x \neq 0)$.*

Proof.

$$x^p/x^q = x^p/x^p = 1.$$

For example,

$$x^3/x^3 = 1.$$

Theorem 3. $(x^p)^q = x^{pq}$.

Proof. We have $(x^p)^q = (x^p)(x^p) \cdots (x^p)$, where there are q such parentheses. Thus,

$$(x^p)^q = (x \cdot x \cdots x)(x \cdot x \cdots x) \cdots (x \cdot x \cdots x) = x^{pq},$$

since there are p x's in each of the q parentheses.

For example, $(x^2)^3 = (x^2)(x^2)(x^2) = (xx)(xx)(xx) = x^6 = x^{2.3}$.

Theorem 4. $(xy)^p = x^p y^p$.

Proof. See section 27.

Exercises

Simplify:

1. $\dfrac{a^8}{a^2}$. **2.** $\dfrac{a^2b^4c^3}{a^6bc^3}$. **3.** $\dfrac{(a^2b)^3}{(ab^3)^2}$. **4.** $(a^3b)(ab^2)$. **5.** $\dfrac{(a^2b)^3(ab)^2}{(ab^2)^2(a^2b)^2}$.

Evaluate:

6. $2^3 \cdot 3^2$. **7.** $8^9/8^7$. **8.** $(-2)^4(-3)^3$. **9.** $3 \cdot 2^3$.
10. $8^4/2^{11}$. **11.** $4 + 2 \cdot 3^2$. **12.** $4 + (2 \cdot 3)^2$. **13.** $(4 + 2) \cdot 3^2$.
14. $(4 + 2 \cdot 3)^2$. **15.** $[(4 + 2) \cdot 3]^2$. **16.** $\dfrac{2^6 \cdot 3^7}{2^4 \cdot 3^6}$. **17.** $\dfrac{8^5 \cdot 9^4}{2^{12} \cdot 3^6}$.

Correct the right member of each of the following, if necessary:

18. $3^2 + 3^3 = 3^5$. **19.** $3^2 + 3^3 = 6^5$. **20.** $3^2 \cdot 3^3 = 3^6$.
21. $3^2 \cdot 3^3 = 9^5$. **22.** $3^8/3^2 = 3^4$. **23.** $(3^4)^2 = 3^6$.
24. $(2^3)^2 = 2^5$. **25.** $6^3/2^3 = 3^3$. **26.** $(2^3)^2 = 2^9$.

53. NEGATIVE INTEGERS AND ZERO AS EXPONENTS

The occurrence of three separate cases in theorem 2, section 52, is a source of inconvenience and it is natural to desire to unify them.

Suppose we attempted to apply the formula of theorem 2(a).

$$\frac{x^p}{x^q} = x^{p-q},$$

mechanically even if $p < q$, in spite of the fact that it does not apply to this case. This would make the exponent $p - q$ negative. For example,

$$\frac{x^2}{x^5} = x^{2-5} = x^{-3}.$$

But an exponent -3 has no sense, since our definition of exponent is necessarily restricted to positive integers, as we have seen. The symbol x^{-3} cannot possibly be interpreted according to definition 1. No one can count out -3 factors, except possibly at a séance; but x^{-3} is not intended to mean the product of the ghosts of three departed x's, or something equally mysterious. The symbol x^{-3} does not come under the jurisdiction of our definition at all and is at present a completely undefined symbol. This is fortunate for since x^{-3} has no pre-assigned meaning we are free to choose a meaning for it to suit ourselves without fear of contradicting previous results. We see at once that we will be able to dispense with theorem 2 (b) if we adopt the following definition.

Definition 2. *If* $-n$ is a *negative integer*, $x^{-n} = \dfrac{1}{x^n}$ $(x \neq 0)$.

Writing $x^2/x^5 = x^{2-5} = x^{-3}$ would now agree with the facts since x^{-3} means $1/x^3$. For example, $2^{-3} = 1/2^3 = 1/8$.

Similarly, if we try to apply the formula of theorem 2(a) mechanically even if $p = q$, although it does not apply to this case either, we would get

$$\frac{x^p}{x^q} = x^{p-q} = x^0$$

since $p = q$. But the symbol x^0 has no sense, under definition 1 or 2. Definition 1 defines positive integral exponents and definition 2 defines negative integral exponents; but 0 is neither positive nor negative. Certainly x^0 cannot mean the result obtained by taking no x's, in some occult way, and multiplying them together. Since the symbol x^0 does not come under the jurisdiction of definitions 1 and 2, we are free to choose any meaning we please for it. We see that we can dispense with theorem 2(*c*) if we adopt the following definition.

Definition 3. $x^0 = 1$, $(x \neq 0)$.

For example, writing $x^3/x^3 = x^{3-3} = x^0$, according to the rule of theorem 2(*a*), is in agreement with the fact that $x^3/x^3 = 1$, for x^0 now means 1. For example, $7^0 = 1$.

By adopting these supplementary definitions 2 and 3, we extend the concept of exponent to allow all integers, positive, negative, or zero, to occur as exponents. At the same time the three parts of theorem 2 reduce to one formula:

$$\frac{x^p}{x^q} = x^{p-q}.$$

Furthermore, this formula in turn reduces to that of theorem 1 since if we apply the rule of theorem 1 mechanically to x^p/x^q we get

$$\frac{x^p}{x^q} = x^p \cdot \frac{1}{x^q} = x^p x^{-q} = x^{p+(-q)} = x^{p-q},$$

which is in agreement with the facts. Thus, *by adopting our supplementary definitions of negative integral and zero we dispense with Theorem 2 entirely.*

Remark. Note that $2^2 = 4$ is half of $2^3 = 8$, and $2^1 = 2$ is half of $2^2 = 4$. By our definitions, $2^0 = 1$ is half of $2^1 = 2$, $2^{-1} = \frac{1}{2}$ is half of $2^0 = 1$, and $2^{-2} = \frac{1}{4}$ is half of $2^{-1} = \frac{1}{2}$ Hence our definitions fit well with our desire for uniformity in the sequence $2^3, 2^2, 2^1, 2^0, 2^{-1}, 2^{-2}$, and so on.

It remains to prove that, for any integral exponents p and q, positive, negative, or zero, the three rules

(1) $$x^p x^q = x^{p+q}$$

(2) $$(x^p)^q = x^{pq}$$

(3) $$(xy)^p = x^p y^p$$

still hold. For example, let us prove (3).

Proof. Case 1. Suppose p is positive. Then it has already been proved in section 52.

Case 2. Suppose p is negative. Then $p = -a$ where a is positive. And

$$(xy)^p = (xy)^{-a} = \frac{1}{(xy)^a} \qquad \text{(by definition 2).}$$

But $(xy)^a = x^a y^a$ by case 1, since a is positive. Therefore

$$(xy)^p = \frac{1}{x^a y^a} = \frac{1}{x^a} \cdot \frac{1}{y^a} = x^{-a} y^{-a} = x^p y^p$$

which was to be proved.

Case 3. Suppose $p = 0$. Then $(xy)^p = 1$, $x^p = 1$, and $y^p = 1$, by definition 3. Thus formula (3) is verified immediately for this case since $1 = 1 \cdot 1$.

The proofs of (1) and (2) are included in the following list of exercises.

Exercises

Evaluate:

1. 4^{-2}. **2.** 5^0. **3.** $(\frac{1}{2})^{-3}$. **4.** $(-2)^{-5}$. **5.** $(\frac{1}{2})^0$.
6. $3 \cdot 2^{-2}$. **7.** $(3 \cdot 2)^{-2}$. **8.** $4 \cdot 10^0$. **9.** $(4 \cdot 10)^0$.

10. $10^0 \cdot 10^5 \cdot 10^{-3}$. **11.** $\dfrac{10^5 \cdot 10^{-2}}{10^3}$. **12.** $\dfrac{10^4 \cdot 10^{-6}}{10^{-4}}$.

13. $\dfrac{(6 \cdot 10^5)(2 \cdot 10^{-3})}{3 \cdot 10^3}$. **14.** $\dfrac{(2 \cdot 10^2)^3 \cdot (4 \cdot 10^{-2})^2}{(2 \cdot 10^3)^{-1}}$.

Simplify by removing zero and negative exponents:

15. $3x^{-2}$. **16.** $(3x)^{-2}$. **17.** $4x^0$. **18.** $(4x)^0$. **19.** $3a^{-3}b^2c^0$.

20. $\dfrac{x^{-1}}{y^{-1}}$. **21.** $\dfrac{a^{-1} + b^{-1}}{a^{-1} - b^{-1}}$. **22.** $\dfrac{1}{a^{-1} + b^{-1}}$. **23.** $\dfrac{(xy^2)^{-3}(x^2y^{-1})^2}{(x^4y^3)^{-1}}$.

24. $(x^{-2})^{-5} + x^{-2}(x^5 + 3x^3 + 5x^2)$.

★25. Prove that formula (1) holds for *all* integral exponents p and q. (Hint: divide the proof into nine separate cases as follows. Case 1(*a*): p positive, q positive. Case 1(*b*): p positive, q negative. Case 1(*c*): p positive, $q = 0$. Case 2(*a*): p negative, q positive. Case 2(*b*): p negative, q negative. Case 2(*c*): p negative, $q = 0$. Case 3(*a*): $p = 0$, q positive. Case 3(*b*): $p = 0$, q negative. Case 3(*c*): $p = 0$, $q = 0$. Imitate the proof of formula (3) in the text as far as possible.)

★26. Prove that formula (2) holds for *all* integral exponents p and q. (See hint for exercise 25.)

54. COMPUTATION WITH POWERS OF TEN

When very large or very small numbers are used in scientific writing it is customary to express them in terms of powers of ten, as follows. Instead of 1,000,000 one would write 10^6. Similarly 378,000,000 might be written as 378×10^6 or 37.8×10^7 or 3.78×10^8; we use the $\times$ sign for multiplication here to avoid confusion with the decimal point. Similarly, .0001 would be written as 10^{-4} and .000378 would be written as 378×10^{-6} or 37.8×10^{-5} or 3.78×10^{-4}. Note that multiplying a number by 10^4 moves the decimal point to the right four places while multiplying by 10^{-4} moves the decimal point to the left four places.

Every positive real number can be expressed as a number between one and ten multiplied by a suitable integral power of ten; when this is done the number is said to be expressed in ***standard form***. For example, $378{,}000{,}000 = 3.78 \times 10^8$, $.000378 = 3.78 \times 10^{-4}$, and $3.78 = 3.78 \times 10^0$. This so-called "standard form" is more compact and more comprehensible than the everyday way of writing such numbers with large numbers of zeros before or after the decimal point. It also lends itself to calculations with cumbersome numbers, large or small, which are made easy by the use of the laws of exponents.

Example. Calculate the value of

$$\frac{378{,}000{,}000{,}000 \times .000004}{2000}.$$

We write

$$\frac{3.78 \times 10^{11} \times 4 \times 10^{-6}}{2 \times 10^3} = 3.78 \times 2 \times 10^{11-6-3} = 7.56 \times 10^2 = 756.$$

The coefficients of the powers of ten have to be multiplied and divided in the ordinary way. How this can be avoided by expressing them also as (fractional) powers of ten will be discussed in sections 57 and 58.

Exercises

Express each of the following in standard form:

1. 300,000. **2.** 5,410,000. **3.** 367,000,000,000. **4.** .5.
5. .056. **6.** .000785. **7.** 3. **8.** 46.73.

Express each of the following in ordinary positional (decimal) notation:

9. 10^5. **10.** 10^{-3}. **11.** 6.78×10^7. **12.** 6.78×10^{-5}.
13. 6.78×10^0. **14.** 3.76×10^{-4}. **15.** 4.68×10^5. **16.** 46.7×10^{-4}.

Calculate, using the laws for exponents, and express the result in ordinary positional (decimal) notation:

17. $\dfrac{(6 \times 10^7) \times (3 \times 10^{-3})}{2 \times 10^3}$. **18.** $\dfrac{(5.2 \times 10^6) \times (4 \times 10^{-8})}{13 \times 10^{-4}}$.

19. If c represents the velocity of radiant energy in a vacuum, L its wave length, and f its frequency, then $f = c/L$. Suppose c is 3×10^{10} centimeters per second and $L = 6 \times 10^{-5}$ centimeters. Find f. (Hint: write $3 \times 10^{10} = 30 \times 10^9$.)

20. The angstrom is a unit of length equal to 10^{-8} centimeters. If one centimeter is .3937 inches, express in inches the wave length of red light with a wave length of 8000 angstroms.

21. A light year is a unit of length equal to 5.88×10^{12} miles. The distance of the cluster of stars called the Pleiades is 1.2936×10^{15} miles. How many light years is this?

22. The Great Nebula in Andromeda is approximately 5.292×10^{18} miles away. How many light years is this? Use the data of exercise 21.

23. If a gram is .002205 pounds and the mass of the earth is 5.97×10^{27} grams, find the mass of the earth in pounds.

24. The mass of the sun is 1.98×10^{33} grams. Find the mass of the sun in pounds. Use the data of exercise 23.

25. One coulomb equals 3.00×10^9 statcoulombs. The charge on an electron is 4.80×10^{-10} statcoulombs. How many coulombs is this?

55. FRACTIONAL EXPONENTS

Since we have successfully extended the concept of exponent to include all integers as exponents, it is natural to ask whether we cannot extend the notion still further, say to fractions. In making such an extension, since if we do it at all we do it for our own convenience, we shall want to preserve the validity of formulas (1), (2), (3) of section 53; just as, when extending the notion of number itself in Chapters 3 and 4 we desired to preserve the validity of such formulas as the associative, commutative, and distributive laws.

Let us experiment with a symbol like $x^{1/2}$. This has no meaning under any of the previous definitions. It certainly cannot mean that we take a product of x's, the number of factors being 1/2. In particular, $X^{1/2}$ does not mean $\wedge$. Since $x^{1/2}$ has no previous meaning, we are free to choose any definition that suits us, and it will suit us to give such a definition, if possible, as will preserve the validity of our three formulas. Consider formula (2). If this is to operate, then $x^{1/2}$, whatever it shall mean, must satisfy the relation $(x^{\frac{1}{2}})^2 = x^{\frac{1}{2}\cdot 2} = x^1 = x$. Thus $x^{1/2}$ will have to mean something which when squared yields x. But this can only be $\sqrt{x}$ or $-\sqrt{x}$. Therefore we choose the *definition*: $x^{1/2} = \sqrt{x}$. For example, $9^{1/2} = 3$. This obviously fits in with formula (1) as well, since $x^{1/2} \cdot x^{1/2} = x^{\frac{1}{2}+\frac{1}{2}} = x^1 = x$. More generally, we choose the definition $x^{\frac{1}{p}} = \sqrt[p]{x}$, where p

is an integer >1, so that rule (2) continues to operate as follows:

$$(\sqrt[p]{x})^p = (x^{\frac{1}{p}})^p = x^{\frac{1}{p}\cdot p} = x^1 = x.$$

Furthermore, if rule (2) is to remain valid we would have

$$(\sqrt[q]{x})^p = (x^{\frac{1}{q}})^p = x^{\frac{1}{q}\cdot p} = x^{\frac{p}{q}}, \qquad \text{and} \qquad \sqrt[q]{x^p} = (x^p)^{\frac{1}{q}} = x^{p\cdot\frac{1}{q}} = x^{\frac{p}{q}}.$$

Since, as is easily proved, $(\sqrt[q]{x})^p = \sqrt[q]{x^p}$ (Exercise 21), we are led to make the following general definition.

Definition 4. $x^{\frac{p}{q}} = (\sqrt[q]{x})^p = \sqrt[q]{x^p}$, *where p and q are any integers* ($q > 1$).

Any rational number can be written in the form p/q where p and q are integers and $q > 0$, that is, with a positive denominator. For example, $3/-4$ can be written as $-3/4$ and $-5/-6$ can be written as $5/6$. Definition 4 therefore extends the notion of exponent to *all* rational numbers. As in section 22, we confine ourselves to roots of positive numbers. Thus, in the present section, the symbols x, a, b represent positive numbers.

For example, $x^{2/3} = \sqrt[3]{x^2} = (\sqrt[3]{x})^2$. Thus $8^{2/3} = (\sqrt[3]{8})^2 = 2^2 = 4$. Similarly, $8^{-2/3} = \sqrt[3]{8^{-2}} = \sqrt[3]{1/8^2} = \sqrt[3]{1/64} = 1/4$.

We must not take it for granted that $x^{2/3}$ means the same thing as $x^{4/6}$, say. This has to be proved. For $x^{2/3}$ means a cube root of x^2, that is, a number a such that $a^3 = x^2$, by definition; while $x^{4/6}$ means a sixth root of x^4. Now squaring a^3 we get $(a^3)^2 = (x^2)^2$ or $a^6 = x^4$. That is, a is a sixth root of x^4. Hence $x^{2/3} = x^{4/6}$. In the same way we can prove the following general theorem.

Theorem A. $x^{\frac{p}{q}} = x^{\frac{pr}{qr}}$ *where p, q, r are integers and q and qr are understood to be positive.*

Proof. By definition $x^{\frac{p}{q}}$ means a number a such that $a^q = x^p$ (that is, a qth root of x^p), while $x^{\frac{pr}{qr}}$ means a qrth root of x^{pr}. Raising a^q to the rth power we obtain $(a^q)^r = (x^p)^r$, or $a^{qr} = x^{pr}$. That is, a *is* a qrth root of x^{pr}. This proves the theorem.

We shall need the following theorem.

Theorem B. *If n is any positive integer,* $\sqrt[n]{a} \cdot \sqrt[n]{b} = \sqrt[n]{ab}$.

Proof. See section 27.

We must not assume naively that the formulas (1), (2), (3) of section 53 remain valid for fractional exponents since they have been proved only for integral exponents. However, we are now in a position to prove them for fractional exponents. For example, let us prove that $x^{1/2} \cdot x^{1/3} = x^{\frac{1}{2}+\frac{1}{3}}$ or $x^{5/6}$ Now $x^{1/2} = x^{3/6}$ and $x^{1/3} = x^{2/6}$ by theorem A. Hence

$$\begin{aligned} x^{1/2}\cdot x^{1/3} &= x^{3/6}\cdot x^{2/6} = \sqrt[6]{x^3}\cdot\sqrt[6]{x^2} && \text{(by definition)}\\ &= \sqrt[6]{x^3\cdot x^2} && \text{(by theorem B)}\\ &= \sqrt[6]{x^5} && \text{(by (1) section 53, since 3 and 2 are integers)}\\ &= x^{5/6} && \text{(by definition).} \end{aligned}$$

Similarly, we can prove that formula (1) of section 53 holds for all fractional exponents, as follows.

Theorem C. $x^{\frac{p}{q}}\cdot x^{\frac{u}{v}} = x^{\frac{p}{q}+\frac{u}{v}}$ *or* $x^{\frac{pv+qu}{qv}}$ *where* p, q, u, v *are integers and* q *and* v *are understood to be positive.*

Proof. By theorem A, $x^{\frac{p}{q}} = x^{\frac{pv}{qv}}$ and $x^{\frac{u}{v}} = x^{\frac{qu}{qv}}$.

$$\begin{aligned} \text{Hence, } x^{\frac{p}{q}}\cdot x^{\frac{u}{v}} &= x^{\frac{pv}{qv}}\cdot x^{\frac{qu}{qv}} = \sqrt[qv]{x^{pv}}\cdot\sqrt[qv]{x^{qu}} && \text{(by definition)}\\ &= \sqrt[qv]{x^{pv}\cdot x^{qu}} && \text{(by theorem B)}\\ &= \sqrt[qv]{x^{pv+qu}} && \text{(by (1), section 53, since } pv \text{ and } qu \text{ are integers)}\\ &= x^{\frac{pv+qu}{qv}} && \text{(by definition).} \end{aligned}$$

We have proved that (1) of section 53 holds for *all* rational exponents. By similar methods we could prove that (2) and (3) of section 53 hold for all rational exponents. We shall not carry out the detailed proofs here; they are included in exercise 20 below.

The validity of these formulas for fractional exponents provides many algebraic simplifications. For example, it is not easy at first glance to simplify such an expression as $(\sqrt[3]{x^2})(\sqrt[5]{x})^3$. But, using fractional exponents it becomes

$$x^{2/3}\cdot x^{3/5} = x^{\frac{2}{3}+\frac{3}{5}} = x^{19/15} = \sqrt[15]{x^{19}} \text{ or } (\sqrt[15]{x})^{19}.$$

We have now extended the concept of exponent to allow all rational numbers as exponents. It is possible to extend it further to allow irrational and even imaginary exponents but this will not be done here.

Exercises

Evaluate:

1. $16^{1/2}$. **2.** $16^{1/4}$. **3.** $8^{1/3}$. **4.** $8^{-1/3}$. **5.** $16^{-1/2}$.
6. $8^{2/3}$. **7.** $8^{-2/3}$. **8.** $16^{3/4}$. **9.** $16^{-3/2}$. **10.** $8^{-4/3}$.
11. $27^{-5/3}$. **12.** $32^{-3/5}$. **13.** $9^{-1/2}$. **14.** $16^{5/4}$.

Simplify:

15. $\sqrt[4]{x^3}\cdot\sqrt[7]{x^5}$. **16.** $\sqrt[5]{x^2}\cdot(\sqrt[5]{x})^3$. **17.** $\sqrt[5]{x^7}/\sqrt[3]{x^4}$.

18. Evaluate $(27^{2/3}+8^{-1/3})\div(8^{3/5}\cdot 8^{2/5})$.

★**19.** Using the definitions, prove, without assuming the validity of formulas (1), (2), and (3) of section 53 for fractional exponents, that:

(*a*) $(x^{1/3})^2 = x^{2/3}$; (*b*) $x^{1/5}\cdot x^{2/5} = x^{3/5}$;
(*c*) $(x^{1/3})^{1/2} = x^{1/6}$; (*d*) $x^{1/4}\cdot x^{2/3} = x^{11/12}$.

★**20.** Prove the following, using the definitions, but not assuming the validity of formulas (1), (2), (3) of section 53 for fractional exponents, p, q, u, v being integers, and q and v being positive:

(*a*) $(x^{\frac{p}{q}})^{\frac{u}{v}} = x^{\frac{pu}{qv}}$; (*b*) $(xy)^{\frac{p}{q}} = x^{\frac{p}{q}}\cdot y^{\frac{p}{q}}$.

21. Prove that $\sqrt[q]{x^p} = (\sqrt[q]{x})^p$.

56. LOGARITHMS

While the algebraic simplifications introduced by the use of fractional and negative exponents are important, even more important is the fact that these exponents provide a foundation for the theory of logarithms which, in turn, must be considered one of the major achievements of the seventeenth century. Logarithms simplified computation to such an extent that it is difficult to estimate the time saved thereby for astronomers and other people who are faced with tedious calculations. The following fundamental definition is important.

Definition 5. *If b is any positive number, different from 1, and $b^y = x$, then the exponent y is called the **logarithm of x to the base b**. In symbols, $y = \log_b x$.*

For example, $3 = \log_2 8$ because $2^3 = 8$. Similarly, $2 = \log_3 9$ because $3^2 = 9$. It is easy to confuse the roles played by the three numbers b, y, and x in this definition unless it is learned carefully. Notice that a logarithm *is* an exponent; that is, $\log_b x$ means the exponent y to which we must raise the base b in order to get the number x. It can be proved that *every positive real number x can be expressed as b^y, where y is a real number, rational or irrational.* This will not be done here.

Exercise. Why do we make the restriction, in definition 5, that $b \neq 1$?

Remarks. There are reasons for restricting b to be positive. For example, if b were negative, b^2 would be positive, b^3 negative, b^4 positive, and so on; and $b^{\frac{1}{2}}$ would be imaginary. This would introduce technical difficulties which are best avoided here. If b is positive, however, and y is real (positive, negative, or zero), x is still positive. We shall confine ourselves to positive x's; that is, we shall speak of $\log_b x$ only when b and x are positive numbers.

How this definition enables us to simplify arithmetical calculations will be made clear in the next section. The simplifications are essentially due to the following theorems.

Theorem 1. $\log_b (xw) = \log_b x + \log_b w.$

Theorem 2. $\log_b (x/w) = \log_b x - \log_b w.$

Theorem 3. $\log_b (x^r) = r \log_b x.$

Since logarithms are nothing but exponents it is natural to expect to prove these theorems by using the laws of operation with exponents. In fact, these three theorems will be seen to be nothing more than the translations (from the language of exponents into the language of logarithms) of the following known laws for exponents:

(a) $$b^y b^u = b^{y+u}$$
(b) $$b^y / b^u = b^{y-u}$$
(c) $$(b^y)^r = b^{yr}.$$

Let us prove our three theorems. Let $y = \log_b x$ and $u = \log_b w$; hence we have $b^y = x$ and $b^u = w$.

Proof of theorem 1. By (a), $xw = b^y b^u = b^{y+u}$. But $xw = b^{y+u}$ says that $\log_b (xw) = y + u$ by definition 5. Substituting for y and u, we get $\log_b (xw) = \log_b x + \log_b w$.

Proof of theorem 2. By (b), $x/w = b^y/b^u = b^{y-u}$. By definition 5, this says that $\log_b (x/w) = y - u = \log_b x - \log_b w$.

Proof of theorem 3. By (c), $x^r = (b^y)^r = b^{yr}$. By definition 5, this says that $\log_b (x^r) = yr = r \log_b x$. (Note: we write $r \log_b x$ to avoid the confusion that would arise from writing $\log_b x \cdot r$ as to whether we meant $\log_b (xr)$ or $(\log_b x)r$.)

Exercises

Express in logarithmic notation:

1. $5^2 = 25$. **2.** $2^6 = 64$. **3.** $10^2 = 100$. **4.** $25^{1/2} = 5$.
5. $8^{1/3} = 2$. **6.** $8^{-1/3} = \frac{1}{2}$. **7.** $5^{-2} = \frac{1}{25}$. **8.** $2^{-3} = \frac{1}{8}$.
9. $7^0 = 1$. **10.** $10^{-1} = \frac{1}{10}$.

Express in exponential notation:

11. $\log_2 16 = 4$. **12.** $\log_{10} 1000 = 3$. **13.** $\log_{10} .01 = -2$.
14. $\log_{10} 10 = 1$. **15.** $\log_{10} 1 = 0$. **16.** $\log_2 8 = 3$.
17. $\log_5 125 = 3$. **18.** $\log_{10} 100 = 2$. **19.** $\log_{10} .1 = -1$.
20. $\log_4 8 = \frac{3}{2}$.

Find:

21. $\log_2 32$. **22.** $\log_{10} .001$. **23.** $\log_8 4$. **24.** $\log_2 1$.
25. $\log_2 2$. **26.** $\log_b b$. **27.** $\log_b 1$. **28.** $\log_b (b^3)$.
29. $\log_{25} 125$. **30.** $\log_9 27$. **31.** $\log_{10} 10{,}000$.
32. $\log_{10} (10^2)$. **33.** $\log_{10} (10^5)$. **34.** $\log_b (b^7)$.

If $\log_{10} 2 = .3010$ *and* $\log_{10} 3 = .4771$, *use theorems 1, 2, 3, to find:*

35. $\log_{10} 6$. **36.** $\log_{10} 4$. **37.** $\log_{10} \frac{3}{2}$.
38. $\log_{10} 9$. **39.** $\log_{10} 12$. **40.** $\log_{10} 20$.
41. $\log_{10} .2$. **42.** $\log_{10} 18$. **43.** $\log_{10} 5$.
44. $10^{2.4771}$.
45. If $\log_2 x = \frac{3}{2}$, show that x is irrational.
46. If $\log_2 x = \frac{4}{3}$, show that x is irrational.

57. COMMON LOGARITHMS

Any positive number $b \neq 1$ can be used as a base for logarithms. An irrational number called e whose decimal expression is $2.71828 \cdots$ is actually used in advanced mathematics for theoretical reasons which cannot be explained here. Logarithms with the base e are called **natural logarithms**, a name that must seem very inappropriate to you, and are closely related to the original systems of Napier and Bürgi. An improvement of Napier's system, which is said to have occurred to both Napier and H. Briggs, an English mathematician, led to the system of logarithms to the base 10, known as **common logarithms**. Logarithms to the base 10 are the most convenient for computation simply because we write our numbers in decimal notation.* It is with this system that we work hereafter. *We shall write* $\log x$, *without any base indicated, to mean* $\log_{10} x$. Thus, we write

* If we were in the habit of writing numbers in the 2 scale, then logarithms to the base 2 would be most convenient for computation.

log 100 = 2 because $10^2 = 100$, log 1000 = 3 because $10^3 = 1000$, log .1 = −1, because $10^{-1} = 1/10 = .1$, and log 1 = 0 because $10^0 = 1$. A rudimentary table of common logarithms is easy to construct:

Table A

x	⋯	.0001	.001	.01	.1	1	10	100	1000	10000	⋯
log x	⋯	−4	−3	−2	−1	0	1	2	3	4	⋯

Since 34.2 is between 10 and 100 it is natural to expect log 34.2 to be between log 10 = 1 and log 100 = 2. That is, in exponential language, since $10^1 = 10$ and $10^2 = 100$ it is natural to expect 10 raised to some exponent between 1 and 2 to be exactly 34.2. This is actually so, but the proof is too difficult to be given here. It can be shown that

$$\log 34.2 = 1.5340$$

approximately; that is, in exponential notation,

$$10^{1.5340} = 34.2 \quad \text{or} \quad 10^{1534/1000} = 34.2$$

approximately; in radical notation

$$\sqrt[1000]{10^{1534}} = 34.2$$

approximately.

We have remarked, in section 54, that every positive number can be expressed as the product of a number between 1 and 10 and an integral power of 10. For example, 34.2 = 3.42(10). Similarly,

$$534 = 5.34(10^2)$$
$$.00534 = 5.34(10^{-3}),$$

and

$$5.34 = 5.34(10^0).$$

By theorem 1, section 56 we have

$$\log 534 = \log 5.34 + \log (10^2),$$
$$\log .00534 = \log 5.34 + \log (10^{-3}),$$
$$\log 5.34 = \log 5.34 + \log (10^0).$$

By the definition of logarithm, or by Table A, above, we obtain

$$\log 534 = \log 5.34 + 2,$$
$$\log .00534 = \log 5.34 + (-3),$$
$$\log 5.34 = \log 5.34 + 0.$$

Therefore we see that we could write down the logarithm of any number if we knew only *the logarithms of numbers from 1 to 10*. The latter are called **mantissas** and a table of mantissas approximated to 4 decimal places (Table I) can be found at the end of this book. They are decimals since the logarithm of a number between 1 and 10 must be between 0 and 1.

From the tables, we obtain $\log 5.34 = .7275$. Hence,

$$\log 534 = 2.7275$$

and

$$\log .00534 = -3 + .7275 = -2.2725.$$

Notice that since the digits of the numbers 5.34, 534 and .00534 are the same their logarithms have the same decimal part (.7275) or mantissa, because any of these numbers can be obtained from any other of them by multiplying by a suitable integral power of 10. Therefore, their logarithms differ only by a whole number. *When a logarithm is expressed so that its decimal part is written positively, the integral part of the logarithm is called its* ***characteristic***. For example, the characteristic of log .00534 is -3, not -2 (see above). The above discussion shows us that *to find the logarithm of a number we have only to estimate its characteristic from Table A* and look up its mantissa in Table I.* For example, log 534 is between 2 and 3 since 534 is between $100 = 10^2$ and $1000 = 10^3$ (see Table A). Hence, the characteristic is 2. The mantissa, as we know from Table I, is .7257. Hence, $\log 534 = 2.7275$. Similarly, log .00534 is between -3 and -2 because .00534 is between. $001 = 10^{-3}$ and $.01 = 10^{-2}$ (Table A). Hence, $\log .00534 = -3 + .7275$. Note that log .00534 is *not* -3.7275; this would be between -3 and -4 instead of between -3 and -2. We usually find it more convenient to write logarithms with negative characteristics, like the latter, in a different way. Instead of writing $\log .00534 = -3 + .7275$ we borrow a trick from the politicians and give 10 with our left hand while taking 10 away with our right, as follows:

$$\log .00534 = 10 - 3 + .7275 - 10 = 7.7275 - 10.$$

The latter form is less clumsy in practice.

* Various rules are often stated for determining the characteristic. For example: if $N \geqq 1$, then the characteristic of $\log N$ is one less than the number of digits in N to the left of the decimal point; but if $N < 1$, and if the first non-zero digit of N is in the kth decimal place then $-k$ is the characteristic of $\log N$. One may also state the rule as follows: express the number N in "standard form," that is, as the product of a number between 1 and 10 and an integral power of 10; then the exponent of 10 is the characteristic of $\log N$. Or, one may state it as follows: move the decimal point to where it would be if we were to write N in "standard form"; if we moved it k places to the left, the characteristic of $\log N$ is k, and if we moved it k places to the right, the characteristic is $-k$. None of these rules need be memorized if one thinks of Table A.

The tables may also be used to find a number whose logarithm is known. If we know that $\log x = 3.7275$ we look up .7275 in the table of mantissas and find that x has the digits 534. The characteristic 3 tells us that x is between $10^3 = 1000$ and $10^4 = 10{,}000$ (Table A) since $\log x$ is between 3 and 4. Hence $x = 5340$, approximately. Similarly, if $\log x = 8.7275 - 10$ the digits are still 534 but the characteristic $8 - 10 = -2$ tells us that x is between $10^{-2} = .01$ and $10^{-1} = .1$ since $\log x$ is between -2 and -1 (Table A). Hence, $x = .0534$, approximately.

If we do not find the exact mantissa in the table, we will take the nearest one to it, since we are interested only in approximate results. If more accuracy is desired one can use tables computed for more than 3 digits and more than 4 decimal places. Another device for obtaining further accuracy from a given table, known as *interpolation*, will be discussed in Chapter 10, section 111.

Notice that while Table I is usually called a table of common logarithms, it is really only a table of mantissas. How these tables are computed will be discussed briefly in Chapter 11, section 134.

Remark. To change logarithms with any base b into logarithms with any other base a it is only necessary to multiply by the constant factor $\log_a b$. That is,

$$\log_a x = \log_b x \cdot \log_a b. \tag{1}$$

For suppose $u = \log_b x$, $v = \log_a x$. Then

$$b^u = a^v$$

since both are equal to x. Taking the logarithm with base a of both sides, we get $u \log_a b = v$, which is (1). For example, $\log_2 x = \log_{10} x \cdot \log_2 10$. But $\log_2 10 = 3.322$, approximately, since $m = \log_2 10$ implies $2^m = 10$, and hence $m \log_{10} 2 = 1$ or $m = 1/.3010 = 3.322$, approximately. Thus approximately, we have

$$\log_2 x = 3.322 \log_{10} x. \tag{2}$$

Exercises

Find:

1. log 124. **2.** log 32.1. **3.** log .0124. **4.** log 456.
5. log 39.6 **6.** log 6.37. **7.** log .0435. **8.** log .489.
9. log .000346. **10.** log 208. **11.** log 360. **12.** log 5000.
13. log .005.

Find the number whose logarithm is:

14. 2.5717. **15.** 1.5211. **16.** 8.6284 − 10. **17.** 9.5211 − 10.
18. 0.7126. **19.** 1.6972. **20.** 0.9415. **21.** 9.7364 − 10.
22. 8.8035 − 10. **23.** 3.9717. **24.** 2.9101.

25. Express the statement $\log 862 = 2.9355$ in exponential notation; in radical notation.

26. Express the statement $\log 631 = 2.8000$ in exponential notation; in radical notation.

27. Prove that if a and b are any positive numbers, different from 1, then $\log_a b = 1/\log_b a$.

58. COMPUTATION WITH LOGARITHMS

Having learned to use the tables, the simplification in computation is obtained by the use of theorems 1, 2, 3 of section 56. Two illustrations will suffice to make the method clear.

Example 1. Calculate

$$\frac{(8.34)(65.2)}{376}.$$

Call the result x. Then by theorems 1 and 2,

$$\log x = \log \frac{(8.34)(65.2)}{376} = \log 8.34 + \log 65.2 - \log 376.$$

Now

$$\begin{aligned} \log 8.34 &= 0.9212 \\ \log 65.2 &= \underline{1.8142} \\ \log 8.34 + \log 65.2 &= 2.7354 \\ \log 376 &= \underline{2.5752} \\ \log x &= 0.1602. \end{aligned}$$

Hence $x = 1.45$, approximately.

Example 2. Find $\sqrt[3]{473}$. Let x be the result. Then

$$x = \sqrt[3]{473} = 473^{1/3}.$$

By theorem 3, $\log x = \frac{1}{3} \log 473 = \frac{1}{3}(2.6749) = 0.8916$. Hence $x = 7.79$, approximately.

Example 2 has been done far more quickly than would be possible by the method of section 31. Even the relatively simple example 1 has been done more quickly than by straightforward arithmetic. This is so essentially because multiplication is replaced by addition of logarithms, division by subtraction of logarithms, and the extraction of roots by simple division of a logarithm by the index of the root. What we have done with our table is to represent every positive number approximately as a power of 10. In example 1, we have

$$8.34 = 10^{0.9212}, \quad 65.2 = 10^{1.8142}, \quad 376 = 10^{2.5752}$$

and hence

$$\begin{aligned}\frac{(8.34)(65.2)}{376} &= \frac{(10^{0.9212})(10^{1.8142})}{10^{2.5752}} \\ &= 10^{0.9212+1.8142-2.5752} \\ &= 10^{0.1602} = 1.45,\end{aligned}$$

approximately.

Needless to say the accuracy obtainable by computation with logarithms is limited by the number of decimal places in the table. But tables are in existence which are carried out to as many places as are needed for all practical purposes.

Remark. Notice that the formula $\log(x + y) = \log x + \log y$, which appears plausible at first glance, is *false*, for $\log x + \log y$ is really $\log(xy)$. If it *were* true we would have an excessively simple table of logarithms. For $\log 1 = 0$; hence $\log 2 = \log(1 + 1) = \log 1 + \log 1 = 0$; and $\log 3 = \log(2 + 1) = \log 2 + \log 1 = 0$, and so on; thus the logarithm of every whole number would be zero and we would need no table of logarithms. If this false formula seemed right to you, it was probably because of its superficial resemblance to the distributive law $g(x + y) = gx + gy$. But the resemblance is no more than superficial. For in the distributive law we are *multiplying* $(x + y)$ by a *number* g, while in the other case we are surely not multiplying by the *word* log.

Exercises

Evaluate by means of logarithms:

1. $\dfrac{(34.2)(1.57)}{31.3}$.

2. $\sqrt[3]{85.2}$.

3. $\sqrt[5]{117}$.

4. $412(1.02)^{16}$.

5. $\dfrac{21.3}{27.2}$.

6. $\dfrac{(629)(52.4)}{(8.26)(55.8)}$.

7. $\sqrt[3]{67300}$.

8. $\sqrt[5]{86300}$.

9. $376(1.06)^{21}$.

10. $\dfrac{(89.6)(43.4)}{53.4}$.

11. $\sqrt[3]{.00857}$.

12. $\sqrt[5]{.0453}$.

59. APPLICATIONS OF LOGARITHMS

An interesting application of logarithms can be made to the compound interest formula. If P dollars are invested at 4% interest compounded annually, the amount at the end of the first year is $P + .04\,P$, or $P(1 + .04)$, or $P(1.04)$.

At the end of the second year the amount is the new principal $P(1.04)$ plus the interest on it, which is $.04\,P(1.04)$; thus the amount at the end of the second year is $P(1.04) + .04\,P(1.04) = P(1.04)(1 + .04) = P(1.04)^2$. At the end of n years we would have the amount $A = P(1.04)^n$.

Example 1. \$100 is invested as a trust fund for a child at 4% interest compounded annually. How much will it amount to in 21 years?

$$A = 100(1.04)^{21}.$$

Therefore,

$$\begin{aligned}\log A &= \log 100 + 21 \log 1.04 \\ &= 2 + 21(0.0170) = 2.3570.\end{aligned}$$

Hence,

$$A = \$228, \text{ approximately.}$$

Example 2. If \$100 is invested at 4% interest compounded quarterly, how much will it amount to in 21 years?

Here the interest will be taken 84 times at the rate of 1% each time. Hence

$$A = 100(1.01)^{84}.$$

Therefore,

$$\begin{aligned}\log A &= \log 100 + 84 \log 1.01 \\ &= 2 + 84(0.0043) = 2.3612.\end{aligned}$$

Hence,

$$A = \$230, \text{ approximately.}$$

If you think of how long it would take to do this by simple arithmetic, multiplying 100 by 1.01 eighty-four times, the time-saving property of logarithms should now be obvious. Other simple applications will be found in the exercises.

The human race has benefited greatly by saving untold hours because of the existence of tables of logarithms. It is said that when Briggs visited Napier, he remarked,* "My lord, I have undertaken this long journey purposely to see your person, and to know by what engine of wit or ingenuity you came first to think of this most excellent help in astronomy, viz. the logarithms; but, my lord, being by you found out, I wonder nobody found it out before, when now known it is so easy." It is worth noting that this remark could be made with equal justice concerning almost any great mathematical invention. For the highways of mathematics are comparatively easy to follow, since each step is merely one of logical reasoning; but the blazing of the original trail may well have demanded the insight and foresight of genius.

Logarithms are of great value in advanced mathematics quite apart from computation.

* F. Cajori, *History of Mathematics*, 2nd edition, Macmillan, N. Y., 1917, pp. 150–151.

Exercises

1. If \$124 is deposited in a bank at 4% interest, compounded semi-annually, what will the amount be in 10 years?

2. It is desired to have a sum of \$2000 in the bank 10 years from now. The bank pays 4% interest compounded annually. How much should we deposit now?

3. If the \$24 which the Indians received in 1626 for Manhattan had been deposited in a bank paying 4% interest compounded annually, what would it have amounted to in 1940?

4. If a person bets 2 cents on April 1st and doubles his bet each day thereafter, how much will his bet be on April 30th?

5. The area of the surface of a sphere is $4\pi r^2$ where r is the radius. Taking $\pi = 3.14$ and assuming that the earth is a sphere of radius 3960 miles, find the area of the earth's surface.

6. The volume of a sphere is $\frac{4}{3}\pi r^3$, where r is the radius. Using the data of exercise 5, what is the volume of the earth?

7. If P dollars are invested in a bank at 4% interest, compounded annually, how long will it take for the amount to be $2P$ (that is, doubled)?

8. If \$852 is deposited in a bank at 4% interest, compounded quarterly, what will the amount be in 5 years?

9. The "period" T measured in seconds of a simple pendulum (that is, the time required for a complete oscillation) of length k is given by the formula $T = 2\pi\sqrt{k/g}$. If $k = 3.26$ feet, $g = 32.2$, $\pi = 3.14$, find T.

10. Find the length of a pendulum whose period is 1 second, using the formula and data of exercise 9.

11. Suppose that an automobile costing \$1000 depreciates at the rate of 20% per year; that is, its value at the end of each year is 80% of its value at the beginning of that year. Find its value at the end of (*a*) 5 years; (*b*) 10 years.

12. The volume of a right circular cylinder is $\pi r^2 h$ where r is the radius of the circular base and h is the height. Taking $\pi = 3.14$, find the volume of a right circular cylinder with $r = 5.47$ inches and $h = 18.4$ inches.

13. If a population increases by 2 percent every year, in how many years will it double itself?

60. CALCULATING MACHINES. THE SLIDE RULE

We have already seen the simplifications introduced into mathematical calculations by the Arabic numerals and by the invention of logarithms. We shall discuss here two important mechanical devices designed to relieve the mind further of the necessity of thinking about boring calculations, thereby freeing it to think about more interesting things. The first device is based essentially on the idea of "carrying" in positional notation (Arabic numerals) while the second is based essentially on the theory of logarithms.

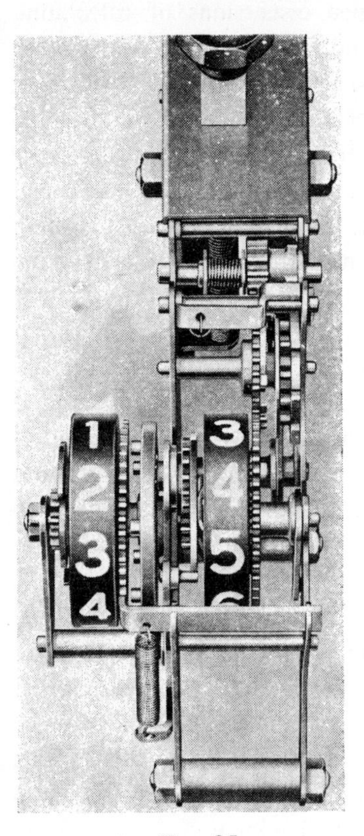

FIG. 35

Calculating machines. The first calculating machines were invented by Pascal and Leibniz in the seventeenth century. The general idea may be explained as follows, without going into mechanical details. A number of wheels are placed next to each other (Fig. 35). On each wheel appear the numbers 0, 1, 2, ⋯, 9. One may imagine a decimal point to be placed between any two of the wheels or at either extreme. A mechanism is arranged so that a number may be registered on the wheels by pressing buttons or some other device; that is, this number is made to appear in a horizontal slit in the machine, say at the top of the wheels. Suppose that the number 13,075 has been recorded on the machine, and that we now wish to add to this the number 67. Pressing the 7 in the "units column" will cause the "units wheel" to rotate through 7 more spaces, thus showing the number 2. The essential point of the machine is that as the units wheel passes from the "nine" to the "zero" it automatically moves the next wheel one space, thus "carrying" one into the "tens column." The machine now reads 13,082. Now pressing the 6 in the "tens column," the "tens wheel" rotates through 6 spaces, thus showing the number 4. But as it passes from the "nine" to the "zero," it automatically moves the next wheel one space, thus "carrying" one into the hundreds column.
The machine now reads 13,142.

Multiplication is done essentially by repeated additions. Subtraction, by turning the wheels in the opposite direction, and division, by repeated subtractions, can also be accomplished on such machines. Needless to say, the actual mechanisms of these machines may be exceedingly ingenious, but at the bottom of the whole thing lies the principle of "carrying" in positional notation. The idea of carrying is also used in the mileage-recorder on an automobile. The

FIG. 36

actual working of a calculating machine is best understood by using one and examining its movements directly. More detailed discussions of calculating machines may be found in the references at the end of the chapter. Many other kinds of calculating machines have been devised to perform various mathematical operations. Calculating machines, in general, not only relieve the mind of the burden of performing fatiguing and uninteresting calculations but also have the additional virtue of being less likely to make a mistake than a human being. Thus it sometimes is advantageous not to think. But it should not be forgotten that only by thinking can one invent, repair, reconstruct, or even understand the machine.

The slide rule. The rectilinear slide rule was invented by Oughtred, an Englishman, in the seventeenth century. On each of two adjacent straight bars C and D we mark numbers so that their distances from the 1 mark are proportional to the logarithms of the numbers (Fig. 37). Since $\log 2 = .301$, $\log 3 = .477$, and $\log 6 = .778$, approximately, we might divide the length of each bar into 1000 equal parts and place the number 2 at the 301st mark, the number 3 at the 477th, and the number 6 at the 778th. The distance of each mark from the end of the bar is proportional to its logarithm. To multiply 2 by 3 we may proceed to slide bar C so that its beginning (1) is directly over the number 2 on bar D. Then we find the product of 2 by 3 on bar D directly under the number 3 on bar C (Fig. 38). Obviously, sliding the bars in this way has the effect of adding the distance between 1 and 2 on bar D to the distance between 1 and 3 on bar C. But this means essentially adding log 2 and log 3. The resulting distance (between 1 and 6 on bar D) must therefore be log 6 since $\log 2 + \log 3 = \log 6$.

Similarly, to divide 6 by 3 we would place the 3 on bar C over the 6 on bar D and read the result on bar D directly under the 1 on bar C. Clearly we have used the fact that $\log 6 - \log 3 = \log 2$. Many other operations can be performed with a slide rule. Further details will best be understood by actually working with one. Since one's eyesight enters into the reading of a slide rule, its accuracy is limited. But it is very useful when great accuracy is not needed, for example, in checking calculations. It is used extensively by engineers and others.

61. ELECTRONIC COMPUTERS

The exorbitant demands for man-hours of computation caused by increased technological needs, especially during World War II, in many fields such as ballistics, aerodynamics, meteorology, etc., stimulated further investigation into means for speedier computation. The calculating machine based on wheels

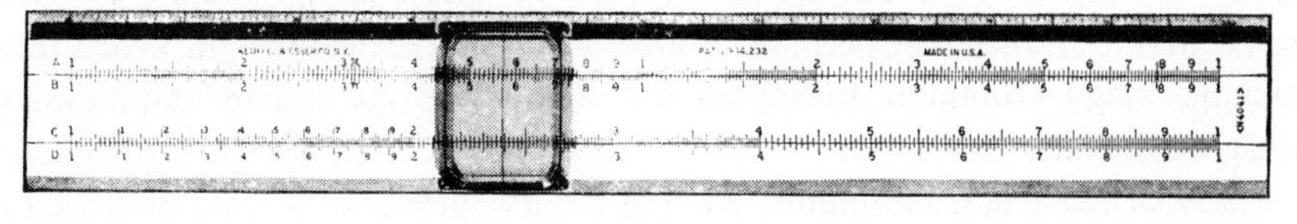

FIG. 37

FIG. 38

and positional notation, discussed in the preceding section and found in many business offices, nowadays using electric power to turn the wheels, was no longer sufficient. The so-called electronic "brains" developed in the 1940's use electricity in a new, more essential way and can do in 1 second arithmetical operations which would take a day with the older office calculators and a week by

FIG. 39
The IBM System 360 Computer

hand with pencil. This enormous increase in speed is, of course, of great practical importance, but perhaps of greater importance is the light which these machines may ultimately throw on the actual nervous system and brain of living organisms.

Many of these new computers use the binary system or 2 scale discussed in section 50 because of its simplicity. Since the only digits needed are 0 and 1, one can represent numbers by means of many devices. A light bulb can represent 0 if dark and 1 if lit; an electric circuit can represent 0 if open (no current) and 1 if closed (current flowing); a switch can represent 0 if open (off) and 1 if closed (on); a location on a punched card can represent 0 if no hole is punched there and 1 if a hole is punched; a location on a magnetic tape can represent 0 if it is not magnetized and 1 if it is magnetized; a location on a storage tube (like a television picture tube) can represent 0 if it carries no spot, 1 if it has a spot; the direction of polarity of the field of a magnetic core can represent 0 in one direction and 1 if reversed. For example, the number thirty-seven can be recorded in binary notation as 100101, hence in a row of bulbs as

or on a punched card as

Furthermore, the addition and multiplication tables for the binary system are so simple (see section 50) that it is not difficult to devise electrical circuits which build these operations into the machine. Hence arithmetical operations are performed with the speed with which electricity passes through the circuits and operates switching devices. Thus it is not difficult to understand how these computers accomplish arithmetical operations with such dazzling speed.

But what else can they do? Is there any justification for calling them "brains" or "thinking machines"? They can certainly do routine arithmetical computations far better than man. They can also store the results of such computations in a record (as magnetic tape, punched cards, etc.) and draw out this information for later use when needed. This is essentially memory and the part of the machine where such information is stored is called its memory. They can also make their

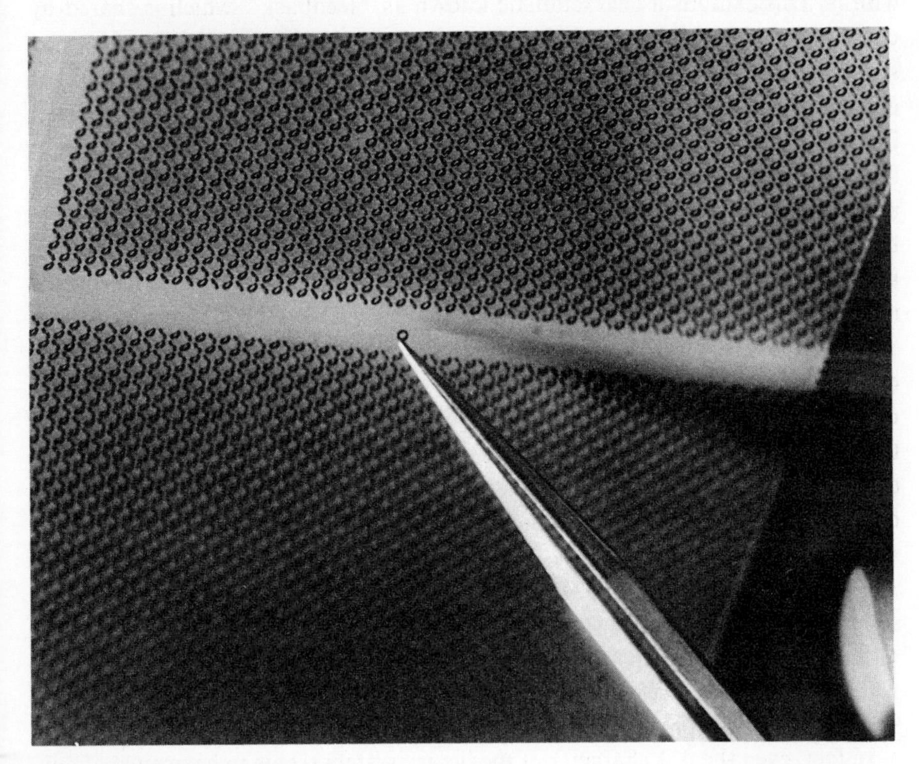

FIG. 40
An IBM System 360 Memory Core

FIG. 41
Enlarged view of magnetic tape, specially treated to make code patterns visible.

own decisions in accordance with previous blanket instructions. For example, they can read the result of one of their own computations and if it is greater than 1000 do one thing with it while if it is not greater than 1000 do another thing with it. This exhibits a characteristic known as "feedback" which is shared by older instruments such as the thermostat in your house or the governor on a steam engine or an automatic pilot. These instruments essentially make decisions depending on their own present state, information about which is "fed back" into their controls. Thus the thermostat turns on the heat when its temperature falls below a predetermined level and shuts it off when the temperature is above another predetermined level. Feedback is obviously a characteristic of the behavior of living organisms as can be observed in the behavior of a dog chasing a rabbit or a man driving a car as they alter their movements in accordance with information received by their sense organs.

Other machines have been built which display other characteristics of living organisms in a rudimentary way, such as adaptive behavior, learning from its own experience, and adjusting itself to injury. A machine has been built which locomotes, gets around obstacles, seeks restoration of its energy from a battery charger when its energy falls below a certain level, and goes away from the charger when its energy rises above a certain level. Thus it exhibits hunger, search for food, and satiation. It has been given the mock-biological name *Machina Speculatrix*.* There are mechanical devices which can reproduce themselves, i.e., assemble another machine like themselves if in an appropriate environment containing the needed parts. We may see later (Chapter 7) that a machine can handle certain formal aspects of reasoning. Computers have also written music and poetry.†

In fact, even the 0, 1 character of the binary system seems to have an analogue in our own nervous system. For it is known that a neuron has an "all or nothing" response; that is, if insufficiently stimulated it discharges no impulse, but if stimulated beyond a certain threshold it transmits an impulse of a fixed intensity. It is clear from the evidence of the electroencephalograph that the behavior of the human brain is in fact associated with electrical phenomena. Thus the behavior of these various mechanisms raises the joint questions. "Can machines think?" and "Are living things really automata (of much greater complexity than any so far built)?"

Man has achieved his ascendancy over the earth and other animals by using tools such as levers, hammers, and steam engines to amplify his puny muscular strength and tools such as microscopes and much laboratory equipment to amplify his observational senses. Perhaps he can also develop tools to amplify his severly limited intelligence. Aristotle claimed that man was a rational animal because he alone could do arithmetic. What would he say if he could see a modern computer?

* See W. G. Walter, *The Living Brain*, Norton, N. Y., 1953.

† Cf. J. R. Pierce, *Electrons, Waves, and Messages*, Hanover House, 1956.

62. INFORMATION THEORY

We have seen how a modern electronic computer can store numerical information in its memory. Now, any sort of information can be coded by means of numbers, so that machines can be made to store and manipulate information coded as numbers and written in the binary scale. Perhaps the simplest piece of information is a yes or no response, as is required in the parlor game "Twenty Questions." This can be made to correspond to a 1 or 0, that is, a binary digit, in a specific location. Thus in the modern theory of information, originated by communication engineers, the usual unit of quantity of information is the **binary digit**, abbreviated **bit**. Thus if a language of signals is devised so that each message is to be composed of three binary digits in succession, the language contains eight different messages, namely, 000, 001, 010, 011, 100, 101, 110, 111, and each message is said to contain three bits of information. Note that this quantity of information is the $\log_2 8$. In general if there are N different messages, the quantity of information in each message is said to be $\log_2 N$. This assumes that all these messages occur with equal frequency, a restriction that will be removed later.

It should be clearly understood that this technical definition of quantity of information ignores completely the question whether or not the information has meaning or significance and whether or not it is of any human value. Thus whether a message spells out (1) a commencement address, (2) a political campaign speech, (3) a page from the telephone book, or (4) a brilliant scientific paper, it may have the same quantity of information, although the meaning, significance, and value in these four cases may be very different and may even, as in case (4), depend upon who is reading it.

Thus quantity of information should not be confused with significant knowledge. For example, consider a poor, dishonest, and desperate student confronted by a multiple-choice question with four parts. He is anxious to obtain not knowledge but only information. Since $\log_2 4 = 2$ he needs two bits of information. This means that he could get the needed information by receiving a yes or no answer to two questions of the "Twenty Questions" type. For instance, he could ask, "Is the number of the correct answer greater than 2?" If the answer were "yes," he could then ask, "Is it greater than 3?" If the answer to his first question were "no," he could then ask, "Is it greater than 1?" In this way a number from 1 to 2^n can be determined by n questions calling for yes or no answers; that is, 2^n numbers contain n bits of information. It goes without saying that if our dishonest student receives his information, he may nevertheless fail to receive much knowledge or value, for he may not even understand the question.

In fact, since in most languages the symbols or messages do not occur with the same relative frequency, they should not be regarded as conveying the same amount of information. For example, if an English word begins with q, it will be found that the second letter will be a u much more often than an x or a z and hence the second symbol does not convey as much information as the first symbol q. For example, if the second were drowned out by noise in a communication system it could easily be supplied. A rare message should be regarded as conveying more information than a commonplace one. A short message such as "Help" or a paragraph of mathematics may convey more valuable information and knowledge than a long one such as a commencement address, a political campaign speech, or one of your sister-in-law's interminable telephone conversations full of repetitious platitudes and predictable nonsense.

If the relative frequencies (fractions or percentages of the times they occur) of n symbols are $p_1, p_2, \cdots, p_n$ $(p_1 + p_2 + \cdots + p_n = 1)$, then the amount of information in the code or system is defined as

$$p_1 \log_2 \frac{1}{p_1} + p_2 \log_2 \frac{1}{p_2} + \cdots + p_n \log_2 \frac{1}{p_n}.$$

If all the relative frequencies are equal $\left(p_1 = p_2 = \cdots = p_n = \frac{1}{n}\right)$, this reduces to the former expression $\log_2 n$. This definition bases amount of information on frequency of occurrence and makes no attempt to distinguish between useful information and nonsense. For further discussion of the idea of relative frequency see Chapter 13 on probability.

Exercises

1. How many questions requiring a yes or no answer will determine a chosen number from 1 to 256? Explain.

2. How many bits of information are needed to pick one card out of a deck of 16 different cards?

3. A single decimal digit can convey ten different signals, namely, 0, 1, 2, 3, 4, 5, 6, 7, 8, 9. How many bits of information does one decimal digit contain? (Hint: see section 57, remark.)

4. Assuming that there are 900,000 known organic (carbon) compounds, how many bits of information are needed to single out one of them? Does this help to explain the notorious length of the names used in organic chemistry?

References

Numbers refer to the bibliography at the end of the book.

Ashby 8, 9
Attneave 10
Berkeley 26
Bowden 35
Brillouin 40
Bronowski 41
Cherry 50
Dantzig 62
Dresden 65
Jacobson 97
Klein 115
Pfeiffer 147
Quastler 151
Rashhevsky 154
Richardson 158
Schrödinger 173
Shannon 175
Shannon and Weaver 176
Sluckin 179
Smith 180
Turing 194
Von Neumann 200, 201
Walter 203
Wiener 208, 209
Young 215

7

The Algebra of Logic and Related Topics

63. INTRODUCTION

In chapters 3, 4, and 5, we were engaged in showing: (1) that algebra has the same kind of logical structure as any other abstract mathematical science; that is, it starts with undefined terms and unproved assumptions or postulates and then proceeds by defining new terms and proving new statements; (2) that the algebraic manipulations with which you have been familiar for years in a mechanical way are logical consequences of our postulates and definitions; (3) that our choice of postulates and definitions has been guided by the concrete applications that we had in mind for our logical system; that is, our postulates and definitions have been suggested by experience. Briefly, we have been concerned with what may be called the *logic of algebra*, where by algebra we mean the familiar algebra of numbers.

We have pointed out (see section 19) that we might very well have used different postulates and different definitions, especially if we had in mind different sorts of applications. We shall now take up briefly actual examples of algebras which in some respects resemble the algebra of numbers and in other respects differ from it sharply, and which really have important applications.

64. THE ALGEBRA OF SETS OR THE ALGEBRA OF LOGIC

The algebra we shall discuss in this section is variously called the **algebra of sets**, the **algebra of classes**, the **algebra of logic**, or **Boolean algebra**, because it was developed by G. Boole about 1850.

George Boole
1815–1864, English

At this point the reader should review section 11, where we introduced the notions of basic collection (universal set), set, subset, union ($\cup$), intersection ($\cap$), contains ($\supset$), etc.

We consider a given basic collection or universal set I, and by capital letters, such as A, B, ..., we denote sets each of which is a subset of I.

The set of all elements in the basic collection I which are not in a given set A is called the **complement** of A and is denoted by A' or $I - A$.

We can now verify that if A, B, C represent any subsets of a given basic collection I, then the following laws are satisfied.

Closure laws.
- I. Given any sets A and B, there is a unique set $A \cup B$.
- I′. Given any sets A and B, there is a unique set $A \cap B$.

Commutative laws.
- II. $A \cup B = B \cup A$.
- II′. $A \cap B = B \cap A$.

Associative laws.
- III. $A \cup (B \cup C) = (A \cup B) \cup C$.
- III′. $A \cap (B \cap C) = (A \cap B) \cap C$.

Distributive laws.
- IV. $A \cap (B \cup C) = (A \cap B) \cup (A \cap C)$.
- IV′. $A \cup (B \cap C) = (A \cup B) \cap (A \cup C)$.

- V. $I \cap A = A$ for all A.
- V′. $\varnothing \cup A = A$ for all A.

$\begin{cases} \text{VI. } I \cup A = I \text{ for all } A. \\ \text{VI}'. \varnothing \cap A = \varnothing \text{ for all } A. \end{cases}$

Idempotent laws. $\begin{cases} \text{VII. } A \cup A = A. \\ \text{VII}'. A \cap A = A. \end{cases}$

Self-distributive laws. $\begin{cases} \text{VIII. } A \cup (B \cup C) = (A \cup B) \cup (A \cup C). \\ \text{VIII}'. A \cap (B \cap C) = (A \cap B) \cap (A \cap C). \end{cases}$

$\begin{cases} \text{IX. } A \cup B \supset A. \\ \text{IX}'. A \cap B \subset A. \end{cases}$

$\begin{cases} \text{X. } A \subset I \text{ for all } A. \\ \text{X}'. A \supset \varnothing \text{ for all } A. \end{cases}$

$\begin{cases} \text{XI. If } A \subset B \text{ then } A \cup B = B. \\ \text{XI}'. \text{If } A \supset B \text{ then } A \cap B = B. \end{cases}$

Complementation law. XII. To each set A there corresponds a set, denoted by A' or $I - A$ and called the complement of A, such that $A \cup A' = I$ and $A \cap A' = \varnothing$.

These can be verified easily by examining Fig. 42 carefully and keeping firmly in mind the meaning of union and intersection. Shading with colored crayons will help you in verifying these facts. For example, IV asserts that if you first take the union of the sets B and C (shaded horizontally in Fig. 43) and consider the common part of this set $B \cup C$ with A (shaded vertically in Fig. 43) then you get exactly the same resulting set (shaded crosswise in Fig. 43) as if you had first taken the set common to A and B (shaded horizontally in Fig. 44) and the set common to A and C (shaded vertically in Fig. 44) and then taken their union $(A \cap B) \cup (A \cap C)$ (the entire shaded set in Fig. 44).

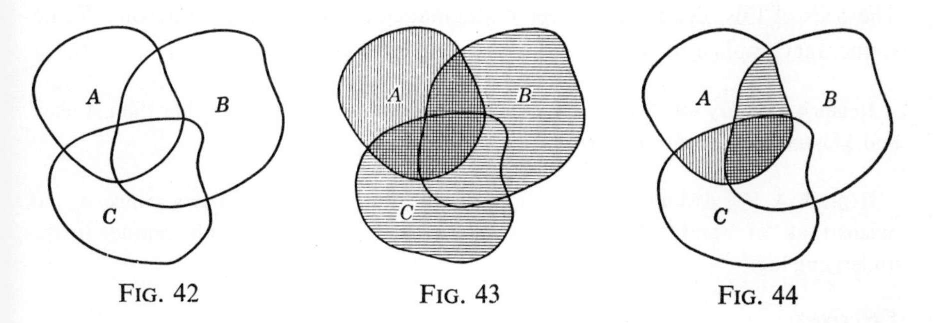

FIG. 42 FIG. 43 FIG. 44

Remark 1. Sometimes $A + B$ is written for $A \cup B$ and AB *or* $A \cdot B$ for $A \cap B$. If the reader will rewrite the numbered properties above in this way, replacing I by 1, $\varnothing$ by 0, $\subset$ by $<$, and the word "set" by the word "number," it will be seen that many of them, such as I, I′, II, II′, III, III′, IV, V, V′, VI′, look formally just like the familiar properties of the ordinary algebra of numbers listed in section 32, while others, such as IV′, VI, VII, VII′, and all the rest are quite different. Also property VIII (*c*) of section 32 does not have an analogue in the algebra of sets; for we can have two sets $A \neq \varnothing$ (that is, not empty) and $B \neq \varnothing$ such that $AB = \varnothing$ (or $A \cap B = \varnothing$). That is to say, they have no elements in common, or their common part is the empty set (see Fig. 45). Some students are of the opinion that if A is the set of mathematics instructors and B is the set of sane and kind-hearted people, then $A \cap B = \varnothing$.

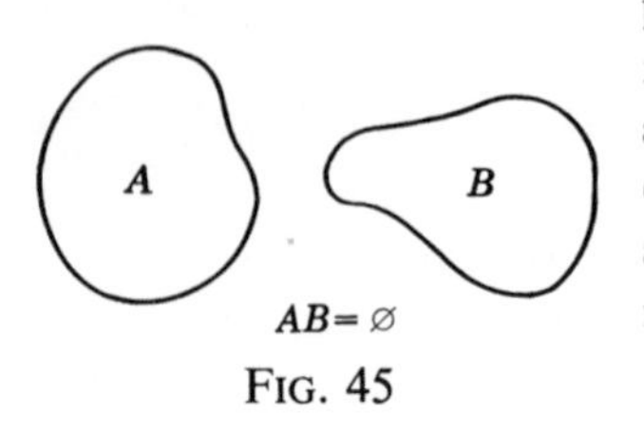

FIG. 45

Remark 2. If we interchange $\cup$ and $\cap$, $\varnothing$ and I, $\subset$ and $\supset$, in any correct formula, we obtain another formula in the algebra of sets. Two formulas thus obtainable from each other are called **duals** of each other. Thus I and I′, II and II′, ..., XI and XI′ are duals of each other, while XII is dual to itself. Since these numbered statements I–XII may be taken as a set of postulates for an algebra, it follows that, in this algebra, the dual of any correct formula is automatically correct.

The algebra of sets therefore cannot be the same as the algebra of numbers. However, it is worth noting that whatever theorems can be deduced by using *only* those properties which both have in common will be true in either system.

We might construct an abstract mathematical science with "set," "union," "intersection," "contained in," "equals," as undefined terms and the above properties as postulates. Actual sets of objects would provide a concrete interpretation of this "algebra." What applications can this queer algebra have? It is clear that we might be able to use it in any situation in which we are concerned with collections of objects whatever the nature of these objects may be. The uses of this algebra in higher mathematics are extremely numerous. Some elementary applications will be discussed in subsequent sections.

Remark 3. Every set A has itself and $\varnothing$ as subsets. A subset of A other than A itself and $\varnothing$ is called a **proper subset** of A.

Remark 4. We assumed the principle of substitution for equal sets. Since $A = B$ means that "A" and "B" are names for the same set, this principle belongs to the underlying logic.

Exercises

1. By shading the indicated sets suitably, on diagrams like that of Figs. 41–43, verify

(*a*) property III; (*b*) property III′; (*c*) property IV′;

(*d*) property VIII; (*e*) property VIII′; (*f*) property XI;
(*g*) property XI′.

2. If A is the set of letters $\{x, y, z, w\}$, B is the set of letters $\{z, w, u, v\}$, and C is the set of letters $\{x, v, r, s\}$, what is

(*a*) $A \cup B$; (*b*) $A \cap C$; (*c*) $A \cup (B \cap C)$;
(*d*) $(A \cup B) \cap C$; (*e*) $(A \cap B) \cap C$; (*f*) $(A \cup B) \cup C$;
(*g*) $(A \cap B) \cup (B \cap C)$; (*h*) $(A \cap C) \cup (B \cap C)$; (*i*) $A \cap B'$;
(*j*) $A' \cap B$?

3. If P, Q, R, S are four points occurring in that order on a straight line I, and if A represents the set of points on the line-segment PR and B represents the set of points on the line-segment QS, what sets of points are represented by

(*a*) $A \cup B$; (*b*) $A \cap B$; (*c*) $A \cap B'$;
(*d*) $A' \cap B$; (*e*) $(A' \cap B) \cap (A \cap B')$; (*f*) $A \cup (A' \cap B)$?

(Hint: a line-segment is understood not to contain its endpoints.)

4. If I represents the set of all real numbers, A represents the set of all real numbers x such that $1 \leqq x \leqq 3$, and B represents the set of all real numbers x such that $2 \leqq x \leqq 4$, what set is represented by

(*a*) $A \cup B$; (*b*) $A \cap B$; (*c*) $A' \cap B$; (*d*) $A \cap B'$; (*e*) $A' \cap B'$;
(*f*) $B \cup (A \cap B')$; (*g*) $A' \cup B'$; (*h*) $(A' \cap B) \cup (A \cap B')$?

5. Show that if $A \cap B = A$ and $A \cap C \neq \varnothing$, then $B \cap C \neq \varnothing$. (Hint: show that the set $A \cap (B \cap C) \neq \varnothing$; from this the conclusion follows. Why?)

From the numbered properties listed above, deduce the following theorems, all letters representing arbitrary subsets of a given basic collection I:

6. If $B = A \cup B$, then $B \supset A$. (Converse of XI. Hint: use IX.)
7. If $B = A \cap B$, then $B \subset A$. (Converse of XI′. Hint: use IX′.)
8. $(A')' = A$.
9. $A \cap B = \varnothing$ implies $B \subset A'$.
10. $A \cup (A \cap B) = A$. (Hint: use IX′ and XI.)
11. $A \cap (A \cup B) = A$. (Hint: use exercise 10.)
12. If $A \subset B$ and $B \subset C$ then $A \subset C$. (Hint: Use XI or XI′.)
13. $(A \cup B)' = A' \cap B'$.
14. $(A \cap B)' = A' \cup B'$.
15. $(A \cup B) \cap ([A \cap B] \cup X) = (A \cap B) \cup ([A \cup B] \cap X)$.

16. Show that property VIII follows from the other postulates. (Hint: use II, III, VII.)

17. Show that property VIII′ follows from the other postulates. (Hint: use II′, III′, VII′.)

18. Rewrite all the numbered properties I, I′ ... , XII, using $+$ for $\cup$, $\cdot$ for $\cap$, 0 for $\varnothing$, 1 for I.

65. AN APPLICATION TO LOGIC

The following indicates why the algebra of the preceding section is sometimes called the algebra of logic.

The reader may have already observed a resemblance between the diagrams of sets of points on the page which have been drawn here and the diagrams used to test reasoning in section 4. Let us see how the familiar statements of logic can be symbolized in our new algebra.

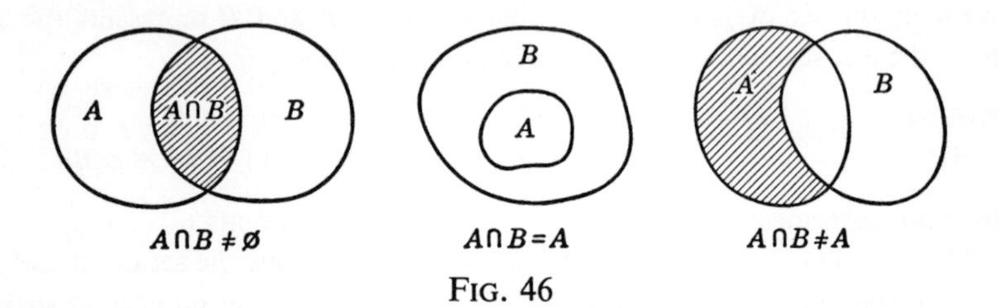

FIG. 46

Let A be the set of all freshmen and B the set of all intelligent people. Then the statement "all freshmen are intelligent" may be written (see Fig. 46) as

$$A \cap B = A,$$

or $A \subset B$, or $A \cup B = B$. "Some freshmen are intelligent" may be written

$$A \cap B \neq \varnothing.$$

"No freshmen are intelligent" becomes

$$A \cap B = \varnothing$$

or $A \subset I - B$. "Some freshmen are not intelligent" becomes

$$A \cap (I - B) \neq \varnothing \text{ or } A \cap B \neq A.$$

It is possible to express the arguments of traditional logic in terms of this algebra, and one can actually reason by manipulating the symbols according to the rules (postulates) of this algebra. In effect, traditional logic can be reduced to the study of this "algebra of logic," or other symbolic "algebras" like it.

Example. Consider the following valid argument.

Hypothesis. (1) All freshmen are undergraduates.

(2) No undergraduates are intelligent.

Conclusion. Therefore no freshmen are intelligent.

First solution. The conclusion of this argument can be obtained algebraically as follows. Let A, B, C be the classes of freshmen, undergraduates, and intelligent people, respectively. Then the two parts of the hypothesis are written as

(1) $$A \cap B = A$$

and

(2) $$B \cap C = \varnothing,$$

respectively. We obtain the conclusion $A \cap C = \varnothing$ as follows. By (1),

$A \cap C = (A \cap B) \cap C$ (substituting $A \cap B$ for A which is its equal by hypothesis (1))

$= A \cap (B \cap C)$ (by the associative law III′)

$= A \cap \varnothing$ (by hypothesis (2))

$= \varnothing$ (by II′ and VI′)

which was to be proved.

Second solution. The hypotheses may be written as

(3) $$A \cup B = B$$

(4) $$B \cap C = \varnothing$$

and the conclusion as $A \cap C = \varnothing$.

By (3), $$(A \cup B) \cap C = B \cap C.$$

By the distributive and commutative laws this becomes

$$(A \cap C) \cup (B \cap C) = B \cap C.$$

By (4), $(A \cap C) \cup \varnothing = \varnothing$. Hence, $A \cap C = \varnothing$.

It is worth noting that this "symbolic logic" grew up not as a mere plaything of the mathematician but as a response to a real need. Many paradoxes and confusions in logic were found to be due to the deficiencies of ordinary language.* Ordinary language evolves from the everyday needs of people to express their ideas, and this does not usually require much in the way of precision or subtle distinctions. Therefore it is natural to expect ordinary language to be poorly adapted to the needs of careful logic. Thus a symbolism was created for the purpose. We have already remarked that the development of satisfactory symbolisms is not without importance.

* A trivial example of verbal confusion is found in the well-known example: "no cat has 8 tails; every cat has one more tail than no cat; therefore every cat has 9 tails."

Exercises

Express each statement in terms of the algebra of sets and obtain algebraically the conclusion of the argument in:

1. Section 4, example 3.
2. Section 4, exercise 5(*a*).
3. Section 4, exercise 5(*b*).
4. Section 4, exercise 6.
5. Section 4, exercise 3(*a*).

*66. BOOLEAN ALGEBRAS

As suggested at the end of section 64, we could set up an abstract mathematical science by taking as undefined terms the terms set, $\cup$, $\cap$, $\subset$, I, $\varnothing$, and assuming properties I, I′, ..., XII as postulates.† Then the class of all subsets of any given set I would constitute a concrete interpretation of this science, although it will be seen to have other interpretations. This science or any interpretation of it may be called a **Boolean algebra**.

Perhaps the simplest interpretation is to consider as I a set with only one element. Then the entire Boolean algebra would have two sets in it, namely, $\varnothing$ and I. If we denote these by 0 and 1, respectively, and write $+$ for $\cup$ and $\cdot$ for $\cap$ we would get the following "tables of addition and multiplication":

(1)

x	y	$x+y$
1	1	1
1	0	1
0	1	1
0	0	0

x	y	$x \cdot y$
1	1	1
1	0	0
0	1	0
0	0	0

For example, the first lines in these tables represent respectively the set-theoretic relationships $I \cup I = I$ and $I \cap I = I$. Let us denote this simple algebra by the symbol B_{01}.

If we were to take as I a set with two elements, say a and b, then the Boolean algebra of all its subsets would contain four sets, namely, $I = \{a, b\}$, $\varnothing$, $A = \{a\}$, and $B = \{b\}$, where the symbol $\{a\}$ means the set consisting of the element a alone, and so on. Thus we would have $A \cup B = I$, $A \cap B = \varnothing$ $I \cap B = B$, and so on.

* This section is needed only for section 68. Otherwise it may be omitted without disturbing the continuity.

† Fewer would do, since they are not independent; compare exercises 16 and 17, section 64.

Exercises

1. In the algebra B_{01}, compute

(*a*) $(1+1)+1$. (*b*) $[(1+1)+1]+1$. (*c*) $(1\cdot 1)\cdot 1$.
(*d*) $[(1\cdot 1)\cdot 1]\cdot 1$. (*e*) $(1+0)+0$. (*f*) $(1\cdot 0)\cdot 1$.

2. Prove that if a and b are any elements of the Boolean algebra B_{01} then

(*a*) $a+ab=a$; (*b*) $a(a+b)=a$.

3. Prove that if a, b, x are any elements of the Boolean algebra B_{01}, then

$$(a+b)(ab+x)=ab+(a+b)x.$$

4. Prove that if a is any element of the Boolean algebra B_{01} and a' is the other element, then

(*a*) $a+a'=1$; (*b*) $aa'=0$.

5. Prove that if a and b are any elements of the Boolean algebra B_{01}, then,

(*a*) $(a+b)'=a'b'$; (*b*) $(ab)'=a'+b'$;

where the prime mark has the same significance as in exercise 4.

6. Write complete tables of "addition" and "multiplication" for the algebra of the four sets $\varnothing$, A, B, I discussed in the preceding paragraph.

*67. THE ALGEBRA OF PROPOSITIONS. TRUTH TABLES

We shall use small letters, such as p, q, r, ..., to represent propositions.† If a proposition p is true, it is said to have the truth value T; if it is false, it is said to have the truth value F. For example, the proposition p: "$2+2=5$" has the truth value F, while the proposition q: "this cat is a feline" has the truth value T.

If p is a proposition, the **negation** or **contradictory** of p is the proposition not-p, which is true when p is false and false when p is true; it is symbolized by $\sim p$. In the examples above, $\sim p$ is the proposition "$2+2\neq 5$," and $\sim q$ is the proposition "this cat is not a feline."

If p and q are propositions, the **disjunction** of p and q is the proposition "p or q," symbolized by $p \vee q$; it is true if *at least* one of the propositions p or q is true and false if both are false. In the examples above, $p \vee q$ is the proposition "$2+2=5$ or this cat is a feline," and is true.

* This section may be omitted without disturbing the continuity.

† Or sometimes, propositional functions (cf. section 5), sentences, or assertions. We avoid discussion of subtle distinctions which need not detain us here. For example, different sentences may express the same proposition.

The **conjunction** of p and q is the proposition "p and q," symbolized by $p \wedge q$; it is true if both p and q are true, and false otherwise. In the examples above, $p \wedge q$ is the proposition "$2 + 2 = 5$ and this cat is a feline," and is false.

The **algebra of propositions** (also called propositional calculus, or calculus of statements, or calculus of sentences) is concerned with compound propositions formed from given propositions by means of the connective symbols $\sim$, $\vee$, $\wedge$.

It is useful to exhibit in tabular form the truth values of a compound proposition for all possible combinations of truth values for the given propositions; such an arrangement is called a **truth table** for the compound proposition. For example, the truth tables for $\sim p$, $p \vee q$, $p \wedge q$ are, respectively:

(1)

p	$\sim p$
T	F
F	T

p	q	$p \vee q$
T	T	T
T	F	T
F	T	T
F	F	F

p	q	$p \wedge q$
T	T	T
T	F	F
F	T	F
F	F	F.

Remark 1. The disjunction $p \vee q$ is true even if both p and q are true. This usage for "or" is the more common one in mathematics and logic, while the exclusive usage meaning "p or q but not both" is frequent in everyday speech.

We assume that the following laws are true for all propositions:

(1) *Law of the excluded middle:* either p is true or not-p is true. Symbolically, we assert $p \vee (\sim p)$.

(2) *Law of contradiction:* not both p and not-p are true. Symbolically, we assert $\sim [p \wedge (\sim p)]$.

We can now use the truth tables (1) to find the truth tables for more complicated compound propositions as in the following examples.

Example 1. Find the truth table for $(\sim r) \vee s$.

Solution. First filling in the first two columns below with all four combinations TT, TF, FT, FF for r and s, we then use the truth table for $\sim p$, above, to fill in the third column, writing r for p and $\sim r$ for $\sim p$. Finally, we use the truth table for $p \vee q$, above, to fill in the fourth column, writing $\sim r$ for p and s for q, obtaining

r	s	$\sim r$	$(\sim r) \vee s$
T	T	F	T
T	F	F	F
F	T	T	T
F	F	T	T.

We take $(\sim r) \vee s$ as the definition of the proposition "r **implies** s" and write it symbolically as $r \rightarrow s$. Thus, the truth table for $p \rightarrow q$ is

(2)

p	q	$p \rightarrow q$
T	T	T
T	F	F
F	T	T
F	F	T.

Remark 2. This meaning for implication is not the usual everyday meaning but it is sufficient for and the most common meaning for mathematics. It is sometimes called "material implication." Note that with this meaning $p \rightarrow q$ is true whenever p is false; that is, a false hypothesis implies any conclusion. For example, "$2+2=5$ implies this cat is a feline" is a correct implication in this sense.

We define "p is **equivalent** to q" or "p **if and only if** q," as $(p \rightarrow q) \wedge (q \rightarrow p)$. In symbols we write this as $p \leftrightarrow q$. For $p \leftrightarrow q$ we obtain the truth table

p	q	$p \rightarrow q$	$q \rightarrow p$	$(p \rightarrow q) \wedge (q \rightarrow p)$
T	T	T	T	T
T	F	F	T	F
F	T	T	F	F
F	F	T	T	T

or

(3)

p	q	$p \leftrightarrow q$
T	T	T
T	F	F
F	T	F
F	F	T.

A compound proposition having a truth table with the last column entirely composed of T's for all combinations of truth values for the given propositions is called a **tautology**. A compound proposition having a truth table with the last column entirely composed of F's for all combinations of truth values for the given propositions is called a **self-contradiction**.

Example 2. Verify that $(r \wedge s) \rightarrow r$ is a tautology.

Solution.

r	s	$r \wedge s$	$(r \wedge s) \to r$
T	T	T	T
T	F	F	T
F	T	F	T
F	F	F	T.

Example 3. Verify that $p \wedge (\sim p)$ is a self-contradiction.

Solution.

p	$\sim p$	$p \wedge (\sim p)$
T	F	F
F	T	F.

We prove the following interesting theorem.

Theorem. *If any one self-contradiction $a \wedge \sim a$ were true, then any proposition p whatever would be true.*

Proof. Since the tautology $a \vee \sim a$ is true, it follows that $a \vee \sim a \vee p$ is true. Therefore, $\sim(a \vee \sim a \vee p)$ is false. Since $\sim(x \vee y)$ implies $(\sim x) \wedge (\sim y)$ (Cf. exercise 18), and since $\sim(\sim a)$ is a, we conclude that $\sim a \wedge a \wedge \sim p$ is false. But $\sim a \wedge a$ is true by hypothesis. Hence $\sim p$ must be false. Therefore p is true.

Remark 3. Since filling out a truth table requires only binary decisions between T and F (which can be symbolized as 1 and 0, ✓ and ×, light on and light off, hole punched in card or not, etc.), it is clear that electronic "brains" can perform such formal reasoning.

Remark 4. If T and F are replaced by 1 and 0, respectively, then the truth tables for $p \vee q$ and $p \wedge q$ are, respectively, the same as the addition and multiplication tables (1) of section 66 for the Boolean algebra B_{01}. Speaking loosely, "or" corresponds to "addition" while "and" corresponds to "multiplication," just as for the algebra of sets.

Remark 5. Let us associate with a propositional function p the set of objects P (in an appropriate universe of discourse or universal set I) for which p is true; and vice versa, to each set P associate the propositional function p which asserts "x is a member of the set P." For example (using the set of all people as the universal set I), if p is the propositional function "x is blonde," then P is the set of blondes; if q is the propositional function "x has blue eyes," then Q is the set of blue-eyed people. It is convenient to write t for a propositional function which is true for all members of I, and f for one which is false for all members of I. Now it can be seen that the following sets are associated with the corresponding propositional functions:

Propositional function	Associated set
p	P
q	Q
(disjunction) $p \vee q$	$P \cup Q$ (union)
(conjunction) $p \wedge q$	$P \cap Q$ (intersection)
(negation) $\sim p$	P' (complement)
t	I
f	$\varnothing$

Hence the algebra of propositional functions is formally the same as the algebra of sets and is thus a Boolean algebra enjoying the properties I, I′, II, ... , XII of section 64 suitably translated by means of the above dictionary, that is, with $\vee$ replacing $\cup$, $\wedge$ replacing $\cap$, and so on.

Exercises

Let p represent the proposition "Thinking is hard work," and let q represent the proposition "I was a fool to take this course." Write out in words the meaning of each of the following symbols:

1. $p \wedge q$. **2.** $p \vee q$. **3.** $(\sim p) \wedge (\sim q)$.
4. $p \rightarrow q$. **5.** $p \wedge (\sim q)$. **6.** $q \rightarrow p$.

Determine the truth table for each of the following compound propositions:

7. $p \vee (\sim p)$. **8.** $p \vee (\sim q)$. **9.** $p \wedge (\sim q)$.
10. $\sim [p \wedge (\sim q)]$. **11.** $(p \wedge q) \vee (p \wedge [\sim q])$. **12.** $(p \wedge q) \vee p$.

Verify by means of truth tables that each of the following is a tautology:

13. $(p \wedge [\sim p]) \rightarrow q$. **14.** $[\sim(\sim p)] \rightarrow p$.
15. $(p \vee q) \leftrightarrow (q \vee p)$. **16.** $(p \wedge q) \leftrightarrow (q \wedge p)$.
17. $[\sim(p \wedge q)] \leftrightarrow [(\sim p) \vee (\sim q)]$. **18.** $[\sim(p \vee q)] \leftrightarrow [(\sim p) \wedge (\sim q)]$.
19. $(p \wedge q) \vee (\sim p) \vee (\sim q)$.
20. $(p \rightarrow q) \leftrightarrow ([\sim q] \rightarrow [\sim p])$. (The two propositions $p \rightarrow q$ and $[\sim q] \rightarrow [\sim p]$ are called **contrapositives** of each other.)
21. $p \rightarrow (q \rightarrow p)$. **22.** $(\sim p) \rightarrow (p \rightarrow q)$.
23. $[(p \rightarrow q) \wedge (q \rightarrow r)] \rightarrow [p \rightarrow r]$. (Hint: the truth table should have eight horizontal lines.)

24. If p and q are propositional functions and P and Q their associated sets (see remark 5):

(*a*) Show that $p \rightarrow q$ is true for all elements of the universal set I if and only if $P \subset Q$;

(*b*) Show that $p \leftrightarrow q$ is true for all elements of the universal set I if and only if $P = Q$.

Using the tabulated dictionary of associated sets and propositional functions of remark 5, find the associated expression in the algebra of sets for each of the following expressions in the algebra of propositional functions:

25. $(p \vee q) \leftrightarrow (q \vee p)$.
26. $[(p \wedge q) \wedge r] \leftrightarrow [p \wedge (q \wedge r)]$.
27. $p \rightarrow (p \vee q)$.
28. $[p \wedge (\sim p)] \leftrightarrow f$.
29. $[p \vee (\sim p)] \leftrightarrow t$.
30. $[\sim(\sim p)] \leftrightarrow p$.
31. $[p \wedge (q \vee r)] \leftrightarrow [(p \wedge q) \vee (p \wedge r)]$.
32. $(p \wedge q) \rightarrow p$.

*68. APPLICATION TO ELECTRICAL NETWORKS

The Boolean algebra B_{01} described in section 66 can be applied to the analysis of switching networks, that is, electrical networks with switches. Two switches A and B are connected in **parallel**, as in Fig. 47, when current will flow from the input N to the output U if either switch A or B (or both) is closed. They are connected in **series**, as in Fig. 48, when current will flow from input to output if and only if both switches are closed. Assign the value 1 to a switch if it is closed, 0 if it is open. Assign the value 1 to the output U if there is current there, 0 if not. We will assume that current is always provided at the input. Then, using the tables of addition and multiplication of B_{01} given in section 66, we see that the value $U = A + B$ when A and B are in parallel, while $U = A \cdot B$ when they are in series. Two switches which are arranged to be always simultaneously open or simultaneously closed may be denoted in a formula by the same letter. On the other hand, if two switches are such that one is open if and only if the other is closed, and vice versa, they may be denoted by A and A', so that when $A = 0$, $A' = 1$ and when $A = 1$, $A' = 0$. Thus $A + A' = 1$, and $AA' = 0$. A switch which is permanently closed may be denoted by 1, and a switch which is permanently open may be denoted by 0.

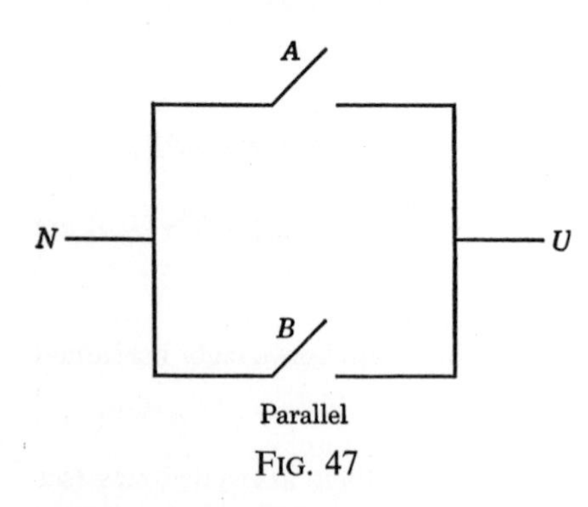

Parallel

FIG. 47

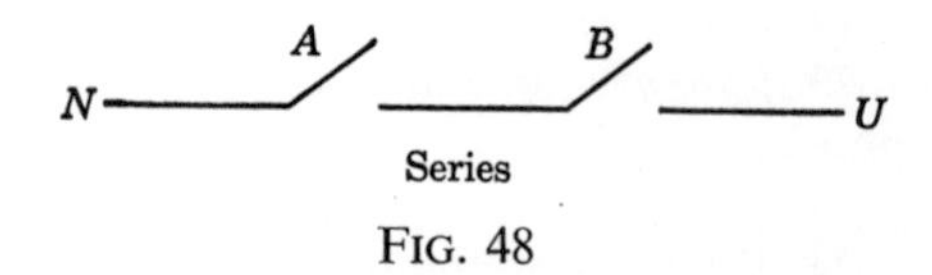

Series

FIG. 48

Each circuit of this sort can be described by a corresponding formula which may be manipulated in accordance with the rules of Boolean algebra and may yield in this way a formula representing a simpler equivalent circuit.

* This section may be omitted without disturbing the continuity.

Example 1. The circuits

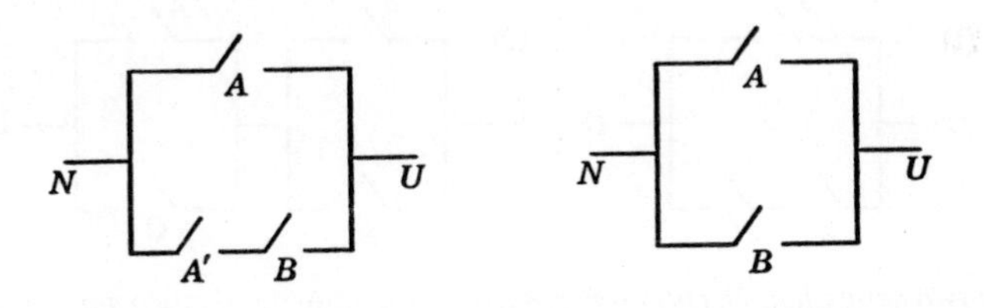

are equivalent. The first has the formula $A + A'B$. The second has the formula $A + B$. But by IV′ of section 64, rewritten with $+$ for $\cup$ and $\cdot$ for $\cap$, we have $A + A'B = (A + A')(A + B) = 1(A + B) = A + B$.

Remark. Note the correspondence, loosely stated, between the following symbols in various contexts:

Ordinary language	*Algebra of sets*	*Algebra of propositions*	*Algebra of switching circuits*
and	$\cap$	$\wedge$	
or	$\cup$	$\vee$	$+$

Exercises

1. (*a*) Write the formula representing each of the following circuits:

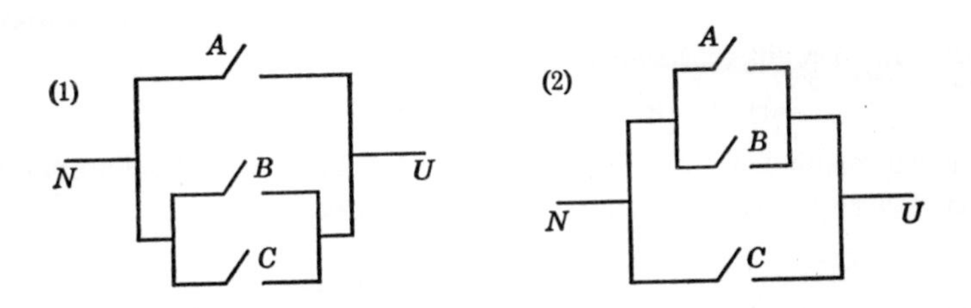

(*b*) Write and name the law of Boolean algebra which states that these two circuits are equivalent.

2. Answer the same questions as in exercise 1 for the following circuits.:

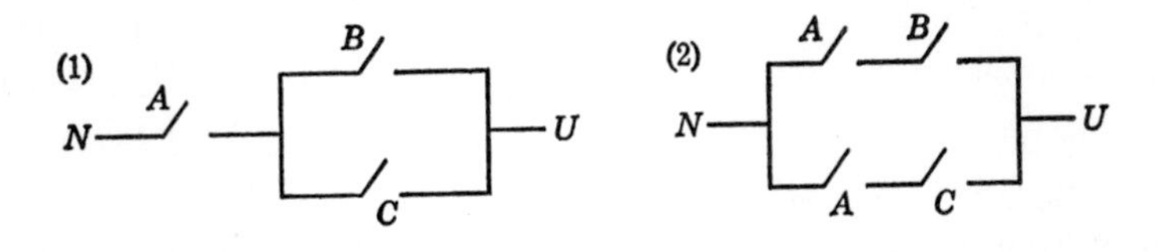

3. Answer the same questions as in exercise 1 for the following circuits:

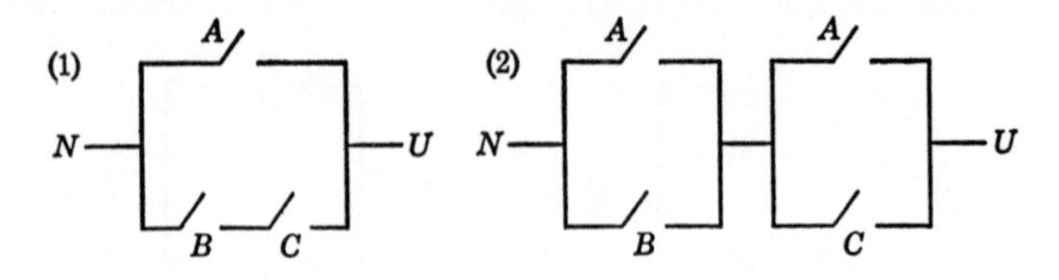

Make up two equivalent circuits representing, respectively, the two sides of the equation:

4. $A + A = A$. **5.** $A \cdot A = A$. **6.** $0 + A = A$.
7. $0 \cdot A = 0$. **8.** $1 + A = 1$. **9.** $1 \cdot A = A$.
10. $A \cdot A' = 0$. **11.** $A + A' = 1$.

12. (*a*) Construct a circuit representing the formula $AB + A'B'$.

(*b*) Show that this circuit will operate a hall light from either an upstairs or downstairs switch.

(*c*) Show that the formula $(A + B')(A' + B)$ is equivalent to that of part (*a*).

13. Show by manipulations of the Boolean algebra B_{01} that

$$(A + B)(AB + X) = AB + (A + B)X$$

and explain how the expression on either side of the equals sign represents the circuit:

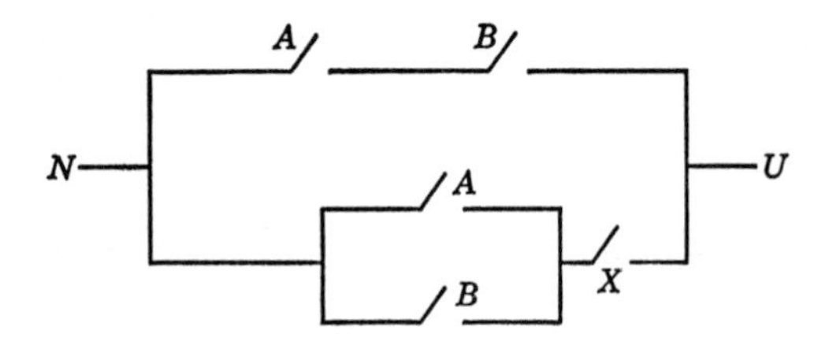

14. (*a*) Draw circuits representing the formulas

$$(1)\ A + B; \qquad (2)\ (A + AC) + (B + A'B).$$

(*b*) Show by manipulations of Boolean algebra that these two circuits are equivalent.

15. (*a*) Write formulas representing the following circuits:

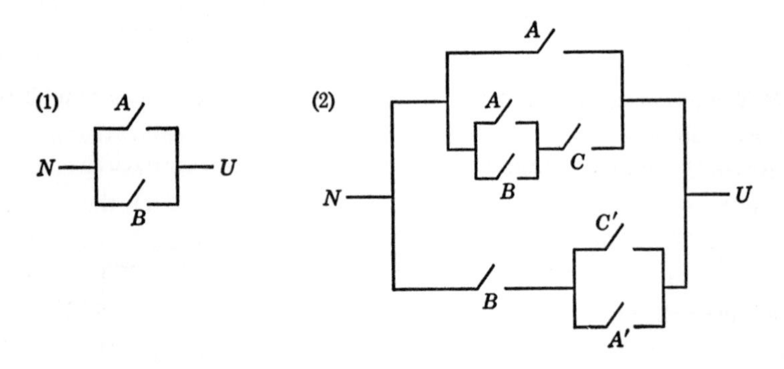

(*b*) Show by manipulations of Boolean algebra that these two circuits are equivalent.

69. THE NUMBER OF ELEMENTS IN A FINITE SET. MEASURES

Suppose we begin again, as children do, to derive the concept of number from concrete objects. A child first learns to associate the number 3 with a set of three apples, say. After some time it makes a tremendous abstraction in recognizing that a set of three apples, a set of three oranges, a set of three fingers, and the set consisting of Smith, Jones, and Brown all have something in common, namely, the property of "threeness." What does it mean to say that these various sets have this property in common? In verifying that the set of three apples has this property in common with the set of three fingers, we pair off each finger with an apple, one for one. This process is called placing the two sets in one-to-one correspondence. In general, two sets of objects are said to be in **one-to-one correspondence** if we have paired off the elements (or members) of one set with the elements of the other set so that to each element of the first set there corresponds exactly one element of the second, and to each element of the second there corresponds exactly one element of the first.

For example, the set of all normal living people is in one-to-one correspondence with the set of all living human heads, for to each person corresponds one head and to each head corresponds one person. In monogamous countries the set of husbands is in one-to-one correspondence with the set of wives if all are law-abiding. The set of all mothers is in one-to-one correspondence with the set of all eldest children. The correspondence between the set of all mothers and the set of all children is not one-to-one but one-to-many.

If two sets A and B can be put into one-to-one correspondence we shall call them **equivalent**; that is, A is equivalent to B or B is equivalent to A. In ordinary language, two equivalent sets **have the same number of elements**. The relation of equivalence for sets is indeed an equivalence relation; that is, it is reflexive, symmetric and transitive. Therefore, all the sets equivalent to a given set S are equivalent to each other, or "have the same number" of elements.

If a set A is equivalent to the set of all natural numbers from 1 up to and including n, then we say that the **number of elements** in A is n. In symbols we may write $N(A) = n$. Thus if the set A consists of Smith, Jones, and Brown, then $N(A) = 3$ since we can put A into one-to-one correspondence with the set consisting of 1, 2, and 3. Setting up this correspondence is known as counting the elements in the set. If there exists a natural number n such that $N(A) = n$, then A is called a **finite set**. We also agree to write $N(\varnothing) = 0$ and to regard $\varnothing$ as a finite set. It is intuitively clear that there exist sets which are not finite, called **infinite** sets, such as the set of *all* natural numbers, or the set of all points on a line. We shall discuss infinite sets in more detail later. *For the remainder of this chapter we shall deal only with finite sets.*

Two sets A and B are called **disjoint** if $A \cap B = \varnothing$, that is, if they have no member in common.

Theorem 1. *If A and B are disjoint, then $N(A \cup B) = N(A) + N(B)$.*

Proof. Suppose $N(A) = n$ and $N(B) = m$. Let A have the elements a_1, $a_2, \ldots, a_n$ and B have the elements $b_1, b_2 \ldots, b_m$. Then since no element of B is also an element of A we may put the set $A \cup B$ into one-to-one correspondence with the set of natural numbers $1, 2, \ldots, n + m$ as follows:

$$\begin{array}{cccccccc} a_1, & a_2, & \ldots, & a_n, & b_1, & b_2, & \ldots, & b_m \\ \updownarrow & \updownarrow & & \updownarrow & \updownarrow & \updownarrow & & \updownarrow \\ 1, & 2, \ldots & & n, & n+1, & n+2, & \ldots, & n+m. \end{array}$$

This completes the proof.

If we have any finite number of sets $A_1, A_2, A_3, \ldots, A_p$ such that every pair of them is disjoint, they are said to be **pairwise disjoint**. If $A_1, A_2, \ldots, A_p$ are pairwise disjoint, then

$$N(A_1 \cup A_2 \cup \cdots \cup A_p) = N(A_1) + N(A_2) + \cdots + N(A_p) \tag{1}$$

as can be seen by repeated application of theorem 1.

The following theorem is more general than theorem 1 since it does not assume that A and B are disjoint.

Theorem 2. $N(A \cup B) = N(A) + N(B) - N(A \cap B)$.

This is intuitively obvious; if one adds $N(A) + N(B)$, the elements in the intersection $A \cap B$ have been counted twice (Fig. 49) and therefore their number $N(A \cap B)$ must be subtracted once in order to arrive at $N(A \cup B)$. A formal proof follows.

Proof of theorem 2. Since every element of A is either in B or in the complement

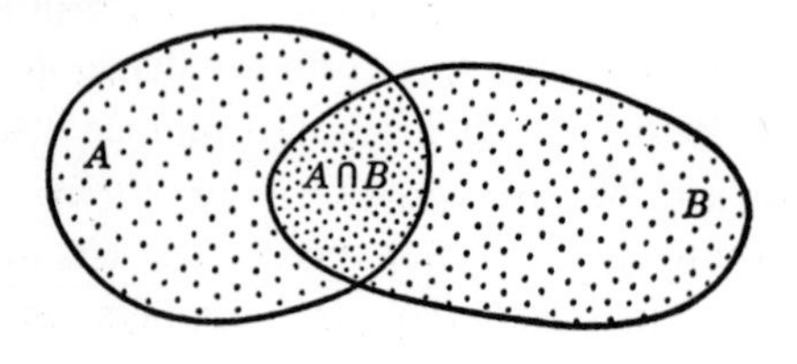

FIG. 49

B' of B, we have $A = (A \cap B) \cup (A \cap B')$, and the two parentheses represent disjoint sets since $B \cap B' = \varnothing$. Hence by theorem 1, we have

$$N(A) = N(A \cap B) + N(A \cap B') \tag{2}$$

or

$$N(A \cap B') = N(A) - N(A \cap B).$$

Similarly, $B = (A \cap B) \cup (A' \cap B)$, so that

$$N(B) = N(A \cap B) + N(A' \cap B) \tag{3}$$

or

$$N(A' \cap B) = N(B) - N(A \cap B).$$

But,

$$A \cup B = (A \cap B') \cup (A \cap B) \cup (A' \cap B)$$

and the sets in the three parentheses are clearly pairwise disjoint. Hence by (1),

$$\begin{aligned} N(A \cup B) &= N(A \cap B') + N(A \cap B) + N(A' \cap B) \\ &= N(A) - N(A \cap B) + N(A \cap B) + N(B) - N(A \cap B) \quad \text{(by (2) and (3))} \\ &= N(A) + N(B) - N(A \cap B). \end{aligned}$$

This completes the proof.

Note that for finite sets we have

$$(N_1) \qquad N(\varnothing) = 0;$$

$$(N_2) \qquad N(X) \geqq 0;$$

$$(N_3) \qquad N(X \cup Y) = N(X) + N(Y) - N(X \cap Y);$$

$$(\mathrm{N}_4) \qquad \text{If } X \subset Y, \text{ then } N(X) \leqq N(Y);$$

and that (N_3) and (N_1) together imply that if $X \cap Y = \varnothing$, then $N(X \cup Y) = N(X) + N(Y)$.

Now consider the collection of sets of points on a line built up from line-segments by means of a finite number of unions and intersections. If X is such a set and $L(X)$ is its total length, then clearly

$$(L_1) \qquad L(\varnothing) = 0;$$

$$L_2) \qquad L(X) \geqq 0;$$

$$(L_3) \qquad (LX \cup Y) = L(X) + L(Y) - L(X \cap Y);$$

and

$$(L_4) \qquad \text{if } X \subset Y, \text{ then } L(X) \leqq L(Y).$$

For example (Fig. 50), if X is the line-segment PR and Y is the line-segment QS then (L_3) holds. While if A is the line-segment PQ and B is the line-segment RS, then $L(A \cup B) = L(A) + L(B)$ since $\mathrm{A} \cap B = \varnothing$.

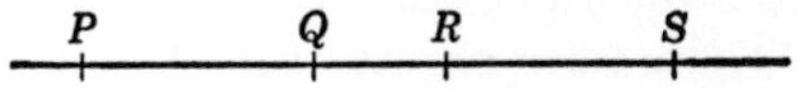

P Q R S

FIG. 50

Consider the collection of sets of points in a plane built up from rectangles, for example, by means of a finite number of unions and intersections. If X is such a set and $m(X)$ is its total area, then again we have analogous formulas

(M_1) $$m(\varnothing)=0;$$

(M_2) $$m(X) \geqq 0;$$

(M_3) $$m(X \cup Y) = m(X) + m(Y) - m(X \cap Y);$$

and,

(M_4) $$\text{if } X \subset Y, \text{ then } m(X) \leqq m(Y).$$

A similar remark can be made for volumes in space.

These four formulas are properties common to all these situations. A real number attached to the sets of a given collection of sets such as those described and satisfying these four formulas is sometimes called a **measure**.

Exercises

1. In a class of 45 girls, each of whom has either blonde hair or blue eyes, 35 are blonde and 20 have blue eyes. How many blue-eyed blondes are there?

2. In a class of 37 students, each of whom must take either English or history, 26 take English and 7 take both English and history. How many take history?

3. In how many ways can we select either a heart or a spade from a deck of 52 playing cards?

4. In how many ways can we select either an ace or a spade from a deck of 52 playing cards?

5. In a certain small college, all freshmen are required to take either English or history. If 30 take English and 25 take history, how many are there in the freshman class provided that

(*a*) The English and history classes meet the same hour?

(*b*) The English and history classes meet at different hours and 10 freshmen take both English and history?

6. (*a*) Prove that if A, B, C are any three sets, then

$$N(A \cup B \cup C) = N(A) + N(B) + N(C) - N(A \cap B) - N(B \cap C) \\ - N(A \cap C) + N(A \cap B \cap C).$$

(Hint: write $A \cup B \cup C$ as $(A \cup B) \cup C$, and apply theorem 2 three times; also use VIII′ of section 64.)

(*b*) Illustrate the theorem of part (*a*) on a diagram showing three overlapping classes.

7. A college requires all students to take either physics, biology, or chemistry. In a graduating class of 300, 220 have taken biology, 180 have taken chemistry, and 70 have taken physics. If 100 have taken both biology and chemistry, 50 have taken both chemistry and physics, and 30 have taken both biology and physics, how many have taken all three subjects? (Hint: use the formula of exercise 6.)

8. In the college of exercise 7, another graduating class has 300 members, of whom 50 have taken physics, 250 have taken biology, 35 have taken both physics and biology, 35 have taken both physics and chemistry, 100 have taken both biology and chemistry, and 30 have taken all three subjects. How many took chemistry?

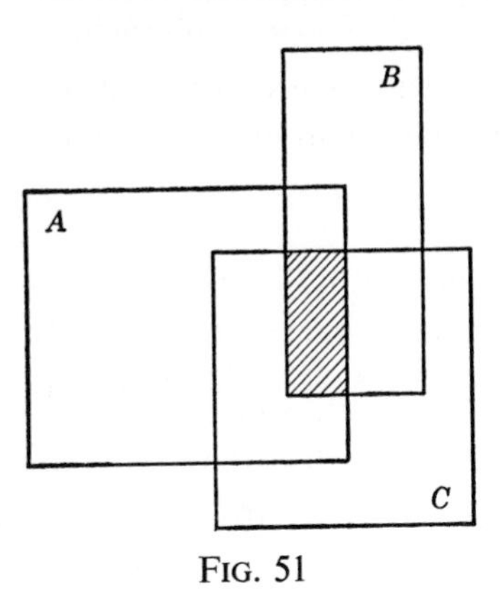

FIG. 51

9. In Fig. 51, the areas of rectangles A, B, and C are $m(A) = 20$, $m(B) = 10$, and $m(C) = 16$ square feet respectively. If $m(A \cap B) = 3$, $m(A \cap C) = 6$, $m(B \cap C) = 4$, and $m(A \cup B \cup C) = 35$ square feet respectively, find $m(A \cap B \cap C)$.

10. At Paradox College, every student is required to take either French, German, or Spanish before being graduated. The registrar reports that in a graduating class of 50, there were 25 who took French, 15 who took German, 35 who took Spanish, 8 who took French and German, 18 who took French and Spanish, 8 who took German and Spanish, and 6 who took all three languages. Criticize his report.

*70. AN APPLICATION TO POLITICAL SCIENCE

Committees, stockholders in corporations, and various governmental bodies frequently make decisions by means of voting rules which may be simple or complicated. It may be strategically useful to examine those subsets of the body which can control the decisions; we call these subsets **winning coalitions.** We assume throughout that there are no abstentions or absences.

Example 1. Consider a committee of three people a, b, c which operates under the ordinary majority rule. Then the winning coalitions are $\{a,b\}$, $\{a,c\}$, $\{b,c\}$, and $\{a,b,c\}$.

Example 2. Consider the same committee, now operating under the following rules: a has 2 votes, b is chairman with 1 vote but also has the power to break ties, and c has 1 vote. One's intuition might now lead one to feel that c's power in this committee has definitely dwindled, while a's and b's have increased, and one might be uncertain as to whether a or b is the strongest. The surprising fact is, however, that nothing has changed! The winning coalitions are still $\{a,b\}$, $\{a,c\}$, $\{b,c\}$, and $\{a,b,c\}$.

* This section is needed only for section 155. Otherwise, it may be omitted without disturbing the continuity.

Thus, the number of votes a person has is not a good measure of his power relative to the other persons. A better measure of power is presented in section 155.

A winning coalition of which no proper subset is winning is called a **minimal** winning coalition. Clearly, if the minimal winning coalitions are specified the others are determined.

Further illustrations will be found in the exercises.

We could set up an abstract mathematical science of such political structures as follows. By a **political structure*** shall be meant a finite set I of elements called **members**, and a collection of non-empty subsets of I called **winning coalitions**, satisfying the following postulates:

Postulate 1. *There is at least one winning coalition.*

Postulate 2. *Any superset of a winning coalition is also a winning coalition.*

Postulate 3. *The complement of any winning coalition is not a winning coalition.*

Any subset of I will be called a **coalition**.

We can now prove some theorems.

Theorem 1. *I is a winning coalition.*

Proof. By postulate 1 there exists a winning coalition W. But $W \subset I$. Therefore by postulate 2, I is a winning coalition.

Theorem 2. *If X is a coalition which is not winning, then no subset Y of X can be winning.*

Proof. If Y were winning then X would be winning by postulate 2. This would contradict the hypothesis. Hence Y is not winning.

Theorem 3. *Any two winning coalitions X and Y must have at least one member in common.*

Proof. Suppose, contrary to the theorem, that $X \cap Y = \varnothing$. Then Y is a subset of the complement X' of X. Since Y is winning, so is X' by postulate 2.

* Political structures are almost the same as, and were suggested by, the so-called *simple games* in J. von Neumann and O. Morgenstern, *Theory of Games and Economic Behavior*, Princeton University Press, Princeton, 1944.

Then X and X' are both winning contrary to postulate 3. Hence the supposition is false and $X \cap Y \neq \varnothing$.

A coalition which is not winning is termed **losing**. A losing coalition whose complement is also losing is called a **blocking** coalition. A member is called a **dictator** if he constitutes a winning coalition by himself, i.e., if all coalitions to which he belongs are winning. A member is called a **dummy** if each winning coalition to which he belongs is also winning without him.

Exercises

1. A committee of four members $\{a,b,c,d\}$ operates under majority rule but a has 1 vote, b has 2 votes, c has 2 votes, and d has 4 votes. (A winning coalition must have at least 5 votes.) List the winning coalitions and state which are minimal.

2. List the winning coalitions and state which are minimal, assuming the same committee as in exercise 1 except that a has 2 votes, b has 2 votes, c has 2 votes, and d has 3 votes.

3. List the winning coalitions and state which are minimal, assuming the same committee as in exercise 1 except that a has 1 vote, b has 2 votes, c has 2 votes, d has 3 votes, and a as chairman may break ties.

4. A committee has six members $\{a,b,c,d,e,f\}$ with 1 vote each. Describe the winning coalitions, the minimal winning coalitions, and the blocking coalitions (a) if a two-thirds majority vote is required to win; (b) if a simple majority vote is required to win but the chairman a can break ties.

5. Prove: (a) a political structure can have no more than one dictator; (b) if there is a dictator, then the other members are dummies.

★6. The Board of Estimate of New York City has eight members with the following numbers of votes: Mayor, 3; Controller, 3; Council President, 3; Borough President of Brooklyn, 2; Borough President of Manhattan, 2; Borough President of Richmond, 1; Borough President of Queens, 1; Borough President of the Bronx, 1. Describe the minimal winning coalitions and the blocking coalitions, assuming (a) majority rule; (b) the same numbers of votes as in (a) except that the Mayor is to have the power to break ties.

★7. The Security Council of the United Nations has 11 members, namely the "Big Five," each of which has the right of veto, and six other nations. A resolution must obtain at least 7 of the 11 votes to pass. Describe the minimal winning coalitions and the blocking coalitions. (Hint: the right of veto means that a "coalition" consisting of a single nation of the "Big Five" is a blocking coalition.)

8. A corporation issues 1000 shares of stock, each carrying one vote. How many shares must a stockholder own to be a dictator and how many to exercise a veto (that is, to constitute a blocking coalition by himself) (a) if a majority rule is in force? (b) if a two-thirds majority rule is in force?

71. A FUNDAMENTAL PRINCIPLE OF COUNTING

The reader should review the definitions of ordered pair and Cartesian product of two sets (section 11) at this point. Clearly the Cartesian product $A \times B$ of the sets $A = \{a, b, c\}$ and $B = \{p, q, r, s\}$, the members of which are listed on page 41, in 3 rows of 4 elements (ordered pairs) each, has $12 = 3 \times 4$ elements.

In general, it is clear that the number of elements $N(A \times B)$ in $A \times B$ is given by

$$N(A \times B) = N(A) \cdot N(B). \quad (1)$$

This leads immediately to the following fundamental principle of counting.

If one thing can be chosen in h different ways, and if, after it has been chosen, another thing can be chosen in k different ways, then both things can be chosen, in the stated order, in $h \cdot k$ different ways.

Example 1. How many different signals, each of two symbols in order, can be formed if each symbol may be either 0 or 1?

Solution. The first symbol can be chosen in two ways, and then the second symbol can be chosen in two ways. Hence by the fundamental principle, there are $2 \cdot 2 = 4$ such signals. They are

$$(0,0), (0,1)$$
$$(1,0), (1,1).$$

If A is the set consisting of 0 and 1, this collection of ordered pairs is precisely $A \times A$.

Example 2. How many different signals, each of three symbols in order, can be formed if each symbol may be either 0 or 1?

Solution. The first symbol can be chosen in two ways, then the second symbol can be chosen in two ways, and finally the third symbol can be chosen in two ways. By the fundamental principle, there are $2 \cdot 2 \cdot 2 = 8$ such signals. They are 000, 001, 010,011, 100, 101, 110, 111. (These are, of course, the numbers from 0 to 7 written in the binary scale.)

Example 3. How many different signals can be registered on a row of n electric bulbs, if each bulb may be either off or on?

Solution. Each bulb may register in two ways. Hence there are $2 \cdot 2 \cdots \cdot 2 = 2^n$ such signals.

Example 4. Two cards are to be drawn in order from a pack of 4 cards (say, an ace king, queen, and jack), the drawn card not being replaced before the second card is drawn. How many different drawings are possible?

Solution. The first card can be drawn in four ways, and then the second card in three ways. By the fundamental principle there are $4 \cdot 3 = 12$ different drawings. (We regard here ace first, king second as a different drawing from king first, ace second.)

If the first card were to be replaced before the second card is drawn, in example 4, then the answer would be $4 \cdot 4 = 16$ different drawings.

Theorem *A set A with n elements has 2^n different subsets (counting the empty set $\varnothing$ and the set A itself as subsets of A).*

Proof. Suppose the elements of A are denoted by

$$a_1, a_2, a_3, a_4, \ldots, a_n.$$

A subset may be indicated by placing under each element a 1 if it is to belong to the subset and a 0 if it is not to belong to the subset. For example, the subset consisting of a_1 and a_3 might be indicated as follows:

$$\begin{array}{l} a_1, a_2, a_3, a_4, \ldots, a_n \\ 1, \ \ 0, \ \ 1, \ \ 0, \ldots, 0. \end{array}$$

Hence the number of subsets is the same as the number of signals in example 3 (0 being represented by a dark bulb, and 1 by a lit one). If every element gets a 1, this indicates the subset A itself; if every element gets a 0, this indicates the empty subset $\varnothing$. Hence the number of subsets is 2^n.

For example, the set I consisting of three elements a, b, c has $2^3 = 8$ different subsets, namely, the empty set $\varnothing$; three sets $\{a\}$, $\{b\}$, $\{c\}$ of one element each; three sets $\{a,b\}$, $\{a,c\}$, $\{b,c)$ of two elements each; and the set $I = \{a,b,c\}$ itself.

Note that once again, speaking loosely, "and" corresponds to multiplication, as in formula (1) or the fundamental principle just below it. Similarly, if one thing can be chosen in h ways and another thing can be chosen in k ways, and if the first h ways and the second k ways are mutually exclusive, then either the first thing *or* the second thing can be chosen in $h + k$ ways. Thus once again, speaking loosely, for mutually exclusive sets, "or" corresponds to addition (compare section 69).

Exercises

1. A cafeteria offers 5 different sandwiches and 3 different beverages. How many different luncheon menus can be arranged, each to consist of a sandwich and a beverage?

2. How many luncheon menus can be arranged, assuming the same cafeteria as exercise 1, except that, because of lack of funds, each luncheon menu is to consist of either a sandwich or a beverage but not both?

3. Two cards are to be drawn from a pack of 20 different cards. How many different drawings are possible: (*a*) if the first drawn card is not replaced before the second drawing; (*b*) if the first drawn card is replaced in the pack before the second drawing?

4. (*a*) How many different signals can be shown on a row of 5 electric bulbs?

(*b*) How many different subsets can be chosen from a set A of 5 distinct objects, including the empty set and the set A itself?

(*c*) How many different natural numbers can be expressed in binary notation using no more than 5 places?

5. In how many ways can 4 students be seated in a row of 4 seats?

6. If a penny, nickel, dime, quarter, and half-dollar are tossed together, in how many different ways can they fall?

7. (*a*) Two cubical dice, 1 red and 1 white, are thrown. In how many different ways can they fall?

(*b*) In how many ways can 3 cubical dice fall?

8. How many different signals can be formed from 5 different flags if each signal is to consist of 3 flags hung in a horizontal row?

9. How many 2-digit numbers can be formed from the digits, 1, 3, 5, 7, 9 (*a*) if each 2-digit number must consist of 2 distinct digits; (*b*) if this restriction is removed?

10. How many different subsets can be chosen from a set of 6 objects?

72. PERMUTATIONS

An arrangement of a set of objects in some order in a straight line is called a **permutation** of these objects. More precisely, if we have a set of n objects and we wish to arrange r of them in some order on a line, each such arrangement is called a **permutation of the n objects taken r at a time.**

Example 1. We have a 3-volume work and a bookshelf with space for only 2 books. The permutations of the 3 volumes of a 3-volume work taken 2 at a time may be written down as follows (1, 2, 3 denoting volumes 1, 2, 3, respectively): 12, 13, 21, 23, 31, 32.

Example 2. The permutations of 4 letters, a, b, c, d taken 3 at a time are:

abc	*abd*	*acd*	*bcd*
acb	*adb*	*adc*	*bdc*
bac	*bad*	*cad*	*cbd*
bca	*bda*	*cda*	*cdb*
cab	*dab*	*dac*	*dbc*
cba	*dba*	*dca*	*dcb.*

We could arrive at the number of permutations of 3 things taken 2 at a time (example 1) as follows. In the first position (on the bookshelf) we can place any one of the 3 books. No matter which choice we made for the first position we could put any one of the 2 remaining books in the second position. By the fundamental principle of section 71, there are $3 \cdot 2$ or 6 different permutations. They are listed in example 1.

Similarly, in example 2, we may place any one of the 4 letters in the first position. No matter which of the 4 choices we make for the first position, we can place any one of the remaining 3 letters in the second position, and then any one of the remaining 2 letters in the third position. By the fundamental principle, there are $4 \cdot 3 \cdot 2 = 24$ permutations. They are listed in example 2.

The number of permutations of n distinct things taken r at a time will be denoted by $P(n,r)$. Clearly, any one of the n things may be placed in the first position, any one of the remaining $(n - 1)$ things may be placed in the second position, any one of the remaining $(n - 2)$ things in the third position, and so on, until we reach the rth position. Hence, by the fundamental principle

$$P(n,r) = n(n-1)(n-2) \ldots \quad \text{(to } r \text{ factors).} \tag{1}$$

Clearly, the rth factor will be $n - (r - 1)$ or $n - r + 1$. Hence (1) may be written as

$$P(n,r) = n(n-1)(n-2) \cdots (n-r+1). \tag{2}$$

The number of permutations of n distinct objects taken *all* at a time is clearly

$$P(n,n) = n(n-1)(n-2) \cdots 3 \cdot 2 \cdot 1. \tag{3}$$

We find it convenient to abbreviate the expression $n(n-1)(n-2) \ldots 3 \cdot 2 \cdot 1$ by defining the symbol $n!$, read "**factorial n**," to mean the product of all the natural numbers from n down to one; that is,

$$n! = n(n-1)(n-2) \cdots 3 \cdot 2 \cdot 1. \tag{4}$$

For example, $3! = 3 \cdot 2 \cdot 1 = 6$, $4! = 4 \cdot 3 \cdot 2 \cdot 1 = 24$, $5! = 5 \cdot 4 \cdot 3 \cdot 2 \cdot 1 = 120$ and so on. Since

$$n(n-1)(n-2) \cdots (n-r+1) =$$

$$\frac{n(n-1)(n-2) \cdots (n-r+1) \cdot (n-r)(n-r-1)(n-r-2) \cdots 3 \cdot 2 \cdot 1}{(n-r)(n-r-1)(n-r-2) \cdots 3 \cdot 2 \cdot 1}$$

$$= \frac{n!}{(n-r)!},$$

we have the following theorem.

Theorem. *The number of permutations of n distinct things taken r at a time is given by*

$$P(n, r) = \frac{n!}{(n-r)!} \qquad \textit{if } r < n$$

while

$$P(n,n) = n!$$

Example 3. The number of arrangements of 7 distinct books on a shelf is $P(7,7) = 7! = 7\cdot6\cdot5\cdot4\cdot3\cdot2\cdot1 = 5040$. The number of arrangements of 7 distinct books taken 4 at a time is

$$P(7,4) = \frac{7!}{(7-4)!} = \frac{7!}{3!} = \frac{7\cdot6\cdot5\cdot4\cdot3\cdot2\cdot1}{3\cdot2\cdot1} = 7\cdot6\cdot5\cdot4 = 840.$$

Exercises

Evaluate each of the following symbols:

1. $6!$. **2.** $\frac{6!}{3!}$. **3.** $\frac{9!}{7!}$. **4.** $P(6,2)$. **5.** $P(9,2)$. **6.** $P(5,5)$.

7. In how many ways can 5 students be seated in a row of 5 seats?

8. How many different signals can be made from 6 different flags if each signal is to consist of 3 flags hung in a horizontal row?

9. How many different numbers of 3 different digits each can be made from the digits 1, 3, 5, 7, 9?

10. How many different signals can be made from 6 different flags if each signal is to consist of one or more flags hung in a horizontal row?

11. How many different symbols each consisting of 4 letters in succession can be formed from the letters *a*, *b*, *c*, *d*, *e*, repetition of a letter in a given symbol being forbidden?

12. How many different symbols each consisting of 4 letters in succession can be formed from the letters *a*, *b*, *c*, *d*, *e*, repetitions being permitted?

13. A telephone dial has 10 holes. How many different signals, each consisting of 7 impulses in succession, can be formed (*a*) if no impulse is to be repeated in any given signal? (*b*) if repetitions are permitted?

14. In how many ways may 6 students be seated in a row of 8 seats?

15. In how many ways can the positions of president, vice-president, and secretary be filled in a club of 20 members?

16. In how many ways may a baseball team be arranged in batting orders if a certain 4 men must occupy the first 4 positions in some order?

17. In how many ways can a party of 5 people be seated in a row of 5 seats (*a*) if a certain 2 insist on sitting next to each other? (*b*) if the same 2 refuse to sit next to each other?

18. In how many ways can a set of 4 different mathematics books and 3 different physics books be placed on a shelf if all the books in the same subject must be placed next to each other?

19. The same as exercise 18, except that the mathematics books must be kept together while the physics books need not be.

20. A careless secretary drops 5 different letters addressed to 5 different people and inserts them into the addressed envelopes. (*a*) In how many ways can this be done? (*b*) How many of these ways send at least one letter to a wrong address? (*c*) How many send exactly one letter to a wrong address?

73. COMBINATIONS

A set of r objects chosen from a given set of n objects, without regard to order, is called a **combination of *n* things taken *r* at a time.**

Example 1. The combinations of 3 distinct volumes (1, 2, 3) taken 2 at a time are 12, 13, and 23. Compare example 1, section 72. The permutations 12 and 21 give rise to only one combination, since order is to be ignored.

Example 2. The combinations of 4 letters a, b, c, d, taken 3 at a time are *abc*, *abd*, *acd*, *bcd*. Compare example 2, section 72. The six permutations in each column of example 2 section 72 give rise to only one combination, since order is to be ignored.

Clearly, any combination of n distinct things taken r at a time gives rise to $r!$ permutations since the set of r objects can be rearranged among themselves in $r!$ ways. Let us denote by $C(n,r)$ the number of combinations of n distinct things taken r at a time. Then, as we have just seen,

$$P(n,r) = r! \cdot C(n,r)$$

or

$$C(n,r) = \frac{1}{r!} \cdot P(n,r)$$

or

$$(1) \qquad C(n,r) = \frac{n!}{r!(n-r)!} \qquad (r < n).$$

Example 3. In example 1 above, the number of combinations of 3 distinct things taken 2 at a time is $C(3,2) = \dfrac{3!}{2!(3-2)!} = \dfrac{3 \cdot 2 \cdot 1}{2 \cdot 1 \cdot 1} = 3$. In example 2 above, the number of combinations of 4 distinct things taken 3 at a time is $C(4,3) = \dfrac{4!}{3!(4-3)!} = \dfrac{4 \cdot 3 \cdot 2 \cdot 1}{3 \cdot 2 \cdot 1 \cdot 1} = 4.$

Remark. Whenever we select a set of r things from a set of n things we automatically select a set of $n - r$ things which are left behind. Therefore $C(n,r) = C(n,n-r)$.

$C(n,r)$ is also denoted by other symbols such as C_r^n, $\binom{n}{r}$, and $C_{n,r}$.

Exercises

Evaluate each of the following symbols:

1. $C(5,2)$. **2.** $C(18,16)$. **3.** $C(20,2)$. **4.** $C(17,16)\cdot C(4,3)\cdot 3!$

In how many ways can we select:

5. A committee of 3 from a group of 10 people?

6. A jury of 12 men from a panel of 20 eligible men?

7. A set of 3 books from a set of 7 different books?

8. A set of 5 or more books from a set of 7 different books?

9. A set of 3 mathematics books and 2 physics books from a set of 7 mathematics books and 5 physics books, all different?

10. A committee of 4 Democrats and 3 Republicans from a group of 8 Democrats and 6 Republicans?

11. A committee of 5 from a group of 10 (*a*) if a certain 2 men insist on serving together or not at all? (*b*) if a certain 2 men refuse to serve together?

12. How many sums of money, each involving 3 coins, can be formed from a cent, a nickel, a dime, and a quarter?

13. (*a*) How many straight lines are determined by 10 points no 3 of which are in the same straight line? (*b*) How many of these lines pass through any given one of these 10 points?

14. From a group of 10 Democrats and 8 Republicans, how many different committes of 7 can be chosen which contain (*a*) at least 4 Democrats? (*b*) at most 4 Democrats? (*c*) exactly 4 Democrats?

15. In how many different orders can we shelve sets of 5 books, each set consisting of 3 mathematics books and 2 physics books, if the books are to be chosen from a set of 10 mathematics books and 8 physics books, all different?

16. How many triangles are determined by the set of vertices of a regular hexagon?

17. (*a*) How many committees of 5 can be chosen from a group of 15 men?
(*b*) How many of these will include a specified man A?
(*c*) From how many will A be excluded?

18. Prove that $C(n-1,r) + C(n-1, r-1) = C(n,r)$.

19. How many minimal winning coalitions are there in the committee of exercise 4(*a*) of section 70?

20. If $P(n,3) = 210$, find $C(n,3)$.

21. If $C(n,4) = 126$, find $P(n,4)$.

22. If $P(n,2) = 156$, find n.

23. If $C(n,2) = 210$, find n.

74. THE BINOMIAL THEOREM

By tedious multiplication we find that

$$(x+h)^1 = x + h$$
$$(x+h)^2 = x^2 + 2xh + h^2$$
$$(x+h)^3 = x^3 + 3x^2h + 3xh^2 + h^3$$
$$(x+h)^4 = x^4 + 4x^3h + 6x^2h^2 + 4xh^3 + h^4$$
$$(x+h)^5 = x^5 + 5x^4h + 10x^3h^2 + 10x^2h^3 + 5xh^4 + h^5,$$

and so on. It is clear that the expansion of $(x + h)^n$, where n is any natural number, begins with x^n and ends with h^n. In the intermediate terms the exponent of x decreases by one with each successive term and the exponent of h increases by one, so that the sum of the two exponents is exactly n in each term. The coefficients may be obtained from the following scheme, known as **Pascal's triangle**, which we shall not justify here,

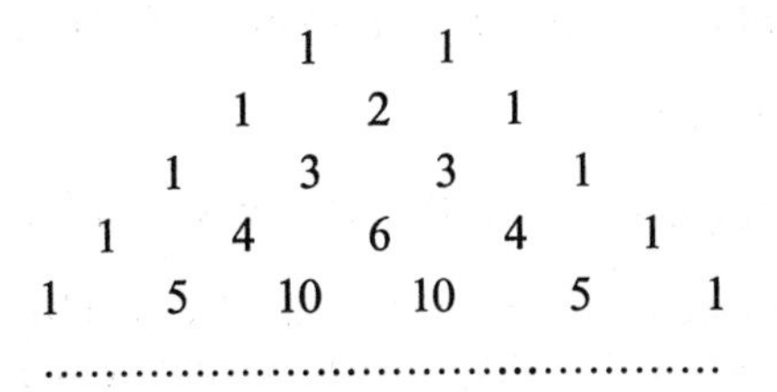

in which each number, except the 1's on the outside, is the sum of the two nearest numbers in the line above. Hence

$$(x+h)^6 = x^6 + 6x^5h + 15x^4h^2 + 20x^3h^3 + 15x^2h^4 + 6xh^5 + h^6.$$

This scheme is, however, not very practical for high exponents n, for to write even the first few terms of $(x + h)^{175}$, say, we should have to work out Pascal's triangle down to the 175th line. A better scheme is given by the following theorem.

Theorem. *If n is a natural number*

$$(x+h)^n = x^n + C(n,1)x^{n-1}h + C(n,2)x^{n-2}h^2 + C(n,3)x^{n-3}h^3 + \cdots + C(n,r)x^{n-r}h^r + \cdots + h^n.$$

This result appears natural if you recall that $(x + h)^n$ means $(x + h)(x + h) \cdots (x + h)$ with n factors. Each term in the result is a sum of terms each of which is a product of one letter from each parenthesis. For example, the term involving h^r will be a sum of terms of the form $x^{n-r}h^r$ each of which is a product of $n - r$ x's (one from each of $n - r$ parentheses) and r h's (one from each of r

parentheses). How many such terms $x^{n-r}h^r$ will there be? Clearly, as many as there are choices of r of the n parentheses from which to take an h. Hence there are $C(n,r)$ such terms and the total coefficient of $x^{n-r}h^r$ in the final result is $C(n,r)$.

Example.

$$(x+h)^6 = x^6 + C(6,1)x^5h + C(6,2)x^4h^2 + C(6,3)x^3h^3 + C(6,4)x^2h^4 + C(6,5)xh^5 + h^6$$
$$= x^6 + 6x^5h + 15x^4h^2 + 20x^3h^3 + 15x^2h^4 + 6xh^5 + h^6.$$

This theorem, known as the **binomial theorem for positive integral exponents,** can be proved by mathematical induction. This will not be done here.

The coefficient of the term involving h^r is $C(n,r)$; this is the $(r + 1)$th term in the expansion. There will be $n + 1$ terms, in all, in the expansion of $(x + h)^n$.

If we define $C(n,0) = C(n,n) = 1$, for convenience, we could write the binomial theorem as

$$(x + h)^n = C(n,0)x^n + C(n,1)x^{n-1}h + C(n,2)x^{n-2}h^2 + \cdots + C(n,n)h^n.$$

Setting $x = h = 1$ we obtain

$$2^n = C(n,0) + C(n,1) + C(n,2) + \cdots + C(n,n).$$

For a given set of n elements, $C(n,r)$ is the number of subsets having r members. Hence the total number of possible subsets, including the set itself (the unique subset of n members) and the empty set $\varnothing$ (the unique subset of 0 members), is 2^n. This is another proof of the theorem of section 71.

Further applications of the material in this section and the preceding ones will be found in later chapters, particularly in connection with probability.

Exercises

Write the expansion of each of the following:

1. $(x+h)^7$. **2.** $(a+b)^8$. **3.** $(p+q)^9$.

4. $(2a+3b)^6$. **5.** $(2a^3+3b^2)^5$. **6.** $\left(\frac{a}{2}+\frac{4b^2}{a}\right)^4$.

7. $(a-b)^3$. (Hint: write $a-b=a+[-b]$.)

8. $(a-b)^6$. **9.** $(a-b)^5$. **10.** $\left(2a^3-\frac{b^2}{2a}\right)^5$.

11. $\left(1+\frac{1}{2}\right)^2$. **12.** $\left(1+\frac{1}{3}\right)^3$. **13.** $\left(1+\frac{1}{4}\right)^4$.

14. $\left(1+\frac{1}{5}\right)^5$.

Write, in simplified form, only the specified terms:

15. The term involving h^3 in the expansion of $(x+h)^{17}$.

16. The term involving b^5 in the expansion of $(a+b)^{20}$.

17. The sixth term of $(x+h)^{15}$.

18. The eighteenth term of $(x+h)^{22}$.

19. The term involving b^6 in the expansion of $\left(\frac{a^2}{2}+2b^2\right)^{10}$.

20. The term involving q^{10} in the expansion of $\left(\frac{p^2}{3}+6q^2\right)^{13}$.

21. The middle term of $(a-b)^8$.

22. The middle terms of $(2a-3b)^9$.

23. The term involving b^3 in $\left(\frac{b}{a}+\frac{1}{b}\right)^9$.

24. Explain the connection between exercise 18 of section 73 and Pascal's triangle.

25. Compute, using only enough terms to get the result accurate to 3 decimal places:

(*a*) $1.01^9=(1+.01)^9$. (*b*) $.99^6=(1-.01)^6$.
(*c*) 1.02^{11}. (*d*) $.98^7$.

26. Prove that

$$C(n,0)+C(n,2)+C(n,4)+\cdots=C(n,1)+C(n,3)+C(n,5)+\cdots.$$

That is, the sum of the $C(n,r)$ for even r is equal to the sum of the $C(n,r)$ for odd r.

References

Numbers refer to the bibliography at the end of the book.

Allendoerfer and Oakley 3
Arnold 5
Bell 16
Bennett and Baylis 23
Berkeley 25
Boole 32
Cohen and Nagel 55
Hohn 95
Kemeny, Snell, and Thompson 107
Richardson 158
Ryser 168
Stabler 184
Stoll 187
Suppes 188
Tarski 190
Wilder 210

8
Impossibilities and Unsolved Problems

75. INTRODUCTION

In sections 30 and 44 we have carefully pointed out that it is one thing to say that a problem has not been solved yet and another thing to say that it is impossible to solve it. For example, we proved that it is impossible for any rational number to satisfy the equation $x^2 = 2$; we did not say merely that no one has yet found such a rational number. The distinction between these two things can hardly be called subtle. It must be regarded as one of the world's wonders that many people blithely assume that all professional mathematicians are incapable of grasping this distinction. Every few years, another crank looses a blast against the professional mathematicians' "smug assertion" that angle-trisection, for example, is impossible "merely because they haven't been able to do it." Many of these amazing people go further and claim actually to do it, and their proposed solutions are solemnly published, sometimes privately and sometimes in the daily press. Moreover, they are difficult to convince. Pointing to the logical proof that angle-trisection, say, is impossible, does no good. On the contrary, they refuse to learn the proof of impossibility and insist that the professional mathematician (if they have been so fleet of foot as to corner one) show them exactly where their methods are wrong. Since their methods usually consist of complicated constructions covering several square yards of paper, this task is not relished by the professional mathematician. Often the misguided zealot has completely misunderstood the problem; it may also happen that he does not grasp how it is possible to prove a thing impossible. The reader has already completed such a proof (section 30).

We shall discuss sketchily some ancient and some modern problems; some are proved impossibilities and others are merely unsolved or open questions at the present time. Among the classical problems are angle-trisection, the duplication of the cube, and squaring the circle, which are known as the "problems of antiquity." Since mathematics is a living science, there are always many unsolved (that is, open) problems. Most of those which are really of importance are far too technical to be discussed here. But there are a few unsolved problems, of little practical importance, which are simple enough to be stated here and which are of interest either because of the stubbornness with which they have resisted solution or because of their unconventional nature. Some of these will be discussed below.

76. CONSTRUCTIONS WITH RULER AND COMPASSES

The ancient Greeks had a predilection for constructing figures with the aid of straight edge and compasses alone. To begin with there is no reason why we should not equally well restrict ourselves to constructions with ruler alone, or compasses alone, or, on the other hand, why we should not permit other mechanical devices. The problem of constructions under these various conditions has been studied in modern times. The Greeks themselves did many construction problems by means of other devices besides ruler and compasses. It may be conjectured that their preference for ruler and compasses is related to their aesthetic appreciation of circles and straight lines which are, perhaps, the simplest figures. Whether this conjecture is correct or not, the construction problems of antiquity, mentioned above, were supposed to be done with ruler (unmarked straight edge) and compasses alone. For roughly 2000 years these problems were considered open questions and remained a thorn in the side of mathematicians because with the synthetic (purely geometric) methods of the Greeks, no way of settling them was found. Only with the application of algebraic methods to geometry were these constructions proved impossible. These methods were not introduced until modern times and will be discussed in the next chapter.

We shall indicate how one can prove the following (loosely stated) criterion for constructibility with ruler and compasses.

Theorem. *We can construct a quantity (length) with ruler and compasses alone if and only if it can be derived from the data (given lengths) by a finite number of rational operations and extractions of square roots.*

This is really a theorem and its converse together (see remark 2, section 5). The converse (the "only if" part of it) will be discussed at the end of the next chapter. The "if" part of it is easy. We have only to show that given any two

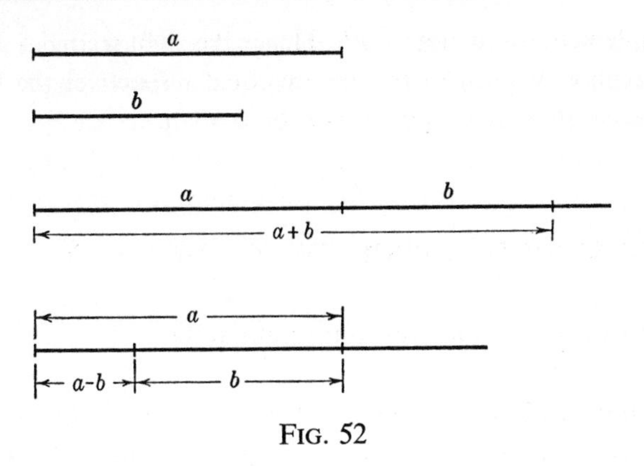

FIG. 52

lengths a and b (and the unit length) we can construct with ruler and compasses the lengths $a + b$, $a - b$, $a \cdot b$, a/b, and $\sqrt{a}$. The constructions of $a + b$ and $a - b$ are obvious (Fig. 52).

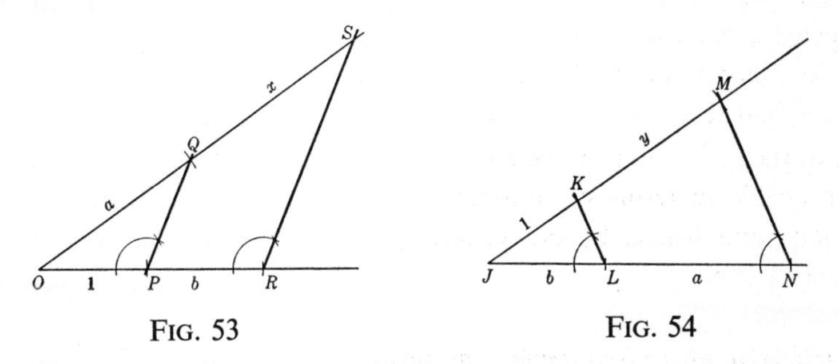

FIG. 53 FIG. 54

To construct $a \cdot b$ we lay off a, the unit length, and b on the sides of an angle as in Fig. 53, join P and Q and construct RS parallel to PQ at R. Then $x/a = b/1$ since parallel lines cut off proportional segments on two transversals. Hence the length $x = a \cdot b$.

To construct a/b we lay off b, the unit length, and a on the sides of an angle as in Fig. 54, join K and L and construct MN parallel to KL at N. Then $y/1 = a/b$ for the reason quoted above. Hence $y = a/b$.

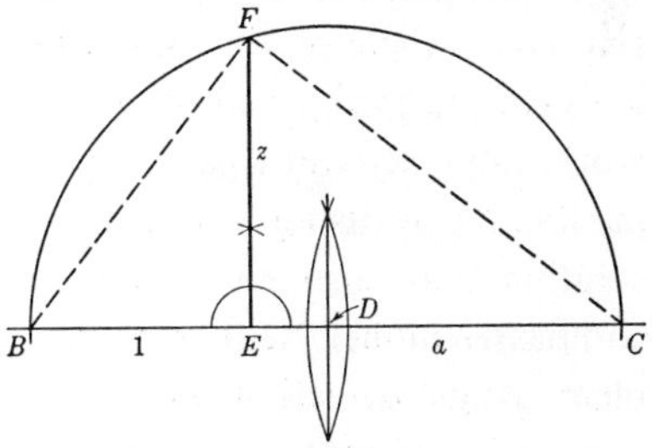

FIG. 55

To construct $\sqrt{a}$ we lay off the unit length and a as in Fig. 55, bisect BC, draw a semicircle with the midpoint D as center, and construct a perpendicular at E. Now angle BFC is a right angle since it is inscribed in a semicircle. Angles BFE and FCE are equal since they are both complementary to angle EFC. Hence the right triangles BFE and FEC are similar because two angles of one are equal respectively to two angles of the other. Hence $a/z = z/1$. Thus $z^2 = a$ or $z = \sqrt{a}$.

77. THE CONSTRUCTION PROBLEMS OF ANTIQUITY

Now let us consider the problems of antiquity.

The duplication of the cube. This problem is known as the Delian problem. It is said that during a plague in Greece, the people went to the oracle at Delos to ask how they might appease the Gods. With the cruel sense of humor often attributed to oracles, it answered that if they would construct a cubical altar with exactly twice the volume of a given cubical altar the plague would stop. The plague ran its course. The people, in their first enthusiasm, are said to have constructed a cube by doubling the side of the given one; but this of course multiplied the volume by 8. Taking the given cube as the unit of volume 1, what they had to do was construct a quantity x to be the side of the doubled cube. But then $x^3 = 2$. The real root of $x^3 = 2$ is $\sqrt[3]{2}$ which can be proved to be not expressible in terms of rational operations and the extraction of square roots only, and hence, by our criterion, is not constructible with ruler and compasses alone.

The trisection of a given angle. The problem is to provide a construction by ruler and compasses alone for the trisection of *any given* angle. To be sure, *some* angles, like 180° or 90°, can be trisected with ruler and compasses alone; that is, an angle of 60° or 30° can be so constructed. But 120° cannot be trisected; that is, an angle of 40° cannot be constructed, with ruler and compasses alone. This can be established by our criterion. It will not be done here. For practical work, anybody can trisect any angle approximately enough by ruler and compasses, or by using a protractor finely enough divided. Theoretically, exact solutions can also be obtained by mechanical devices other than ruler and compasses alone. Neither of these solutions have to do with the classical problem. Angle-trisection and circle-squaring are still popular sports among the vast army of amateur cranks; a proposed "solution" for one or the other appears every few years.

Squaring the circle. The problem is to construct a square whose area is exactly equal to that of a given circle. Let the radius of the circle be 1. Then the area of the circle is π. But if x is the side of the square to be constructed we must have $x^2 = \pi$. If we could construct a length equal to π we could also construct $x = \sqrt{\pi}$, and conversely. But it can be shown that x is not constructible because π is not constructible by ruler and compasses alone. In fact, not only is π inexpressible in a finite number of rational operations and square roots, but it is even inexpressible in terms of roots of any index. This is a consequence of the theorem that π does not satisfy any polynomial equation with integral coefficients, proved by Lindemann in 1882. There are, however, mechanical devices which can construct π.

A number which satisfies a polynomial equation with integral coefficients is called an **algebraic number**. A number satisfying no such equation is called a **transcendental number**. Hence π is a transcendental number. A rational number $x = p/q$, where p and q are integers, by definition; hence x satisfies the equation $qx - p = 0$ with integral coefficients. It follows that every rational number is algebraic, and hence that every transcendental number is irrational. On the other hand, $\sqrt{2}$ is algebraic, although irrational, since it satisfies the equation $x^2 - 2 = 0$ with integral coefficients. Whether the number π^π is algebraic or transcendental is still unknown today.

78. CONSTRUCTION OF REGULAR POLYGONS. PROBLEMS ABOUT PRIME NUMBERS

A polygon is called **regular** if its sides and angles are all equal. By using our criterion it can be shown that while regular polygons of 4, 5, 6, 10 sides and others can be constructed, a regular polygon of 7 sides cannot. It was proved by Gauss, at the age of 19, that a regular polygon of 17 sides can be constructed, a fact which was not previously suspected. He also gave such a construction. In fact, Gauss proved that if the number $X = 2^{2^n} + 1$ is prime then a regular polygon of X sides can be constructed. A **prime number** is a natural number, greater than one, which has no factors except 1 and itself, like 2, 3, 5, 7, 11, 13, 17, 19, ... For $n = 1$ and $n = 2$, respectively, $X = 5$ and $X = 17$. For $n = 3$, $X = 257$, a prime number. Detailed discussions of the construction of the regular polygon of 257 sides have been given. For $n = 4$, $X = 65{,}537$ is also prime. The regular polygon of 65,537 sides has been discussed. If a prime number X is not expressible as $2^{2^n} + 1$, then a regular polygon of X sides cannot be constructed with ruler and compasses alone.

This suggests that it might be desirable to know for what natural numbers n the number $2^{2^n} + 1$ is prime. Fermat believed that $2^{2^n} + 1$ was prime for all

Leonhard Euler
1707–1783, Swiss

natural numbers n. Euler (1707–1783) showed that this is not so by finding that 641 is a factor of $2^{2^5} + 1 = 4,294,967,297$. However, there remains the question of whether the unending sequence of numbers $2^{2^n} + 1$ as $n = 1, 2, 3, 4, 5, \ldots$ contains only a finite (limited) number of primes or an infinite number of primes. This question is still an open or unsolved problem.

There are many unsolved problems connected with prime numbers such as the following:

(1) Is every even number, greater than 2, the sum of two primes? (Goldbach's conjecture, 1742.) For example, $4 = 2 + 2$, $6 = 3 + 3$, $8 = 5 + 3$, $10 = 7 + 3$, $12 = 7 + 5$. No one has ever found an even number greater than 2 which is not so expressible, but neither has anyone been able to *prove* that they all can be so expressed.

(2) Find a formula for the number of primes between two given natural numbers.

(3) Is there an infinite number of pairs of primes differing by two? For example, 11 and 13, 17 and 19, 29 and 31.

(4) How can one decide practically whether or not a given natural number is prime? Clearly one can decide whether or not any natural number is prime by actually trying to divide it by every smaller natural number.* But this is not practical for large numbers. A mechanical device has been invented by D. H. Lehmer which can decide question 4 in a short time for many very large numbers. For example, it factored $2^{93} + 1$ into 529,510,939 times 2,903,110,321 times 715,827,883 times 3^2 in 3 seconds.†

(5) *Fermat's last theorem.* Pierre de Fermat (1601–1665) was a lawyer and councillor for the parliament of Toulouse, whose leisure time was given largely

* Actually, one need never try any number greater than the square root of the given number (Why?), but it remains impractical for very large numbers.

† Ball, *Mathematical Recreations and Essays*, 11th edition, Macmillan, London, 1939, p. 61. For a description of the machine see D. H. Lehmer, A Photo-Electric Number Sieve, *Amer. Math. Monthly*, vol. 40, 1933, pp. 401–406.

to mathematics. He left his mark on many branches of mathematics but had the annoying habit of making brief marginal notes of his discoveries. One of these marginal notes, discovered after his death, asserted the following theorem: *if n is a natural number greater than 2 there cannot be three natural numbers x, y, and z, such that* $x^n + y^n = z^n$. (Notice that for $n = 2$ there *are* such numbers; for example $3^2 + 4^2 = 5^2$.) He wrote that he had a remarkable proof for this for which there was no room in the margin. Whether or not Fermat actually had a proof remains exceedingly doubtful because no one has yet proved the theorem, although many erroneous proofs have been proposed in the intervening three centuries. The theorem *has* been proved for *certain* values of n including every value from 3 up to 25000.* Note also that if the theorem has been proved for any value of n it is automatically proved for all multiples of that value. For example, having proved the theorem for $n = 3$ it is automatically proved for $n = 6$. For if there *were* integers x, y, z satisfying $x^6 + y^6 = z^6$, then the integers x^2, y^2, z^2 would satisfy the relation $(x^2)^3 + (y^2)^3 = (z^2)^3$. Therefore, it would be sufficient to prove it for all prime exponents, but this has never been done. It is interesting to note that while the problem itself is not of great practical importance, the attempts to solve it have been the source of many important mathematical researches. Large prizes were once but are no longer offered for the solution of this problem. It remains an open question.

Pierre de Fermat
1601–1665, French

79. THE EUCLIDEAN ALGORITHM

Let a positive integer a be divided by a positive integer b, so that $a = bq + r$, where $0 \leqq r < b$.

Theorem 1. *Any common factor c of a and b is a factor of r.*

* See J. L. Selfridge, C. A. Nicol, and H. S. Vandiver, *Proc. Nat. Acad. Sci.*, Vol. 41, 1955, pp. 970–973, for proof up to 4002. See J. L. Selfridge and B. W. Pollack, Abstract No. 608–138, *Notices of the American Mathematical Society*, vol. 11, No. 1. Part 1, January 1964, page 97, for the announcement up to 25000.

Proof. By hypothesis, there exist positive integers x and y such that $a = cx$ and $b = cy$. Then $cx = cyq + r$, or $r = c(x - yq)$. Since $x - yq$ is an integer, c is a factor of r.

Theorem 2. *Any common factor d of b and r is a factor of a.*

Proof. By hypothesis, there exist positive integers u and v such that $b = du$ and $r = dv$. Then $a = duq + dv = d(uq + v)$. Hence, d is a factor of a.

Theorems 1 and 2 imply that *the highest common factor* (*H. C. F.*) *of a and b is also the highest common factor of b and r*. Given two positive integers a and b with $a > b$, their highest common factor may be found by means of the following process called the **Euclidean algorithm.**

Divide a by b obtaining

$$a = bq_1 + r_1 \qquad (0 \leqq r_1 < b). \tag{1}$$

If r_1 is positive, divide b by r_1, obtaining

$$b = r_1q_2 + r_2 \qquad (0 \leqq r_2 < r_1). \tag{2}$$

If r_2 is positive, divide r_1 by r_2, obtaining

$$r_1 = r_2q_3 + r_3 \qquad (0 \leqq r_3 < r_2). \tag{3}$$

If r_3 is positive, divide r_2 by r_3, obtaining

$$r_2 = r_3q_4 + r_4 \qquad (0 \leqq r_4 < r_3), \tag{4}$$

and so on until a remainder r_{n+1} equal to zero is reached; that is,

$$r_{n-1} = r_nq_{n+1}. \tag{5}$$

Theorem 3. *The last non-zero remainder r_n is the highest common factor of a and b.*

Proof. We know that the H. C. F. of a and b is equal to the H. C. F. of b and r_1 by (1). But (2) implies that the H. C. F. of b and r_1 is the H. C. F. of r_1 and r_2. And so on, until we conclude that the H. C. F. of a and b is the H. C. F. of r_{n-1} and r_n. But (5) shows that this is r_n itself since r_n is a factor of r_{n-1}.

Example. Find the H. C. F. of 78 and 144.

Solution. The successive divisions may be arranged compactly, as follows

```
      1
78)144
    78
   ---
         1
   66)78
      66
      --
           5
     12)66
        60
        --
             2
        6)12
          12
          --
           0
```

Therefore, 6 is the H. C. F. of 78 and 144.

Theorem 4. *If h is the H. C. F. of a and b, then there exist integers s and t such that* $h = sa + tb$.

Proof. Suppose, to simplify the discussion, that the euclidean algorithm terminates with $r_4 = 0$, so that $r_3 = h$. From (1), we have $r_1 = a - bq_1$. From (2),

$$r_2 = b - r_1 q_2 = b - (a - bq_1)q_2 = (-q_2)a + (1 + q_1 q_2)b.$$

From (3),

$$r_3 = r_1 - r_2 q_3 = (a - bq_1) - [(-q_2)a + (1 + q_1 q_2)b]\, q_3$$
$$= (1 + q_2 q_3)a + (-q_1 - q_3 - q_1 q_2 q_3)\, b.$$

Since the symbols in the parentheses in the last expression represent integers, we have $r_3 = sa + tb$. The proof for any value of n is similar.

Two different positive integers are termed **relatively prime** if and only if their H. C. F. is 1.

Theorem 5. *If a and b are relatively prime but a is a factor of bc, then a is a factor of c.*

Proof. Since the H. C. F. of a and b is 1, theorem 4 implies that there exist integers s and t such that $1 = sa + tb$. Multiplying both sides by c, we have $c = sac + tbc$. By hypothesis there exists an integer x such that $bc = ax$. Hence, $c = sac + tax = a(sc + tx)$. Hence a is a factor of c.

The proofs of theorems 6–8 are left as exercises.

Theorem 6. *If p is a prime and p is a factor of ab, where a and b are positive integers, then either p is a factor of a or p is a factor of b.*

Theorem 7. *If p is a prime and p is a factor of abc ... l, all letters representing positive integers, then p is a factor of at least one of the numbers a, b, c, ..., l.*

Theorem 8. *If p is a prime and p is a factor of abc ... l, where all letters represent primes, then p is equal to at least one of the numbers a, b, c, ..., l.*

Exercises

By means of the Euclidean algorithm, find the H. C. F. of each of the following pairs of numbers:

1. 60, 105.
2. 48, 576.
3. 36, 132.
4. 77, 400.
5. 91, 225.
6. 729, 147.
7. Prove theorem 6.
8. Prove theorem 7.
9. Prove theorem 8.
10. Prove that if a, b, c are positive integers and a and b are relatively prime and if a and b are both factors of c, then ab is a factor of c.

80. THE UNIQUE FACTORIZATION THEOREM

The following theorem is attributed to Euclid.

Theorem 1. *There are infinitely many primes.*

Proof. Suppose there were only a finite (limited) number of primes. Let all of them be 2, 3, 5, 7, ..., p where p is the largest of them. Consider the number $q = 2 \cdot 3 \cdot 5 \cdot 7 \cdots p + 1$. If q were prime, we would have a contradiction since $q > p$. If q is not prime, then it must have some factor other than 1 and itself and hence some prime factor. But none of the numbers 2, 3, 5, 7, ..., p is a factor of q, since, if q is divided by any of them, there is a remainder of 1. This contradicts the hypothesis that all prime numbers were included in the list 2, 3, 5, 7, ..., p.

All primes less than a given number may be found by a simple process called the **sieve of Eratosthenes** (Greek 275–194 B.C.), which we illustrate by finding all primes up to 60. Write all natural numbers up to 60:

2 3 ~~4~~ 5 ~~6~~ 7 ~~8~~ ~~9~~ ~~10~~ 11 ~~12~~ 13 ~~14~~ ~~15~~ ~~16~~
17 ~~18~~ 19 ~~20~~ ~~21~~ ~~22~~ 23 ~~24~~ ~~25~~ ~~26~~ ~~27~~ ~~28~~ 29 ~~30~~ 31
~~32~~ ~~33~~ ~~34~~ ~~35~~ ~~36~~ 37 ~~38~~ ~~39~~ ~~40~~ 41 ~~42~~ 43 ~~44~~ ~~45~~ ~~46~~
47 ~~48~~ ~~49~~ ~~50~~ ~~51~~ ~~52~~ 53 ~~54~~ ~~55~~ ~~56~~ ~~57~~ ~~58~~ 59 ~~60~~.

Then leave 2 but cross out every second number thereafter. Then leave the next uncrossed number, 3, but cross out every third number thereafter. Then leave the next uncrossed number, 5, but cross out every fifth number thereafter, and so on. The numbers remaining uncrossed at the end are primes.

Any positive integer n can be expressed as a product of prime factors. Arrange the prime numbers less than or equal to n (less than or equal to $\sqrt{n}$ will do; why?) in order of magnitude. Divide n by the first prime, 2, if possible. Then divide the quotient by 2 again if possible. Do this until the resulting quotient is not divisible by 2. Then try the next prime, 3, and so on. For example, $80 = 2 \cdot 2 \cdot 2 \cdot 2 \cdot 5 = 2^4 \cdot 5$; and $63 = 3 \cdot 3 \cdot 7 = 3^2 \cdot 7$.

The following so-called **unique factorization theorem** is fundamental to the study of the integers, called the theory of numbers or higher arithmetic.

Theorem 2. *Every integer x greater than 1 can be expressed as a product of primes in one and only one way, apart from the order of the factors.*

Proof. If p_1 is the smallest prime factor of x, we have $x = p_1 q$. If p_1 is a factor of the quotient $q = x/p_1$, then $q = p_1 q_1$ and $x = p_1 p_1 q_1$. When no more factors equal to p_1 can be thus split off, we proceed to the next larger prime factor p_2 of the quotient present at that stage. Thus we arrive at an expression $x = p_1 p_1 \cdots p_1 p_2 p_2 \cdots p_2 \cdots p_n$, or, if one prefers, $p_1^{a_1} p_2^{a_2} \cdots p_n^{a_n}$, where the p_1, $p_2, \ldots, p_n$ are distinct prime factors and $a_1, a_2, \ldots, a_n$ are positive integers.

We now prove that there cannot be two different such factorizations into primes apart from the order in which the factors are written. For, suppose that there were two. Let us write them as $c_1 c_2 \ldots c_h$ and $d_1 d_2 \ldots d_k$, where the primes $c_1, c_2, \ldots, c_h$, not necessarily all distinct, are written in order of magnitude, as are the primes $d_1, d_2, \ldots, d_k$. By theorem 8, section 79, every c_i is equal to some d_j and every d_i is equal to some c_j. Since x is given by

$$c_1 c_2 \cdots c_h = d_1 d_2 \cdots d_k,$$

the smallest prime factor c_1 of x must equal some d_i. Dividing both sides by c_1, we have, on renaming the d's, if necessary, x/c_1 given by

$$c_2 \cdots c_h = d_2 \cdots d_k.$$

Repeat this process of canceling the smallest present prime factor c_2 of x/c_1, and so on, until one side or the other is reduced to 1 by canceling all its prime factors. Then the other side must be 1 also and, hence, the numbers h and k of prime factors on both sides must have been the same and each factor on one side must have been equal to a factor on the other.

An immediate corollary is the following.

Theorem 3. *If a positive integer n is the product of prime factors p, q, r, ..., then n^2 is the product of the same prime factors, each occurring twice as often.*

Proof. If $n = p \cdot q \cdot r \cdots$, then $n^2 = p^2 \cdot q^2 \cdot r^2 \cdots$.

This enables us to give a rapid proof of the theorem that it is impossible that a rational number be a square root of 2. For, suppose p/q were such a rational number, where p and q are positive integers. Then $p^2/q^2 = 2$ or $p^2 = 2q^2$. By theorem 3, both p^2 and q^2 have 2 as a factor an even number of times, if at all. But then the right member $2q^2$ has 2 as a factor an odd number of times, while the left p^2 has it an even number of times. This contradicts theorem 2. A similar method now yields the more general theorems of exercises 10 and 12 below.

Exercises

1. Use the sieve of Eratosthenes to find all primes less than 100.

Find the prime factorization of each of the following:

2. 18. **3.** 110. **4.** 650. **5.** 720.
6. 812. **7.** 513. **8.** 585. **9.** 539.

★**10.** Prove that if a positive integer m is not the square of a positive integer, then $\sqrt{m}$ is not rational.

11. Prove that if a positive integer n is the product of prime factors $p, q, r, \ldots$, then n^k, where k is a positive integer, is the product of the same prime factors, each occuring k times as often.

★**12.** Prove that if a positive integer m is not the kth power of a positive integer, then $\sqrt[k]{m}$ is not rational. (Hint: use exercise 11.)

81. NETWORKS OR LINEAR GRAPHS

A **simple arc** PQ joining a pair of points P, Q is an arc having P and Q as endpoints and having no intersection with itself (Figs. 56, 57). The endpoints themselves are understood not to belong to the arc. If the endpoints coincide ($P = Q$), then the arc PQ is called a **loop** (Fig. 58).

By a **network**, or **linear graph**, or simply a **graph*** is meant a finite (limited) set of points in ordinary space called vertices, some pairs of which are joined by (simple) arcs† (Fig. 59).

The **degree** or **valence** of a vertex v is the number of arcs having v as an end-point. For example, in Fig. 59, the degree of P and R are 2 and 3, respectively. A loop is counted twice; the degree of Q is 3 in Fig. 59. That is, the degree of a vertex is the number of arcs emanating from it as counted by a myopic observer at the vertex.

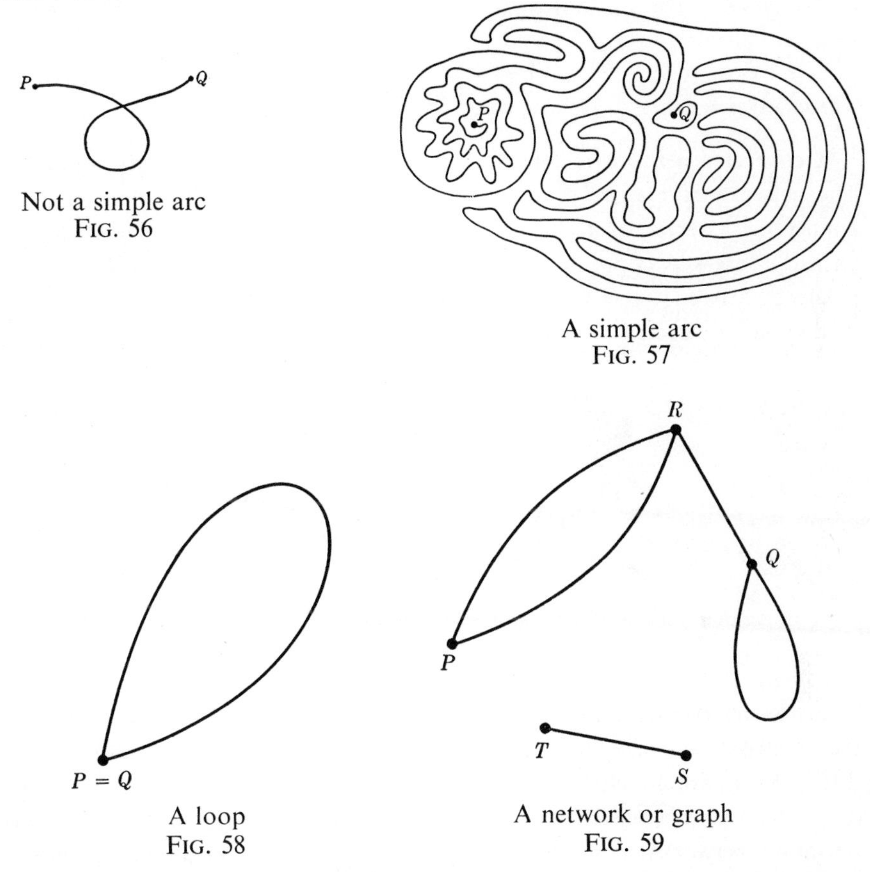

Not a simple arc
FIG. 56

A simple arc
FIG. 57

A loop
FIG. 58

A network or graph
FIG. 59

Two vertices P and Q of a network are said to be **connected** if there exists a succession of arcs beginning at P and ending at Q of which each consecutive pair have a common vertex. Thus, P and Q in Fig. 59 are connected but P and S are not.

* This should not be confused with the graph of an equation, a term in somewhat more common use.

† The terms nodes or points for vertices, and edges or links or lines for arcs are also used.

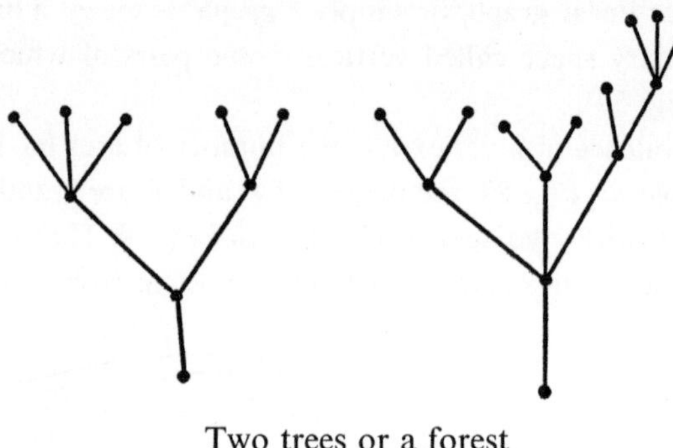

Two trees or a forest
FIG. 60

A **connected network** is a network in which every two vertices are connected. The network of Fig. 59 is not connected. A succession of distinct arcs thus connecting a vertex to itself is termed a **cycle**. If a network has no cycle, it is termed a **forest**. A connected forest, that is, a connected network with no cycle, is termed a **tree** (Fig. 60). If arrowheads are attached to the arcs of a network, it is termed a **directed** or **oriented network** (Fig. 61).

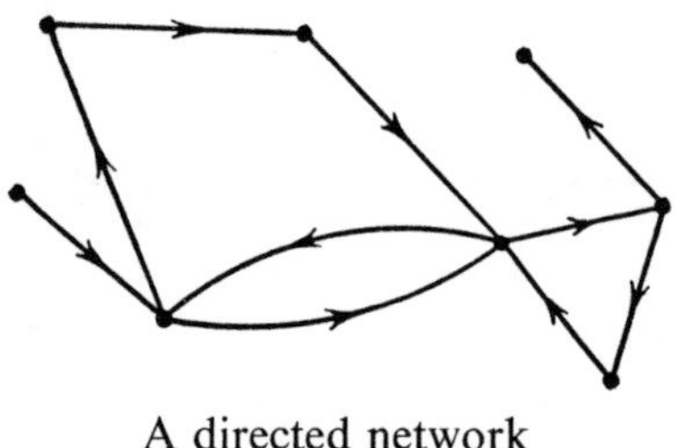

A directed network
FIG. 61

Any binary relation R (*section* 12) *may be represented by a directed network*; the elements involved are represented by vertices X, Y, Z, ... and we join X to Y by an arc directed from X to Y if XRY.

The theory of networks can be applied to problems of traffic flow and transportation networks, communication networks such as telephone systems or the nerve networks of animals, charts of organizations such as chains of command or channels of information flow in an army or corporation, charts of the interconnections of components of a complex machine like an electronic computer or a biological organism, graphs of the connections among the possible positions in a game like chess or tic-tac-toe, genealogical charts, graphs of preference orders (see chapter 18) such as "pecking orders" of chickens in a barnyard or dignitaries at a diplomatic party, the graphs of chemical isomers and many others.

Remark. Two graphs are called **isomorphic** if the vertices of one can be matched, one for one, with the vertices of the other, so that two vertices of one graph are joined by arc if and only if the matching vertices of the other graph are joined by an arc. The locations of the vertices and shapes of the arcs are irrelevant. Thus the graphs

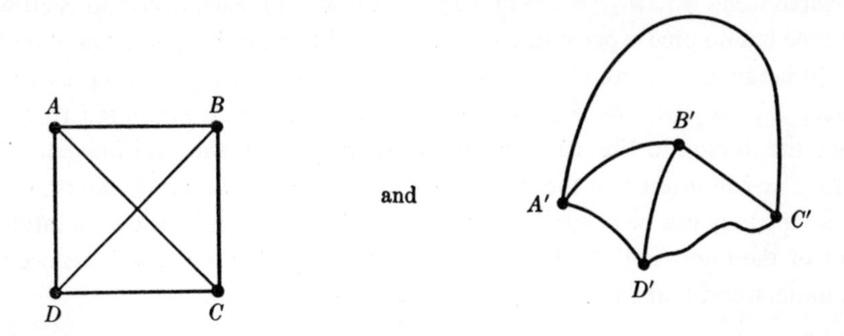

are isomorphic, each vertex of the left-hand one being matched with the one labeled with the same letter with prime attached in the right-hand one.

Exercises

1. Show that the sum of the degrees of all the vertices of any graph is even, and is twice the number of arcs.

2. Use the result of exercise 1 to show that a graph cannot have an odd number of vertices of odd degree.

3. Show that a tree with m arcs has $m + 1$ vertices.

4. (*a*) Draw a directed graph representing the binary relation $<$ for the numbers $\{1,2,3,4\}$, where each number in the set is represented by a vertex.

(*b*) Is the graph connected?

(*c*) Is it a tree?

5. (*a*) Draw a directed graph representing the binary relation x is a proper factor of y (that is, a factor other than 1 or y) for the set of numbers $\{2,3,4,5,6\}$.

(*b*) Is the graph connected?

(*c*) Is it a forest?

6. (*a*) Draw a directed graph whose 4 vertices represent the various subsets of a set $I = \{x,y\}$ with 2 elements, including $\varnothing$, and representing the binary relation $\subset$.

(*b*) Is it connected?

(*c*) Is it a tree?

7. Show that in any set of 6 people, either some trio are mutual acquaintances, or some trio are total strangers. (Hint: represent the people as vertices of a regular hexagon with all diagonals drawn. Color an arc of this graph with 6 vertices and 15 arcs black if the two people represented by its endpoints are acquainted, and grey if they are strangers. Then show that no matter in what way all the arcs are colored either black or grey there must be either a black triangle or a grey triangle.)*

8. Show that the statement of problem 7 would not be true for 5 people.

* A version of this problem appeared on the 1953 William Lowell Putnam Mathematical Competition. (Cf. *American Mathematical Monthly*, vol. 60 (1953), pp. 539–542.)

82. THREE HOUSES AND THREE WELLS

The following is a very familiar puzzle. There are three houses, H_1, H_2, H_3 and three wells W_1, W_2, W_3 (Fig. 62). We are to join each house to each well by a pipe but no pipe is permitted to cross any other pipe. Translated into mathematical language, we are to join each of the vertices H_1, H_2, H_3 to each of the vertices W_1, W_2, W_3 by a simple arc, no two arcs being permitted to cross. Hence the joining in Fig. 62 is *not* permissible. Experiments will indicate (Fig. 63) that we can insert 8 of the 9 arcs without crossings, but not the ninth. (Note that a pipe may not be passed under a house.) We will sketch below an intuitive proof of the impossibility of this problem. Some preliminaries will be needed. It is understood that the entire graph is to lie in one plane.

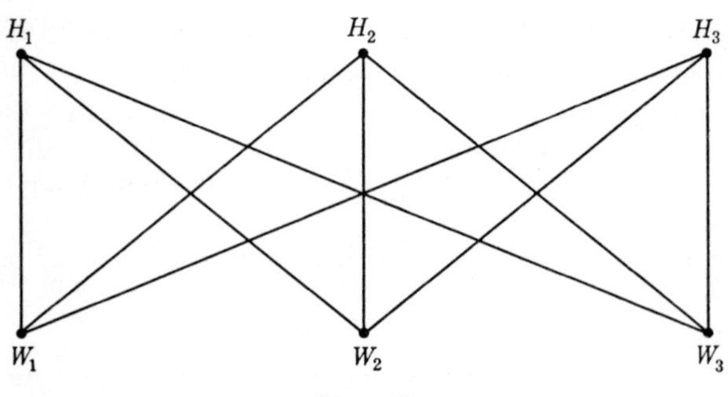

FIG. 62

Consider the figure consisting of a single vertex or point. Any connected network can be built up from this single vertex by a succession of the following two operations (see Figs. 64, 65, and 66):

(1) Adding a new vertex and joining it to an old vertex by a simple arc not crossing any existing arc, as in Fig. 65;

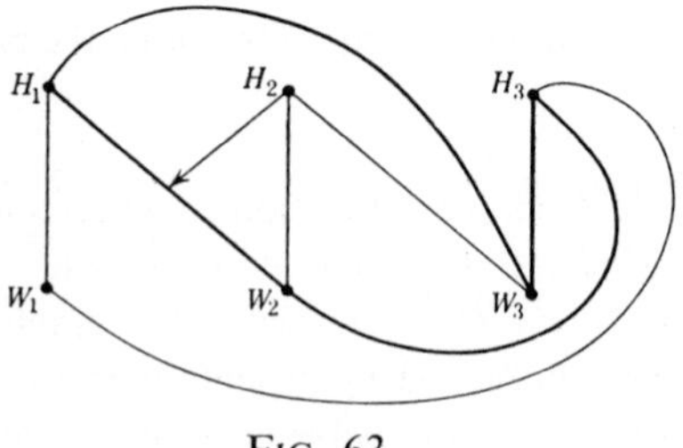

FIG. 63

(2) Joining two existing vertices by a new simple arc not crossing any existing arc, as in Fig. 66.

We have the following theorem due to Euler.

Theorem. *Let V be the number of vertices, and E the number of arcs in any connected network situated in a plane. If the network divides the plane into F regions, then $V - E + F = 2$.*

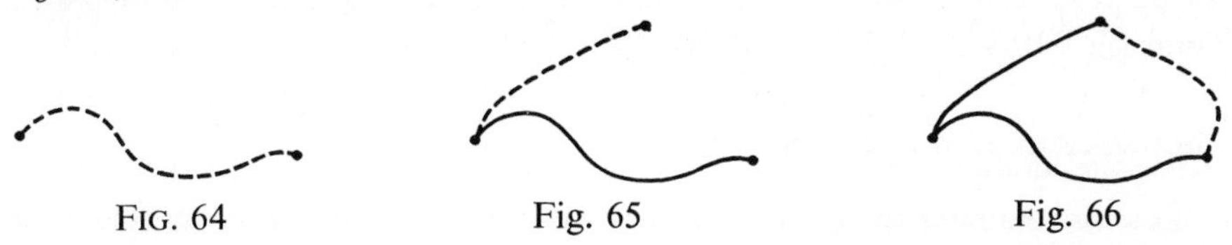

FIG. 64 Fig. 65 Fig. 66

For example, the single vertex has $V = 1$, $E = 0$, $F = 1$, and the network in Fig. 64 has $V = 2$, $E = 1$, and $F = 1$ since it "divides" the plane into one region, that is, leaves the plane undivided; clearly, $2 - 1 + 1 = 2$, The network in Fig. 65 has $V = 3$, $E = 2$, $F = 1$; obviously $3 - 2 + 1 = 2$. The network in Fig. 66 has $V = 3$, $E = 3$, and $F = 2$ since it divides the plane into two regions, an inside and an outside. In the network of Fig. 67, before inserting the dotted arc AB by means of operation (1) and the dotted arcs CD and EF by means of operation (2), we have $V = 8$, $E = 10$, $F = 4$, and $8 - 10 + 4 = 2$. After inserting the dotted arcs we have $V = 9$, $E = 13$, $F = 6$ and $9 - 13 + 6 = 2$.

To prove the above theorem we reason as follows. The single vertex, like the network of Fig. 64, clearly yields 2 as the value of the expression $V - E + F$. But every connected network can be built up from this one by means of operations (1) and (2), in the plane. Now operation (1) cannot alter the value of $V - E + F$ since it leaves F unchanged but increases V by one and E by one, and V and E have opposite signs. Similarly, operation (2) leaves the value of $V - E + F$ unaltered since it leaves V unchanged but increases E by 1 and clearly increases F by 1; but E and F have opposite signs. It follows that every connected network must have the same value for $V - E + F$ as the network of Fig. 64, namely 2. This completes the proof of Euler's theorem.

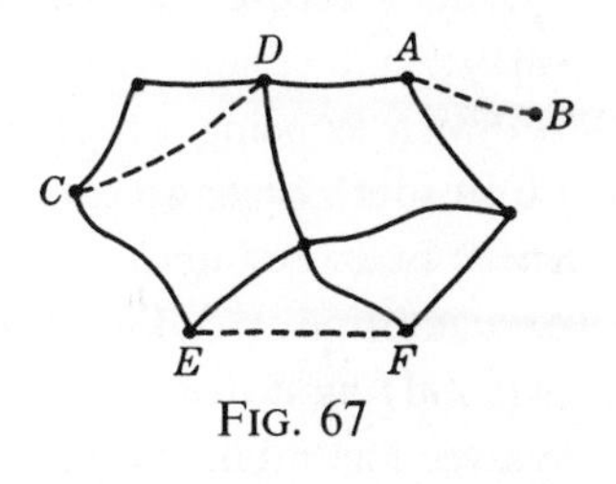

FIG. 67

We are now in a position to establish that the 3 houses and 3 wells puzzle is impossible, by means of an indirect proof (*reductio ad absurdum*). Suppose it were possible. Then we would have a network in the plane with 6 vertices and 9 arcs. That is, $V = 6$, and $E = 9$. From Euler's theorem we have $6 - 9 + F = 2$; hence $F = 5$. Inspection of Fig. 62 reveals that there are no three vertices each pair of which are joined by an arc; that is, there are no "triangular" regions. That is, there are no regions bounded by exactly 3 arcs. Similarly, inspection reveals that there are no regions bounded by exactly 2 arcs; that is, there is no pair of vertices joined by exactly 2 arcs. Therefore each region must be bounded by at least 4 arcs. Since there are 5 regions, we might now be tempted to think that there must be at least $4 \cdot 5 = 20$ arcs; but this would be wrong because each arc is on the boundary of exactly two regions and has therefore been counted twice. It *is* correct, however, to say that there must be at least half of $4 \cdot 5$ arcs, or at least 10 arcs. This contradicts the hypothesis that our network is to have exactly 9 arcs. Since our supposition that the problem is possible leads to a contradiction, it must be impossible.

Exercise. Imitating the proof in the preceding paragraph as far as possible, show that it is impossible to join each of the five vertices of a pentagon to every other vertex by simple arcs (in a plane) which do not cross each other. (Hint: if it could be done there would be a network with $V = 5$, $E = 10$. See Fig. 68.)

A remarkable and difficult theorem proved by Kuratowski in 1930 asserts that any network which cannot be drawn in a plane, without crossings, must contain in it either the network of Fig. 62 or that of Fig. 68.

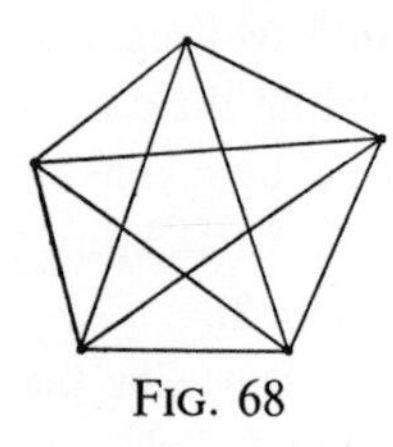

FIG. 68

While *our* interest in networks has been due to a mere puzzle, it is worth remarking that networks were studied by Kirchoff to good advantage in connection with his work of electrical circuits (1874).

Euler's theorem applies equally well to a connected network drawn on the surface of a sphere. If one thinks of the part of the plane in which our network is drawn as being a square sheet of rubber on which we place a sphere, resting on its south pole, we can stretch the rubber sheet over the surface of the sphere and "button it up" at the north pole, without altering the numbers V, E, F. Now imagine an ordinary polyhedron (like a cube, or a pyramid) made of rubber and placed within a glass sphere. The rubber polyhedron can be blown up until it clings to the inner surface of the glass sphere. Then the vertices, edges, and faces of the polyhedron appear as vertices, arcs, and regions of a network on the sphere. Hence, for any polyhedron which can be so deformed into a sphere we have $V - E + F = 2$ where V is the number of vertices, E the number of edges, and F the number of faces. For example, a cube has 8 vertices, 12 edges, and 6 faces, and $8 - 12 + 6 = 2$. Euler's theorem is *not* true for networks drawn on the surface of a doughnut or inner tube, for example. Therefore, the corresponding theorem for polyhedra like that of a picture frame (Fig. 69), which could be placed within

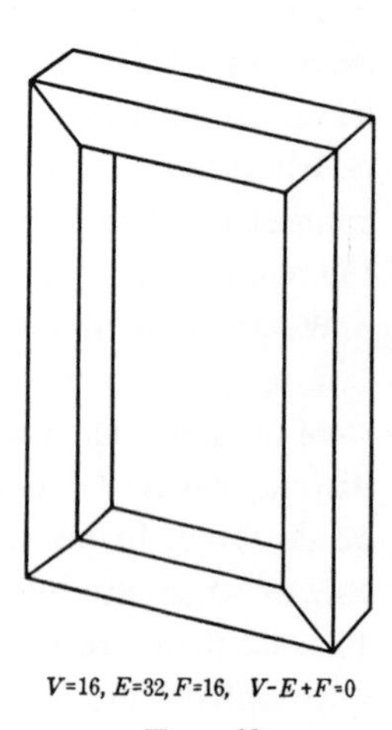

FIG. 69

an inner tube and blown up as above, is no longer true. For such networks or polyhedra we have $V - E + F = 0$. Other surfaces yield different values for the number $V - E + F$.

83. THE SEVEN BRIDGES OF KÖNIGSBERG

The city of Königsberg, in the eighteenth century, had 7 bridges situated as in Fig. 70. The problem is: can a pedestrian cross all 7 bridges without crossing any one of them twice? The pedestrian may start anywhere and finish anywhere. This problem was solved in 1736 by Euler, who proved it impossible.

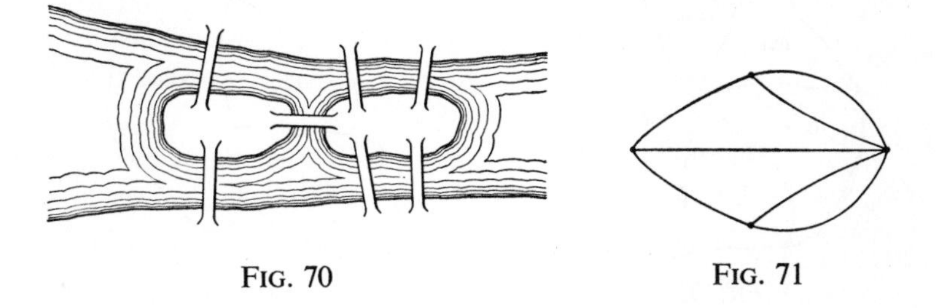

FIG. 70 FIG. 71

The problem may be studied as follows: choose one point or vertex on each island and on each shore and join these vertices by arcs across the bridges. We get thus the figure in Fig. 71, consisting of 4 points joined by 7 arcs. The question becomes: can we trace these arcs with a pencil without lifting the pencil from the paper and without tracing any arc twice. Many problems of this nature appear in our newspapers. They may be settled as follows. A vertex is called **even** or **odd** according as it has an even or odd number of arcs emanating from it. Then it is not hard to prove that a figure can be traversed exactly once, as required above, if and only if the number of odd vertices is either 0 or 2. In fact, if the number of odd vertices is zero, then we may start at any vertex and end at the same place; if the number of odd vertices is 2, we may start at one of them and end at the other. Thus the figure in Fig. 72 can be traversed exactly once beginning at the odd vertex A and ending at the odd vertex B. Try to see why this is so. The bridge problem above is an impossibility, and not an open question, since there are 4 odd vertices. Further details may be found in the references.

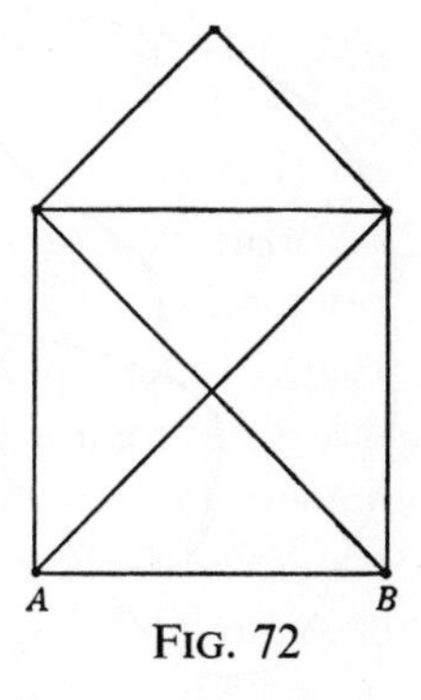

FIG. 72

84. THE FOUR-COLOR PROBLEM

The following problem might have originated in a printing shop which made colored maps. Suppose we agree to color every map according to the following rules:

(1) If two countries have a strip of boundary in common they *must* have different colors;

(2) If two countries have only isolated points of boundary in common they *may* have the same color.

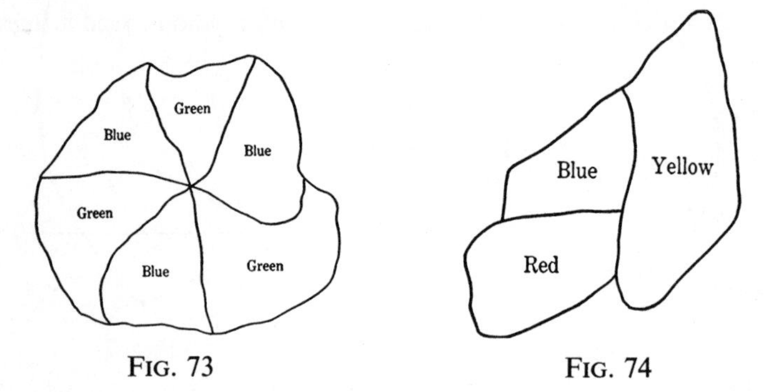

FIG. 73

FIG. 74

Each country is understood to be in one connected piece. For example, the coloring of Fig. 73 is permissible. Notice that the map in Fig. 73 cannot be colored with less than 2 colors. The map in Fig. 74 *requires* 3 colors. The map in Fig. 75 *requires* 4 colors. The problem is: does there exist a map which *requires* 5 colors? Or to put it another way: *can* every map be colored with only 4 colors? This problem can be traced back to about 1840. Many people have proposed proofs that every map can be colored with 4 colors; all these proofs have been erroneous. It *has* been proved that every map can be colored with 5 colors, but no one has ever produced a map that really *required* 5 colors; all known maps, at the present writing, *can* be colored with only 4 colors. Whether the number is 4 or 5 remains an open question today. Curious partial results have been proven. For example, it has been proved recently that if there

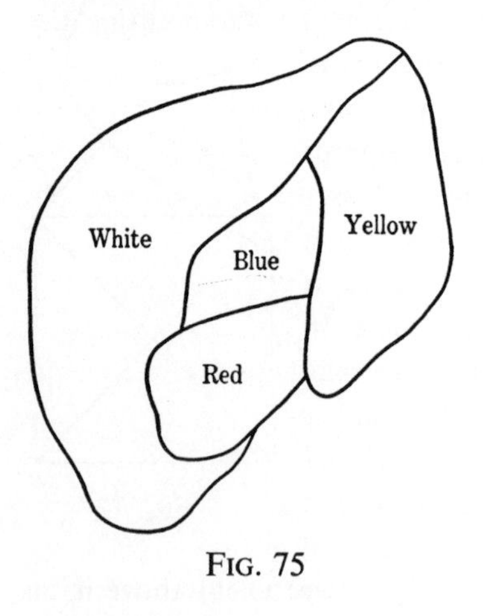

FIG. 75

were a map requiring 5 colors it would have to have at least 36 countries on it. The problem has an extensive literature. It can be converted into a problem about networks in a plane by the following device. Choose a capital city in each country and join each pair of capital cities of adjacent countries (i.e., countries with a common border line) by a railroad line crossing the common border. Represent each capital city by a vertex and each railroad line by an arc. We then

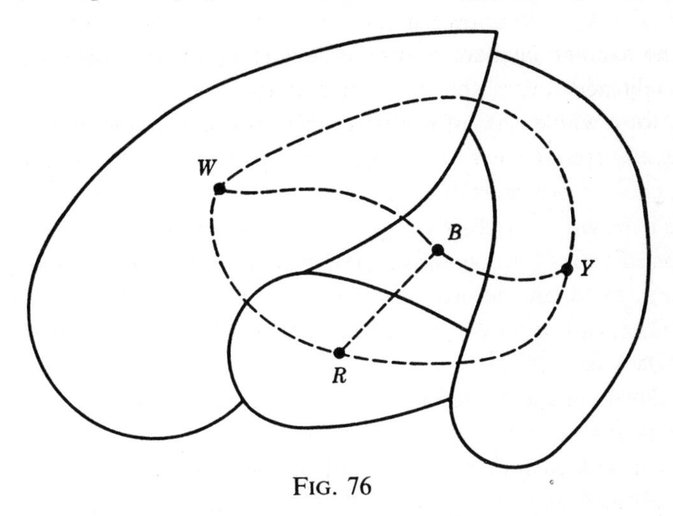

FIG. 76

get a network. For example, the map of Fig. 75 or 76 yields the network of Fig. 77. The problem becomes that of coloring the vertices of the network so that no two adjacent vertices (i.e., vertices joined by an arc) have the same color.

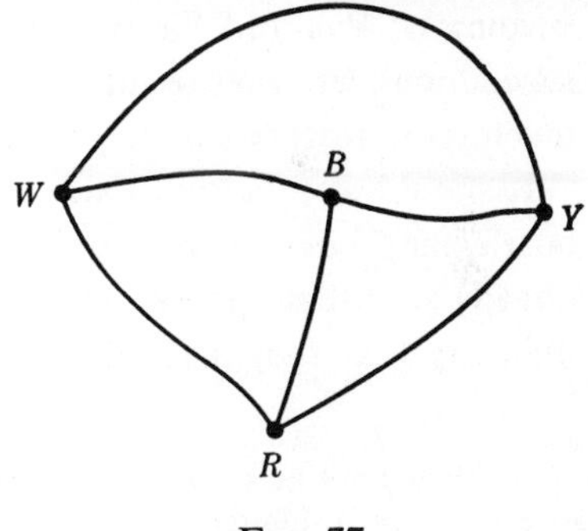

FIG. 77

Exercise. Show that in a plane there cannot exist 5 countries such that every pair are adjacent. (Hint: use the "railroad" construction of the preceding paragraph to produce a network with 5 vertices and 10 edges. Then use the exercise of section 82. Note that this result does not settle the four-color conjecture.)

85. PUZZLES

Many of the problems mentioned in this chapter are of interest only as puzzles rather than because of any practical value. As we pointed out before, this is partly because unsolved problems of practical value would be too technical to discuss here. One should not get the impression that mathematicians concern themselves exclusively with problems like those in this chapter. In fact, a student who brings a puzzle to his teacher is frequently met with rebuff. This is often due to the fact that most puzzles which circulate among laymen either depend on a play of words or joke of some sort, or, if legitimate, are easily soluble by well-known mathematical methods. For the mathematician, unlike the average layman, is not content to solve an individual puzzle; he immediately generalizes the problem and tries to find a general method of solution for a whole class of similar problems. For example, Euler did not stop with the solution of the Königsberg bridge problem but found the solution of a whole class of problems of that sort.

While it would be frightfully wrong to regard mathematics as nothing but a collection of tricks for solving puzzles, an unfortunate impression which some students seem to get, nevertheless there is something to be said for the lowly puzzle. There can be no doubt that the personal satisfaction derived from a successful attack on a puzzle is a universal and human emotion. In fact, the somewhat childish "I-can-do-something-you-can't-do" spirit may have stimulated mathematical research considerably.* For example, during the 16th and 17th centuries it was customary for a mathematician who had solved a new and difficult problem to withhold his method of solution and challenge all comers to solve the problem. This custom led to many entertainingly undignified and often violent disputes, but it also served to stimulate other mathematicians who frequently advanced the progress of mathematics by their efforts. In modern times, however, new results are published for all to read; this seems to be a much more mature way to cooperate for the advancement of science.

It should also be said that even the lowliest and most unimportant looking puzzle may possibly lead to general and important considerations. We have already seen that apparently simple problems have led to mathematics of such difficulty that they are still unsolved. In any case, much ingenuity has been

* It should not be supposed, however, that mathematicians are *never* actuated by a pure love of science. A. Einstein says in his prologue to M. Planck's *Where is Science Going?* (Norton, N. Y., 1932): "Many kinds of men devote themselves to science, and not all for the sake of science herself. There are some who come to her temple because it offers them the opportunity to display their particular talents. To this class of men science is a kind of sport in the practice of which they exult, just as an athlete exults in the exercise of his muscular prowess. There is another class of men who come into the temple to make an offering of their brain pulp in the hope of securing a profitable return. . . . Should an angel of God descend and drive from the Temple of Science all those who belong to the categories I have mentioned, I fear the temple would be nearly emptied. But a few worshippers would still remain—some from former times and some from ours."

expended on what may be called mathematical amusements or recreations. Hosts of people have found in mathematical puzzles and in mathematics in general a never-failing source of enjoyment. As a hobby, mathematics has the very desirable characteristic of being inexhaustible. For even if you were to solve all the problems in existence at the moment (an unlikely eventuality), you could proceed to invent more problems for yourself.

References

Numbers refer to the bibliography in the back of the book.

Arnold 6
Avondo-Bodino 11
Ball 12, 13
Bell 16
Berge 24
Cajori 46, 47
de Morgan 63
Eves 70
Flament 76
Ford and Fulkerson 77
Harary, Norman, and Cartwright 91
Hobson 94
Jones 100
Kasner and Newman 103
Kemeny and Snell 106
Klein 116
Newman 140
Niven 141
Ore 143, 144, 145
Rademacher and Toeplitz 152
Seshu and Reed 174
Smith 180, 181
Stein 185
Steinhaus 186
Tucker and Bailey 193
Young 216

9
Analytic Geometry

86. INTRODUCTION

The geometry of the ancient Greeks was the outstanding scientific achievement of the human race up to their time and for hundreds of years thereafter. The long period called the Dark Ages began, so far as mathematics is concerned, roughly with the fall of Greek civilization. The Romans, pre-occupied with military conquest, governmental affairs, and the acquisition of riches, contributed nothing to the progress of science. In 529 A.D., the emperor Justinian expressed his disapproval of heathen learning by closing the schools at Athens. Europe, for roughly a thousand years, preserved in its monasteries barely enough science, and that often copied rather than understood, to calculate the calendar in order to ascertain the dates of religious holidays. Not only were no improvements made in mathematics but the excellent work of the Greeks was forgotten or degraded throughout Europe. Only the Arabs kept alive an interest in science and they preserved much of the Greek work together with Hindu arithmetic during these centuries. With the beginning of the Renaissance, progress in mathematics revived along with progress in other fields. The algebra we have studied was developed largely from the thirteenth century to the first years of the seventeenth century, its slow advance suffering long interruptions due to frequent periods of war and religious strife.

Yet, almost miraculously, the thread of science has persisted through the centuries, often disappearing almost entirely. To be sure, much ancient work has been lost. A considerable number of Greek works were destroyed, for example, in the tragic burning of the great library at Alexandria, containing hundreds of thousands of books collected for many centuries, in the seventh century A.D. by the Mohammedan conquerors. Their leader is said to have held that if the books disagreed with the Koran they lied and should be destroyed whereas if they agreed with the Koran they were superfluous. The books were therefore burned to heat water for the soldiers' baths. This was more serious than similar modern instances of religious, racial, and nationalistic intolerance since it occurred before the invention of the printing press, so that few, if any, copies of any given work could be expected to exist. The early Mohammedans were not the first to damage the treasures of the Alexandrian library; they were merely the last and possibly the most thorough. The library had been subjected to vandalism before by other zealots. Fortunately, copies of some Greek masterpieces remained unharmed, sometimes in remote places. One of Archimedes' works, for example, was found at Constantinople as recently as 1906 by Heiberg.

René Descartes
1596–1650, French

The fifteenth and sixteenth centuries saw the invention of the printing press, the circumnavigation of the earth, and the beginning of the struggle against dogmatism and repressive authority. The Renaissance, in all its phases, got fairly under way. With the seventeenth century, there began a period of tremendous mathematical activity which is still in progress today. A great deal of modern mathematics has its roots in the seventeenth century and came to flower in the eighteenth and nineteenth centuries. The feats of engineering, the wonders of mathematical physics and astronomy, the manifold applications of mathematics to the field of statistics, all of which are so commonplace today, were made possible by mathematical researches which began in the seventeenth century.

Until the seventeenth century, geometry had been thought of as dealing with figures in space and algebra as dealing with numbers, and no one had thought of studying geometry systematically by means of algebra. In the first half of the seventeenth century, however, several people, notably Descartes and Fermat, saw that geometric theorems could be interpreted algebraically, and that algebraic theorems could be interpreted geometrically. In 1637, Descartes published a famous work on geometry in which he studied with great ease, by his algebraic methods, geometrical problems which demanded the greatest ingenuity when attacked solely with the purely geometrical methods of the Greeks. This so-called *analytic geometry*, *coordinate geometry*, or *Cartesian geometry* was part of the foundation on which the calculus of Newton and Leibniz was reared in the latter half of the seventeenth century. In fact, it may be said to mark a turning point in the development of mathematics. Its importance lies in the fact that it unifies algebra and geometry. Let us see how this union of algebra and geometry was accomplished.

Since elementary algebra is principally concerned with numbers (or expressions involving numbers) and geometry deals chiefly with points (or figures composed of points), it is natural to expect the union of the two subjects to be achieved by somehow associating points with numbers. This is done essentially by attaching to each point at least one label, each label consisting of one or more numbers. The numbers composing a label attached to a given point are called **coordinates** of the point. When we have attached such numerical coordinates to all our points in any way whatever we say that we have set up a **coordinate system** in our geometry. Such an association or correspondence between numerical labels and points may be made in any manner whatever; but if it is to be useful, a coordinate system should have certain regular properties. For example, if P and Q are different points, no label attached to P should be exactly the same as any label attached to Q. Also, if two points are near to each other, they should have coordinates which do not differ very much. In setting up such a coordinate system we can hardly meander about tying labels to points in a haphazard way, one point at a time. Hence we use some device or scheme which enables us to attach coordinates to all points in a systematic way, so that we can determine the coordinates of any given point or the point having any given coordinates easily. Hence we may identify any point by means of its numerical coordinates or label. Some of the usual schemes for doing this will now be taken up.

87. ONE-DIMENSIONAL GEOMETRY

Consider a single straight line. We have already seen how we can associate a real number with every point on it, after having chosen a starting point or origin, a unit of length, and a positive direction. It is customary to assign positive numbers to the right side of the line.* The real number attached to a given point is called its **coordinate**. To each point on the line there corresponds a definite real number and to each real number there corresponds a definite point on the line. This *one-to-one correspondence* between real numbers and

* If you turn the page upside down, or stand on your head, the "right" side becomes the "left." This cannot affect the geometry of the figures we study since the figures are surely unconcerned about our posture.

points on the line is called a **one-dimensional coordinate system**, *one*-dimensional because each point is associated with a *single* number. If we had chosen a different point as origin, or a different unit of length, or a different positive direction, we would have obtained a different one-dimensional coordinate system for the same line.

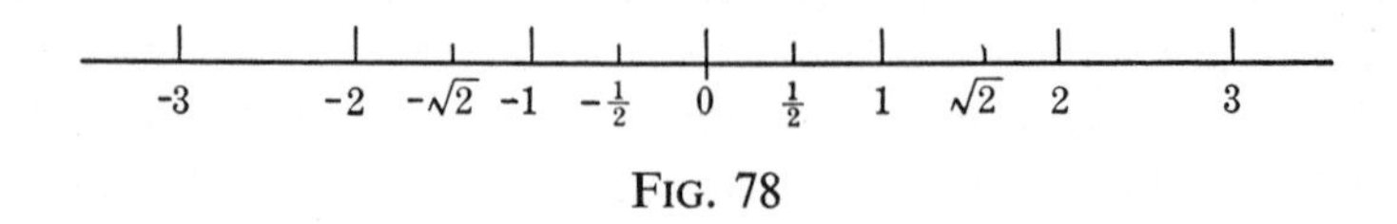

FIG. 78

Let us choose a definite one-dimensional coordinate system on our line. The distance from the origin to the point whose coordinate is 3 is 3. The distance from the origin to the point whose coordinate is -3 is also 3, since distance is always understood to be a positive number. By the **absolute value** of the real number x we mean x itself if x is not negative, or the positive number $-x$ if x is negative. We denote the absolute value of x by $|x|$. For example, $|3| = 3$ and $|-3| = 3$. **The distance from the origin of the point whose coordinate is x is $|x|$.**

The distance between the points whose coordinates are 1 and 3, respectively, is $|1 - 3| = |-2| = 2$. The distance between the points whose coordinates are -1 and -3, respectively, is $|(-1) - (-3)| = |2| = 2$. The distance between the points whose coordinates are 1 and -3, respectively, is $|1 - (-3)| = |4| = 4$. We could prove the following theorem.

Theorem 1. *The distance between two points P_1 and P_2 the coordinates of which are x_1 and x_2, respectively, is $|x_1 - x_2|$.*

This theorem may also be stated as follows: *the distance between the points P_1 and P_2 whose coordinates are x_1 and x_2, respectively, is whichever of the two numbers $x_1 - x_2$ or $x_2 - x_1 = -(x_1 - x_2)$ happens to be positive.* If the point with coordinate x_1 is to the right of the point with coordinate x_2, then $x_1 - x_2$ is positive. *Another way to indicate $|x_1 - x_2|$ symbolically is $\sqrt{(x_1 - x_2)^2}$*, since we have agreed that the radical sign denotes the positive square root, whenever possible. For example,

$$|(-3) - (-1)| = \sqrt{[(-3) - (-1)]^2} = \sqrt{[-2]^2} = 2.$$

Let x_1 and x_2 be the coordinates of two different points. Let x' be the coordinate of their midpoint; that is, the point midway between them. Then

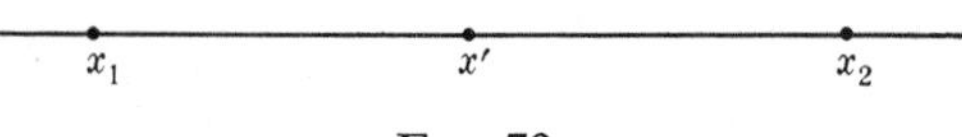

FIG. 79

either $x_1 < x' < x_2$ or $x_1 > x' > x_2$. Suppose the first case holds (Fig. 79). Then $x' - x_1$, being positive, is the distance between those two points, and $x_2 - x'$, being positive, is the distance between these two points. But x' is the midpoint. Hence we must have

$$x' - x_1 = x_2 - x'. \tag{1}$$

Hence,

$$x' + x' = x_1 + x_2$$

or

$$2x' = x_1 + x_2.$$

Finally,

$$x' = \frac{x_1 + x_2}{2}.$$

Exercise. The other case, where x_1, x', x_2 are in order from right to left, proceeds similarly. Give the proof for this case.

We have the following theorem.

Theorem 2. *The coordinate x' of the midpoint between the points the coordinates of which are x_1 and x_2 is given by $x' = \frac{1}{2}(x_1 + x_2)$; that is, it is the average of the given coordinates.*

For example, the coordinate of the midpoint between the points whose coordinates are 5 and (-3) is $[5 + (-3)]/2 = 1$.

Exercises

Find (a) the distance between the points whose coordinates are given: (b) the coordinate of their midpoint:

1. 7 and 5. **2.** 8 and -2. **3.** -3 and -7. **4.** 2 and 8.
5. -3 and 7. **6.** -7 and -1. **7.** 8 and 0. **8.** -6 and 0.
9. 5 and 2. **10.** -5 and 8.

11. The point whose coordinate is 2 is the midpoint between the point whose coordinate is -3 and another point. Find the coordinate of the other point.

12. If particles with positive weights w_1 and w_2 are placed at the points P_1 and P_2 with coordinates x_1 and x_2 respectively (Fig. 79), then the point P with coordinate $\bar{x} = \dfrac{w_1x_1 + w_2x_2}{w_1 + w_2}$ is called the **centroid** (or **center of gravity**) of the two particles.* The centroid is the point at which to place the fulcrum or balancing point of a lever or seesaw or teeterboard in order to balance these weights.

* The number $\bar{x}$ is called the **weighted average** or **weighted arithmetic mean** of x_1, x_2 with weights w_1, w_2. Compare section 163.

(*a*) Show that the centroid divides the line-segment P_1P_2 in the ratio w_2/w_1; that is, $\dfrac{\bar{x} - x_1}{x_2 - \bar{x}} = \dfrac{w_2}{w_1}$, and conversely.

(*b*) Show that the centroid is the midpoint of P_1P_2 if the weights are equal.

(*c*) If a weight of 60 pounds is put at one end of a seesaw 8 feet long and a 100-pound weight is put at the other end, where should the fulcrum be placed so that they will balance?

(*d*) If the fulcrum of a lever is 6 inches from the end at which a 100-pound weight is attached, how far from the fulcrum must a 30-pound weight be placed in order to balance it?

13. If particles with non-negative weights $w_1, w_2, \ldots, w_n$, not all zero, are placed at the points with coordinates $x_1, x_2, \ldots, x_n$, respectively, the point with coordinate $\bar{x} = \dfrac{w_1x_1 + w_2x_2 + \cdots + w_nx_n}{w_1 + w_2 + \cdots + w_n}$ is called the **centroid** of the system.

(*a*) Find the centroid of the system of weights 5, 10, 20 placed at the points with coordinates -20, 20, 10, respectively.

(*b*) A 40-pound boy sits at the end of a 12-foot seesaw and a 60-pound boy sits 3 feet away from him nearer the fulcrum, which is located at the middle of the seesaw. How heavy must a boy be to balance them by sitting at the other end of the seesaw?

14. Prove that $|x + y| \leqq |x| + |y|$ if x and y are any real numbers. (Hint: divide the proof into cases according as the numbers are positive, negative or zero.)

15. Prove that if x, y, z, are any real numbers then $|x - y| + |y - z| \geqq |x - z|$. (Hint: use exercise 14.)

88. TWO-DIMENSIONAL GEOMETRY

We now turn to plane geometry with which we shall be occupied for most of this chapter. We may introduce coordinates into the plane as follows.

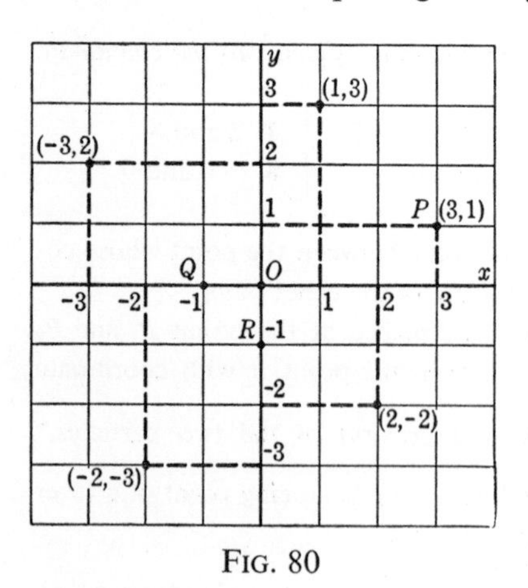

FIG. 80

Choose two perpendicular lines and a unit of length. Call one of the lines the ***x*-axis** and the other the ***y*-axis**, and call their point of intersection the **origin**. Choose a positive direction on each of the axes and, by means of the chosen unit of length, set up a one-dimensional coordinate system on each axis. It is customary to consider the x-axis horizontal and the y-axis vertical, and their positive directions as being to the right and up, respectively,* as in Fig. 80. Now

* See footnote on page 257.

consider any point P in the plane. Draw a line through P perpendicular to the x-axis. The number attached to the point on the x-axis where this perpendicular meets it is called the **x-coordinate** or **abscissa** of P. Similarly, draw a line through P perpendicular to the y-axis; the number attached to the point on the y-axis where this perpendicular meets it is called the **y-coordinate** or **ordinate** of P. Thus the abscissa of the point P in Fig. 80 is 3 and its ordinate is 1; *we indicate these facts briefly by writing that the coordinates of P are* (3,1), *writing the x-coordinate first*. Thus the coordinates of Q in Fig. 80 are $(-1,0)$, the coordinates of R are $(0,-1)$, and the coordinates of the origin are (0,0). Clearly, each point in the plane has a definite pair of coordinates, and every pair of real numbers determines a definite point in the plane. This *one-to-one correspondence* between the points of the plane and ordered pairs of numbers (x,y) is called a **two-dimensional coordinate system**, *two*-dimensional because each point is identified by an *ordered pair* of real numbers. If we had chosen a different pair of axes, or a different unit of length, or different positive directions, we would have obtained a different two-dimensional coordinate system for the same plane. In most of this chapter we shall suppose that we have chosen a definite two-dimensional coordinate system. We shall speak loosely of the point (x,y) or the point (2,3),

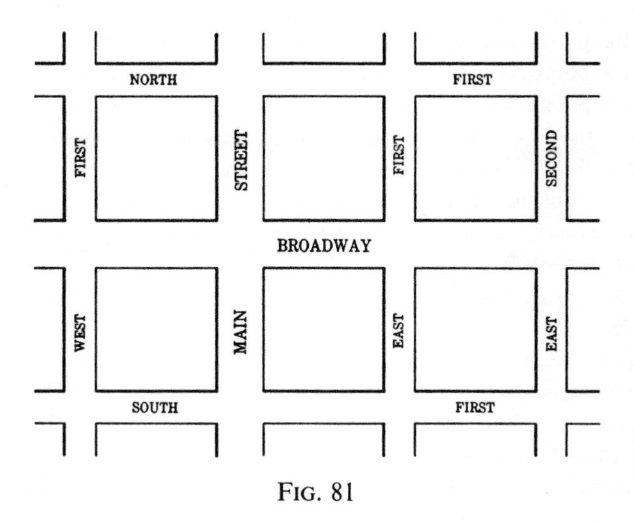

FIG. 81

meaning the point whose coordinates are (x,y) or (2,3), respectively. Lines parallel to the x-axis are called **horizontal** and lines parallel to the y-axis are called **vertical**. A line which is neither horizontal nor vertical is called **oblique**.

The idea of coordinates introduced here is nothing but a systematization of the way in which we might locate a certain corner in a city with rectangular streets, such as the corner of East 2nd St. and South 1st St. To reach this corner from Main and Broadway, we go 2 blocks east and 1 block south. Similarly, to say that the coordinates of a point are $(2, -1)$ means that to reach it, starting from the origin, we must proceed 2 units in the direction of the positive side of the x-axis and then 1 unit in the direction of the negative side of the y-axis. Marking a point with given coordinates is called **plotting** the point.

In this simple idea of coordinates we have the germ of the unification of geometry and algebra. Although geometry may be concerned with points and algebra with numbers, we have now identified each point in the plane with an ordered pair of numbers and conversely. It remains now to exploit and develop this idea. In particular, we shall see how various geometric concepts can be translated into algebraic terms, by means of this simple device of coordinates, and studied by algebraic means. It may be difficult to see how so simple a notion can lead to anything important. This, however, can be said of many great scientific ideas. It takes insight and imagination to see in a simple idea its implications and potentialities.

Remark. Squared graph paper will be useful for the exercises in this chapter. A diagram should be made for each exercise.

Exercises

1. Plot the points whose coordinates are $(1,2)$, $(2,1)$, $(-1,2)$, $(2,-1)$, $(-2, -1)$.

2. Plot the points whose coordinates are $(3,2)$, $(2,3)$, $(3,-2)$, $(-3,2)$, $(-3,-2)$.

3. Plot the points whose coordinates are $(3,0)$, $(0,3)$, $(-3,0)$, $(0,-3)$, $(0,0)$.

4. What is the y-coordinate of any point on the x-axis?

5. What is the x-coordinate of any point on the y-axis?

6. What are the coordinates of the origin?

7. If two points are on the same vertical line what can be said about their x-coordinates?

8. If two points are on the same horizontal line, what can be said about their y-coordinates?

9. A square has its center at the origin. (The center of a square is the point at which its diagonals interesect.) The sides of the square are parallel to the x- and y-axes, respectively. If one of the vertices of the square is the point $(3,3)$, find the coordinates of each of the other three vertices.

10. A rectangle has vertices at $(0,0)$, $(5,0)$, $(0,3)$. Find the coordinates of the fourth vertex.

89. OTHER TYPES OF COORDINATE SYSTEMS

The two-dimensional coordinate systems introduced into the plane in the preceding section are known as **rectangular coordinate systems** because the axes are perpendicular. We digress for a moment to point out that other types of

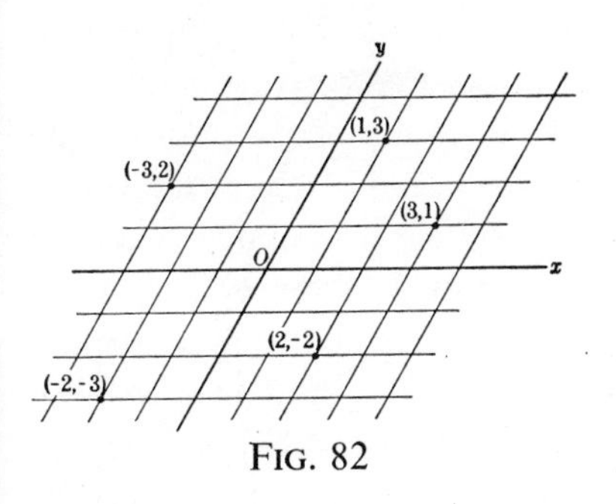

FIG. 82

coordinates can be used. For example, we might use what are called **oblique** coordinate axes as in Fig. 82.

Or, instead of saying that a certain point may be reached by proceeding 1 mile east and 1 mile north (rectangular coordinates), we might say walk at an angle of 45° between north and east for a distance of $\sqrt{2} = 1.414 \ldots$ miles (Fig. 83). This would be most natural in open country, for example. This suggests that any point in the plane can be specified by stating the angle A (measured in the counter-clockwise direction, say) with a chosen fixed direction, and the distance r to be traversed from the origin O, or starting point, in the direction given by the angle (Fig. 84). If we specify our points

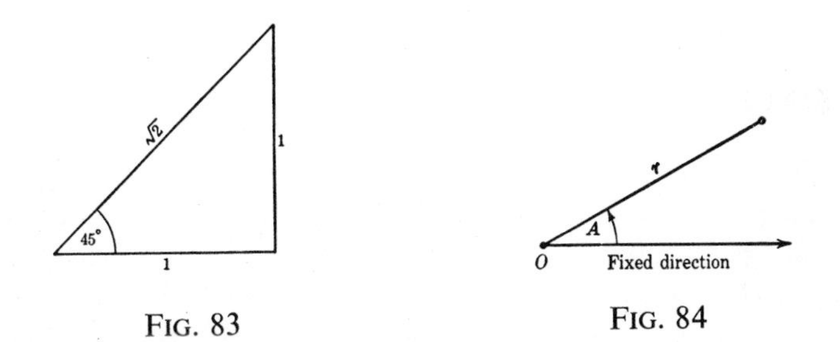

FIG. 83

FIG. 84

by such a pair (A,r) we call the resulting correspondence between number-pairs (A,r) and points a **polar coordinate system.**

Other systems, such as various kinds of **curvilinear coordinates**, are sometimes used in which systems of curves take the place of the straight lines on ordinary graph paper (Fig. 85). If one were studying the geometry of figures on a curved surface of some sort instead of a plane (flat surface), we might naturally employ some sort of curvilinear coordinates. An example of this is our system of latitude and longitude on the surface of the earth. When we specify a place as 60° west longitude and 42° north latitude we are using the curvilinear coordinate system pictured in Fig. 86 with the equator and Greenwich meridian as x and y axes, respectively. The "parallels" of latitude and "meridians" of longitude form the network of curves. Degrees are used in this system because longitude and latitude signify angles at the center C of the earth as indicated in Fig. 86.

In plane geometry, the rectangular coordinates introduced in the preceding section are the easiest to use. Hence in our study of plane geometry here, *we shall use rectangular coordinates exclusively.*

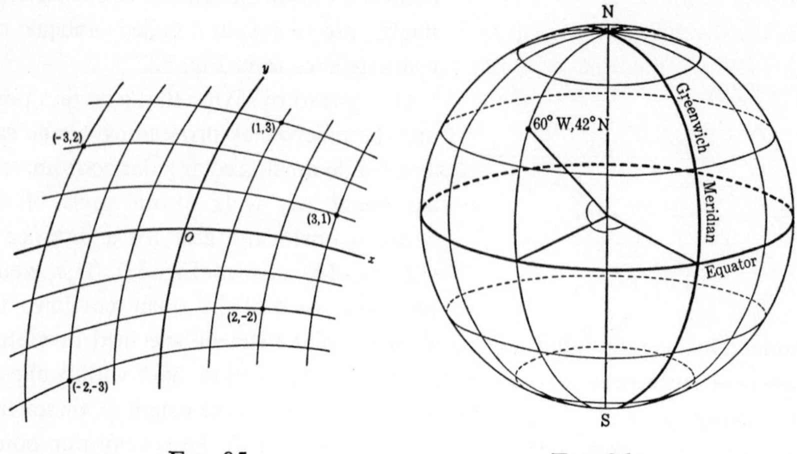

FIG. 85

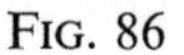

FIG. 86

90. DISTANCE

Let P_1 be a point whose coordinates are (x_1,y_1), and let P_2 be a second point with coordinates (x_2,y_2). Since P_1 and P_2 are different points, we cannot have both the equalities $x_1 = x_2$ and $y_1 = y_2$ although we may have one or the other or neither. We shall discuss these three cases separately.

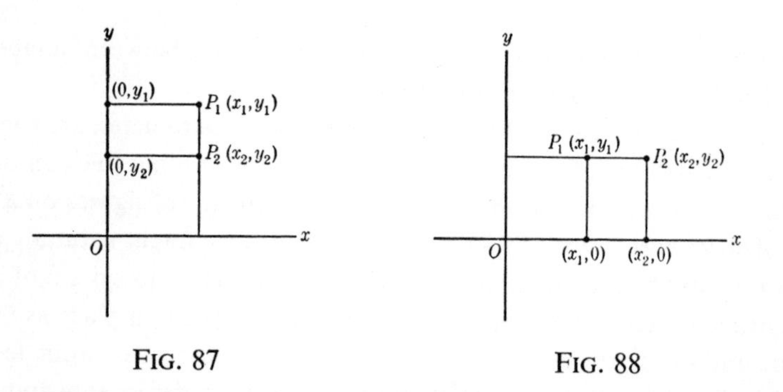

FIG. 87

FIG. 88

Case 1. Suppose $x_1 = x_2$; that is, P_1 and P_2 are on the same vertical line. Then the distance P_1P_2 is equal to the distance between the points $(0,y_1)$ and $(0,y_2)$. (Why? See Fig. 87.) But by theorem 1, section 87, this distance is $|y_1 - y_2|$ or $\sqrt{(y_1 - y_2)^2}$.

For example, the distance between the points $(1,-3)$ and $(1,2)$ is $|(-3)-2| = |-5| = 5$.

Case 2. Suppose $y_1 = y_2$; that is, P_1 and P_2 are on the same horizontal line. Then the distance P_1P_2 is equal to the distance between the points $(x_1,0)$ and $(x_2,0)$. (Why? See Fig. 88.) But by section 87, this distance is $|x_1 - x_2|$ or $\sqrt{(x_1 - x_2)^2}$.

For example, the distance between the points $(-2,4)$ and $(1,4)$ is $|(-2)-1| = |-3| = 3$.

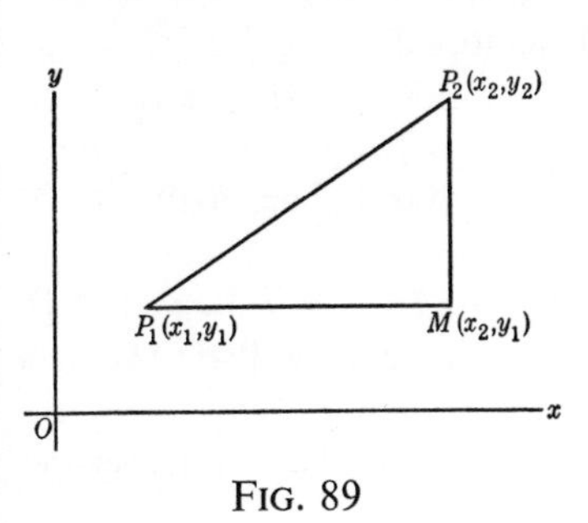

FIG. 89

Case 3. The only remaining possibility is that $x_1 \neq x_2$ and $y_1 \neq y_2$. Then the line P_1P_2 is oblique, that is, neither horizontal nor vertical. Draw a horizontal line through P_1 and a vertical line through P_2. These lines meet at a point M whose coordinates are (x_2,y_1); see Fig. 89 (the student should verify that our statements are true even when P_1 and P_2 are in positions other than those pictured). Therefore by the two previous cases, P_1M is $\sqrt{(x_1 - x_2)^2}$ and MP_2 is $\sqrt{(y_1 - y_2)^2}$. Thus we have $(P_1M)^2 = (x_1 - x_2)^2$ and $(MP_2)^2 = (y_1 - y_2)^2$. Since angle M is a right angle we have $(P_1P_2)^2 = (P_1M)^2 + (MP_2)^2$ by the Pythagorean theorem. Therefore

$$(P_1P_2)^2 = (x_1 - x_2)^2 + (y_1 - y_2)^2,$$

or

$$P_1P_2 = \sqrt{(x_1 - x_2)^2 + (y_1 - y_2)^2}. \tag{1}$$

For example the distance between the points $(1,-1)$ and $(4,3)$ is

$$\sqrt{(1-4)^2 + (-1-3)^2} = \sqrt{(-3)^2 + (-4)^2} = 5.$$

Note that formula (1), which was derived from the hypothesis of case 3, applies also to cases 1 and 2. If (1) is applied to case 1 where $x_1 = x_2$, the term $x_1 - x_2 = 0$ and (1) reduces to $\sqrt{(y_1 - y_2)^2}$; thus the formula (1) yields the correct result for case 1.

Exercise. Verify that the formula (1) yields the correct result for case 2.

We have proved the following theorem.

Theorem 3. *If P_1 and P_2 are any two points with coordinates (x_1,y_1) and (x_2,y_2) respectively, the distance P_1P_2 between them is given by*

$$P_1P_2 = \sqrt{(x_1 - x_2)^2 + (y_1 - y_2)^2}.$$

Exercises

Find the distance between each of the following pairs of points:

1. (3,7) and (−2,−5).
2. (0,0) and (−5,12).
3. (−2,2) and (2,2).
4. (0,2) and (−1,5).
5. (2,3) and (2,−7).
6. (3,−1) and (−9,−1).
7. (0,0) and (−4,0).
8. (0,0) and (0,−8).

9. Show that the triangle whose vertices are (−1,−2), (3,−2), (1,5) is isosceles. Is it also equilateral?

10. Find the lengths of the sides of the triangle whose vertices are (0,0), (0,−5) and (−12,0).

11. Let A, B, C be points whose coordinates are (−2,3), (−6,−3), and (1,1), respectively. Use the converse of the Pythagorean theorem to show that ABC is a right triangle.

12. As in exercise 11, show that the points (−4,−3), (6,−5), (−3,2) are the vertices of a right triangle.

13. (*a*) Show that the points (3,1) and (−3,1) are on a circle whose center is (0,5).
(*b*) What is the radius of this circle?
(*c*) Does the point (−4,−2) lie on this circle?
(*d*) Does the point (2,4) lie on this circle?
(*e*) Does the point (−4,2) lie on this circle?

14. Find a point on the x-axis equidistant from the points (5,4) and (6,−3). (Hint: let the desired point be $(x,0)$ and find x.)

15. Find a point on the y-axis equidistant from the points (3,1) and (4,−6). (Hint: let the desired point be $(0,y)$ and find y.)

16. Show that the points (−3,−3), (3,5), and (6,9) lie in a straight line. (Hint: the sum of the lengths of any two sides of a triangle must be greater than the length of the third side.)

★17. (*a*) Show that if x_1, y_1, x_2, y_2 are any real numbers, then

$$\sqrt{x_1^2+y_1^2}+\sqrt{x_2^2+y_2^2} \geqq \sqrt{(x_1+x_2)^2+(y_1+y_2)^2}.$$

(Hint: assume the contrary and arrive at a contradiction.)
(*b*) Interpret the theorem of part (*a*) geometrically.

18. Show that if P,Q,R are any three points in the plane with coordinates (a,b), (c,d), (e,f) respectively, then the distances PQ, QR, RP satisfy the so-called triangle inequality: $PQ + QR \geqq RP$. (Hint: use the result of exercise 17, noting that $(a-c)+(c-e)=(a-e)$ and $(b-d)+(d-f)=(b-f)$.)

91. MIDPOINT OF A LINE-SEGMENT

Let $P'(x',y')$ be the mid-point of the line-segment joining $P_1(x_1,y_1)$ and $P_2(x_2,y_2)$. We shall find expressions for the coordinates of P' in terms of the coordinates of P_1 and P_2.

Case 1. Suppose P_1P_2 is neither horizontal nor vertical. Draw vertical lines through the points P_1, P', P_2 intersecting the x-axis at $A(x_1,0)$, $B(x',0)$, $C(x_2,0)$, respectively. Clearly, B is the midpoint of AC since if parallels intercept equal segments on one transversal (P_1P_2), they intercept equal segments on any transversal (the x-axis). Thus, by theorem 2, section 87, we have

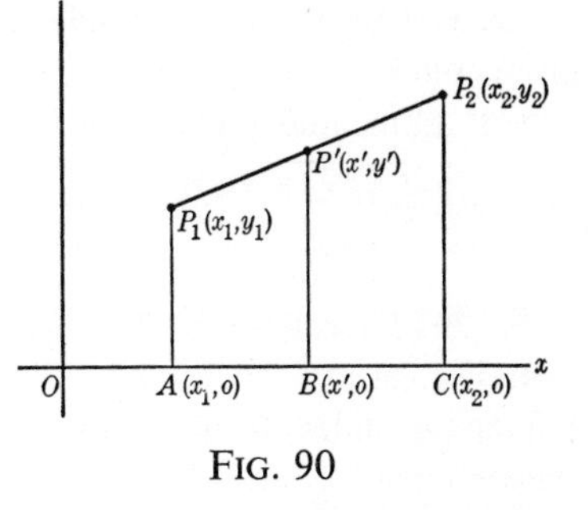

FIG. 90

$$x' = \frac{x_1 + x_2}{2}. \tag{1}$$

Similarly, by drawing three horizontal lines through P_1, P', P_2, we would obtain

$$y' = \frac{y_1 + y_2}{2}. \tag{2}$$

The proof of (2) is left to the student.

Case 2. Suppose P_1P_2 is horizontal. Then $y_1 = y' = y_2$. Hence $y' + y' = y_1 + y_2$ by substitution. Thus $2y' = y_1 + y_2$ and $y' = \frac{1}{2}(y_1 + y_2)$. Hence the same formula (2) applies in this case.

Formula (1) can be derived just as in case 1.

Case 3. Suppose P_1P_2 is vertical. Then $x_1 = x' = x_2$. As in case 2, we may prove that formula (1) holds in this case as well. The derivation of formula (2) in this case is the same as in case 1.

Exercise. Complete the proofs in detail for each case.

Hence we have the following theorem.

Theorem 4. *The coordinates (x', y') of the midpoint of the line-segment whose endpoints are (x_1, y_1) and (x_2, y_2) are given by*

$$x' = \frac{x_1 + x_2}{2}, \qquad y' = \frac{y_1 + y_2}{2}. \tag{3}$$

In other words, the abscissa of the midpoint is the average of the abscissas of the endpoints, and the ordinate of the midpoint is the average of the ordinates of the endpoints.

Exercises

1. Find the coordinates of the midpoint of the line-segment joining $(-1,-3)$ and $(7,11)$. Use the distance formula to verify that this midpoint is equidistant from the given points.

2. Find the midpoints of the sides of the triangle in:

(*a*) exercise 9, section 90; (*b*) exercise 10, section 90;
(*c*) exercise 11, section 90; (*d*) exercise 12, section 90.

3. Find the lengths of the 3 medians in each of the triangles of exercise 2.

4. For each of the triangles of exercise 2, show that the length of the line-segment joining the midpoints of any two sides of the triangle is equal to half the length of the remaining side.

5. The point $P(3,5)$ is on a circle whose center is $(-1,2)$. Find the coordinates of the other end of the diameter passing through P.

6. The points $(-2,6)$ and $(4,-2)$ are opposite ends of a diameter of a circle. Show that $(6,2)$ lies on the circle. Does $(2,6)$ lie on the circle?

7. Write the coordinates of the midpoint of the line-segment joining (a,b) and (c,d).

8. If particles of positive weights $w_1, w_2 \ldots, w_n$ are placed at the points $P_1, P_2, \ldots, P_n$, the coordinates of which are $(x_1,y_1), (x_2,y_2), \ldots, (x_n,y_n)$, respectively, the **centroid** (or **center of gravity**) of the set of particles is the point P' with coordinates (x',y') given by the formulas

$$x' = \frac{w_1x_1 + w_2x_2 + \cdots + w_nx_n}{w_1 + w_2 + \cdots + w_n}, \qquad y' = \frac{w_1y_1 + w_2y_2 + \cdots + w_ny_n}{w_1 + w_2 + \cdots + w_n}.$$

(*a*) Show that for $n = 2$ and equal weights $w_1 = w_2$, the centroid is the midpoint of P_1 and P_2.

(*b*) Find the centroid of the system of three particles with equal weights at the points $(0,0)$, $(6,0)$, $(2,4)$, respectively.

(*c*) Find the centroid of the system of four particles with weights 1, 2, 3, 4 at the points $(1,2)$, $(3,5)$, $(7,-1)$, $(5,-4)$, respectively.

92. SLOPE

We have already seen how the familiar geometric concepts of distance and midpoint of a line-segment may be treated algebraically. In this section we shall discuss a means of treating algebraically problems connected with the idea of the direction of a line, in particular, problems of parallel and perpendicular lines.

If a hill rises 15 feet vertically for every 100 feet of horizontal progress, it is customary to say that it has a slope of 15/100. If it were steeper, rising, say, 30 feet for every 100 feet of horizontal progress, it would have the larger slope 30/100. In Fig. 92, the line-segment P_1P_2 rises exactly $y_2 - y_1$ units (that is, the distance QP_2) while making horizontal progress of $x_2 - x_1$ units (that is, the distance P_1Q). Hence it is natural to make the following definition.

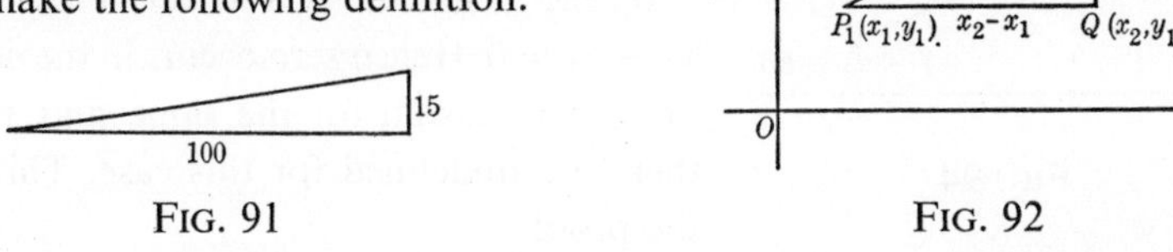

FIG. 91

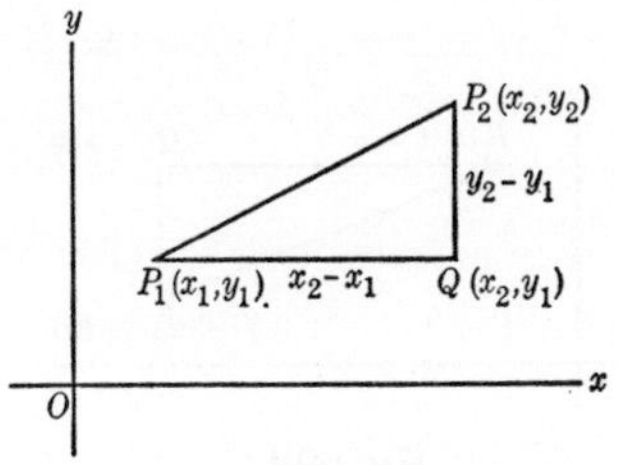

FIG. 92

Definition 1. *By the* ***slope of the line-segment*** *joining the points* $P_1(x_1, y_1)$ *and* $P_2(x_2, y_2)$, *we shall mean the number* $\dfrac{y_2 - y_1}{x_2 - x_1}$, *provided this number exists.*

Exercise. Prove that $\dfrac{y_2 - y_1}{x_2 - x_1} = \dfrac{y_1 - y_2}{x_1 - x_2}$. It follows that it does not matter which of the two given points we take as P_1 in applying the definition.

Example. The slope of the line-segment joining the points (5,3) and (8,1) is $\dfrac{1-3}{8-5} = \dfrac{-2}{3}$. If we had taken the second point as P_1, we would obtain $\dfrac{3-1}{5-8} = \dfrac{2}{-3} = -\dfrac{2}{3}$, just as before. However, the slope of the line-segment joining (2,1) and (5,3) is $\dfrac{3-1}{5-2} = \dfrac{2}{3}$. (See Fig. 93.)

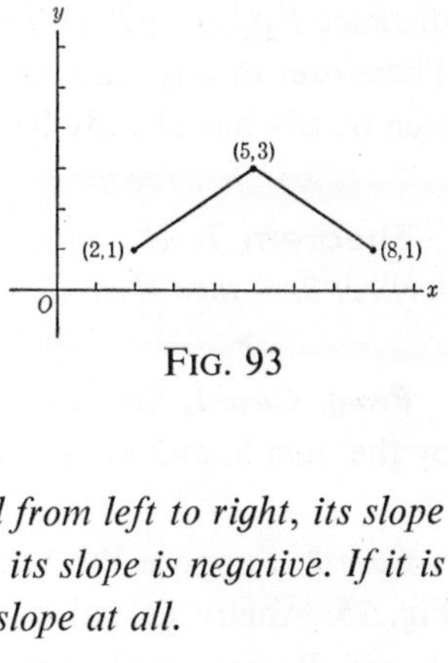

FIG. 93

The geometric significance of our definition will be brought out by the next two theorems.

Theorem 5. *If a line-segment rises as we proceed from left to right, its slope is positive. If it sinks as we proceed from left to right, its slope is negative. If it is horizontal, its slope is zero. If it is vertical, it has no slope at all.*

Proof. Let $P_1(x_1, y_1)$ be to the left of $P_2(x_2, y_2)$. Then $x_1 < x_2$, or $x_2 - x_1$ is positive. If the segment P_1P_2 rises as we proceed from left to right, then $y_2 > y_1$, or $y_2 - y_1$ is positive (Fig. 92). Hence the slope is positive since it is obtained by dividing one positive number, $y_2 - y_1$, by another, $x_2 - x_1$.

If the segment sinks as we proceed from left to right, then $y_2 < y_1$ and $y_2 - y_1$ is negative (Fig. 94). Hence the slope is negative since it is obtained by dividing a negative number, $y_2 - y_1$, by a positive number, $x_2 - x_1$.

By the exercise above, the slope is the same whether we take P_1 to be the left-hand point or the right-hand point.

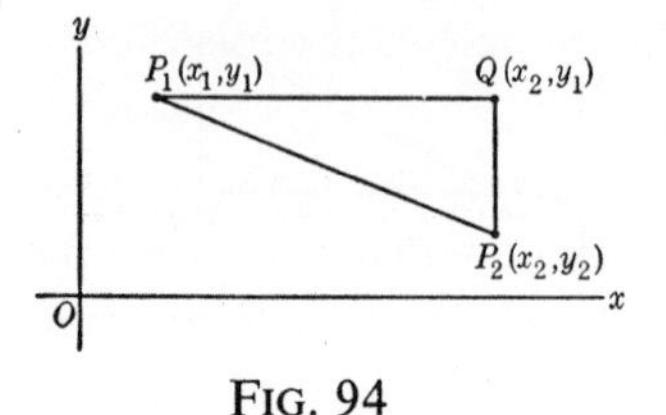

FIG. 94

If the segment is horizontal, then $y_2 = y_1$, or $y_2 - y_1 = 0$. Hence the slope is zero.

If the segment is vertical, then $x_2 = x_1$, or $x_2 - x_1 = 0$. Hence zero occurs in the denominator of the expression for the slope and the slope is therefore undefined for this case. This completes the proof.

The converses of the statements in theorem 5 are also correct but we shall not prove them here.

Theorem 6. *Let the line-segment P_1P_2 be oblique. Draw a horizontal line through P_1 and a vertical line through P_2, meeting at Q. Then the slope of the segment P_1P_2 is equal to* $+(P_2Q/P_1Q)$ or $-(P_2Q/P_1Q)$ *according as the segment rises or sinks as we proceed from left to right.*

Proof. Clearly the coordinates of Q are (x_2, y_1). Hence $y_2 - y_1$ is either the distance P_2Q or $-P_2Q$. Similarly, $x_2 - x_1$ is either the distance P_1Q or $-P_1Q$. Therefore, in any case, the slope is either $+P_2Q/P_1Q$ or $-P_2Q/P_1Q$. Which sign occurs has already been determined in theorem 5.

Theorem 7. *If two line-segments P_1P_2 and P_3P_4 are on the same non-vertical line, then their slopes are equal.*

Proof. Case 1. Suppose the line is horizontal. Then both slopes will be zero, by theorem 5, and are consequently equal.

Case 2. Suppose the line is oblique. Draw horizontal and vertical lines as in Fig. 95. Angles Q and R are right angles. Angles P_1 and P_3 are equal since they are corresponding angles of parallel lines. Hence the right triangles are similar since two angles of one are equal to two angles of the other. Now, it is a theorem of plane geometry that if two triangles are similar, the ratio of the lengths of any pair of sides of one triangle equals the ratio of the lengths of the corresponding pair of sides of the other triangle. Hence $P_2Q/P_1Q = P_4R/P_3R$. By theorem 6,

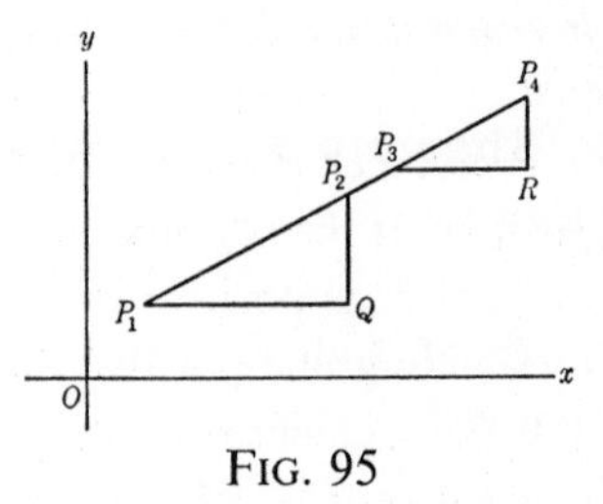

FIG. 95

these expressions are either the slopes of the segments P_1P_2 and P_3P_4 or the negatives of these slopes, according as the line rises or sinks as we proceed from left to right. In either case, the slopes are equal. This completes the proof.

By theorem 7, the slope of any line-segment on a given line is the same as the slope of any other line-segment on the same line. This makes possible the following natural definition.

Definition 2. *The* ***slope of a line*** *shall mean the slope of any line-segment on it.*

That the converse of theorem 7 is false is apparent from the following theorem.

Theorem 8. *If two non-vertical lines l and l' are parallel, then they have the same slope.*

Proof. Case 1. If the lines are horizontal, then their slopes are both zero.

Case 2. Suppose the lines are oblique. Since they are parallel, they either both rise or both sink as we proceed from left to right. Thus their slopes must have the same sign. Let P_1 and P_1' be the points where l and l' meet the x-axis, respectively. Let P_2 and P_2' be any other points on l and l', respectively. Let Q and Q' be the points where the vertical lines through P_2 and P_2' meet the x-axis, respectively. The angles P_1 and P_1' are equal, since l and l' are parallel, and Q and Q' are both right angles. Therefore the right triangles are similar. Hence $P_2Q/P_1Q = P_2'Q'/P_1'Q'$. By theorem 6, this implies that l and l' have the same slope.

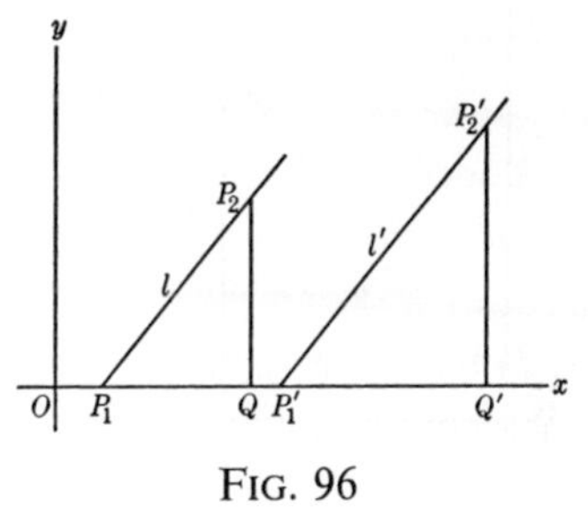

FIG. 96

Theorem 9. *If two distinct* non-vertical lines l and l' have the same slope, then they are parallel.*

Proof. Case 1. If their slope is zero, the lines are both horizontal and hence parallel.

* Two lines are called **distinct** if they are different, that is, if they do not coincide. Two distinct lines may very well have one point in common, however.

Case 2. If their slope is not zero, the lines either both rise or both sink as we proceed from left to right, according as the slope is positive or negative. Draw right triangles P_1P_2Q and $P_1'P_2'Q'$ just as in the preceding theorem (Fig. 96). Since the slopes of l and l' are equal, we have $P_2Q/P_1Q = P_2'Q'/P_1'Q'$. Angles Q and Q' are equal, since they are both right angles. It is a theorem of plane geometry that, if one angle of a triangle equals one angle of another triangle, and the ratio of the sides including the first angle equals the ratio of the sides including the other, then the triangles are similar. Hence the triangles P_1P_2Q and $P_1'P_2'Q'$ are similar. Therefore, angle P_1 is equal to angle P_1'. Hence l and l' are parallel, because a pair of corresponding angles made by a transversal (the x-axis) are equal. This completes the proof.

If two line-segments have the same slope they are either on the same line or on parallel lines.

Theorem 10. *Let l and l' be two oblique lines whose slopes are denoted by m amd m', respectively. If $mm' = -1$, then the lines are perpendicular.*

Proof. Since $mm' = -1$, by hypothesis, m and m' are of opposite sign. Suppose, for example, m is positive. Then l rises and l' sinks as we proceed from left to right; hence they must intersect at some point A. Choose another point B on l. Draw a vertical line through B; this line must meet l' at some point C, since l' is not vertical. Draw a horizontal line through A meeting BC at D. By theorem 6, $m = BD/AD$ while $m' = -DC/AD$. By hypothesis, $mm' = -1$ or $m = -1/m'$. Thus

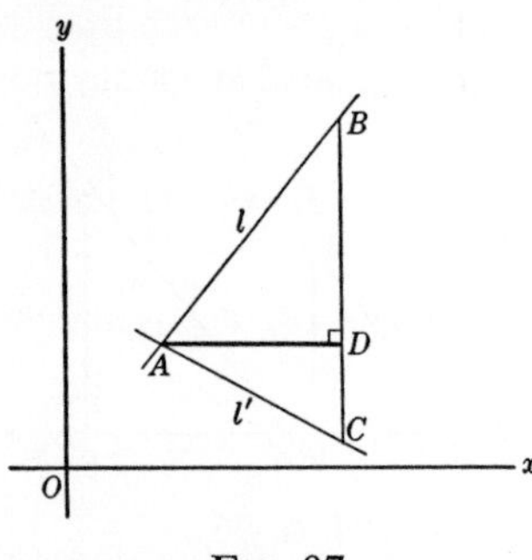

FIG. 97

$$\frac{BD}{AD} = \frac{-1}{-DC/AD}, \quad \text{or} \quad \frac{BD}{AD} = \frac{AD}{DC}.$$

Since angles BDA and ADC are right angles, it follows that the right triangles BAD and CAD are similar, by the theorem of geometry quoted in the preceding proof. Hence angle BAD is equal to angle C since corresponding angles of similar triangles are equal by definition. Now since triangle CAD is a right triangle, we have

$$\sphericalangle DAC + \sphericalangle C = 90^\circ. \tag{2}$$

Substituting in (2), we have $\sphericalangle DAC + \sphericalangle BAD = 90^\circ$. Therefore, $\sphericalangle BAC = 90^\circ$. This is what we had to prove.

The converse of theorem 10 is also true but we shall not prove it here.

Example. Let the points, A, B, C, D have the coordinates (2,3), (4,7), (6,6), (4,2), respectively. Show that $ABCD$ is a rectangle. (The student should draw the figure.)

The slope of AB is 2; the slope of BC is $-\frac{1}{2}$; the slope of CD is 2; the slope of DA is $-\frac{1}{2}$. Since the slopes of AB and CD are equal, AB and CD are either parallel or on the same straight line; but they are not on the same straight line since the slope of BC is not also 2. Hence AB and CD are parallel. Similarly, AD and BC are parallel. Therefore, the figure is a parallelogram. But the slope of AB multiplied by the slope of BC yields -1. By theorem 10, AB and BC are perpendicular. Therefore $ABCD$ is a rectangle.

Exercises

1. Show that the slope of the segment joining (1,2) and (3,8) is equal to the slope of the segment joining (4,10) and (8,22). Establish whether or not all four points are on the same line.

2. Show that the slope of the segment joining (1,2) and (2,6) is equal to the slope of the segment joining (4,14) and (9,34). Establish whether or not all four points are on the same line.

3. Find the slopes of the sides of the triangles in: (*a*) exercise 12, section 90; (*b*) exercise 11, section 90; (*c*) exercise 10, section 90; (*d*) exercise 9, section 90.

4. Find the slope of the lines joining the midpoints of the sides of each triangle in exercise 3. Establish in each triangle that the line joining the midpoints of any two sides of the triangle is parallel to the third side.

5. Prove that the points $(-2,-2)$, $(-5,1)$, $(-4,5)$, and $(-3,-6)$ are vertices of a parallelogram.

6. Using theorem 10, show that the triangles given in (*a*) exercise 11, section 90, (*b*) exercise 12, section 90, are right triangles.

7. Show that $A(1,6)$, $B(4,5)$, $C(1,-4)$, and $D(-2,-3)$ are the vertices of a rectangle.

8. Draw a line through the point (2,3) having (*a*) the slope 2; (*b*) the slope $\frac{1}{2}$; (*c*) the slope $-\frac{1}{2}$; (*d*) the slope -2.

9. Draw a line through the point (1,3) having (*a*) the slope $\frac{2}{5}$; (*b*) the slope $-\frac{5}{2}$; (*c*) the slope $-\frac{2}{5}$; (*d*) the slope $\frac{5}{2}$.

10. If A, B, C, D have the coordinates $(-2,0)$, (2,4), (6,0), and $(2,-4)$, respectively, show (*a*) that $ABCD$ is a square; (*b*) that the diagonals of this square are equal and perpendicular to each other; (*c*) that the diagonals bisect each other.

11. If A, B, C, D have the coordinates $(-1,0)$, (3,4), $(7,-2)$, $(4,-3)$, respectively, show that the line-segment joining the midpoints of AB and BC is equal and parallel to the line-segment joining the midpoints of CD and DA.

12. State and prove the converse of theorem 10.

93. PROOFS OF THEOREMS

By analytic methods (that is, the use of coordinates) we can prove easily theorems in geometry which demand considerable ingenuity when attacked by the "synthetic" methods of the ancient Greeks. We shall take up some simple examples here. It will be useful to remember that we may choose our axes wherever we wish. We shall usually find it convenient to choose axes in such a way that as many coordinates as possible are zero.

Example. Prove that the length of the line-segment joining the midpoints of two sides of a triangle is half the length of the third side.

Proof. Choose the line of the third side as our x-axis and let one vertex be the origin. Then the coordinates of the other two vertices may be denoted by $(a,0)$ and (b,c) where $a > 0$. By theorem 4, section 91, the midpoints M and N have coordinates $(b/2,c/2)$ and $\left(\frac{b+a}{2}, \frac{c}{2}\right)$, respectively. Hence, by theorem 3, the distance

$$MN = \sqrt{\left(\frac{b+a}{2} - \frac{b}{2}\right)^2 + \left(\frac{c}{2} - \frac{c}{2}\right)^2} = \sqrt{\left(\frac{a}{2}\right)^2} = \frac{a}{2}.$$

But the length of the third side is $a - 0 = a$. This proves the theorem.

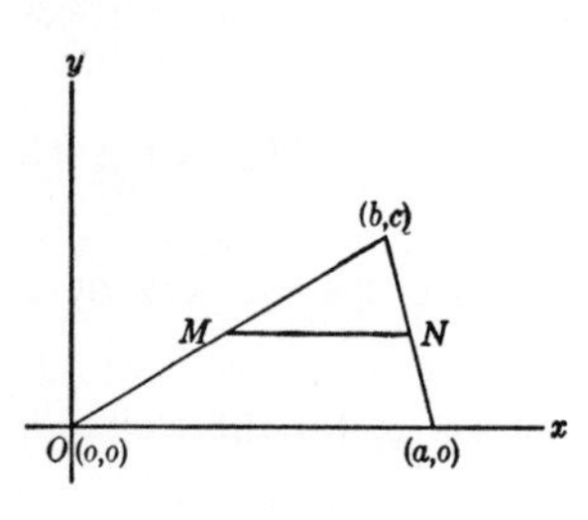

Fig. 98

If we had assigned definite numerical coordinates to the vertices, we would have proved the theorem only for a particular triangle. By using unspecified literal coordinates we prove the theorem in all generality.

Note that our proof is much shorter than the proof you learned in high school, which involved making judiciously chosen construction lines and a more or less ingenious argument. Here we have only to apply our formulas.

Exercises

1. Prove the theorem above, using the other pairs of sides in Fig. 98.

2. Prove the following theorems analytically, remembering to choose the axes in a convenient position:

(a) The diagonals of a rectangle are equal.

(b) The diagonals of a rectangle bisect each other.

(*c*) The midpoint of the hypotenuse of a right triangle is equidistant from the three vertices.

(*d*) Two medians of an isosceles triangle are equal.

(*e*) The diagonals of a square are perpendicular.

(*f*) The line-segments joining the midpoints of the sides of any quadrilateral in succession form a parallelogram.

(*g*) The line-segments joining the midpoints of opposite sides of any quadrilateral bisect each other.

(*h*) If the diagonals of a rectangle are perpendicular, then the figure is a square. (Hint: use the converse of theorem 10, section 92.)

(*i*) The sum of the squares of the diagonals of any parallelogram is equal to the sum of the squares of the four sides.

(*j*) If two medians of any triangle are equal, the triangle is isosceles.

94. THE GRAPH OF AN EQUATION

We have already seen that points in a plane may be identified with pairs of real numbers, and that certain geometric concepts, like distance, etc., may be studied by means of algebraic formulas. To see how other geometrical considerations may be reduced to algebraic problems, we need the following definition.

Definition. *By the* ***graph*** *or* ***locus*** *or* ***curve of an equation*** *in two variables x and y we mean the set of (1)* ***all*** *those points, and (2)* ***only*** *those points, whose coordinates satisfy* the equation.*

Example 1. Consider the equation $x + y = 5$. The point (2,3) is in the locus of this equation since $2 + 3 = 5$. That is, the pair of values $x = 2$, $y = 3$ satisfies the equation $x + y = 5$, or converts it into a true statement. So are the points (3,2), (1,4), (−2,7), (6,−1). But the point (1,3) is not in the graph since $1 + 3 \neq 5$. Clearly, we may substitute any value for x and obtain a corresponding value for y from the relation $y = 5 - x$. Many corresponding pairs of values may be tabulated as follows.

x	2	3	1	−2	6	⋯
y	3	2	4	7	−1	⋯

Marking these points on the graph (Fig. 99) we see that the graph seems to be a straight line.

* A pair of values for x and y is said to **satisfy** an equation if the equation becomes a true statement when these values are substituted in it. Thus, the graph of an equation is the truth-set of the propositional function expressed by the equation.

Note that both conditions (1) and (2) are important. Thus, the set of the 5 points which we actually plotted *alone* would satisfy condition (2) but not condition (1). On the other hand, the set of all points on the line in Fig. 99 together with the point (1,3) would satisfy condition (1) but not condition (2).

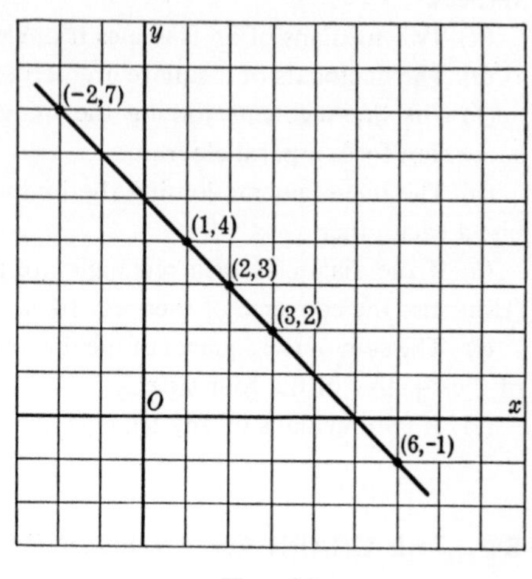

FIG. 99

To plot the graph of an equation, we usually substitute arbitrary values for x (or y) and calculate corresponding values of y (or x) from the equation. Many such substitutions must be made before we can form an idea of the shape of the curve. In joining the isolated points we have plotted by a "smooth" curve, we are assuming that the curve does not behave queerly between these points. The question of whether this is justified, and the question of how many points are necessary before the shape of the curve can be roughly determined, will be discussed in the next chapter. The coordinates of the points to be plotted are conveniently arranged in a table as in the following examples.

Example 2. Plot the graph of $y = x^2$. Substituting various numbers for x, we obtain the following table

x	0	1	−1	2	−2	3	−3	...
y	0	1	1	4	4	9	9	...

from which we get the graph in Fig. 100.

Example 3. Plot the graph of $x^2 + y^2 = 25$. We solve for y in terms of x as follows:

$$y^2 = 25 - x^2,$$

$$y = \pm\sqrt{25 - x^2}.$$

Substituting for x, we obtain the following table:

x	0	±5	3	4	−3	−4	+2	−2	...
y	±5	0	±4	±3	±4	±3	$\pm\sqrt{21}$	$\pm\sqrt{21}$	...

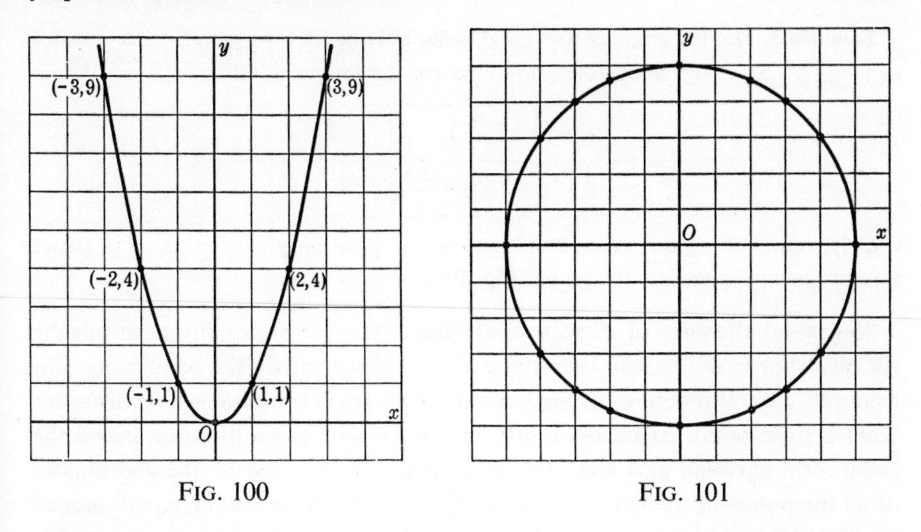

FIG. 100

FIG. 101

Clearly, for any value of x greater than 5 or less than -5, the values of y will be imaginary. Hence no such points appear on the graph, since our coordinates are exclusively real numbers. We get the graph in Fig. 101.

Example 4. Plot the graph of $xy = 1$. Solving for y, we get $y = 1/x$. Clearly, for $x = 0$, there is no point of the graph since $1/0$ is not defined. The following table may be obtained by substitution:

x	1	2	3	4	5	$\frac{1}{2}$	$\frac{1}{3}$	$\frac{1}{4}$	$\frac{1}{5}$	-1	-2	-3	$-\frac{1}{2}$	$-\frac{1}{3}$	$-\frac{1}{4}$	...
y	1	$\frac{1}{2}$	$\frac{1}{3}$	$\frac{1}{4}$	$\frac{1}{5}$	2	3	4	5	-1	$-\frac{1}{2}$	$-\frac{1}{3}$	-2	-3	-4	...

We get the graph in Fig. 102.

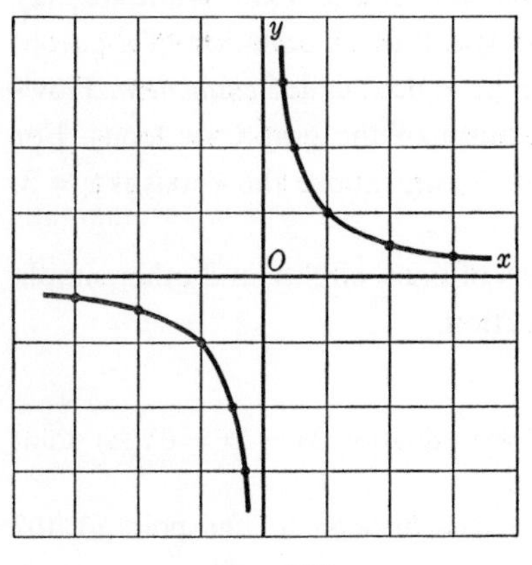

FIG. 102

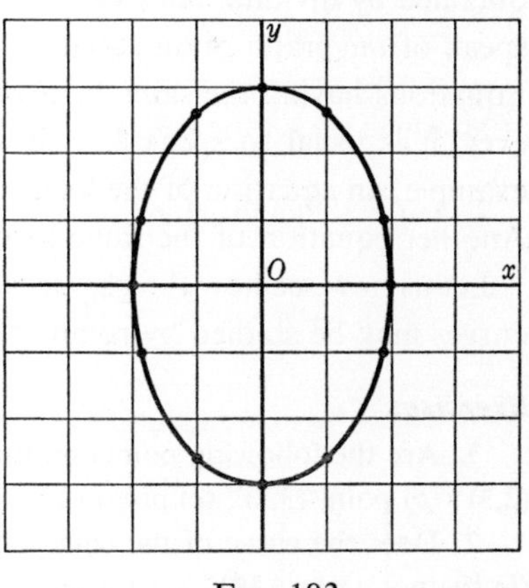

FIG. 103

Example 5. Plot the graph of $9x^2 + 4y^2 = 36$. Solving for y we get $y^2 = (36 - 9x^2)/4$ or $y = \pm\frac{1}{2}\sqrt{36 - 9x^2}$. Substituting for x we get the following table:

x	0	± 1	± 2	$\cdots$
y	± 3	$\pm\frac{3}{2}\sqrt{3}$	0	$\cdots$

Clearly, values of x greater than 2 or less than -2 yield imaginary values of y. Hence no such points appear on the graph (Fig. 103).

In general, the **locus** of all points satisfying certain given conditions means the set of all those points and only those points which satisfy the conditions. For example, a *circle* is defined as the locus of all points in the plane whose distances from a fixed point, called the center, are equal to a given distance, called the radius. An **equation of a locus** means an equation satisfied by the coordinates of all the points of the locus and of no other points. Note that an equation may be altered by multiplying or dividing both sides of it by the same constant ($\neq 0$) without affecting the graph. For, if x and y are numbers for which the given equation is true, then the new equation must be true as well, since if equals are multiplied or divided by equals the results are equal. For example, if the point (x, y) satisfies the equation

$$x + y = 5, \tag{1}$$

it also satisfies the equations

$$3x + 3y = 15,$$

obtained by multiplying both sides of (1) by 3, and

$$\frac{x}{2} + \frac{y}{2} = \frac{5}{2},$$

obtained by dividing both sides of (1) by 2, and conversely. Thus, while we may speak of *the* graph of an equation, we should speak of *an* equation of a graph. Equations having the same truth-set or graph have been called *equivalent*. However, it is usual to speak loosely of the equation of the graph, or locus. For example, an equation of the locus of all points 3 units above the x-axis is $y = 3$. Another equation of the same locus is $2y = 6$.

Let us now see how the geometric properties of lines, circles, and other simple curves may be studied by means of their equations.

Exercises

1. Are the following points on the graph of the equation $3x - 2y = 0$? (*a*) point (2,3)? (*b*) point (3,2)? (*c*) point (4,6)?

2. Does the curve of the equation $y = x^2 + 1$ pass through (*a*) the point (3,10)? (*b*) the point (3, -10)? (*c*) the point (-3,10)?

Plot the graphs of the following equations:

3. $2x - 3y = 6.$ **4.** $2x + 3y = 6.$ **5.** $x^2 + y^2 = 100.$
6. $10y = x^3.$ **7.** $y = 2x^3 + 3x^2 - 36x.$ **8.** $xy = 8.$
9. $4x^2 + 9y^2 = 36.$ **10.** $x^2 - y^2 = 4.$ **11.** $y^2 = 10x.$
12. $10y = -x^2.$ **13.** $y^2 = -10x.$

Write in simple form an equation of each of the following loci, and plot the graph:

14. The locus of all points 3 units to the right of the y-axis.

15. The locus of all points 3 units below the x-axis.

16. The locus of all points 4 units to the left of the y-axis.

17. The locus of all points whose abscissas and ordinates are of the same sign and which are equidistant from the x and y axes.

18. The locus of all points whose abscissas and ordinates are of opposite sign and which are equidistant from the x and y axes.

19. The locus of all points whose abscissas and ordinates are of the same sign and which are twice as far from the x-axis as from the y-axis.

20. Show that $x^2 - y^2 = 0$ is an equation of the locus of all points equidistant from the x and y axes. Plot the locus.

21. (*a*) Show that the values $x = 2$, $y = 3$ satisfy both the equations $2x + 3y = 13$ and $2x - y = 1$. Plot the graphs of both equations and discuss the geometric significance of the preceding statement.

(*b*) The values $x = 5$, $y = 1$ satisfy one of these equations but not the other. What is the geometric significance of this statement?

(*c*) The point (3,5) is on one of these graphs but not the other. What is the algebraic significance of this statement?

(*d*) The point (1,−1) is on neither graph. What is the algebraic significance of this statement?

95. EQUATION OF A STRAIGHT LINE

Case 1. Horizontal lines. Every point on a horizontal line has the same y-coordinate as every other point on it, and all points with this y-coordinate are on the line. Hence the equation of a horizontal line is of the form

(1) $$y = k$$

where k is a constant.

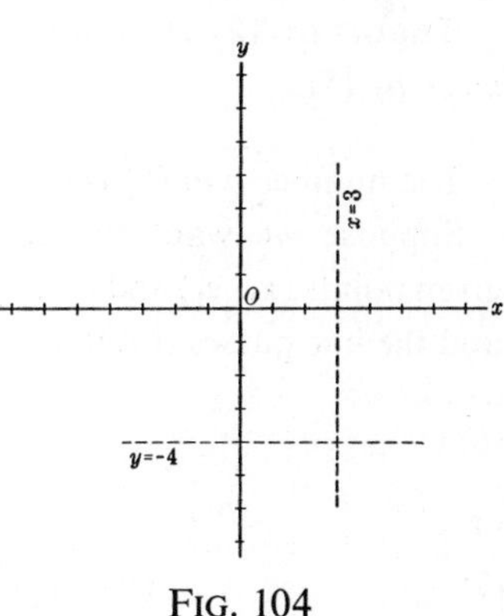

FIG. 104

Case 2. Vertical lines. Similarly, every vertical line has an equation of the form

(2) $$x = k$$

where k is a constant.

Case 3. Oblique lines. These lines have a slope different from zero. Consider the line having a given slope m and passing through a given point (x_1, y_1). Let (x, y) be any *other* point on the line. Then the line-segment joining (x, y) to (x_1, y_1) must have the slope m, or

$$\frac{y - y_1}{x - x_1} = m. \tag{3}$$

Thus any point (x, y) on the line other than (x_1, y_1) satisfies the equation

$$y - y_1 = m(x - x_1). \tag{4}$$

The point (x_1, y_1) itself clearly satisfies (4) as we see by direct substitution. Hence, every point on the line satisfies equation (4). Conversely, if (x, y) is any point, other than (x_1, y_1), satisfying (4), then (x, y) also satisfies (3); hence the segment joining (x, y) and (x_1, y_1) has the slope m and (x, y) is on the line. Thus (4) is an equation of the line passing through the point (x_1, y_1) with slope m. We have proved the following theorem.

Theorem 11. *An equation of the line passing through (x_1, y_1) with slope m is given by (4). Horizontal and vertical lines have equations of the form (1) and (2), respectively.*

Note that equation (4) applies equally well to the case of horizontal lines, taking $m = 0$.

As a special case, consider the equation of the line passing through a given point $(0,p)$ on the y-axis, with slope m. From (4) we see that its equation is $y - p = m(x - 0)$, or

$$y = mx + p. \tag{5}$$

Hence we have the following theorem.

Theorem 12. *An equation of the line passing through $(0,p)$ with slope m is given by (5).*

The number p in (5) is called the ***y*-intercept** of the line.

Suppose we want the equation of the oblique line passing through two given points (x_1, y_1) and (x_2, y_2). The slope of the line must be $(y_2 - y_1)/(x_2 - x_1)$ and the line passes through (x_1, y_1). Hence, by (4) the equation of the line is

$$y - y_1 = \frac{y_2 - y_1}{x_2 - x_1}(x - x_1) \tag{6}$$

or

$$(y - y_1)(x_2 - x_1) = (y_2 - y_1)(x - x_1). \tag{7}$$

Note that the latter form of the equation may be applied to all lines through two given points, oblique or not; if the two points are on the same vertical line, then $x_2 - x_1 = 0$ and (6) cannot be used while (7) can. Hence, we have the following theorem.

Theorem 13. *An equation of the line through two points (x_1, y_1) and (x_2, y_2) is given by (7).*

In practice, it is unnecessary to use (7) for, given the coordinates of two points, one can get the slope and then use (4).

Examples. The equation of the line through (2, −3) with slope 4 is $y + 3 = 4(x - 2)$, by (4). The equation of the line through (0,2) with slope $\frac{1}{3}$ is $y = \frac{1}{3}x + 2$, by (5). The line through the points (2,3) and (4, −5) is $(y - 3)(4 - 2) = (-5 - 3)(x - 2)$, or $4x + y = 11$, by (7). The line through (3,1) and (3,5) is $(y - 1)(3 - 3) = (5 - 1)(x - 3)$ or $x = 3$ by (7).

Since every line is either horizontal, vertical, or oblique, we have incidentally proven the following theorem.

Theorem 14. *Every straight line has an equation of the first degree in x and y.*

Exercises

Write equations of the lines satisfying the following conditions:

1. Passing through (5,1) with slope 2.
2. Passing through (−1,−2) with slope $\frac{1}{3}$.
3. Passing through (3,2) with slope 0.
4. Passing through (3,2) parallel to the y-axis.
5. Passing through (2,3) and (5,6).
6. Passing through (2,−3) and (−1,4).
7. Passing through (2,−3) and (2,5).
8. Passing through (3,−4) and (−1,−4).
9. Passing through (0,4) with slope 3.
10. Passing through (3,4) with slope 1.
11. Passing through (−3,3) with slope −1.
12. Passing through (5,3) parallel to the x-axis.
13. If the line $y = 3x + p$ passes through (1,2), find p.
14. If the line $y = mx + 3$ passes through (4,2), find m.
15. If the line $y = mx + p$ passes through (1,2) and (3,5), find m and p.
16. If the line $y = mx + p$ passes through (2,4) and (4,3), find m and p.

96. THE GENERAL EQUATION OF THE FIRST DEGREE

We shall now prove the converse of theorem 14.

Theorem 15. *Every equation of the first degree in x and y has a straight line as its graph.*

Proof. Every equation of the first degree in x and y can be written in the form $ax + by = c$, a, b, and c being constants where not both a and b are zero. (Why do we make the latter restriction?) Either $b \neq 0$ or $b = 0$.

Case 1. *Suppose $b \neq 0$.* Then we may divide both sides of the equation $ax + by = c$ by b obtaining

$$\frac{a}{b}x + y = \frac{c}{b}$$

or

$$y = -\frac{a}{b}x + \frac{c}{b}.$$

But this is the equation of a line with slope $-a/b$ passing through the point $(0, c/b)$, by theorem 12, section 95.

Case 2. *Suppose $b = 0$.* Then $a \neq 0$ since not both a and b can be zero. Then $ax + by = c$ becomes $ax = c$; since $a \neq 0$, we may divide through by a, obtaining

$$x = \frac{c}{a},$$

which by (2) of section 95, is the equation of a vertical line through $(c/a, 0)$.
This completes the proof.

An equation of the first degree is often called a **linear equation**. To plot such an equation it is only necessary to compute the coordinates of two points on the graph since we know that the graph is a straight line and two points determine a line. *The slope of the graph of a linear equation is most easily found by expressing the equation in the form $y = mx + p$; then the coefficient of x is the slope, and the constant p is the y-intercept.*

Remark. Note that the line $y = -2x$ with slope -2 and passing through the origin has on it the points $(3,-6)$, $(2,-4)$, $(1,-2)$, $(0,0)$, $(-1,2)$, $(-2,4)$, $(-3,6)$, since $(-2)3 = -6$, $(-2)2 = -4$, $(-2)1 = -2$, $(-2)0 = 0$, $(-2)(-1) = 2$, $(-2)(-2) = 4$, $(-2)(-3) = 6$. This linear equation would not have a straight line for its graph were it not for the "rule of signs" for multiplication of signed numbers (section 24) which *defines* the products of signed numbers in the familiar way. This is perhaps the most important motivation for choosing the definition of multiplication of signed numbers as we did.

Exercises

Find the slope of the following lines, wherever possible, and plot the graph:

1. $2x - 3y = 6$. **2.** $2x + 4y = 11$. **3.** $3x = 1$. **4.** $2y = -10$.
5. $x + 2y = 0$. **6.** $5x - y = 0$.

7. What is the equation of the x-axis? the y-axis?

8. Write the equation of a line passing through $(-2,5)$ and parallel to the line $9x - 3y = 2$.

9. Write the equation of a line passing through $(3,2)$ and parallel to the line $6x + 3y = 5$.

10. Write the equation of a line passing through $(-2,5)$ and perpendicular to the line $6x - 3y = 2$.

11. A triangle has vertices $A(-2,0)$, $B(0,8)$, $C(4,2)$. Find the equations of (*a*) its sides; (*b*) its altitudes; (*c*) its medians; (*d*) its perpendicular bisectors.

12. Answer the questions of exercise 11 for the triangle with vertices $(-2,-4)$, $(2,12)$, $(6,-2)$.

Write in simple form an equation of each of the following loci, and plot the graph:

13. The locus of all points which are equidistant from the points $(1,2)$ and $(3,4)$. Is the point $(4,2)$ on this locus? the point $(6,-1)$?

14. The locus of all points equidistant from the points $(-1,2)$ and $(3,-4)$. Is the point $(7,3)$ on this locus? the point $(4,6)$?

15. The locus of all points whose distance from the origin is 5. Is the point $(3,4)$ on this locus? the point $(4,2)$?

16. The locus of all points whose distance from the point $(2,1)$ is 5. Is the point $(5,5)$ on this locus? the point $(6,4)$?

97. EQUATION OF A CIRCLE

By the **circle** with radius r and center at the point C we mean the set of all those points and only those points which are at a distance r from C. Let the coordinates of C be (h,k) and let the coordinates of any point P on the circle be (x,y). Then the distance PC must be r. Thus x and y must satisfy the equation

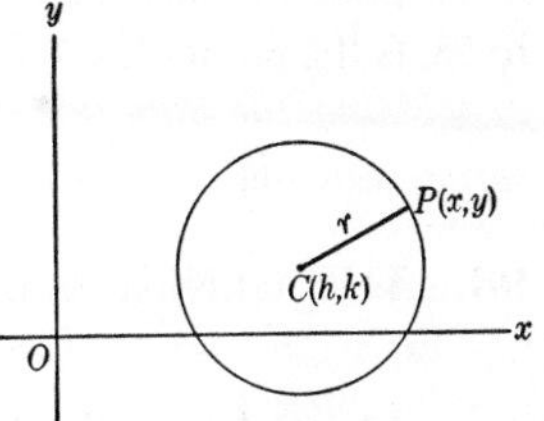

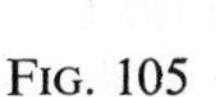
FIG. 105

$$\sqrt{(x-h)^2+(y-k)^2} = r,$$

or

$$(x-h)^2+(y-k)^2 = r^2. \qquad (1)$$

Conversely, if (x,y) satisfy (1), then the distance from (x,y) to (h,k) must be r ($-r$ cannot be regarded as a distance since it is negative). Hence (x,y) is on the circle. We have proved the following theorem.

Theorem 16. *An equation of the circle with center at (h,k) and radius r is (1).*

Example. An equation of the circle with center at $(3,-2)$ and radius 5 is $(x-3)^2 + (y+2)^2 = 25$.

Exercises

Write equations of the following circles:

1. With center at $(-1,3)$ and radius 4.
2. With center at $(2,-3)$ and radius 5.
3. With center at $(0,0)$ and radius 2.
4. With center at $(0,3)$ and radius 4.
5. With center at $(-2,0)$ and radius 2.
6. With center at $(4,1)$ passing through $(3,5)$.
7. With center at $(-2,-3)$ passing through $(3,9)$.
8. With $(-2,3)$ and $(6,-7)$ as ends of a diameter.

Find the center and radius of the circle whose equation is:

9. $(x-2)^2+(y+5)^2=16.$ **10.** $x^2+(y-5)^2=1.$
11. $(x-1)^2+y^2=9.$ **12.** $x^2+y^2=16.$
13. $x^2-6x+y^2-2y=-6.$ (Hint: complete the square for both the x terms and the y terms.)
14. $x^2+8x+y^2-4y=5.$

Write in simple form an equation of each of the following loci, and plot the graph:

15. The locus of all points which can be the third vertex of a right triangle whose hypotenuse is the line-segment joining $(-5,0)$ and $(5,0)$. Is the point $(4,-3)$ on this locus? the point $(3,-4)$?

16. Given the points $A(0,10)$, $B(0,-10)$, and $P(x,y)$. Find the equation of the locus of all points P such that PA is perpendicular to PB. Is the point $(4,5)$ on this locus? the point $(6,-8)$?

17. Given the points $A(-2,0)$, $B(2,0)$, and $P(x,y)$. Find the equation of the locus of all points P such that the sum of the squares of the distances PA and PB is equal to 58. Is the point $(4,-3)$ on this locus? the point $(0,5)$?

98. THE GENERAL EQUATION OF DEGREE TWO

In the last section we saw that the equation of every circle is quadratic; that is, of degree two. The converse proposition (namely, that the graph of every quadratic equation in x and y is a circle) is *false*. However, it *can* be proved that every quadratic equation in x and y has a graph which is a **conic section** (that is, a curve which can be obtained as the intersection of a plane with a cone) except for trivial exceptional cases.* Let us discuss these curves in further detail.

* For example, the quadratic equation $x^2+y^2=-1$ has no locus at all since, x and y being real, neither x^2 nor y^2 can be negative and therefore no point can satisfy the equation.

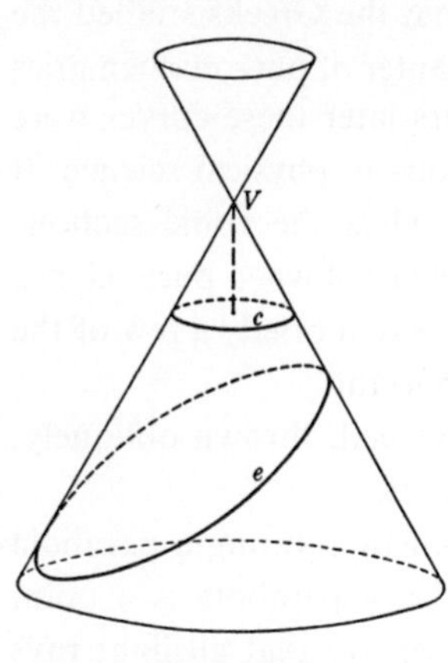

FIG. 106

Take a circle C (Fig. 106) in a horizontal plane and a point V, called the *vertex*, directly over the center of the circle. Consider all the lines, called *generators*, joining the vertex to the points on the circumference C. The set of all the points on these lines is called a **cone** (more precisely, a *right circular cone*).

It is intuitively clear that every horizontal plane section of the cone is a circle, unless it be the vertex itself. A non-horizontal plane section cutting through two opposite generators is called an **ellipse** (e, Fig. 106). A plane parallel to a generator intersects the cone in a curve called a **parabola** (p, Fig. 107). A plane cutting both the upper and lower parts of the cone intersects the cone in a curve called a **hyperbola**, a curve which falls into two branches (h, Fig. 107).

Examples 2, 3, 4, 5 of section 94 are a parabola, circle, hyperbola, and ellipse, respectively. These are the only types of conic sections, save for trivial special cases.*

The conic sections were studied by the ancient Greeks by "synthetic" methods such as those you used in high school. A splendid book on the subject was written by Apollonius of Perga (about the third century B.C.) in which a wealth of knowledge about the conic sections was obtained with great ingenuity. The analytic methods of Descartes enable us to study these curves with ease by means of quadratic equations, and furthermore to discover algebraically many theorems about them that the

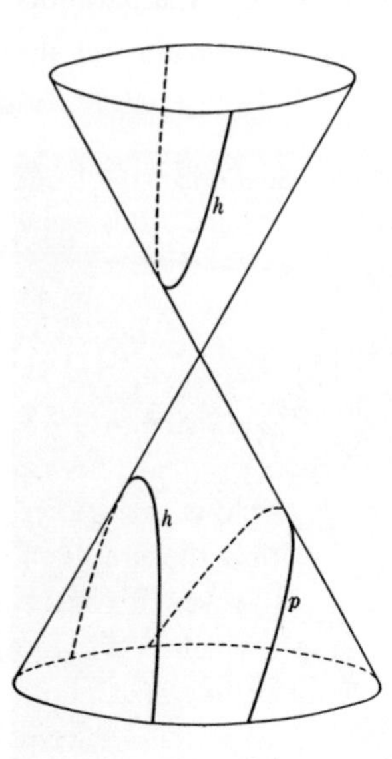

FIG. 107

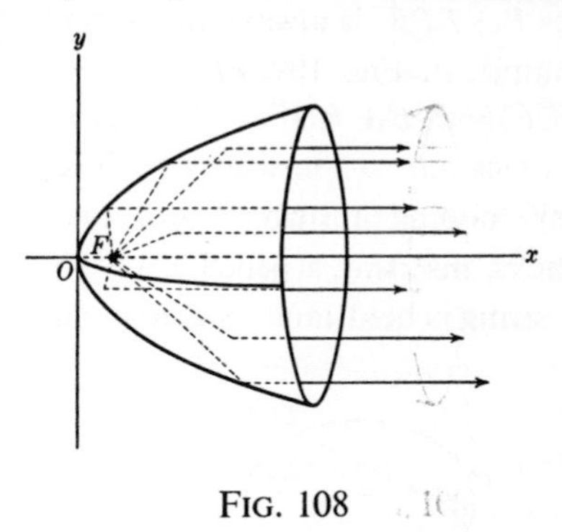

FIG. 108

* If the cutting plane passes through the vertex of the cone, the intersection may consist of a pair of straight lines, a single straight line, or a single point.

Greeks had never suspected. It is interesting to note that the Greeks studied the geometry of the conic sections merely as a beautiful chapter of pure mathematics and had no thought of applications. About 1800 years later these curves were found to have the most important practical applications in physical science. It is, in fact, difficult to exaggerate their importance. Thus the conic sections provide striking evidence for the thesis that one can never tell when pure science may find unsuspected practical applications. We shall sketch briefly a few of the many connections in which the conic sections are important.

The path of a projectile, like a baseball or a cannon ball, thrown obliquely, is a parabola, neglecting the influence of air resistance, etc.

Searchlight reflectors are parabolic surfaces obtained by rotating a parabola about its axis (the x-axis in Fig. 108). Associated with a parabola is a point called its *focus*. This point (F in Fig. 108) has the property that all light rays emanating from it will be reflected in the same direction, thus concentrating the beam of the searchlight in that direction and preventing it from spreading. For the same reason the mirrors in reflecting telescopes used in astronomy are parabolic. For the light rays entering the telescope from a distant star are, practically, parallel. Hence the parabolic reflectors concentrate all these rays at the focus.

The cable of a suspension bridge is, under certain circumstances, a parabola. Arches are sometimes parabolic in shape.

Associated with an ellipse there are two points within it called the *foci* of the ellipse (F and F' in Fig. 109). The ellipse has the property that, for any point P on it whatever, the sum of the distances $P + FPF'$ is always the same. For example, in Fig. 109, $PF + PF' = P'F + P'F' = P''F + P''F'$. This property enables one to construct an ellipse easily by looping a string about two thumbtacks, inserting a pencil point so that the string is held taut, and moving

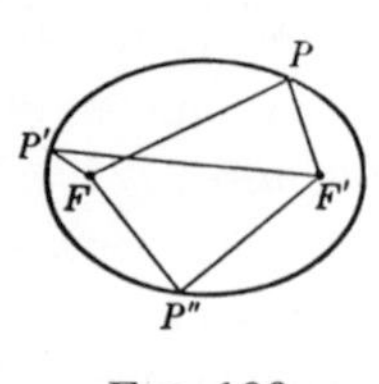

FIG. 109

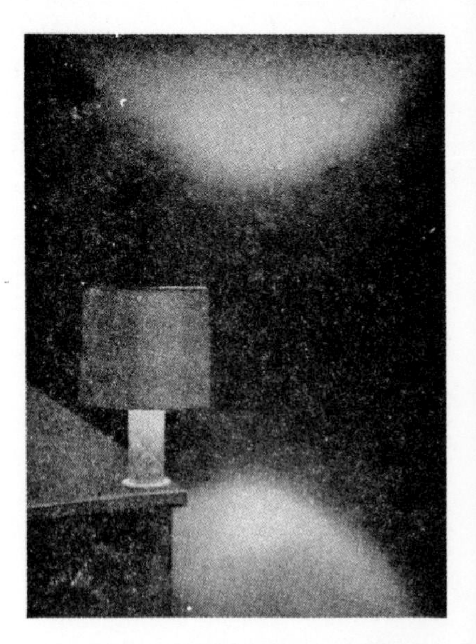

FIG. 110

the point about. Thus one gets an ellipse with the two tacks as foci.

The orbits of the planets are ellipses with the sun at one focus. This alone is sufficient to explain the overwhelming importance of ellipses since the seventeenth century when Kepler and Newton did their monumental work in astronomy.

The ellipse has interesting reflecting properties. It can be shown that all rays of light, or sound waves, emanating from one focus must collect again at the other focus. This explains the amusing phenomenon of the whispering gallery. If the walls or ceiling of a hall are elliptical, then a whisper at one focus may not be audible at all at a nearby place but may nevertheless be audible far off at the other focus, since all the individually weak sound waves scattering over the room will gather together there (Fig. 109). One such whispering gallery exists in Statuary Hall, Washington, D. C.

The orbits of some meteors are parabolas while others are branches of hyperbolas. Many scientific laws are expressed as quadratic equations involving two variable quantities, and hence their graphs are conic sections. But the applications of the conic sections in modern science are too numerous to list.

Fairly good approximations of the various conic sections may be seen by shining a flashlight on a wall in an otherwise dark room and varying the angle at which the flashlight is held. This is so because the light emanates from the circular opening of the flashlight in an approximate cone and the wall plays the role of the intersecting plane. Both branches of a hyperbola may be seen when a lamp with a cylindrical shade is placed near a wall (Fig. 110).

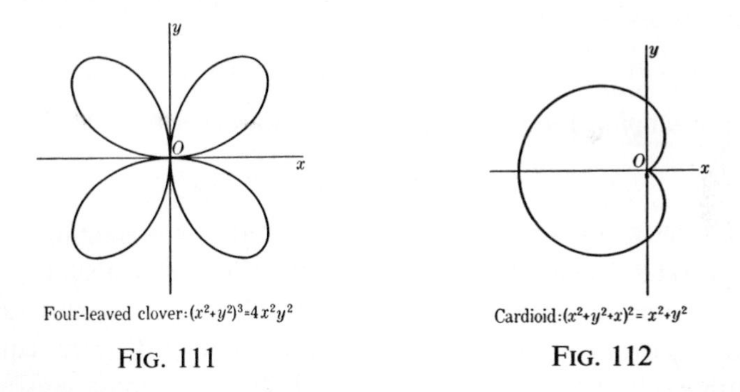

Four-leaved clover: $(x^2+y^2)^3=4x^2y^2$

FIG. 111

Cardioid: $(x^2+y^2+x)^2=x^2+y^2$

FIG. 112

After discovering the connection between conic sections and equations of the second degree in x and y, the mathematician's desire to obtain general results naturally leads him to investigate the geometric properties of the graphs of equations of higher degree. This study is called the *theory of algebraic curves* and is a very difficult and intricate branch of modern mathematics in which research is still being done. Many parts of modern mathematics, like this one, arise from elementary problems which come up naturally in elementary work.

Exercises

Plot the following curves:

1. The parabola $y = 10 - \frac{1}{2}x^2$.

2. The parabola $y = \frac{1}{2}x^2 - 10$.

3. The hyperbola $xy = 10$.

4. The hyperbola $x^2 - y^2 = 1$.

5. The ellipse $4x^2 + 25y^2 = 100$.

6. The ellipse $25x^2 + 4y^2 = 100$.

Write in simple form an equation of each of the following loci and plot the graph:

7. The locus of all points P whose distances from the line $x = -2$ and from the point (2,0) are equal.

8. The locus of all points P such that the distance from P to the point $(-4,0)$ is equal to $\frac{4}{5}$ of the distance from P to the line $x = -\frac{25}{4}$.

9. The locus of all points P such that the distance from P to the point (5,0) is equal to $\frac{5}{4}$ of the distance from P to the line $x = \frac{16}{5}$.

10. The locus of all points P such that the lines joining P to (4,3) and $(-4,-3)$, respectively, are perpendicular.

99. COMMON CHORD OF TWO INTERSECTING CIRCLES

Consider any two circles

$$(1) \qquad (x - h)^2 + (y - k)^2 = r^2,$$

$$(2) \qquad (x - H)^2 + (y - K)^2 = R^2,$$

intersecting at two points. Form a new equation by subtracting (2) from (1), obtaining

$$(3) \qquad (x - h)^2 - (x - H)^2 + (y - k)^2 - (y - K)^2 = r^2 - R^2,$$

which can be simplified to the form

$$(4) \qquad (2H - 2h)x + (2K - 2k)y = r^2 - R^2 - h^2 - k^2 + H^2 + K^2.$$

This is a linear equation in x and y (the other letters representing constants). Suppose (x_1, y_1) is a point of intersection of the two circles; then (x_1, y_1) must satisfy both (1) and (2); hence it must satisfy (3) since if equals are subtracted from equals the results are equal. Therefore it must satisfy (4). By the same argument, the second point of intersection (x_2, y_2) must satisfy (4). But (4) is a linear equation and its graph is therefore a straight line. Now, two points determine a straight line and we already know that our two points of intersection are on this line (4). Hence (4) is an equation of the line joining the two points of intersection of

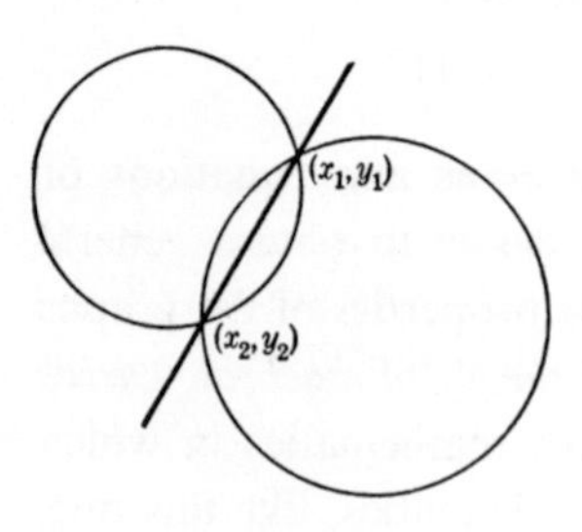

FIG. 113

the given circles. This line is called the **common chord** of the two circles. We have proved the following theorem.

Theorem 17. *An equation of the common chord of two circles intersecting at two points may be obtained by subtracting the equation of one circle from the equation of the other circle (provided they are written so that the coefficients of x^2 and y^2 are the same in both equations) and simplifying.*

Exercises

Find an equation of the common chord of the given circles and plot:

1. $(x-3)^2+(y-5)^2=25.$
$(x-5)^2+(y-3)^2=25.$

2. $(x+1)^2+(y-2)^2=16$
$(x-1)^2+(y+2)^2=9.$

3. $x^2+y^2=16$
$(x+2)^2+(y-2)^2=9.$

4. $(x+2)^2+(y-1)^2=5$
$x^2+y^2=10.$

100. INTERSECTION OF TWO CURVES

Consider the graphs of two equations. By a point of intersection of the two curves we mean a point on both of them; that is, a point belonging to the intersection of the truth-sets of the two equations. If (x_1, y_1) is such a point, then $x=x_1$ and $y=y_1$ must satisfy both equations because the point is on both curves. Conversely, if $x=x_1$ and $y=y_1$ are real numbers which satisfy both equations, then (x_1, y_1) is a point on both curves. Thus *the coordinates of the points of intersection of two curves are merely the real common solutions of the two equations; to find the points of intersection we have only to solve the two equations simultaneously.*

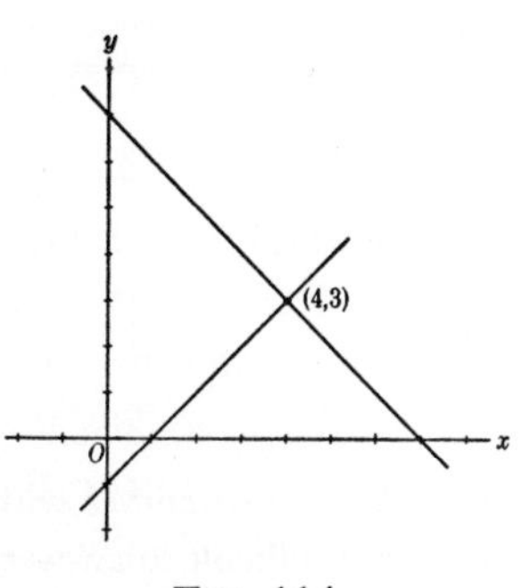

FIG. 114

Example 1. Let the curves be straight lines: say $x+y=7$ and $x-y=1$. From the first equation we obtain $y=7-x$. Substituting this in the second equation, and solving as in section 45, we have $x=4$ and $y=3$. Hence (4,3) is the point of intersection. The student should work out the details.

Example 2. Consider a straight line and a conic section: say

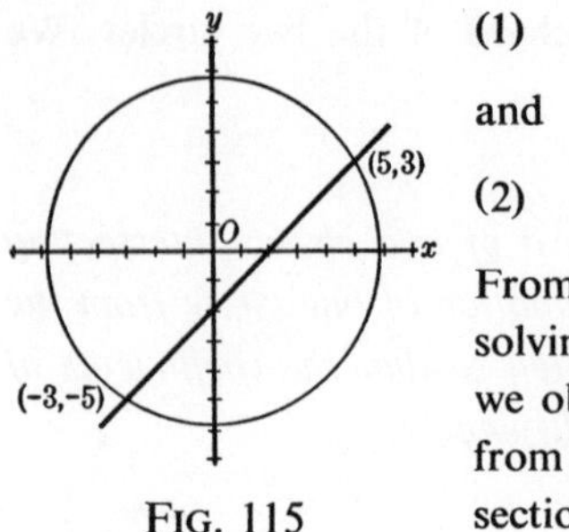

FIG. 115

(1) $$x - y = 2$$

and

(2) $$x^2 + y^2 = 34.$$

From (1) we obtain $y = x - 2$. Substituting this in (2), and solving as in section 46, we find $x = 5$ or $x = -3$. For $x = 5$, we obtain $y = 3$ from (1); for $x = -3$ we obtain $y = -5$ from (1). Hence (5,3) and $(-3,-5)$ are the points of intersection. The student should complete the solution in detail.

Example 3. To find the intersections of two circles we have only to find the equation of their common chord (theorem 17, section 99) and find the points of intersection of this line with one of the circles as in example 2. Thus, the circles

(3) $$(x - 2)^2 + y^2 = 5$$

(4) $$x^2 + (y - 1)^2 = 10$$

have the common chord

(5) $$2x - y = 4.$$

The points of intersection of this line with the circle (3) are found to be (3,2) and $(1,-2)$. Hence these are the points of intersection of the two given circles. The details of the solution should be worked out by the student.

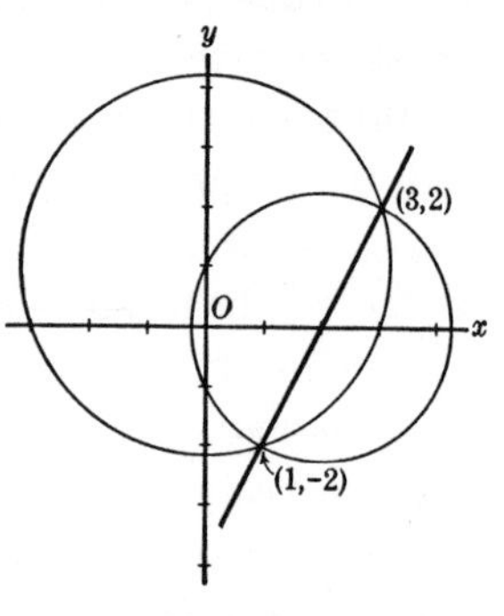

FIG. 116

The general problem of finding the points of intersection of any two curves with equations of arbitrary degree is a very natural one to think of but difficult to answer. See section 46.

Exercises

Find all the points of intersection of the following curves and plot:

1. $2x - 3y = 4$
$3x + 4y + 11 = 0.$

2. $3x - 2y = 5$
$x + 5y = 1.$

3. $2x - 5y = 3$
$3x + y = 4.$

4. $y^2 = 4x$
$x + y = 3.$

5. $y^2 = 4x$
$y = 2.$

6. $y^2 = 4x$
$x = 1.$

7. $x^2 + y^2 = 25$
$4x - 3y = 0.$

8. $xy = 12$
$x + y = 7.$

9. $x^2 + y^2 = 41$
$x + y = 9.$

10. $x^2 - y^2 = 5$
$3x + y = 11.$

11. $y^2 = x$
$y - 4x + 3 = 0.$

12. $(x - 3)^2 + (y - 4)^2 = 4$
$x + y = 16.$

13. $(x - 2)^2 + (y - 5) = 0$
$y = x + 1.$

14. $(y + 1)^2 = x - 2$
$y + 12 - 4x = 0.$

15. $(x + 2)^2 + y^2 = 5$
$x^2 + (y - 1)^2 = 10.$

16. $(x + 1)^2 + (y + 1)^2 = 5$
$(x + 3)^2 + y^2 = 10.$

17. $(x \times 2)^2 + y^2 = 5$
$x^2 + (y + 1)^2 = 10.$

18. $(x + 2)^2 + (y - 1)^2 = 5$
$x^2 + y^2 = 10.$

19. Plot the graphs of $x + y = 3$ and $x + y = 7$. Explain the geometric interpretation of the fact that these equations are incompatible (see section 45).

20. Plot the graphs of $x + 2y = 3$ and $2x + 4y = 6$. Explain the geometric interpretation of the fact that these equations are dependent or equivalent (see section 45).

21. In the triangle whose vertices are (0,0), (6,0), and (2,4):

(*a*) Find the coordinates of the midpoints of the sides;
(*b*) Find the equations of the medians;
(*c*) Find the point of intersection of two of the medians (compare exercise 8(*b*) of section 91);
(*d*) Show that the three medians are concurrent;
(*e*) Show that the distance from each vertex to the point of intersection of the medians is 2/3 of the length of the corresponding median.

22. In the triangle of exercise 21,

(*a*) Find the equations of the three altitudes;
(*b*) Show that they are concurrent.

23. In the triangle of exercise 21.

(*a*) Find the equations of the three prependicular bisectors of the sides;
(*b*) Show that they are concurrent;
(*c*) Show that the point of intersection of the altitudes (found in exercise 22), the point of intersection of the medians (found in exercise 21), and the point of intersection of the perpendicular bisectors all lie on the same straight line.

24. If A, B, C have the coordinates (2,1), (5,4), (7,−3), respectively, find the coordinates of:

(*a*) The vertex D of the parallelogram $ABCD$;
(*b*) The vertex E of the parallelogram $ABEC$;
(*c*) The vertex F of the parallelogram $AFBC$.

***25.** Prove that in any triangle:

(*a*) The three medians are concurrent;
(*b*) The three perpendicular bisectors of the sides are concurrent;
(*c*) The three altitudes are concurrent.
(*d*) Show that the three points found in parts (*a*), (*b*), and (*c*) lie on the same straight line.

(Hint: assign coordinates (0,0),($2a$,0), ($2b$,$2c$) to the three vertices.)

*101. GRAPHS OF INEQUALITIES

Let us locate the set of all points of the plane whose coordinates satisfy the inequality $x + 3y > 6$; that is, the truth-set of the propositional function expressed by the inequality. Using the rules for manipulating inequalities, which the student should now review (sections 28 and 32), this set is the set such that $y > -\frac{1}{3}x + 2$. For any given value of x, the point on the line l with equation $y = -\frac{1}{3}x + 2$ lying on the same vertical line V as $(x,0)$ has the y-coordinate $y = -\frac{1}{3}x + 2$. All points on this vertical line V lying above l have y-coordinates such that $y > -\frac{1}{3}x + 2$; these points occupy the dotted portion of V (Fig. 117). All points on V lying below l have y-coordinates such that $y < -\frac{1}{3}x + 2$; these occupy the dashed portion of V (Fig. 117). Thus the set of all points such that

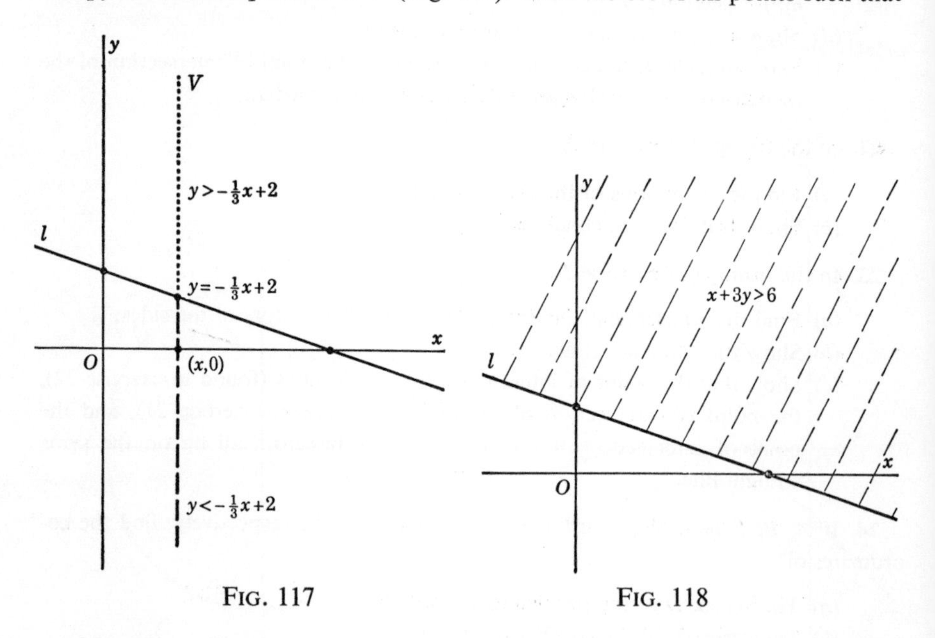

FIG. 117 FIG. 118

* This section is needed only for section 102. Otherwise it may be omitted without disturbing the continuity.

$y > -\frac{1}{3}x + 2$, or equivalently $x + 3y > 6$, is the set of all points lying above l indicated by shading in Fig. 118. The unshaded region below l is similarly the graph of the inequality $x + 3y < 6$, or $y < -\frac{1}{3}x + 2$. The graph of $y \geqq -\frac{1}{3}x + 2$, or $x + 3y \geqq 6$, is the set of points lying above or on l; i.e., the union of the graph of $x + 3y > 6$ and the graph of $x + 3y = 6$.

Example 1. The graph of the system

$$\begin{cases} x + 3y > 6 \\ y < x - 2 \end{cases}$$

that is, the set of points satisfying both inequalities is the intersection of the truth-set of $x + 3y > 6$ with the truth-set of $y < x - 2$. This is the cross-hatched region R in Fig. 119.

Clearly, any straight line $ax + by = c$ divides the rest of the plane into two regions satisfying the inequalities $ax + by > c$ and $ax + by < c$, respectively. These are the two "sides" of the line.

Similarly, the circle $x^2 + y^2 = 1$ divides the rest of the plane into two regions, satisfying the inequalities $x^2 + y^2 < 1$ and $x^2 + y^2 > 1$, respectively. Since $x^2 + y^2$ is the square of the distance of (x, y) from the origin, these regions are clearly the "inside" and "outside" of the circle, respectively.

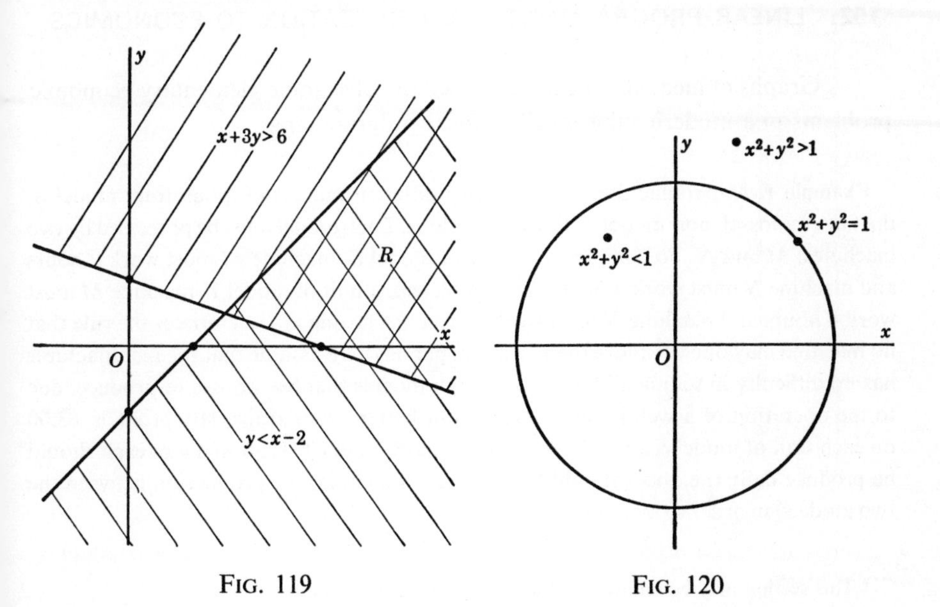

FIG. 119

FIG. 120

Exercises

Indicate, by shading, the regions described by the following inequalities:

1. $x + y \geqq 7$. **2.** $x + y < 7$. **3.** $2x - y \geqq 3$.
4. $2x - y \leqq 3$. **5.** $x^2 + y^2 \leqq 9$. **6.** $x^2 + y^2 > 9$.

7. (*a*) $\begin{cases} x + y \geqq 7 \\ x - y \geqq 1 \end{cases}$ (*b*) $\begin{cases} x + y \geqq 7 \\ x - y \leqq 1 \end{cases}$ (*c*) $\begin{cases} x + y \leqq 7 \\ x - y \geqq 1 \end{cases}$ (*d*) $\begin{cases} x + y \leqq 7 \\ x - y \leqq 1. \end{cases}$

8. $\begin{cases} x \geqq 0 \\ y \geqq 0 \\ x + y \leqq 3. \end{cases}$ **9.** $\begin{cases} x \geqq 0 \\ y \geqq 0 \\ x \times y \geqq 3. \end{cases}$ **10.** $\begin{cases} x \geqq 0 \\ y \geqq 0 \\ x + 2y \leqq 6 \\ 2x + y \leqq 6. \end{cases}$

11. $\begin{cases} x \geqq 0 \\ y \geqq 0 \\ x + 2y \geqq 6 \\ 2x + y \geqq 6. \end{cases}$ **12.** $\begin{cases} x^2 + y^2 \leqq 4 \\ x + y \leqq 2 \\ x \geqq 0. \end{cases}$ **13.** $\begin{cases} x^2 + y^2 \leqq 4 \\ x + y \geqq 2. \end{cases}$

14. $\begin{cases} y \geqq x^2 \\ y \leqq x. \end{cases}$ **15.** $\begin{cases} 2x + 3y \leqq 12 \\ 2x + y \leqq 8 \\ x \geqq 0 \\ y \geqq 0 \end{cases}$ **16.** $\begin{cases} x \geqq 0 \\ y \geqq 0 \\ x \leqq 4 \\ y \leqq 3 \\ x + y \leqq 5. \end{cases}$

*102. LINEAR PROGRAMMING. AN APPLICATION TO ECONOMICS

Graphs of inequalities can be applied to solve some elementary economic problems in a modern subject called linear programming.

Example 1. A manufacturer produces two different models of mousetrap, model S, the Supercolossal, and model T, the Tremendous. Each model must be processed by two machines, M and N. To complete one unit of model S, machine M must work 2 hours and machine N must work 4 hours. To complete one unit of model T, machine M must work 4 hours and machine N must work 2 hours. A strong union enforces the rule that no machine may operate more than 12 hours per day. We assume that the manufacturer has no difficulty in selling all the units of both models that he chooses to produce, due to the operation of a well-known adage about better mousetraps. His profit is \$3.00 on each unit of model S and \$5.00 on each unit of model T. How many of each should he produce daily (i.e., how should be allocate his facilities for production between the two models) in order to maximize his profit?

* This section may be omitted without disturbing the continuity.

Solution. Let x be the number of units of model S and y the number of units of model T produced daily. His daily profit is then

$$P = 3x + 5y. \tag{1}$$

We must find values of x and y which will maximize P subject to the constraints

$$x \geqq 0 \tag{2}$$

$$y \geqq 0 \tag{3}$$

$$2x + 4y \leqq 12 \tag{4}$$

$$4x + 2y \leqq 12. \tag{5}$$

The constraints (2) and (3) express the fact that it is impossible to manufacture a negative number of either model. Constraints (4) and (5) indicate that machines M and N, respectively, may not operate more than 12 hours per day. Any point (x,y) in the plane satisfying the constraints (2), (3), (4), (5), is termed a **feasible point.** The set of feasible points consists of the shaded region in Fig. 121, including its boundary. For a given value of P, say $P = 10$, the points (x,y) yielding $P = 10$ constitute a straight line (Fig. 121). For a larger value of P, say $P = 12$, they lie on a parallel line with a higher y-intercept, since the y-intercept of (1) is $P/5$. For various values of P we get a family of parallel lines. It is clear from the figure, and it can be proved, that the line of this family with highest y-intercept, and therefore highest P, which contains a feasible point on it must intersect the feasible (shaded) region at a corner point. (If the family of lines happens to be parallel to a side of the feasible polygonal region then the same maximum value is attained at both corner points and, indeed, all along this side; but it is still sufficient to check the corner points.) Checking the corner points we find that (2,2) is the point required since for (2,2) we have $P = 16$ while for the other corners we get lower values of P, namely, 0, 9, and 15. Hence this manufacturer should produce equal numbers of both models; that is, he should produce them in the ratio 2:2. A hasty decision to produce more of model T because of the larger profit from each unit of model T would have yielded him less profit. The point (2,2) which maximizes (1) subject to the given constraints is termed **optimal.**

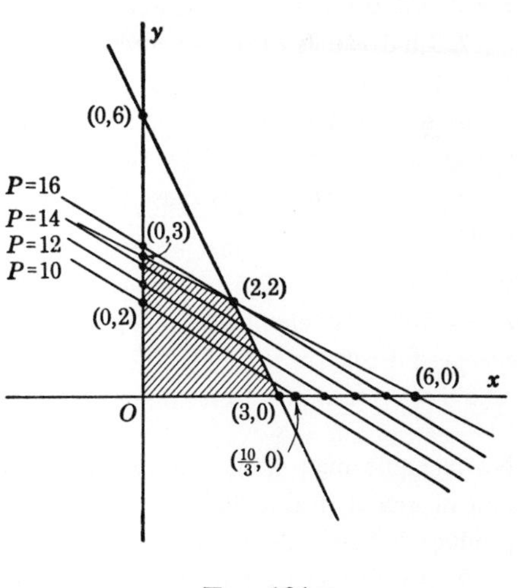

FIG. 121

In general, a problem in which it is required to determine unknowns $x, y, z, \ldots$ so as to maximize or minimize a linear expression

$$ax + by + cz + \cdots \tag{6}$$

subject to linear inequalities or constraints is termed a **linear programming** problem. The points satisfying the constraints are termed **feasible**. A feasible point which maximizes or minimizes the expression (6) as required is termed **optimal**. When the number of unknowns is more than two, the simple graphical method used above is inadequate, but a systematic study may be made of the analogous analytic geometry of space of three or more dimensions, the number of dimensions corresponding to the number of unknowns (see section 106 and Chapter 14). The subject has been successfully applied in large-scale allocation, supply, and other problems of business and military establishments.

Exercises

1. Find x and y so as to maximize $Q = x + y$, and find the maximum value of Q, subject to the constraints, $x \geqq 0$, $y \geqq 0$, $x + 3y \leqq 9$, $2x + y \leqq 8$.

2. Find x and y so as to maximize $C = x + y$, and find the maximum value of C, subject to the constraints $x \geqq 0$, $y \geqq 0$, $x \leqq 6$, $y \leqq 3$, $x + 2y \leqq 8$.

3. Find x and y so as to maximize $K = x + 4y$, subject to the same constraints as in exercise 2.

4. Find x and y so as to minimize $Q = x + y$, and find the minimum value of Q, subject to the constraints $x \geqq 0$, $y \geqq 0$, $2x + y \geqq 4$, $x + 3y \geqq 7$.

5. Find x and y so as to minimize $C = 2x + 3y$, and find the minimum C, subject to the constraints $x \geqq 0$, $y \geqq 0$, $2x + y \geqq 6$, $x + 3y \geqq 8$.

6. Find values of x and y which minimize $C = x + y$ subject to the constraints $x \geqq 0$, $y \geqq 0$, $3x + 4y \geqq 24$, and $x + 2y \geqq 10$, and find the minimum value of C.

7. Find values of x and y which maximize $C = x + y$ subject to the constraints $x \geqq 0$, $y \geqq 0$, $3x + 4y \leqq 24$, $x + 2y \leqq 10$, and find the maximum value of C.

8. A manufacturer produces two different models A and B of a product. Each model must be processed by two machines I and II. To complete one unit of each model, the two machines must work the number of hours indicated in the following table:

	A	B
I	3	1
II	1	3

No machine may operate more than 12 hours per day. The profit is \$3.00 on each unit of model A and \$6.00 on each unit of model B. How many of each should be produce daily in order to maximize his profit?

9. An animal feed is to be a mixture of two foodstuffs A and B each ounce of which contains protein, fat, and carbohydrate in the tabulated numbers of grams:

	A	B
Protein	10	5
Fat	0.1	0.9
Carbohydrate	15	20

The costs of foodstuffs A and B are 4 and 3 cents per ounce, respectively. Each bag of the resulting mixture is to contain at least 50 grams of protein, 1.8 grams of fat, and 150 grams of carbohydrates. Find the numbers x and y of ounces of A and B, respectively, which will produce a mixture satisfying these minimum requirements which will minimize the cost.

10. A manufacturer makes two models A and B of a product. Each model must be processed by 3 machines I, II, III. The number of hours each machine must be used on each unit of each model is given by the table:

	A	B
I	39/5	1
II	20/3	20/3
III	1	19/2

No machine may work more than 40 hours per week. The profit on each unit is $20 for model A and $30 for model B. How many of each model should the manufacturer produce per week in order to maximize his profit?

11. A company has 16 tons of a commodity of which 10 tons are in one warehouse W_1 and 6 tons in another warehouse W_2. It must all be delivered to three company stores S_1, S_2, S_3 in the amounts 5 tons, 7 tons, 4 tons, respectively. The cost per ton of transporting from the two warehouses to the three stores is given by the table:

	S_1	S_2	S_3
W_1	$7.00	$5.00	$8.00
W_2	$2.00	$3.00	$4.00

Find the amounts to be shipped from each warehouse to each store in order to make the transportation costs minimum, and find the minimum cost. (Hint: let the number of tons to be shipped from the warehouses to the stores be given by the table:

	S_1	S_2	S_3
W_1	x	y	$10 - x - y$
W_2	$5 - x$	$7 - y$	$6 - (5 - x) - (7 - y)$.

The cost $C = 7x + 5y + 8(10 - x - y) + 2(5 - x) + 3(7 - y) + 4(x + y - 6)$ is to be minimized subject to the constraints $x \geqq 0$, $y \geqq 0$, $5 - x \geqq 0$, $7 - y \geqq 0$, $10 - x - y \geqq 0$, $x + y - 6 \geqq 0$.)

103. TRANSLATION OF AXES. INVARIANTS

All our work has been based on a definite set of axes (that is, a definite coordinate system) although we have at times allowed ourselves to choose these axes in a convenient position. Suppose, now, that we change from our given coordinate system to a new coordinate system whose origin is at the point (2,3) and whose axes are parallel to the old axes and have similar positive directions. Call the old system the xy-system (Fig. 122), and the new one the $x'y'$-system. A change of coordinate system where the new axes are parallel to the old, with similar positive directions, is called a **translation** of axes. Consider the point P (Fig. 122) whose coordinates are (3,9) in the xy-system; clearly, its coordinates in the $x'y'$-system are (1,6). Similarly, the point Q whose coordinates in the xy-system are (6,5) has the coordinates (4,2) in the $x'y'$-system. Thus the values of the coordinates of a point depend upon where the pair of axes or "frame of reference" is located. However, consider the distance PQ. Using the xy-system,

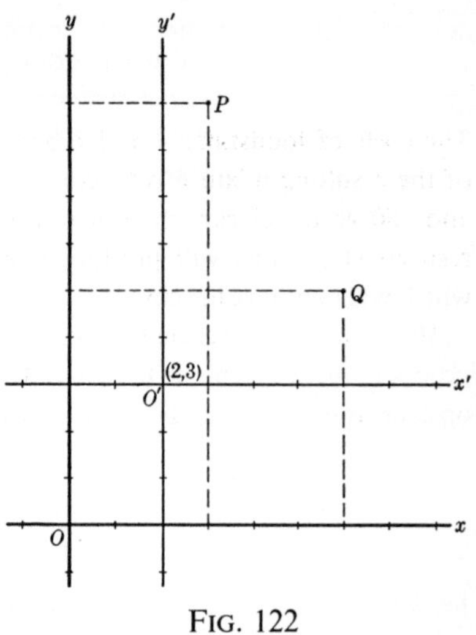

FIG. 122

$$PQ = \sqrt{(3-6)^2 + (9-5)^2} = \sqrt{(-3)^2 + (4)^2} = 5;$$

and using the $x'y'$-system,

$$PQ = \sqrt{(1-4)^2 + (6-2)^2} = \sqrt{(-3)^2 + (4)^2} = 5.$$

This suggests that, while the coordinates of a point change when we make a translation of axes, the distance between the two points remains unchanged or **invariant**; that is, the expression for the distance gives the same value in either system.

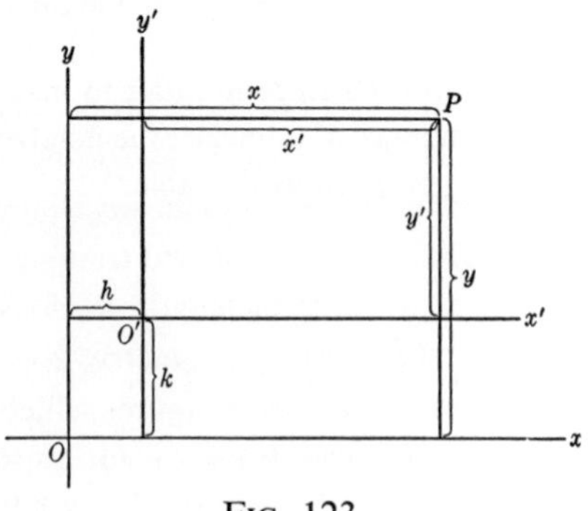

FIG. 123

In general, if we translate our axes so that the new origin is at a point whose old coordinates are (h,k), then for any point P with coordinates (x, y) in the old system and coordinates (x', y') in the new system, we have (Fig. 123)

$$\text{(1)} \qquad \begin{cases} x = x' + h \\ y = y' + k \end{cases}, \quad \text{or} \quad \begin{cases} x' = x - h \\ y' = y - k. \end{cases}$$

Thus the coordinates of an individual point are altered by the translation. Let P_1 and P_2 be points whose old coordinates are (x_1, y_1) and (x_2, y_2) and whose new coordinates are (x_1', y_1') and (x_2', y_2'), respectively. Then by (1) we have

$$\text{(2)} \qquad \begin{array}{ll} x_1 = x_1' + h, & x_2 = x_2' + h, \\ y_1 = y_1' + k, & y_2 = y_2' + k. \end{array}$$

In the xy-system the distance

$$\text{(3)} \qquad P_1P_2 = \sqrt{(x_1 - x_2)^2 + (y_1 - y_2)^2},$$

and in the $x'y'$-system the distance

$$\text{(4)} \qquad P_1P_2 = \sqrt{(x_1' - x_2')^2 + (y_1' - y_2')^2}.$$

Substituting the values given by (2) in (3) we obtain

$$\sqrt{(x_1 - x_2)^2 + (y_1 - y_2)^2} = \sqrt{(x_1' + h - x_2' - h)^2 + (y_1' + k - y_2' - k)^2}$$
$$= \sqrt{(x_1' - x_2')^2 + (y_1' - y_2')^2}.$$

This proves that the value of the expression called the distance formula is unaltered by a translation of the axes; that is, it yields the same numerical value no matter in which of the two coordinate systems we apply it. With a little more technical knowledge than we assume here, it can be proved that the distance formula also remains invariant or unaltered if we rotate our axes (Fig. 124). On the other hand, the numerical value of the distance formula would not remain unchanged if we chose a different unit of length. Thus the points (2,0) and (4,0) have a distance of 2; but if we doubled the size of the unit of length they would have coordinates (1,0) and (2,0), respectively, and their distance would be 1. But even a change of unit will leave the ratio of two lengths invariant.

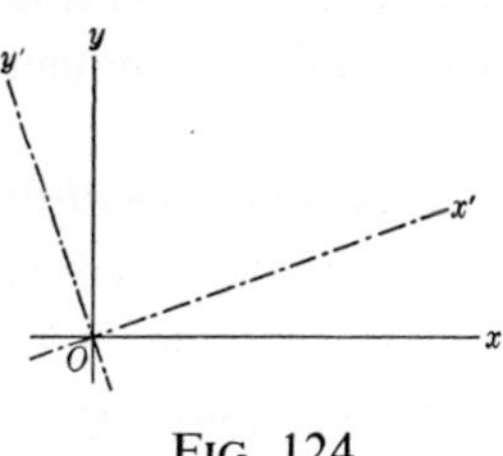

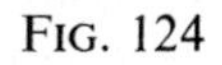
FIG. 124

From one point of view, the study of geometry is the study of those properties of figures which remain invariant under various kinds of changes. Thus distances (as we have proved), areas, angles, etc., are properties which remain invariant when translations (or rotations) of axes are made. The property of two triangles being similar remains invariant even under changes of units of length, as does the size of an angle, while length and area do not. Elementary geometry, considered from this point of view, is the study of those properties of figures which remain invariant under the types of changes or "transformations" mentioned above.

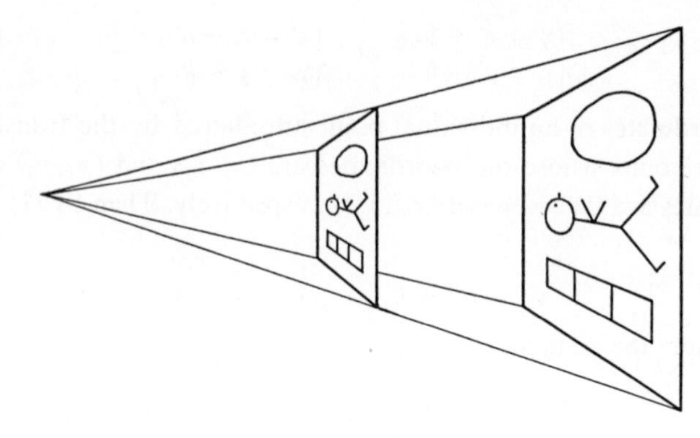

FIG. 125

A figure on a flat piece of moving picture film is said to be *projected* into its image on a flat screen which may or may not be parallel to the film (Fig. 125). If one figure can be obtained from another by a number of such projections, the second is said to have been transformed into the first by projection. The study of those properties of figures which remain invariant or unchanged by projections is called **projective geometry**. Clearly, the property of being a circle is not invariant under projections, as may be seen from section 98. But the property of having a second degree equation (that is, of being a conic section) is invariant under projections. Thus a circle can be projected into an ellipse or a parabola, etc., but not into a curve whose equation is of the third degree, say. A classic work on projective geometry was written by the French mathematician Poncelet (1788–1867) while he was a prisoner of war in Russia.

A very general kind of geometry, developed largely in the twentieth century is called **topology** or **analysis situs**. This subject may be partially described as the study of those properties of figures which remain invariant when the figure is deformed in any "continuous" way. Thus, if we imagine our figures to be made of rubber, we may think of them as being folded, stretched, bent, crumpled,

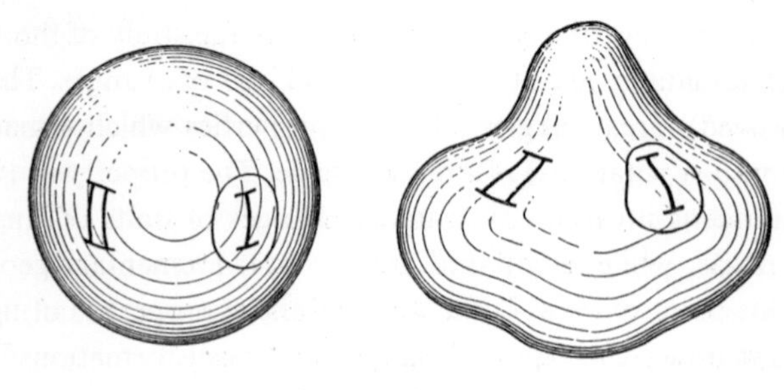

FIG. 126

and deformed in any way at all as long as they are not punctured or torn. It may be difficult to imagine that such drastic changes will leave any properties of the figure unchanged or invariant. But there are some. Thus a simple property of a spherical surface like a rubber balloon is that if we cut it along any "closed" curve like a circle, the surface will fall apart into two pieces (Fig. 126). This property will be preserved under deformations of the sphere. Notice that this property of falling into two pieces when cut along a closed curve is not possessed by a doughnut surface or inner tube; thus if the latter is cut along the circle C in Fig. 127, it still hangs together in one piece. The property of being inseparably linked, as the two links of a chain in Fig. 128, is unchanged no matter how we deform continuously the shapes of the links. Topology has been called the science of carelessly drawn figures, since a topologist would not distinguish between the two figures in Fig. 128, for example, because he is interested only in properties which are preserved when one of these figures is deformed into the other. Similarly, he would not distinguish between a doughnut and a coffee cup. The 4-color problem, the problem of the 7 bridges of Königsberg, and the problem of 3 houses and 3 wells discussed in Chapter 8 are problems of topology since the actual rigid shape of the figures in question may be deformed continuously without affecting the problem. The study of topology is one of the most recent kinds of geometry to be developed and has proved to be of importance even in application to physical science.

The idea of invariants occurs in physical science itself. Our measurements of the position and velocity of a star, say, depend on the axes or frame of reference

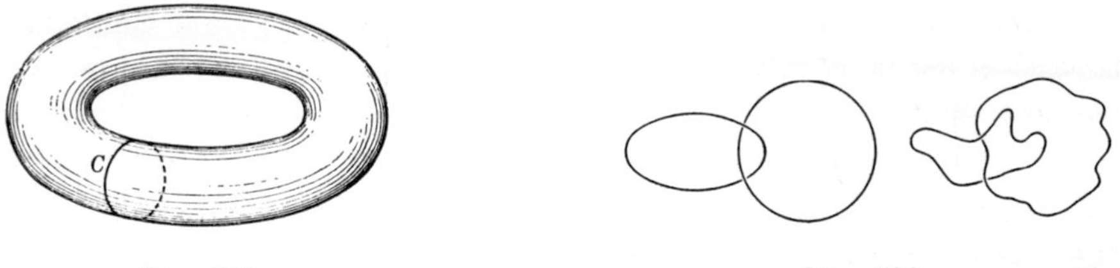

FIG. 127

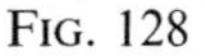

FIG. 128

to which we refer its coordinates. This depends on the position and motion of the observer, among other things. But we would like our "laws of nature" to be independent of the observer. Hence we would like "laws of nature" to be expressible as formulas which are invariant under changes of frame of reference. Of course, in a broad sense, the task of the scientist is the search for invariant relationships under varying conditions; it is the search for permanence in a changing world.

104. THREE DIMENSIONAL OR SOLID GEOMETRY

Just as we associate an ordered pair of coordinates with a point in a plane, we can associate an ordered triplet of coordinates with a point in space. Taking three mutually perpendicular lines as x-axis, y-axis, and z-axis, respectively, we locate the point whose coordinates are $(2,3,-4)$ by proceeding 2 units in the direction of the positive x-axis, 3 units in the direction of the positive y-axis, and 4 units in the direction of the negative z-axis (Fig. 129). Because each point in space is thus identified by means of three coordinates, the geometry of space is called 3-dimensional. It can be proved that the distance between two points (x_1, y_1, z_1) and (x_2, y_2, z_2) is

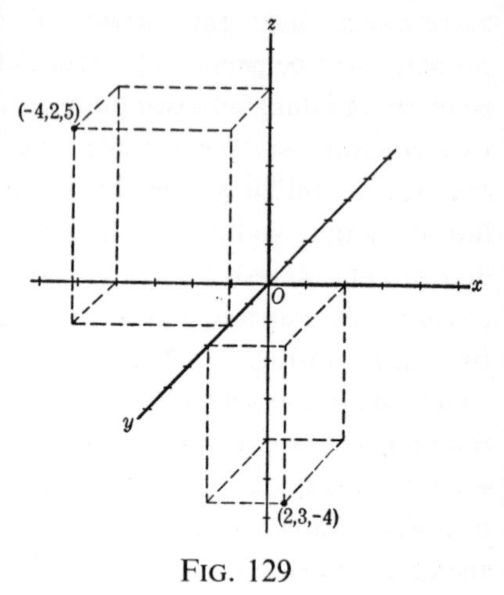

FIG. 129

$$\sqrt{(x_1 - x_2)^2 + (y_1 - y_2)^2 + (z_1 - z_2)^2};$$

that the set of all points satisfying an equation of the first degree, such as $x + 2y - 3z = 4$, constitutes a plane; that the set of all points satisfying the equation $x^2 + y^2 + z^2 = 25$ constitutes the surface of a sphere of radius 5 with center at the origin; and so on. Thus the study of solid geometry, which requires considerable ingenuity when attacked by methods of the ancient Greeks, is reduced to the study of algebra with three variables, a subject which can be studied systematically with much less difficulty.

105. ANALYTIC GEOMETRY AS A CONCRETE INTERPRETATION OF THE POSTULATES FOR GEOMETRY

We have said that any theorem that can be proved in geometry by means of the methods of the ancient Greeks can also be proved by means of coordinates. How can we be sure that this is so? This question can be answered simply by approaching analytic geometry from a slightly different point of view.

Let us recall the postulates for geometry given in Chapter 2. We considered the words "point" and "line" as undefined terms and we assumed about these undefined terms such properties as the following:

Postulate 1. *Given two distinct points, there is at least one line containing them.*

The postulates and their logical consequences, the theorems, constitute the abstract mathematical science known as geometry. As we pointed out in Chapter 2, we usually give a concrete interpretation of this abstract mathematical science by assigning the meanings "dot" and "streak" to the undefined terms "point" and "line"; thus we interpret the whole geometry as applying to the diagrams we draw. But let us now give a different concrete interpretation to our abstract mathematical science, geometry, by assigning different meanings to the undefined terms "point" and "line," as follows. Let "point" mean an ordered pair of real numbers (x, y). Let "line" mean a set of all those and only those "points" (that is, ordered pairs of real numbers) which satisfy a given equation $ax + by = c$ of the first degree, where a, b, and c are all real constants and not both a and b are zero. It is not difficult to verify that the postulates become true statements when these meanings are substituted for the undefined terms.

For example, let us verify postulate 1. Let (x_1, y_1) and (x_2, y_2) be any two distinct given "points." We have only to show that there exists at least one equation of the first degree in x and y which is satisfied by both of these given ordered pairs of numbers. But

$$(y - y_1)(x_2 - x_1) = (x - x_1)(y_2 - y_1)$$

is such an equation (see theorem 13, section 95), for it is clearly satisfied by both $x = x_1$, $y = y_1$, and $x = x_2$, $y = y_2$, as we see by direct substitution. That the coefficients of x and y in this equation cannot both be zero follows at once from the hypothesis that (x_1, y_1) and (x_2, y_2) are distinct points, so that we can have one or the other or neither of the equalities $x_1 = x_2$ and $y_1 = y_2$ but not both.

Similarly, all the other postulates can be verified algebraically if we interpret the undefined terms as having the above meanings. But if all the postulates are true statements for these meanings then so are all the theorems, for the theorems follow from the postulates by pure logic. Hence, analytic geometry may be regarded as a concrete interpretation of the abstract mathematical science discussed in Chapter 2.

106. GEOMETRY OF MORE THAN THREE DIMENSIONS

In the last section we indicated how we might set up 2-dimensional (plane) analytic geometry by defining "point" to mean "ordered pair of real numbers." Similarly, we might set up 3-dimensional (solid) geometry by defining "point" to mean "ordered triplet of real numbers." But there is now nothing to stop us from defining "point" to mean an "ordered set of 4 real numbers," like (x, y, z, u), or "ordered set of 17 real numbers," or an "ordered set of n real numbers" where n is any natural number. If we did this we would be beginning the study of geometry of 4 or 17 or n dimensions. Thus, developing the subject in ways analogous to our study of 2-dimensional analytic geometry, the study of 4- or 17- or n-dimensional geometry is nothing more than the study of algebra with 4 or 17 or n variables. This presents little difficulty. That is all there is, essentially, to the study of geometry of many dimensions.* The use of geometric terminology, such as calling an ordered set of 17 real numbers a "point," is merely a convenience. As you see, there is nothing mysterious about this unless, indeed, you try to imagine, in some mysterious way, what 4-dimensional or 17-dimensional space looks like pictorially. Even mathematicians, whose eyes are constructed in the same way as yours, are unable to do that; in fact, there is no reason why they should want to, and they don't. Our visual spatial intuition is 3-dimensional and, indeed, even in 3-dimensions, our intuition cannot be trusted without the aid of reasoned ideas of perspective, etc.

If you now understand that "point in space of 5 dimensions" is taken to mean ordered set of 5 real numbers and "space of 5 dimensions" is taken to mean merely the totality of all such "points" or ordered sets of 5 real numbers (x, y, z, u, v), you may fairly ask, "How can such a 5-dimensional geometry be applied practically?" The answer is that it may be very convenient to represent as a "point" in 5-dimensional space anything that can be specified by an ordered set of 5 real numbers. For example, if we were making a statistical study of people with respect to their height, weight, age, blood pressure, and income, and were interested in no other properties, we might specify each person by an ordered set of 5 real numbers (h, w, a, b, i); it might then be convenient to represent each person as a "point" in 5-dimensional space.

This kind of thing has actually been found to be of the greatest convenience in the study of dynamics. For example, consider 3 billiard balls moving on a table. At any instant, the position of each ball can be specified by its two coordinates. Thus the "position" of the dynamical system consisting of the 3 moving balls at any instant can be specified by 6 coordinates and might be represented by a "point" in 6-dimensional space. In fact, physicists are usually interested not only in position but in velocity as well. Now in the above example the velocity of each ball at any instant can be specified by two coordinates (component velocities). The position and velocities of the system together are called

* The subject may be approached from many different viewpoints, however.

the "phase" of the system. In the above example the "phase" of the system at any instant may be represented as a point in 12-dimensional space, that is, as a set of 12 real numbers. Physicists call this 12-dimensional space the phase-space of the dynamical system. The totality of phases for all instants forms some kind of a locus in the 12-dimensional phase-space, and the physical properties of the dynamical system may be studied by means of the geometric properties of this locus. This is actually done in advanced physics.

Another example of the use of many dimensions in physics occurs in the special theory of relativity. This example has needlessly bewildered many people. In this subject, the things being studied are "events," such as the flashing of a light signal at a given time and place. The word "event" is not used here in its everyday sense as something unusual; the mere existence of a particle of matter in a certain place at a certain time is an "event." Thus, an event may be specified by 4 real numbers: three of them, x, y, and z, say, are coordinates of the place where the event occurs, and the fourth, t, say, tells the time of its occurrence. Hence an "event" may be represented as a "point" in a "space" of 4 dimensions. (In the later general theory of relativity the four coordinates lose their individual meanings, because of certain changes or transformations of the coordinate system, but we cannot go into details here.) Let us hope that this brief explanation will dispel any aura of mystery surrounding the Fourth Dimension (always spelled with capitals to make it seem mysterious) about which many people, who have had the courage of their confusion, have written a great deal of nonsense. If you observe anyone talking or writing about the Fourth Dimension in an exalted, mystic tone you may bet with a fair degree of safety that he is not a mathematician but a bohemian philosopher, possibly with a concentrated solution of alcohol in his bloodstream. It is also worth pointing out that brilliant new ideas lie at the foundation of the theory of relativity but mere use of 4-dimensional space is not one of them. Mathematicians have studied the geometry of many-dimensional space since the middle of the nineteenth century and physicists have been using spaces of more than 4 dimensions, as phase-spaces, for example, about as long. The fact that 4 dimensions are convenient in relativity is something of a triviality; the excellence of the theory is to be found elsewhere.

Space of many dimensions is also used in actual problems of linear programming of greater complexity than those studied in section 102, problems in the theory of games of strategy more complicated than those studied in sections 157 and 158, and problems in psychology. Further study of this subject is found in Chapter 14.

107. CONSTRUCTIONS WITH RULER AND COMPASSES

Now that we know a little analytic geometry, we can indicate how the criterion for constructibility by ruler and compasses (which was discussed in section 76, Chapter 8) may be established. This criterion says, essentially, that *we can construct, with ruler and compasses alone, all those and only those quantities which can be obtained from the given quantities by a finite number of rational operations and extractions of square roots.* The "all those" part of this statement was established in section 76; there remains only the "only those" part of it to be discussed. Now, in constructing a figure with ruler and compasses one deals exclusively with the intersection of two lines, the intersections of a line with a circle, and the intersections of two circles. Finding the intersection of two lines amounts algebraically to solving simultaneously two linear equations in x and y. This (see section 100, example 1) is accomplished with the help of rational operations (addition, subtraction, multiplication, and division) alone (see section 45). Finding the intersections of a line with a circle amounts to solving simultaneously a linear and a quadratic equation in x and y. This (see section 100, example 2) reduces to the solution of a quadratic equation in one variable which, as you know, may be solved by a formula (section 42) which involves only rational operations and the extraction of a square root. Finding the intersections of two circles reduces to finding the intersections of one of the circles with their common chord (see section 100, example 3). This also involves only rational operations and square roots. This brief discussion is hardly a formal proof of our underlined statement, but it is not hard to see that these considerations might lead to a proof.

References

Numbers refer to those in bibliography at end of book.

Abbott 1
Allen 2
Arnold 6
Baumol 14
Bell 16
Boulding and Spivey 34
Courant and Robbins 58
Dantzig 61
Dorfman, Samuelson, and Solow 64
Dresden 65
Einstein and Infeld 68
Eves 70
Ficken 73
Gale 81
Glicksman 87
Hadley 89
Kasner and Newman 103
Kemeny, Snell and Thompson 107
Kline 117
Koopmans 118
Luce and Raiffa 128
Manning 129
Russell 167
Spivey 183
Tucker and Bailey 193
Vajda 195, 196, 197, 198
Whitehead 206

10

Functions

108. VARIABLES AND FUNCTIONS

By a **variable** we mean a symbol which may represent (many) different objects during the same discussion. By a **constant** we mean a symbol which may represent only one definite object during the same discussion. It is customary to use early letters of the alphabet like a, b, c for constants and later letters like x, y, z for variables. The set of all objects which a variable is permitted to represent during a discussion is called the **domain** of the variable. Any object which the variable may represent (that is, any object in its domain) is called a **value** of the variable. The "objects" in the domain will usually be numbers. Note that a and b stand for constants even though their values are not stated. Of course, definite numbers like 2 or $\frac{3}{2}$ are constants.

Let the variable x have the domain X, and let the variable y have the domain Y. A **function** f from X to Y is a set of ordered pairs (x, y) with the property that to each x in X there corresponds one and only one y in Y such that the ordered pair (x, y) is in the set f. *If* (x, y) *is in* f, *we write* $y = f(x)$ *and* y *is called the* **value** *of the function* f *at* x. The set X is called the **domain** of the function f and the set Y is called the **range** of the function f. The subset of Y consisting of those elements y for which there is an x in X such that $y = f(x)$ is called the **image** of X under f.

A function from X to Y is also called a **mapping** from X to Y or a **functional relation** from X to Y. It is a special kind of relation from X to Y in the sense of the remark of section 12.

A function f *from* X *to* Y *may be defined by any scheme (rule, or correspondence) whereby to each* x *in* X *there corresponds a unique* y *in* Y *to be paired with* x *in an ordered pair* (x, y). The variable x is called the **independent variable** and y

is called the **dependent variable,** because the value of y is determined when a value of x is chosen. *Sometimes y is said to be a function of x when $y = f(x)$.* The significance of these definitions will become clear as soon as we examine some concrete examples.

Remark. The word function is used here in a technical sense quite different from its everyday meaning as in the statements "digestion of starch is a function of the saliva," or "passing bills is a function of the legislature," or "the Senior Prom was the outstanding function of the school year."

Example 1. Let the domain X of x and the range of Y of y be the set of all integers. Then the function f defined by the relation $y = 2x + 1$ associates with each value of x just one value of y. The image of X under the function f is the set of odd integers. For example, to the value $x = 3$, it associates the value $y = 7$; to the value $x = 2$, it associates the value $y = 5$. Thus, the ordered pairs (3,7) and (2,5) belong to f, and we write $7 = f(3)$ and $5 = f(2)$. We might have allowed the domain of x to be the set of all rational numbers, or all real numbers, or all complex numbers, at the same time changing the range of the function accordingly, of course.

Example 2. Consider the function f defined by the relation $y = 1/(x - 3)$. For $x = 3$ this function is not defined. (Why?) We may let the domain of x be the set of all real numbers except 3.

Example 3. Let the domain of x be the set of all objects for sale in a certain department store. Let the value of y corresponding to each value of x (that is, each object) be the price of x. This functional relation defines y as a function of x.

Example 4. Let the domain of x be the set of husbands in a given country. Let y be the "wife of x." This relation defines y as a function of x if the domain of x is the set of law-abiding husbands in a monogamous civilization. Notice that this would still be a (single-valued) function in polyandrous civilizations but not in polygamous civilizations.

Example 5. Let the domain of x be the set of all positive numbers with three consecutive significant digits; for example, 278 or .00278. Then the table of logarithms, properly read, associates with each such number x a number called its logarithm. Thus $y = \log x$ defines y as a function of x. Actually the domain of this function can be taken as the set of all positive real numbers. But our table tells us the (approximate) value of $\log x$ only for the domain stated above.

Example 6. Let the domain of x be the set of years between 1930 and 1936. If y is the number of Fourth of July accidents in the year x, then the correspondence given by the following (fictitious) table

x	1930	1931	1932	1933	1934	1935	1936
y	420	350	358	200	250	262	276

defines y as a function of x for the given domain of x.

Example 7. Let x be the age of a certain baby, measured in days, and let y be its weight, measured in pounds, at 5 P.M. of the corresponding day. Consider the table:

x	0	7	14	21	28	35	42	49
y	$7\frac{13}{16}$	$8\frac{4}{16}$	$8\frac{9}{16}$	$9\frac{2}{16}$	$9\frac{9}{16}$	$10\frac{1}{16}$	$10\frac{9}{16}$	11

Here y is a function of x, for the given domain of x.

Example 8. Let x be the number of days a patient has been in the hospital for a certain illness. Let y be the temperature of the patient, taken at noon, for the corresponding day. Consider the table:

x	1	2	3	4	5	6	7	8
y	102	103	103	101	100	99	98.6	98.6

Here y is a function of x, for the given domain of x.

Example 9. Let the domain of x be the set of all places in the United States. Let the domain of y be the set of all points on a map of the United States. Let "$y =$ the point on the map corresponding to the place x" be the functional relation. Then y is a function of x, since to each place x there corresponds just one point y on the map.

Example 10. Let the domain X of x be the set of all normal human beings. Let the domain of y be the set of all feet. The functional relation "y is the right foot of x" determines y as a function of x, for which the image of X under the function is the set of all right feet of normal humans.

Example 11. Let the domain X of x be the class of all finite sets, and let $y = N(x)$ be the number of elements in the set x. Then y is a function of x and the image of X under the function is the set of all non-negative integers 0, 1, 2, 3, ...

The extremely general idea of a function given here is a modern one. It may seem too general to be of much practical value. However, even these very general functions can be studied to good advantage. In elementary mathematics and for many applications *we can and will restrict ourselves to functions where the domains of both variables are sets of real numbers.*

If we have occasion to mention more than one function in the same problem or discussion, we may use different letters, such as f, g, F, f_1, f', h, *etc., for the different functions.* Thus, let f be defined by the relation $y = f(x) = (12 - x)/x$, where X is the set of all non-zero real numbers and Y is the set of all real numbers, and let g be defined by the relation $y = g(x) = 2x + 1$, where X and Y are both the set of all real numbers. If a is any value of x (that is, any number in the domain of x) then $f(a)$ *means the value of the dependent variable* (*that is, the value of the function*) *corresponding to the value* $x = a$ *of the independent variable. That is,* $f(a)$ *is the value of* $f(x)$ *when* x *is replaced by* a. Thus, $f(3) = (12 - 3)/3 = 3$, $f(4) = (12 - 4)/4 = 2$, $f(2) = (12 - 2)/2 = 5$, $f(1) = (12 - 1)/1 = 11$, $f(12) = (12 - 12)/12 = 0$, and $f(0)$ does not exist, since 0 cannot be in the domain of x for this function. (Why?) Also, $g(1) = 3$, $g(2) = 5$. Hence, $f(3) = g(1)$ and $f(2) = g(2)$ in our examples. This functional notation is very compact and convenient.

Remark. The functions just discussed are sometimes called **single-valued functions** because each value of x is paired with exactly one value of y. If we allow the same value of x to occur in ordered pairs with more than one value of y, we may speak of **many-valued functions.** But a many-valued function from X to Y may be regarded as a single-valued function from X to the set S of all subsets of Y. For example, if X and Y are both the set of non-negative real numbers, then the relation $y^2 = x$ or $y = \pm\sqrt{x}$ defines y as a many-valued function from X to Y, or equivalently as a single-valued function from X to the set S of all subsets of Y. Thus, to the value $x = 9$ corresponds the set $\{+3, -3\}$ of values of y. That is, the ordered pair (9,3) and (9,−3) are both in the (many-valued) function. *We shall usually be concerned here with single-valued functions only.*

Exercises

In each of exercises 1–8 find the largest possible set of real numbers which can be taken as the domain of x *if the image of* X *under the function* f *for which* $y = f(x)$ *is to be confined to real numbers:*

1. $y = 2x + 1$. **2.** $y = x^2$. **3.** $y = \sqrt{x}$. **4.** $y = 1/x$.

5. $y = \sqrt{9 - x^2}$. **6.** $y = \sqrt{x^2 - 9}$. **7.** $y = \dfrac{1}{x - 2}$.

8. $y = \sqrt{x - 2}$.

9. Give three examples each of (*a*) variables, (*b*) constants, (*c*) functions, which occur in any connection or subject whatever.

10. If $f(x) = 2x^2 - 3x + 4$, find: (*a*) $f(0)$; (*b*) $f(1)$; (*c*) $f(2)$; (*d*) $f(-2)$; (*e*) $f(\frac{1}{2})$.

11. If $f(x) = 8^x$, find: (*a*) $f(1)$; (*b*) $f(2)$; (*c*) $f(0)$; (*d*) $f(\frac{1}{3})$; (*e*) $f(-\frac{2}{3})$; (*f*) $f(-2)$.

12. If $g(x) = \dfrac{1}{x-2} + \dfrac{3}{x-5}$, find: (*a*) $g(1)$; (*b*) $g(3)$; (*c*) $g(7)$; (*d*) $g(\frac{1}{2})$. (*e*) What numbers must be excluded from the range of x?

13. (*a*) If $f(x) = x^2 + 1$ and $g(x) = 9 - x^2$ show that $f(2) = g(2)$ and $f(-2) = g(-2)$. (*b*) Plot the graphs of both functions on the same coordinate system and interpret the latter statements graphically. (*c*) Is $f(-2) = -f(2)$?

14. If $f(x) = 3x^2 + 2x + 3$, find: (*a*) $f(2)$; (*b*) $f(a)$; (*c*) $f(a + h)$; (*d*) $f(a + h) - f(a)$; (*e*) $[f(a + h) - f(a)]/h$.

Find the value of $[f(x + h) - f(x)]/h$ *for each of the following functions:*

15. $f(x) = x^2$. **16.** $f(x) = x^3$. **17.** $f(x) = 3x^2 + 5x + 1$.

18. $f(x) = 1/x$. **19.** $f(x) = 3 - 4x - 2x^2$. **20.** $f(x) = 1/x^2$.

109. THE GRAPH OF A FUNCTION

The study of functions began to be very important in the seventeenth century when scientists became greatly interested in the study of varying quantities. The invention of the pendulum clock, the problems of trans-oceanic navigation, the study of the motions of cannon balls and planets, and other physical phenomena, all contributed to the need for this study. If y is a function of x, we say that the value of y depends on the value of x. Speaking loosely, we might say that *y varies with x*; or a change in x *induces* a corresponding change in y. This statement is not strictly true, for we might have a function which assigns the same value to y no matter what value is given to x. Such a function might be called a *constant function*; its graph would be a horizontal straight line. But, it will do no great harm if you think of the value of y changing when the value of x changes provided you agree that the change in y may be zero.

Examples of functions important in physical science are extremely numerous. Thus the distance through which a body falls at a given place on the earth's surface depends on the number of seconds during which it falls. The length of a steel bar depends on its temperature. The time required for a complete oscillation of a pendulum depends on the length of the pendulum. The distance through which a cannon ball, fired with a given initial velocity, will travel depends on the angle at which it is fired; the area of a square depends on the length of its side; and so on. However, to know merely that one quantity, y, depends on another, x, is hardly enough. It is usually essential to know whether y increases or decreases as x increases, and whether these changes are rapid or slow. More precisely, we might want to know how much y increases or decreases when

x increases a certain amount; or how fast y is changing near a given value of x. We might want to know whether or not y has maximum or minimum values, and, if so, what they are; and so on. Some of these questions will be answered by a careful study of functions in Chapter 11.

For the present, we can see that a rough idea of how a function f given by the relation $y = f(x)$ varies may be obtained from its graph in a rectangular coordinate system. Graphical methods are used extensively in many fields, especially where approximate results are desired.

Example 1. Consider the function given by $y = 10 - x^2$. To draw its graph we first choose a number of values of x and calculate the corresponding values of $y = f(x)$; these results may be put into a table:

x	0	1	−1	2	−2	3	−3	4	−4
$y = f(x)$	10	9	9	6	6	1	1	−6	−6

Plotting these points (x,y), we obtain several points of the graph. If we have enough points to give us a fairly accurate idea of the shape of the curve, we join them by a "smooth" curve (Fig. 130). We may now use the graph to estimate values of y corresponding to values of x not in the table. Thus for $x = 1.5$ we might estimate $y = 8$ from the graph (Fig. 130); this is not correct, but it is not far wrong. From the actual formula for the function we obtain for $x = 1.5$ the value $y = 10 - (1.5)^2 = 7.75$. Naturally, the more points we actually plot and the more carefully we plot them, the more accurate our graphical estimates will be. We could judge from the graph that 10 is the maximum value of y and that there is no minimum value.

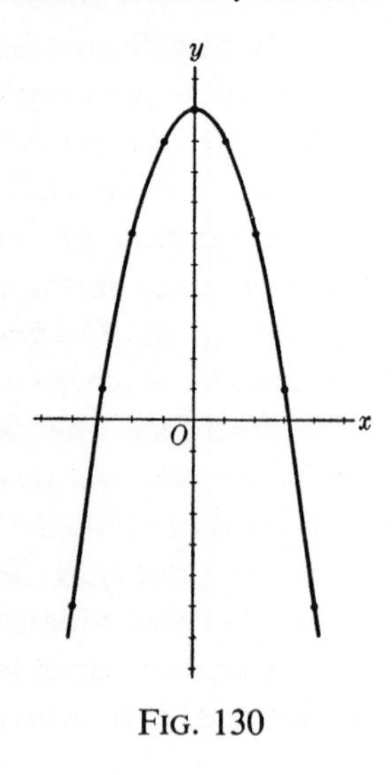

FIG. 130

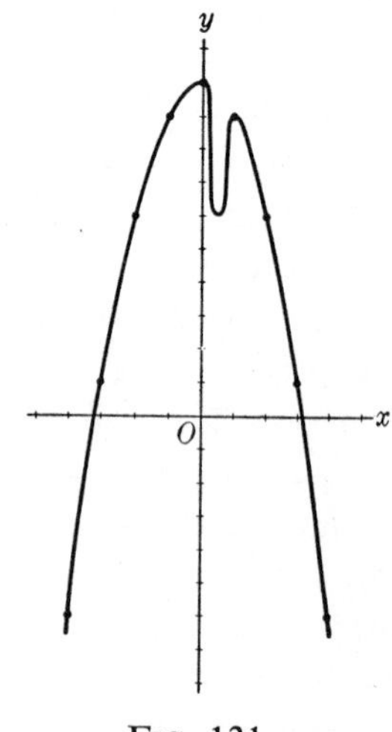

FIG. 131

When we join our plotted points by a smooth curve, we really assume a great deal. For instance, we assume that the curve does not behave queerly between the plotted points, as in Fig. 131. In fact, we cannot be sure of this without a much deeper study of the function than we can make here. It is certainly clear that if we plot points corresponding to values of x which are too far apart, we may get an erroneous idea of the shape of the curve. But it is not always obvious how close together the values of x must be in order to avoid being "too far apart"; consider the following examples. *Note that it is often advisable to use units of different lengths on the two axes in order to confine the graph to a moderate space.*

Example 2. Let the function be given by $y = 4x^3 - x$. As usual, we obtain a table:

x	0	1	-1	2	-2	...
y	0	3	-3	30	-30	...

If we plotted these points we might be tempted to join them as in Fig. 132. This would give us a *false* impression of the shape of the curve as we can see by using values of x chosen closer together, as in the following table, from which we see that the part of the graph between $x = -1$ and $x = 1$ (drawn on a different scale, for convenience) should look like Fig. 133:

x	0	$\frac{1}{4}$	$-\frac{1}{4}$	$\frac{1}{2}$	$-\frac{1}{2}$	$\frac{3}{4}$	$-\frac{3}{4}$	1	-1	$\frac{3}{2}$	$-\frac{3}{2}$	2	-2
y	0	$-\frac{3}{16}$	$\frac{3}{16}$	0	0	$\frac{15}{16}$	$-\frac{15}{16}$	3	-3	12	-12	30	-30

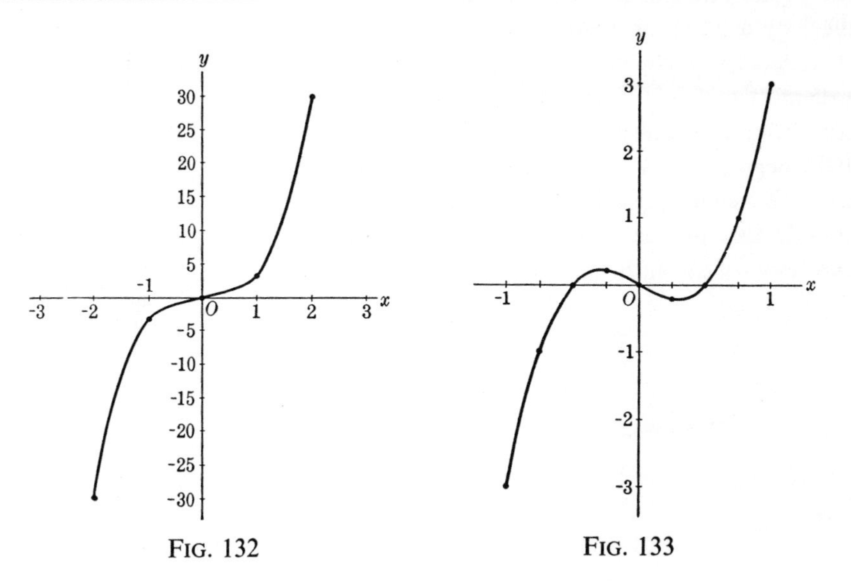

FIG. 132

FIG. 133

Example 3. Let the function be given by $y = 1/(2x - 3)$. We might obtain the following table:

x	0	1	-1	2	-2	3	4	$\cdots$
y	$-\frac{1}{3}$	-1	$-\frac{1}{5}$	1	$-\frac{1}{7}$	$\frac{1}{3}$	$\frac{1}{5}$	$\cdots$

Plotting these points we might suppose that the curve looked like Fig. 134. But, plotting more carefully, we see that for $x = \frac{3}{2}$ there is no point of the curve. A more complete table would be:

x	0	1	$\frac{5}{4}$	$\frac{11}{8}$	$\frac{23}{16}$	$\cdots$	$\frac{3}{2}$	$\cdots$	$\frac{25}{16}$	$\frac{13}{8}$	$\frac{7}{4}$	2	3
y	$-\frac{1}{3}$	-1	-2	-4	-8	$\cdots$	no value	$\cdots$	8	4	2	1	$\frac{1}{3}$

This gives rise to the curve in Fig. 135. The curve is a hyperbola and has two separate branches.

Often we draw graphs for functions which are given originally in the form of a table. For example, let us plot a graph for example 8 of section 108. Having plotted the points given in the table, we usually join them by a curve or a broken line (Fig. 136). If we want to estimate the temperature of the patient at midnight of the fifth day, we might read from the graph that it was approximately 100.5 degrees. But this might be wrong for the patient's temperature might have fluctuated considerably between noon of the fourth day and noon of the fifth. However, if we plotted

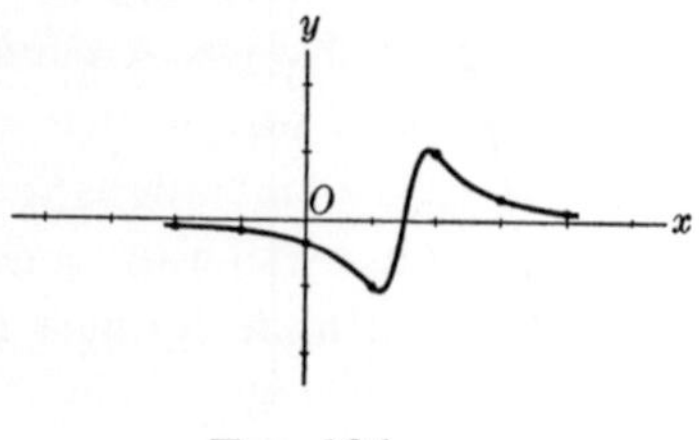

FIG. 134

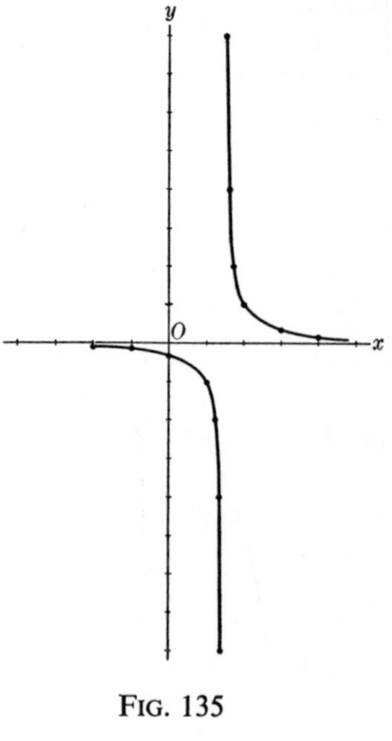

FIG. 135

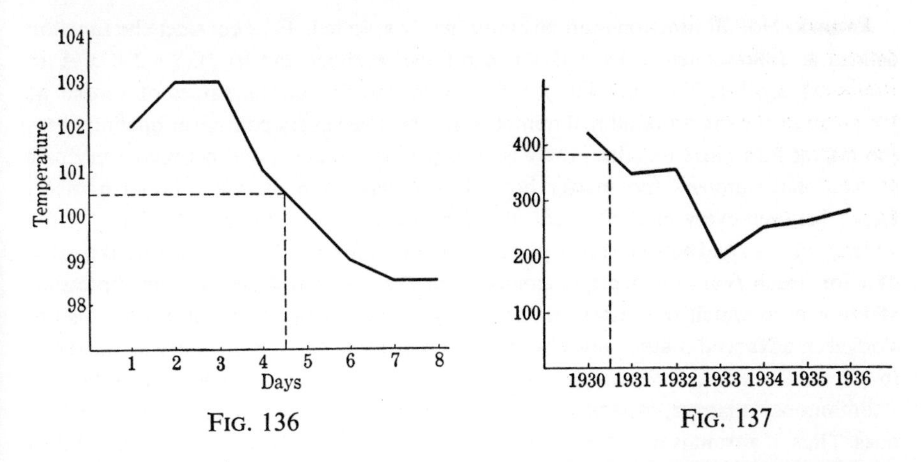

FIG. 136

FIG. 137

a graph for example 7, section 108, it would be more reliable to estimate the weight between the actually plotted points because we do not expect a baby's weight to undergo abrupt fluctuations. Thus, *great care must be exercised in reading from a graph more than has been put into it.* It is even possible to get complete nonsense if one is not careful. For example, a graph for example 6, section 108, is given in Fig. 137. If we were to use the graph to estimate values of the function between the plotted points, we might conclude that there were approximately 385 Fourth of July accidents at Christmas 1930. In this example, joining the points by a line serves no purpose beyond that of a purely visual aid in seeing at a glance the trend of the function.

In most of our examples the function was defined or given by means of a definite rule, or formula, or by a table, and the graph was derived from the definition of the function. However, a function may be defined by means of a graph directly and an approximate table of values, or an approximate formula may be derived from the graph. This actually occurs in various practical situations. Thus, a seismograph records on a strip of moving tape the graph of a function representing the vibrations of an earthquake. Similarly, a cardiograph records on a strip of paper the graph of a function representing the vibrations of the heart beat, and an electroencephalograph records electrical vibrations in the brain. In the same manner, an instrument called a phonodeik records a graph of the vibrations of the air produced by a sound wave. A phonograph record is essentially a graph of the sound scratched in wax so that a needle retracing the scratch (or graph) will reproduce the original vibrations and sound wave. In all these cases, the function is given originally as a graph and conclusions are drawn from the graph. For most purposes, a definite formula is more desirable than either a table or a graph since from it one can obtain as exactly as one pleases the value of y corresponding to any value of x.

Remark. Not all functions can be conveniently graphed. Thus consider the function defined as follows: let $f(x) = 1$ if x is a rational number and let $f(x) = 2$ if x is an irrational number. This function $y = f(x)$ is defined for all real values of x; that is, the range of x is the set of all real numbers. But between every pair of rational numbers (no matter how close together) there is an irrational number; and between every pair of irrational numbers (no matter how close together) there is a rational number. Hence between every pair of values of x for which $f(x) = 1$ there is a value of x for which $f(x) = 2$; and between every pair of values of x for which $f(x) = 2$ there is a value of x for which $f(x) = 1$. A graph cannot be drawn which will give a clear impression of the way in which this function varies. Such "pathological" functions as this are studied in advanced mathematics but are of no importance in elementary applications to physical science, for example, where most functions are supposed to vary in a "continuous" manner, instead of jumping fitfully between two values as this function does. Thus, if a train is traveling from Washington to New York, we do not expect it to move gradually from Washington to Philadelphia and then suddenly disappear from Philadelphia and pop up in New York without any lapse of time and without traversing the intervening territory. We expect it to move continuously over all the places between Philadelphia and New York.

Exercises

1. For each of the following functions (*a*) plot the graphs between $x = -5$ and $x = 5$, if possible; (*b*) estimate from the graph the values of x for which $y = 1$, $y = \frac{3}{2}$, $y = 0$; (*c*) describe how y changes as x goes from -5 to $+5$. For what values of x does y appear to be a maximum? minimum?

(*i*) $y = 10 - \frac{1}{2}x^2$. (*ii*) $y = 4 - 2x$. (*iii*) $y = x^3 - 9x^2 + 24x - 7$.
(*iv*) $y = 8^x$. (Hint: plot values of x at intervals of $\frac{1}{3}$.)
(*v*) $y = \log x$. (Hint: use table of logarithms.)
(*vi*) $y = 10^x$. (Hint: use table of logarithms.) (*vii*) $y = 1/(x - 2)$.

2. In the function $y = ax^2$, a being a constant different from zero, how does y change when x is doubled? tripled?

3. The distance s, measured in feet, through which a body falls in t seconds is found experimentally to be given approximately by the function

$$s = 16t^2. \tag{1}$$

(*a*) Make a graph of this function, plotting integral values of t from $t = 0$ to $t = 4$.

(*b*) Estimate from the graph how high a cliff is if a body dropped from it reaches bottom in 1.5 seconds.

(*c*) If the cliff is 104 feet high, in how many seconds will the body reach bottom?

4. (*a*) A bomb is dropped from an airplane 1600 feet high. In how many seconds will it reach the earth? (Use formula (1) of exercise 3.)

(*b*) If a bomb strikes the earth in 6 seconds, how high was the airplane when the bomb was dropped?

5. If a ball is thrown directly upward from an initial height of h_0 feet, with an initial velocity of v_0 feet per seond, its height h, measured in feet, after t seconds is found to be given by the function

$$h = h_0 + v_0 t - 16t^2. \tag{2}$$

Assume $h_0 = 5$ feet, and $v_0 = 128$ feet per second.

(*a*) Make a graph of this function.
(*b*) After how many seconds will the ball strike the ground?
(*c*) After how many seconds will the ball reach its maximum height? What is the maximum height?
(*d*) After how many seconds will the ball be 85 feet high?

6. Make a graph of the function in example 7, section 108. Estimate from the graph, the approximate weight of the baby at 5 P.M. of the 24th day; the 26th day.

7. A rectangular area is to be enclosed by 40 feet of fence.

(*a*) Express the area A as a function of the length x of one side of the rectangle.
(*b*) Make a graph of this function using a horizontal x-axis and a vertical A-axis.
(*c*) From the graph, estimate the value of x which will make A a maximum and estimate the maximum value of A.

8. An open box is to be made from a square piece of cardboard 18 inches on each side by cutting out equal squares from the corners and folding up the sides.

(*a*) Express the volume V of the box as a function of the length x of the edge of the cut-out square.
(*b*) Make a graph of this function using a vertical V-axis and a horizontal x-axis.
(*c*) From the graph, estimate the value of x which will make V a maximum, and estimate the maximum value of V.

9. A closed box with a square base is to have a volume of 64 cubic feet.

(*a*) Express the total area A of the top, bottom, and four sides as a function of the length x of the base.
(*b*) Make a graph of the function, using a vertical A-axis and a horizontal x-axis.
(*c*) Estimate from the graph the value of x which will make A a minimum, and estimate the minimum value of A.

10. An open box with a square base is to be made from 400 square inches of material.

(*a*) Express the volume V as a function of the length x of the base.
(*b*) Make a graph of this function with a vertical V-axis.
(*c*) From the graph, estimate the value of x which will make V maximum, and estimate the maximum value of V.

11. For a box with square ends to be sent by parcel post, the sum of its length and girth (perimeter of a cross section) must not exceed 84 inches. Suppose a box has for its sum of length and girth exactly 84 inches.

(*a*) Express the volume V of the box as a function of the length x of the edge of the square ends.

(*b*) Make a graph of this function, with a vertical V-axis.

(*c*) Estimate from the graph the value of x which will make V maximum, and estimate the maximum value of V.

12. Plot the graphs of the functions given in

(*a*) Exercise 2, section 108. (*b*) Exercise 3, section 108.
(*c*) Exercise 4, section 108. (*d*) Exercise 5, section 108.
(*e*) Exercise 6, section 108. (*f*) Exercise 7, section 108.

110. AVERAGE RATES

If an automobile travels 360 miles in 9 hours, we say that its average speed for the trip was 40 miles per hour. In general, *if y is a function of x, and y changes from y_1 to y_2 as x changes from x_1 to x_2, then $(y_2 - y_1)/(x_2 - x_1)$ is called the* ***average rate of change of y with respect to x for the interval between x_1 and x_2***. That is, the average rate is simply the change in y divided by the change in x, or the change in y per unit change in x, for the interval in question. If the graph of the function $y = f(x)$ happens to be a straight line, this average rate is clearly the slope of the line. If the graph is not a straight line, the average rate of change of y with respect to x for the interval between x_1 and x_2 is easily seen (Fig. 138) to be the slope of the chord joining the points (x_1, y_1) and (x_2, y_2). Thus average rates may be estimated from the graph.

Example. A falling body traverses s feet in t seconds, where $s = 16t^2$ approximately. From the table

t	0	1	2	3	4
s	0	16	64	144	256

the average speed for the first second is 16 feet per second; for the second second it is 48 feet per second; for the first two seconds it is 32 feet per second.

Exercises

1. In the above example, find the average speed for (*a*) the third second; (*b*) the fourth second; (*c*) the first three seconds; (*d*) the first four seconds.

2. From the graph of example 1, section 109, find the average rate of change of y with respect to x for the interval between (*a*) $x = 1$ and $x = 2$; (*b*) $x = 1$ and $x = 3$. (*c*) What is the significance of the fact that these rates are negative?

3. From the graph of example 7, section 108, find the average rate of change of the weight per day for (*a*) the first 7 days; (*b*) the first 14 days; (*c*) the first 3 weeks.

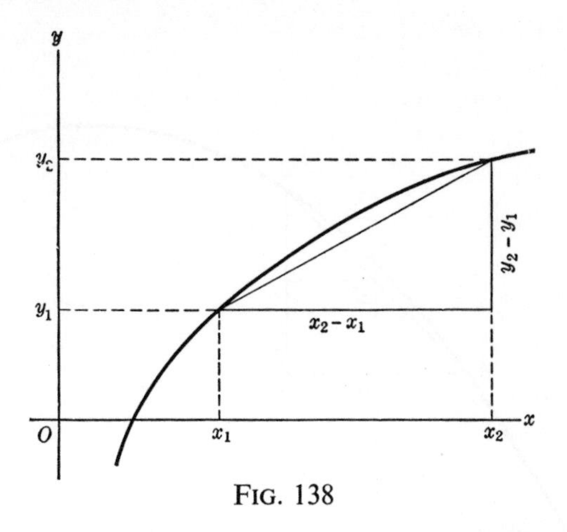

FIG. 138

4. From the graph of exercise 3, section 109, find the average rate of change for (*a*) the first second; (*b*) the first two seconds; (*c*) the interval between $t = 4$ and $t = 5$.

5. From the graph of exercise 5, section 109, find the average rate of change for (*a*) the first second; (*b*) the first two seconds; (*c*) the interval between $t = 2$ and $t = 4$.

111. INTERPOLATION AND EXTRAPOLATION

The act of estimating values y of a function corresponding to values of x *between* those actually plotted or calculated is called **interpolation**. We have seen how we may interpolate roughly by reading from the graph of the function. Let us examine another method of interpolation that is used frequently, namely, the method of **proportional parts.** We shall illustrate this method by the following example.

Example. Consider the function given by $y = 1 + 6x - x^2$, from which we get the following table:

x	0	1	2	3	4
y	1	6	9	10	9

For $x = 1.5$ we might obtain an estimate of the corresponding y as follows. As x goes from 1 to 2, y goes from 6 to 9; that is, y increases 3 units. Now $x = 1.5$ is halfway between 1 and 2; hence we might take a value of y half-way between 6 and 9, that is, $y = 7.5$, as our approximate value. Similarly, for $x = \frac{4}{3}$ which is $\frac{1}{3}$ of the way between 1 and 2 we take for y a value $\frac{1}{3}$ of the way between 6 and 9 or $y = 7$. These values can be seen to be inaccurate since we have a formula for the function which enables us to compute directly that for $x = 1.5$, $y = 7.75$ and for $x = \frac{4}{3}$, $y = \frac{65}{9} = 7\frac{2}{9}$; but they are

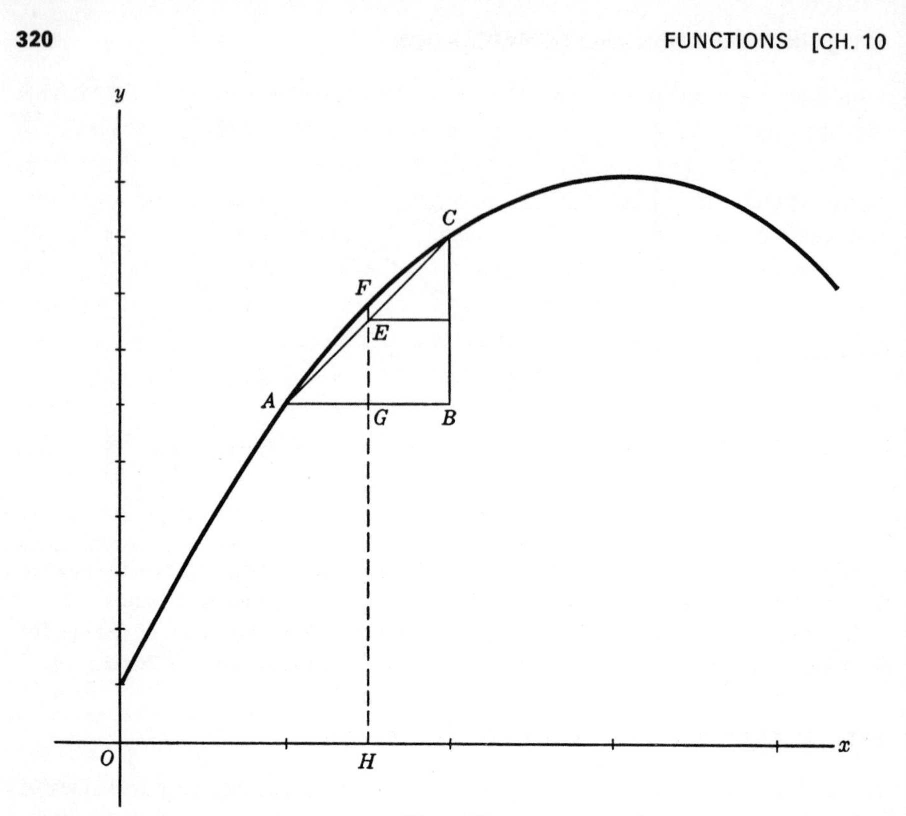

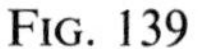
FIG. 139

not far wrong. Let us see why this is so. Draw the chord (straight line-segment) joining our two plotted points A and C (Fig. 139). For $x = 1.5$, the true value of y is the length of HF. But the midpoint E of the chord AC has the coordinates (1.5, 7.5). This may be seen by means of the similar triangles AEG and ACB.

In general, *the method of interpolation by proportional parts amounts to using the ordinate of the point on the chord with the given abscissa instead of the ordinate of the point on the curve with the given abscissa. The accuracy of this method clearly depends on how closely the chord approximates the curve.* Thus if we interpolated by proportional parts for the value of y corresponding to the value $x = 1.5$ by using the points (0,1) and (3,10) we

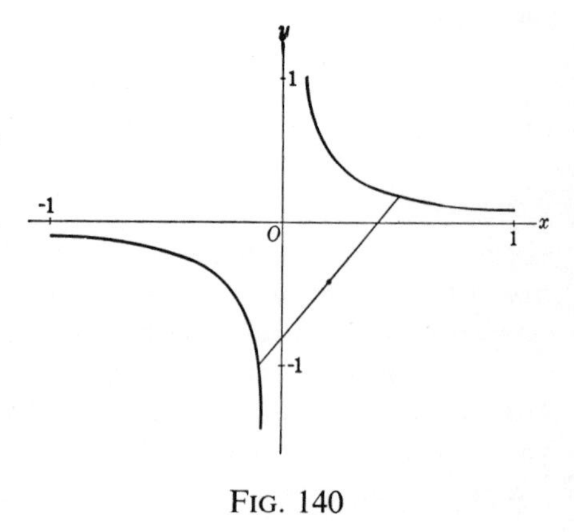

FIG. 140

would get the result $y = 5.5$ which is far from the correct value $y = 7.75$. This is so because the chord joining the points (0,1) and (3,10) does not remain close to the curve. In general, the closer together are the values of x between which we interpolate, the closer will the chord approximate the curve. However, this statement cannot be relied on completely without further knowledge of the function or curve we are considering. For example, consider the function $y = 1/10x$. For $x = -.1$ we have $y = -1$ and for $x = .5$ we have $y = .2$. Suppose we were to interpolate by proportional parts to obtain an approximation for the value of y at $x = .2$, which is halfway between $-.1$ and .5. We obtain the value $y = -.4$ which is halfway between the values -1 and .2. But this is far from the true value $y = .5$. This happens because the chord is not at all close to the curve even though the values of x used are close together (Fig. 140). However, the method of interpolation by proportional parts can be shown to give a good approximation for most of the functions used in elementary mathematics and physics provided we interpolate between values of x that are close enough together.

Because interpolation by proportional parts amounts to using the chord instead of the curve, it is often called **linear interpolation.**

The act of estimating values of a function *beyond* the range of values of x actually plotted or calculated is called **extrapolation**. Thus if we had plotted the curve of Fig. 139 only for $x = 0, 1, 2$, we might feel that since the curve is rising at $x = 2$, it will probably continue to rise as we proceed further to the right, at least for a short interval. Such a conclusion can often be justified, so far as the functions we meet in elementary mathematics and physics are concerned, but only for a *short* interval, as we see from Fig. 139 in this case. As for functions defined by a table of statistical observations, such extrapolation is extremely dangerous, even for a short interval. Thus if the fictitious graph in Fig. 141 represented the average price of securities on the stock market from 1917 to 1932, we see how mistaken were the people who, in 1929, extrapolated incautiously and came to the conclusion that the rising trend would continue a while longer. To be at all secure in extrapolation, even more than in interpolation, one must know, by some means, the nature of the function one is dealing with. Thus in making predictions in physical science by extrapolation beyond our past and present observations in the case, say, of the return of a comet, or the occurrence of an eclipse, we are very safe, because we have a great deal of information as to the

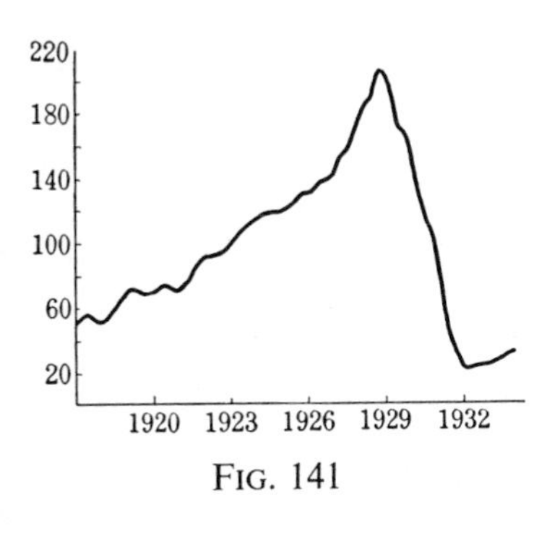

FIG. 141

nature of the functions involved. But prediction by extrapolation from statistical data is not safe unless supported by sufficient additional knowledge of the functions involved.

Exercises

1. In the illustrative example $y=1+6x-x$; above, interpolate by proportional parts from the given table for the value of y corresponding to (*a*) $x=2.5$; (*b*) $x=2.3$; (*c*) $x=3.5$; (*d*) $x=.5$; (*e*) $x=.2$.

2. In example 7, section 108, interpolate by proportional parts to obtain the approximate weight of the baby at 5 P.M. on (*a*) the 11th day; (*b*) the 15th day. Extrapolate to obtain the approximate weight of the baby on (*c*) the 33rd day; (*d*) the 37th day. (*e*) Would we be justified in extrapolating to estimate the weight of the baby on the 400th day? its 20th birthday?

3. Interpolate to find (*a*) log 15.15; (*b*) log 15.12; (*c*) log 15.125; (*d*) 15.175.

4. Interpolate to find the number whose logarithm is (*a*) 1.6024; (*b*) 2.6925; (*c*) 2.6731.

5. Interpolate to find the number whose logarithm is (*a*) 1.6924; (*b*) 2.6922; (*c*) 2.6926.

6. In how many years will any sum of money, invested at 3% interest compounded annually, double itself?

7. If $100 is invested at 4% interest compounded annually, how much will the amount be after 21 years?

8. If it is desired to have a sum of $1000 in the bank ten years from now and the bank pays 3% interest compounded annually, how much should be desposited now?

112. CLASSIFICATION OF FUNCTIONS

An important chapter of pure and applied mathematics consists of the study of functions. To facilitate this study, it is convenient to classify functions in various ways.

One way is to distinguish between continuous and discontinuous functions. A function $y=f(x)$ may be called **continuous at the point (a,b)** if the dependent variable has the value $y=b$ corresponding to the value $x=a$ of the independent variable, and if the graph of the function consists of one connected piece in a small neighborhood of the point (a,b); otherwise it is called **discontinuous at $x=a$**. Thus the function $y=1/x$ is discontinuous at the point where $x=0$ but continuous for all other values of x. Most of the functions

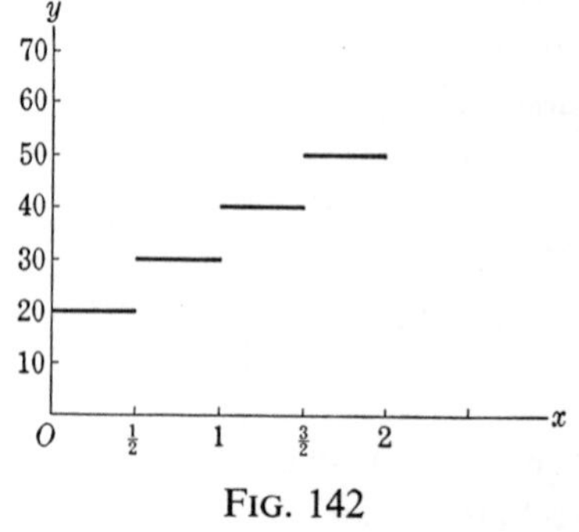

FIG. 142

studied in elementary mathematics and its applications are continuous except possibly for isolated values of x. Polynomials are continuous for all values of x. In the next chapter we shall give a more precise definition of continuous function.

Example. The cost y of a taxi ride is a function of the distance x traversed. Suppose the cost is 20 cents for the first half mile and 10 cents for each succeeding half mile. Then the graph of this function is given in Fig. 142. Here y is a discontinuous function of x since the value of y jumps at the end of each half mile.*

Other modes of classification are often convenient. A function for which $f(x)$ can be expressed as a quotient of two polynomials in x is called a **rational function of x**. It can be shown that rational functions are continuous for all values of x except those for which the denominator becomes zero. A function for which $f(x)$ can be expressed as a polynomial in x is called an **integral rational function**. These terms are analogous to the terms rational number and integer. A function for which $f(x)$ can be expressed as a polynomial of the first degree is called a **linear function**. If y is a (possibly many-valued) function of x such that the values of y corresponding to every x can be obtained as roots of the same equation

$$f_0(x)y^n + f_1(x)y^{n-1} + \cdots + f_{n-1}(x)y + f_n(x) = 0$$

where the functions $f_0(x), f_1(x), \ldots, f_n(x)$ are polynomials in x, then y is called an **algebraic function of x**. For example, $y = \sqrt{\dfrac{x^2+1}{x^2-1}}$ is an algebraic function of x since $(x^2-1)y^2 + (-x^2-1) = 0$; here $f_0(x) = x^2 - 1, f_1(x) = 0$, and $f_2(x) = -x^2 - 1$. All rational functions are algebraic, for if $y = p(x)/q(x)$ where $p(x)$ and $q(x)$ are polynomials, then $q(x)\cdot y - p(x) = 0$; here $f_0(x) = q(x)$ and $f_1(x) = -p(x)$. The functions $\log x$, 10^x, and the trigonometric functions which will be taken up in Chapter 12, can be shown to be not algebraic; they belong to a class of functions called **transcendental**. The terms algebraic function and transcendental function are analogous to the terms algebraic number and transcendental number introduced in section 77.

Functions like 10^x or c^x where c is any constant are called **exponential functions** because the independent variable x occurs as an exponent. They are important in many applications of mathematics, such as the following example.

* Whether the value of this function y is 30 or 40 at the exact value $x = 1$, may depend on the size of the taxi driver (see Fig. 142).

Example. The number n of bacteria in a given culture at the end of t hours is given by $n = 100 \times 10^{.243t}$. Find (*a*) how many bacteria there are at $t = 0$; (*b*) at $t = 3$; (*c*) how many hours will be required for the number of bacteria to double itself.

(*a*) At $t = 0$ there are $n = 100 \times 10^0 = 100$ bacteria; (*b*) at $t = 3$ there are $n = 100 \times 10^{.729}$. Now $\log n = \log 100 + \log 10^{.729} = 2 + .729 \log 10 = 2.729$. Therefore, $n = 536$, approximately. (*c*) n will be 200, as required, when t satisfies the equation $200 = 100 \times 10^{.243t}$. Hence $\log 200 = \log 100 + .243\, t \log 10$ or $2.301 = 2 + .243\, t$. Hence $t = .301/.243 = 1.24$ hours, approximately.

Special terminology is often used in physical science to refer to special types of functions which occur often. For example, if y is a linear function of x of the special form $y = cx$ where c is any constant whatever, then it is customary to say that ***y* varies directly as *x***. The graph of this function is a straight line through the origin with slope c. If $y = c/x$ where c is any constant whatever, it is customary to say that ***y* varies inversely as *x***. Thus Boyle's law for enclosed gases says that (at a given temperature) the pressure p varies inversely as the volume v; that is, $p = c/v$ where c is a constant. The graph of this function is a branch of a hyperbola, since only positive numbers are used. Newton's law of gravitation says that the gravitational force F exerted between any two particles whatever varies directly as the product of their masses m_1 and m_2 and inversely as the square of their distance d; that is, $F = Gm_1m_2/d^2$, where G is a constant. The constant G is known as the gravitational constant; when the units employed are centimeters, grams, and seconds, then $G = 6.66 \times 10^{-8}$, approximately. Note that if we ignore the decimal point (quite common practice among numerologists) then the gravitational constant is nothing more than the Number of the Beast (666) discussed in section 34. We leave this bit of information to any numerologist in good standing who wishes to make something of it.

Remark. The function $y = cx$ is a generalization of the multiplication table. For if c is a natural number, say 2, and if x takes only natural numbers as its values, the values of y are the results found in the "two times" table.

In the next chapter, we shall indicate some ways in which functions may be studied.

Exercises

1. If y varies directly as x and if $y = 21$ when $x = 7$,

(*a*) Express y as a function of x.
(*b*) Find the value of y when $x = 6$.
(*c*) How is y affected if x is tripled?

2. If y varies inversely as x and if $y = 8$ when $x = 3$,

(*a*) Express y as a function of x.
(*b*) Find the value of y when $x = 6$.
(*c*) How is y affected if x is doubled?

3. The maximum range of a projectile varies directly as the square of its initial velocity. If the maximum range is 15,000 feet when the initial velocity is 300 feet per second:

(*a*) Write the range r as a function of the initial velocity v.
(*b*) What is the range when $v = 500$ feet per second?
(*c*) What is v when $r = 60{,}000$ feet?

4. Using Boyle's law above, assume that an enclosed gas kept at constant temperature has a volume v of 600 cubic inches when the pressure is 24 pounds per square inch.

(*a*) Express p as a function of v.
(*b*) Find p when $v = 720$ cubic inches.
(*c*) Find v when $p = 100$ pounds per square inch.

5. Neglecting air resistance, the distance a body falls from rest varies directly as the square of the time. If a body falls 64 feet in the first 2 seconds, how far will it fall in the first 5 seconds?

6. The period T of a simple pendulum (that is, the time required for a complete oscillation) varies directly as the square root of the length L of the pendulum. If $T = 1.5$ seconds when $L = 2$ feet, find T when $L = \frac{9}{2}$ feet.

7. The weight of a body is essentially the gravitational force exerted on it by the earth. Hence, as a special case of Newton's law of gravitation above we deduce that the weight w of a body varies inversely as the square of its distance d from the center of the earth. Assuming this to be true and taking the radius of the earth as 4000 miles, how much would a girl weigh at a height of 100 miles above the surface of the earth, if she weighs 100 pounds on the surface of the earth?

8. Show that if y varies directly with x and if $y = y_1$ when $x = x_1$, and $y = y_2$ when $x = x_2$, then $y_1/y_2 = x_1/x_2$. That is, corresponding values of x and y are in proportion.

9. Show that if y varies inversely as x and if $y = y_1$ when $x = x_1$, and $y = y_2$ when $x = x_2$, then $y_1/y_2 = x_2/x_1$.

10. Using the same axes, draw the graphs of both $y = x^2$ and $y = 2^x$, between $x = 0$ and $x = 5$.

11. Using the same axes, draw the graphs of both $y = x^{-2}$ and $y = 2^{-x}$, between $x = 0$ and $x = 5$.

12. The number n of bacteria in a culture at the end of t hours is given by $n = 100 \times 10^{.0492t}$.

(*a*) Find the number present at the start ($t = 0$).
(*b*) How many were present at the end of 4 hours?
(*c*) In how many hours will the number present be 300?

13. A star loses heat in such a way that its temperature y, measured in degrees, at the end of x millions of years is given by $y = 15{,}000 \times 10^{-.075x}$. Find its temperature at the end of 10 million years.

14. If the population P of a country, during a certain interval of time, is represented approximately by the formula $P = 3{,}500{,}000 \times 10^{.015t}$ where t is measured in years, find the population after 7 years.

15. If radium decomposes so that the number y of milligrams remaining at the end of t centuries is given by $y = 50 \times 10^{-.017t}$,

(*a*) How many milligrams were there at the start ($t = 0$)?
(*b*) How many milligrams were left at the end of 15 centuries?

113. GRAPHICAL SOLUTION OF EQUATIONS

Let $f(x)$ be any function of x. If the value of the function becomes zero when the number r is substituted for x, then r is said to be a **root** of the equation $f(x) = 0$. That is, by definition, a root of the equation $f(x) = 0$ is a number r such that $f(r) = 0$.* If r is a real number and r is a root of the equation $f(x) = 0$, then the graph of the function $y = f(x)$ must have a point in common with the x-axis at $x = r$. Therefore *the real roots of an equation $f(x) = 0$ are the x-coordinates of the points of intersection of the curve $y = f(x)$ with the x-axis* (Fig. 143). Consequently the real roots of an equation may be estimated graphically. Note that imaginary roots cannot be found in this way since on our graph x and y range only over real numbers.

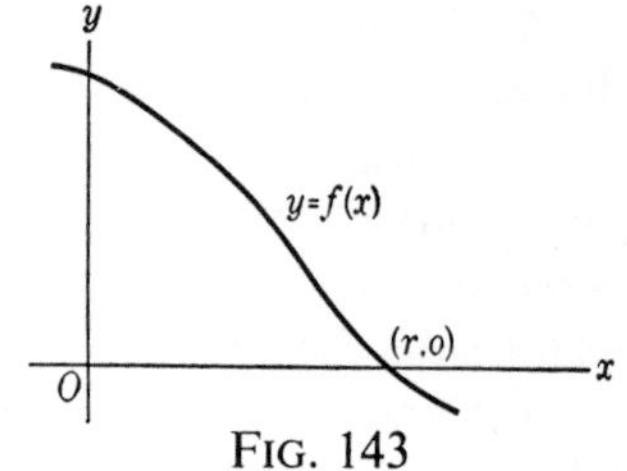

FIG. 143

Example 1. The roots of the equation $4x^3 - x = 0$ are $x = 0$, $x = \frac{1}{2}$, and $x = -\frac{1}{2}$. See Fig. 133.

Example 2. Consider the equation $x^3 - x^2 - 5x + 5 = 0$. Plotting the graph of the function $y = x^3 - x^2 - 5x + 5$ for integral values of x we find the table:

x	0	1	2	3	−1	−2	−3
y	5	0	−1	8	8	3	−16

* Note that the statement $f(x) = 0$ is a propositional function since it contains the variable x, while the statement $f(r) = 0$ where r is a definite number or constant is a proposition.

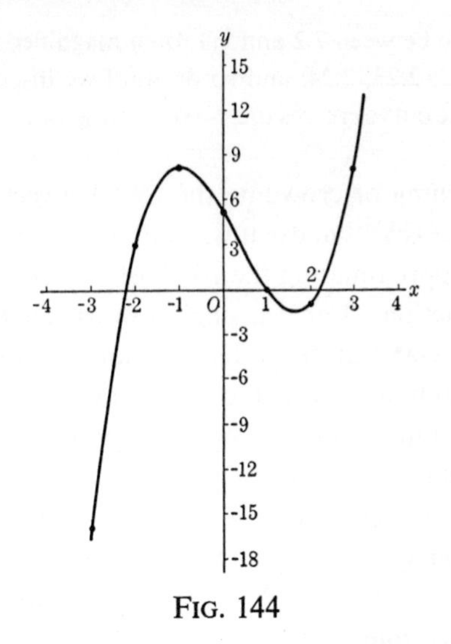

FIG. 144

From the graph (Fig. 144) we see that one root of the equation is 1, while there is another root between -2 and -3 and a third between 2 and 3. We could guess at the value of the root between 2 and 3, for example; but if we would like to get a closer estimate of this root we can locate it beween successive tenths by plotting the graph (on a magnified scale, if desirable) for every tenth between 2 and 3, obtaining the table

x	2	2.1	2.2	2.3
y	-1	-0.649	-0.192	.377

This shows (Fig. 145) that the root of the equation between 2 and 3 is really between 2.2 and 2.3. If we wanted to approximate the root between successive hundredths we

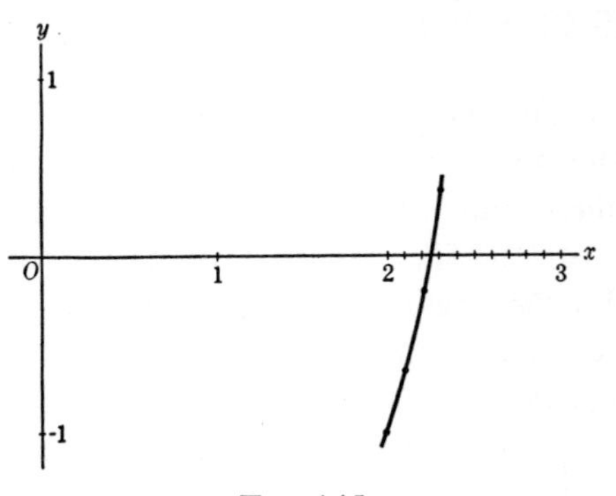

FIG. 145

could now plot the curve between 2.2 and 2.3 (on a magnified scale, if desirable) using the values $x = 2.21, 2.22, 2.23, 2.24$, and so on until we discover between which two successive hundredths the curve crosses the x-axis; and so on.

The process of pinching or crowding the root between two successive units, successive tenths, successive hundredths, and so on, used in example 2, is a standard method of approximating the roots of any equation involving single-valued continuous functions. For if a single-valued function is continuous and its graph is below the x-axis at one value of x and above the x-axis at another value of x, then the graph must cross the x-axis at least once somewhere between these two values of x. This method of hemming in the root, much as one runs down a baserunner caught between first and second base, is very useful although tedious. We have already used it in section 31 to approximate numbers like $\sqrt{2}$, $\sqrt[3]{2}$, etc. Note that $\sqrt{2}$ is a root of the equation $x^2 - 2 = 0$ and $\sqrt[3]{2}$ is a root of the equation $x^3 - 2 = 0$, and so on. Slight improvements in technique can be made which save some time but we shall not go into them here.

Exercises

Solve the following equations graphically:

1. $4x^2 - 8x + 3 = 0.$ **2.** $2x^3 - 3x^2 - 3x + 2 = 0.$
3. $x^3 - 4x^2 + x + 6 = 0.$ **4.** $2x^3 - 5x^2 - 9x + 9 = 0.$
5. $2x^3 - 3x^2 - 9x + 10 = 0.$ **6.** $4x^3 - 5x^2 - 6x = 0.$

Locate the real roots of the following equations between successive tenths:

7. $x^3 - 3x^2 - 2x + 6 = 0.$ **8.** $x^3 - 4x + 2 = 0.$ **9.** $x^3 - 3x + 11 = 0.$
10. $x^4 - 4x - 5 = 0.$ **11.** $2^x + 3x - 6 = 0.$ **12.** $2^x - 8 + 4x = 0.$
13. $3^x + 5x - 10 = 0.$

114. FUNCTIONS OF SEVERAL VARIABLES

It is frequently necessary to study functions of more than one independent variable. Thus the area of a rectangle is a function of its length x and width y, given by the formula $A = xy$. The perimeter of the rectangle is given by the formula $P = 2x + 2y$. The volume of a rectangular box is a function of three independent variables, the length x, width y, and height z, given by the formula $V = xyz$. The surface area of the box is given by $S = 2xy + 2xz + 2yz$. The amount of money A in a bank account on which interest is compounded annually is a function of three independent variables, the original principal P, the number n of years, and the rate r per cent at which interest is paid; this function is given by the formula $A = P\left[1 + \frac{r}{100}\right]^n$. The study of functions of more than one independent variable presents technical difficulties very soon, and *we shall therefore confine ourselves, in our further study of functions, to functions of one independent variable.*

115. THE APPLICATION OF FUNCTIONS IN PRACTICAL SCIENCE

We have already indicated how widespread are the applications of functions in science. We must again emphasize, however, the distinction between pure and applied mathematics. For example, the distance s, measured in feet, through which a falling body falls in t seconds is given approximately by $s = \frac{1}{2}gt^2$ where the constant g is found experimentally to be about 32. (Note: g is the acceleration, measured in feet per second per second, due to gravity.) Now we may use this formula to predict that a body will fall 64 feet in 2 seconds, 144 feet in 3 seconds, and so on. But even if our arithmetical calculations based on this formula are flawless, we must not be misled into believing that our results are perfectly accurate with respect to the physical facts. For the study of the *function* $s = 16t^2$ belongs to pure mathematics while the question whether or not the given function fits the physical facts accurately is a question of applied mathematics. In fact, careful experimentation would show that $g = 32.2$ would fit the facts more accurately than $g = 32$. Further experiment would show that the value $g = 32.1724$ is a still better approximation. In fact, the value g varies slightly depending on the latitude of the place on the earth where the body is falling and on the height above sea level. Thus one should not confuse accuracy insofar as the purely logical perfection of pure mathematics is concerned with the accuracy with which the pure mathematics fits the concrete application.

On the other hand, the accuracy of some of the formulas employed in physical science is amazing. The most familiar of these spectacular achievements are probably those of astronomy, wherein eclipses, etc., are predicted at long range. One of the most dramatic triumphs of applied mathematics was the discovery of the planet Neptune by Leverrier and Adams, about 1846. The planet Uranus had exhibited distressing unwillingness to move as the theory of gravitation said it should. It was suggested that the deviations might be due to the gravitational pull of some other body whose existence had not hitherto been suspected. Leverrier and Adams, independently of each other, performed the difficult mathematical task of calculating how large a body would have to be and how it would have to move in order to produce exactly the observed deviations in the orbit of Uranus. Leverrier wrote to an astronomer Galle telling him that this hypothetical body should be found at a certain place at a certain time. Galle looked with his telescope and there it was! Thus the discovery of the planet Neptune, which had never been seen before that time, was made by purely mathematical prediction.

References

Numbers refer to the bibliography at the back of the book.

Allendoerfer and Oakley 3
Bell 19
Cooley, Gans, Kline, and Wahlert 56
Whitehead 206

11

Limits and the Calculus

116. INTRODUCTION

We have seen how important the study of varying quantities was in the physical science of the seventeenth century when the motions of planets, pendulums, cannon balls, sounds, etc., came to be of central interest. Both the physics of a changing world and the study of problems connected with tangents to curves, which arose in the analytic geometry of Descartes and Fermat, led to the invention of the calculus. The invention of the (differential and integral) calculus was accomplished by the mathematician and physicist Isaac Newton (1642–1727), most famous for his remarkable theory of gravitation, and Gottfried Wilhelm Leibniz (1646–1716), the mathematician and philosopher. Needless to say, neither Newton nor Leibniz created the calculus out of thin air. Other people, Fermat, for example, had some of the ideas of the calculus before these two, and some of the problems involved had been attacked with partial success years earlier. Newton

Isaac Newton
1642–1727, English

himself is said to have remarked "If I have seen a little farther than others it is because I have stood on the shoulders of giants." The fact that progress is seldom independent of the past is amply illustrated in the history of science. This in no way detracts from the gigantic contributions of Newton and Leibniz. They developed and organized the subject, making it one of the most powerful chapters of mathematics. The invention of the calculus initiated a period of exceedingly rapid development both in mathematics and in its applications to physics, astronomy, engineering, etc. In the latter half of the seventeenth century and the entire eighteenth century, much effort was devoted to the important task of developing further the ideas of Newton and Leibniz and their manifold applications in physical science.

Gottfried Wilhelm Leibniz
1646–1716, German

That the ideas of the calculus were "in the air" in the seventeenth century is partly indicated by the fact that Newton and Leibniz obtained their results independently of each other, although at the time each was accused of plagiarizing from the other. This controversy developed into one of the most heated feuds in the history of science (which is rich in disputes about priority) and helped to create an almost complete schism between British and German mathematicians. The unworthy kind of nationalism which displayed itself in this and other such controversies is merely evidence that mathematicians are also human beings often subject to the same weaknesses as other mortals. What is more inspiring, however, is the fact that the thread of scientific progress has persisted through the ages and has been contributed to by many different civilizations, nationalities, races, and creeds and has come to be one of the most precious parts of man's heritage.

The entire calculus is based on the concept of function and the concept of "limit." The notion of "limit" was, in fact, familiar to the ancient Greek philosophers and mathematicians. Indeed, some of them had some of the essential ideas of the calculus. But they failed to develop any usable technique in connection with their ideas and hence made little progress.

117. LEAST UPPER BOUNDS. THE ARCHIMEDEAN PROPERTY

Let X be any subset of the system R of rational numbers or of the system R^1 of real numbers. If a number u of the system is such that $x \leqq u$ for all x in X, then u is termed an **upper bound** of the set X, and the set X is called **bounded above**. If a set has an upper bound u, then it has many upper bounds since any number larger than u is certainly an upper bound. If b is an upper bound of set X, but no number smaller than b is also an upper bound, then b is termed the **least upper bound** of X. For example, let X be the set of all rational numbers x such that $1 < x < 3$ considered as a subset of the system of rational numbers. Then any rational number greater than 3 is an upper bound of X but 3 is the least upper bound. For, if r is any member of X less than 3, then $(r + 3)/2$ lies between r and 3 and is a member of X, so that r cannot be an upper bound of X. These statements are equally true if the word "rational" is replaced by the word "real" throughout.

Both the system R and the system R^1 have all the properties I through XXI of section 32. The system R^1 of real numbers can be distinguished from the system R of rational numbers by the fact that it has the additional property:

XXII. Every non-empty set of real numbers which is bounded above has a least upper bound in the system of real numbers.

The system R^1 of real numbers has the following property called the **Archimedean property** (although Archimedes attributes it to Eudoxus):

Theorem. *If a is a positive real number, no matter how small, and u is a positive real number, no matter how large, then there exists a positive integer n such that $na > u$.*

That is, if one adds up enough a's their sum will exceed u. For instance, enough pennies will add up to more than the federal budget.

Proof of theorem.* Of course, if $u \leqq a$, then $2a$ is already $> u$. Suppose $a < u$. Let X be the set of all positive integral multiples of a. Suppose, contrarywise, that no element of X is $> u$. Then all of them are $\leqq u$, so that u is an upper bound of set X. By the completeness postulate (XXII) X has a least upper bound b. Let

$$c = b - \frac{a}{2}. \tag{1}$$

Then $c + a = b + \dfrac{a}{2} > b$, or $c > b - a$. Since $c < b$ by (1), c is not an upper

* May be omitted without disturbing the continuity of the discussion.

bound for X. Hence, there must exist an element na of X which is $>c$. But $na > c$ implies $na + a > c + a > b$, so that the element $(n+1)a$ of X is $>b$, contradicting the assertion that b is an upper bound of X.

Corollary. *No matter how small a positive number h is, there exists a positive integer n such that $\frac{1}{n} < h$.*

Proof. By the Archimedean property, there is an n such that $nh > 1$. Dividing both sides by n, we have the corollary.

To show that XXII would not be correct in the system of rational numbers, consider the set X of all positive rational numbers x such that $x^2 < 2$. Every positive rational number r is either such that $r^2 < 2$ (i.e. in X) or such that $r^2 > 2$, since we already know that no rational number is such that $r^2 = 2$ (section 30). It is clear that the positive rational numbers r whose squares are greater than 2 are upper bounds for the set X, since $x^2 < 2 < r^2$ implies that $x < r$. We now prove by *reductio ad absurdum* that X has no least upper bound in the system R of rational numbers.

No upper bound of the set X belongs to X. For, if r is such that $r^2 < 2$, then let s be a positive integer such that $\frac{1}{s} < \frac{2-r^2}{2r+1}$. Such an s exists by the corollary above. Let $t = r + \frac{1}{s}$. Then, $t > r$, but

$$t^2 = r^2 + \frac{2r}{s} + \frac{1}{s^2} = r^2 + \frac{1}{s}\left(2r + \frac{1}{s}\right) < r^2 + \frac{1}{s}(2r+1) < r^2 + (2 - r^2) = 2.$$

Hence t is in X, and r is not an upper bound of X.

Suppose now that r were a rational least upper bound of X, with $r^2 > 2$. Let

$$s = r - \frac{r^2 - 2}{2r} = \frac{r}{2} + \frac{1}{r}.$$

Then s is positive and rational since $r/2$ and $1/r$ are both positive and rational. Also $s < r$, since $r^2 - 2$ and hence $(r^2 - 2)/2r$ are positive, and $s = r$ minus the positive number $(r^2 - 2)/2r$. But

$$s^2 = \left(r - \frac{r^2-2}{2r}\right)^2 = r^2 - 2r\,\frac{r^2-2}{2r} + \left(\frac{r^2-2}{2r}\right)^2$$

$$= r^2 - (r^2 - 2) - \left(\frac{r^2-2}{2r}\right)^2 = 2 + \left(\frac{r^2-2}{2r}\right)^2 > 2.$$

Since $s^2 > 2$, s is an upper bound for X. But since $s < r$, this contradicts the supposition that r is the least upper bound.

In the system R^1, of course, the real, irrational number $\sqrt{2}$ is the least upper bound of the set X. In fact, *the system R^1 of all real numbers is completely characterized by properties I through XXII. That is, I–XXII may be taken as a set of postulates for the system of real numbers.* Postulate XXII is often called the **completeness postulate.**

Exercises

1. Find the least upper bound of the set X of all real numbers x such that $1 \leqq x < 3$; of the set Y of all real numbers y such that $1 < y \leqq 3$.

2. If the least upper bound of a set is an element of the set, it is called the **maximum** element of the set. Which of the sets in exercise 1 has a maximum element? What is the maximum of this set?

3. A set X of real numbers is termed **bounded below** if there exists a real number l such that $l \leqq x$ for all x in X, and l is termed a **lower bound** for the set X. Prove that if a non-empty set of real numbers is bounded below then it has a **greatest lower bound** (that is, a lower bound such that no greater number is also a lower bound).

4. Find the greatest lower bound of each of the sets in exercise 1.

5. If the greatest lower bound of a set is an element of the set, it is called the **minimum** element of the set. Which of the sets in exercise 1 has a minimum element? What is the minimum of this set?

6. If a set is bounded below and bounded above it is called **bounded.** Describe a subset of R^1 which is

(*a*) bounded above but not bounded;
(*b*) bounded below but not bounded;
(*c*) bounded;
(*d*) neither bounded below nor bounded above.

7. Prove that if a and b are any two positive real numbers with $a < b$, no matter how small $b - a$ may be, there exists a rational number r between a and b (that is, such that $a < r < b$). (Hint: let q be a positive integer such that $\frac{1}{q} < b - a$, and consider the smallest positive integer p such that $p \cdot \frac{1}{q} > a$.)

8. Prove that if a and b are any two real numbers with $a < b$, there exists a rational number between a and b. (Hint: use the result of exercise 7. Consider all possible cases, such as $a < b < 0$, $a < 0 < b$, $a = 0 < b$, etc.)

9. Prove that if a and b are any two real numbers with $a < b$, there exists an irrational number s between a and b. (Hint: use exercise 8 to show the existence of a rational number r such that $a\sqrt{2} < r < b\sqrt{2}$. Then divide by $\sqrt{2}$.)

118. SEQUENCES

By a **sequence** (or an **infinite sequence**) of numbers we mean an unending succession of numbers $x_1, x_2, x_3, \ldots$, where the dots mean "and so on." The subscript n merely indicates the position of the number x_n in the sequence. Thus x_1 is the first term, x_2 is the second term, x_3 is the third term. The term x_n is called the ***n*th term** or the **general term**. A sequence may be defined by stating its general term. For example, the sequence whose general term is $\frac{n}{n+1}$, is the sequence $\frac{1}{2}, \frac{2}{3}, \frac{3}{4}, \frac{4}{5}, \frac{5}{6}, \ldots, \frac{n}{n+1}, \ldots$. The sequence whose general term is $1 - \frac{1}{10^n}$ has for its first few terms the numbers .9, .99, .999, .9999, .99999, .999999, ... The sequence whose general term is $\frac{(-1)^n}{n}$ has for its first few terms the numbers $-\frac{1}{1}, \frac{1}{2}, -\frac{1}{3}, \frac{1}{4}, -\frac{1}{5}, \frac{1}{6}, \ldots$.

A sequence can be regarded as a single-valued function of n where the domain of n is the set of all natural numbers; to each natural number n there corresponds a number x_n, the nth term in the sequence. Thus the symbol x_n might have been written as $x(n)$ to emphasize that it is a function of n.

Remark. Infinite sequences may arise outside of what is usually considered to be mathematics. For example, if a label on a can has on it a picture of the can, it gives rise to an infinite sequence of pictures of the can.

Exercises

Write the first five terms of the sequence whose general or nth term is:

1. $2 + \frac{1}{10^n}$. **2.** $1/2^n$. **3.** $\frac{2^n - 1}{2^n}$. **4.** $2 - \frac{1}{10^n}$.

5. $\frac{(-1)^n}{2^n}$. **6.** $\frac{(-1)^{n+1}}{10^n}$. **7.** $1/n$. **8.** $3 + \frac{(-1)^n}{n}$.

9. $1 + \frac{1}{2^n}$. **10.** $1 + \frac{(-1)^n}{2^n}$.

119. LIMIT OF A SEQUENCE

Let us mark on a line the numbers of the sequence whose nth term is $2 - \frac{1}{10^n}$; that is, 1.9, 1.99, 1.999, 1.9999, ... It is intuitively clear from Fig. 146

that as n increases indefinitely, the numbers $2 - \frac{1}{10^n}$ become closer and closer to 2; furthermore, it can be shown that $2 - \frac{1}{10^n}$ becomes *as close as we please to* 2 *if n is taken great enough*. Therefore, we say that 2 is the *limit* of the sequence. The latter condition is important, for $2 - \frac{1}{10^n}$ also gets closer and closer to 3 as

1   1.9   1.99   2

FIG. 146

n increases indefinitely but it does not get as close as we please to 3, since for any value of n the number $2 - \frac{1}{10^n}$ is more than 1 unit away from 3. In other words as n becomes large, the distance between 2 and the numbers $2 - \frac{1}{10^n}$ becomes as small as we please. Now the words small and large have only comparative, not absolute, meaning. Thus .001 is small compared with 1,000,000 but large compared to .00000000001; a hundred miles is a large distance to a lame man who has to walk it, but an insignificantly small distance to an astronomer. The condition that the terms of the sequence get as close to 2 as you please can be formulated as a game, as follows: if you choose a "small number" h, we can find a natural number N such that all the terms after the Nth are closer to 2 than the distance h. Thus if you choose $h = .001$ we can take $N = 3$, and it is clear that every term after $2 - \frac{1}{10^3}$ is closer to 2 than the distance .001 (that is, lies between $2 - .001$ and $2 + .001$). If you choose $h = .00001$ the value $N = 3$ will no longer do, but we can take $N = 5$, say. That is, having chosen a "degree of closeness" h we can find a place in the sequence so that every term thereafter is closer to 2 than the preassigned amount h. This leads us to the formal definition of the limit of a sequence.

* **Definition.** *The number a will be called the* ***limit of the sequence*** x_1, x_2, x_3, ..., x_n, ... *provided that, given any positive number h, no matter how small, there exists a corresponding term of the sequence* x_N *such that every succeeding term* x_m $(m > N)$ *lies between the numbers* $a - h$ *and* $a + h$ (*that is, the distance* $|x_m - a|$ *of every* x_m, *with* $m > N$, *from a is less than the preassigned amount h*).

* The formal definition may be omitted without disturbing the continuity of the chapter.

This definition may seem complicated at first because of the unfamiliar precise language in which it is couched, but the idea is really simple. Intuitively it means that *the numbers x_n get to be as close as we please to a as n increases indefinitely.* Let us see what it means in an example.

Example 1. Prove that the sequence $-1, \frac{1}{2}, -\frac{1}{3}, \frac{1}{4}, \ldots, (-1)^n/n, \ldots$ has the limit 0. To do this we must show that given any positive number h, there exists a term of the sequence $1/N$ such that every succeeding term $1/m$ $(m > N)$ lies between $0 - h$ and $0 + h$. This is clearly so. We have only to choose N so that $1/N$ is smaller than h (Fig. 147).

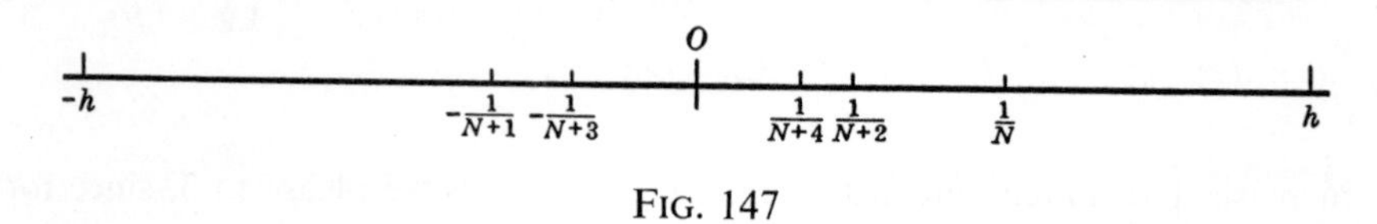

FIG. 147

That such an N exists follows from the Archimedean property: taking $a = h$ and $u = 1$, the Archimedean property assures the existence of an N such that $Nh > 1$ from which $1/N < h$ follows. If $m > N$, then $1/m < 1/N < h$. For example, if we choose $h = .001$, we have only to take $N = 10{,}000$, since $+1/10000$, $-1/10001$, ... are all nearer to 0 than the distance .001. If we choose $h = .00001$, then $N = 10{,}000$ will not do, but we have only to take $N = 1{,}000{,}000$, say, since $1/1000000$, $-1/1000001$, ... are all nearer to 0 than the distance .00001.

If the sequence $x_1, x_2, x_3, \ldots, x_n, \ldots$ has the limit a, we write

$$x_1, x_2, x_3, \ldots, x_n, \ldots \to a \text{ (read, approaches } a\text{)}$$

or

$$\text{as } n \uparrow, x_n \to a \text{ (read, as } n \text{ increases indefinitely } x_n \text{ approaches } a\text{)}$$

or

$$\lim_{n\uparrow} x_n = a, \quad \text{(read, the limit of } x_n \text{ as } n \text{ increases indefinitely is } a\text{)}$$

or simply

$$\lim x_n = a, \quad \text{(read, the limit of the sequence } x_n \text{ is } a\text{).*}$$

We say that x_n **tends to a** or **converges to a** or **approaches a as a limit as n increases indefinitely**. In this case we say the sequence is **convergent;** otherwise **divergent.**

* The notation

$$\lim_{n\to\infty} x_n = a \quad \text{(read, the limit of } x_n \text{ as } n \text{ becomes infinite is } a\text{)}$$

is also widely used, but it often misleads the unwary student into believing that there is a peculiar number, called "infinity" and denoted by a lazy eight ∞, which n approaches. This is, of course, not the case.

Thus the sequences

$$1, 2, 3, 4, \ldots, n, \ldots$$
$$2, 4, 6, 8, \ldots, 2n, \ldots$$
$$1, 4, 9, 16, \ldots, n^2, \ldots$$
$$-1, 1, -1, 1, \ldots, (-1)^n, \ldots$$
$$-1, 2, -3, 4, \ldots, (-1)^n n, \ldots$$

are not convergent since there is clearly no number to which the terms of these sequences get as close as we please. Note that we may have $\lim x_n = a$ even though none of the numbers x_n in the sequence is equal to a. That is, *the limit of a sequence need not be a term of the sequence.*

* **Example 2.** If c is a positive number less than 1, then the sequence $x_n = c^n$ of positive integral powers of c ($c^1, c^2, c^3, \ldots, c^n, \ldots$) has the limit 0.

Proof. Since $c < 1$, we have $1/c > 1$, and we may write $1/c = 1 + p$ where p is positive. For every integer $n > 2$, the binomial theorem asserts

$$(1 + p)^n = 1 + np + \frac{n(n-1)}{2} p^2 + \cdots + p^n.$$

Hence, for $n > 2$, $(1 + p)^n > 1 + np$. Hence,

$$c^n = \frac{1}{(1 + p)^n} < \frac{1}{1 + np} < \frac{1}{np}.$$

Applying the Archimedean property with $a = 1$ and $u = 1/ph$, we are assured of the existence of a positive integer N such that $N > 1/(ph)$. Hence, for any $n > N$, we have $n > 1/(ph)$ or $1/(np) < h$. Hence, for all $n > N$, we have $c^n < 1/(np) < h$ which completes the proof.

Thus the sequence $\frac{1}{2}, \frac{1}{4}, \frac{1}{8}, \ldots, 1/2^n, \ldots$ has the limit 0, as does $1/10, 1/10^2, 1/10^3, \ldots, 1/10^n, \ldots$, and many others.

It is not always easy to prove that a sequence has a limit. However, in a more advanced course we would rest a great deal of work on this definition of limit. In fact, the entire subject of calculus may be based on it. Because of the technical difficulties, we shall here employ the idea of limit intuitively.

Exercises

1–10. What does the limit of each of the ten sequences given in the exercises in section 118 appear to be? What does this mean in terms of the definition of limit?

Make up a sequence whose limit is:

11. Five. **12.** Three. **13.** Zero. **14.** Ten.

* May be omitted without disturbing the continuity of the chapter.

Prove each of the following theorems:

15. If $\lim a_n = a$, then $\lim (-a_n) = -a$.

16. If $\lim a_n = 0$ and $b_n = ca_n$, then $\lim b_n = 0$.

17. If all $|x_n| \leqq K$ and $\lim b_n = 0$, then $\lim x_n b_n = 0$.

★**18.** If $\lim a_n = a$, then there exists a positive K such that all $|a_n| \leqq K$.

★**19.** If $\lim x_n = x$ and $\lim y_n = 0$, then $\lim x_n y_n = 0$.

★**20.** If $\lim a_n = a$ and $\lim b_n = b$, then $\lim (a_n + b_n) = a + b$. (Hint: take $h' = h/2$ and use exercise 14 of section 87.)

★**21.** If $\lim a_n = a$ and $\lim b_n = b$, then $\lim (a_n - b_n) = a - b$. (Hint: write $a_n - b_n = a_n + (-b_n)$ and use exercise 15.)

★**22.** If $\lim a_n = a$ and $\lim b_n = b$, then $\lim a_n b_n = ab$. (Hint: write $a_n b_n - ab = a_n b_n - a_n b + a_n b - ab = a_n(b_n - b) + (a_n - a)b$, and use exercises 18, 17, 20 and 16.)

★**23.** If all $b_n \neq 0$ and $\lim b_n = b \neq 0$, then $\lim \dfrac{1}{b_n} = \dfrac{1}{b}$.

★**24.** If $\lim a_n = a$ and $\lim b_n = b \neq 0$ and all $b_n \neq 0$, then $\lim \dfrac{a_n}{b_n} = \dfrac{a}{b}$. (Hint: use exercises 23 and 22.)

120. LIMIT OF A FUNCTION

Consider a sequence of values of x approaching a as a limit: $x_1, x_2, x_3, \ldots, x_n, \ldots \to a$. Suppose that every term x_n of the sequence is in the domain of the independent variable x for a given function $f(x)$; that is, $f(x_n)$ is defined. Then it may be that the sequence $f(x_1), f(x_2), \ldots, f(x_n), \ldots$ converges to a limit L. If $x_1', x_2', x_3', \ldots x_n', \ldots$ is another sequence of values of x converging to a, it might be

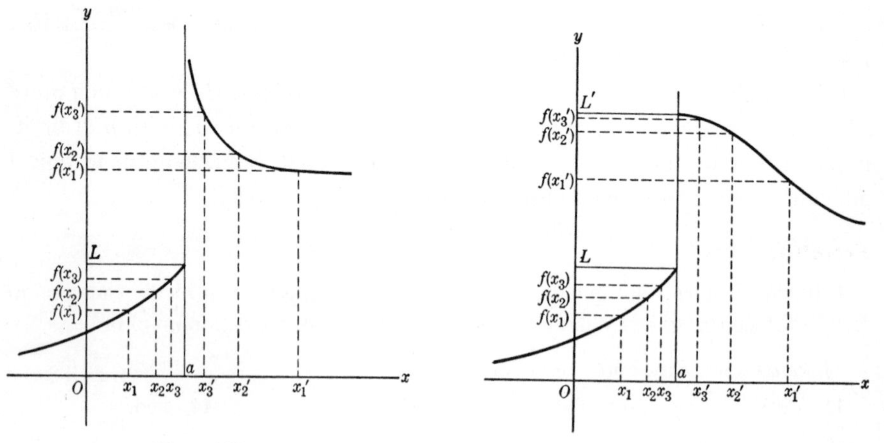

FIG. 148 FIG. 149

that the sequence $f(x_1'), f(x_2'), \ldots, f(x_n'), \ldots$ does not converge at all, or possibly converges to a limit $L' \neq L$. These things happen in the functions whose graphs are given in Figs. 148 and 149, respectively. But it *may* happen that, no matter what sequence of x's we take converging to a, the corresponding values of the function will converge to the limit L. In this case, we say that $f(x)$ approaches the limit L as x approaches a. Precisely, we make the following definition.

* **Definition.** *If for **every** sequence $x_1, x_2, x_3, \ldots, x_n, \ldots \to a$ (where each $x_n \neq a$), all x_n's being in the domain of the independent variable x, we have $f(x_1), f(x_2), \ldots, f(x_n), \ldots \to L$, then we say that L is the **limit of $f(x)$ as x approaches a.** In symbols we write $\lim_{x \to a} f(x) = L$, or $f(x) \to L$ as $x \to a$.*

Intuitively, the statement $\lim_{x \to a} f(x) = L$ means that *the value of $f(x)$ gets close to L as the value of x gets close to a.* One reason for the parenthetical remark in the definition is that we do not require that the number a be in the domain of the independent variable at all; that is, $f(a)$ need not be defined. We want to discuss what happens as we approach a even if we cannot be at a. This is illustrated in the following example.

Example 1. Let $f(x) = \dfrac{x^2 - 9}{x - 3}$. This function is defined for all values of x except $x = 3$. (Why?) For any $x \neq 3$, in fact, the value of $f(x)$ is the same as for the (different) function $y = x + 3$. Thus the graph of $y = \dfrac{x^2 - 9}{x - 3}$ is the same as the straight line $y = x + 3$ except that the point (3,6) is removed, since our function is not defined for $x = 3$. Nevertheless, $\lim_{x \to 3} \dfrac{x^2 - 9}{x - 3}$ exists and is 6. That is, as x approaches 3, $f(x)$ becomes as close as we please to 6. Thus we see that $\lim_{x \to a} f(x)$ can exist even when $f(a)$ does not.

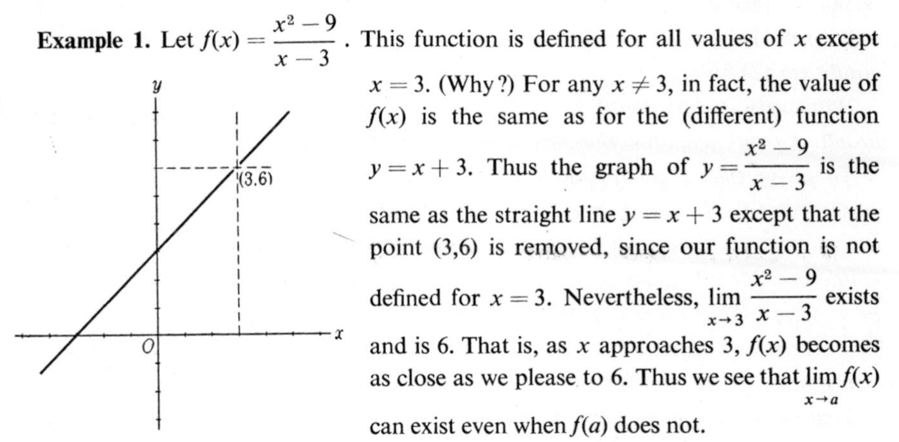

FIG. 150

Notice that $\lim_{x \to 3} (x^2 - 9) = 0$ and $\lim_{x \to 3} (x - 3) = 0$; yet, $\lim_{x \to 3} \dfrac{x^2 - 9}{x - 3} = 6$.

Example 2. Consider the function defined as follows:

$$f(x) = \begin{cases} \dfrac{x^2 - 9}{x - 3} & \text{for all } x \neq 3 \\ 1 & \text{for } x = 3. \end{cases}$$

* The formal definition may be omitted without disturbing the continuity of the chapter.

This function is defined for *all* values of x. Its graph is given in Fig. 151. The point (3,6) is not in the graph while the isolated point (3,1) is in the graph. For this function we have $f(3) = 1$ while $\lim_{x \to 3} f(x) = 6$. This situation obviously corresponds to the "jump" in the graph at $x = 3$.

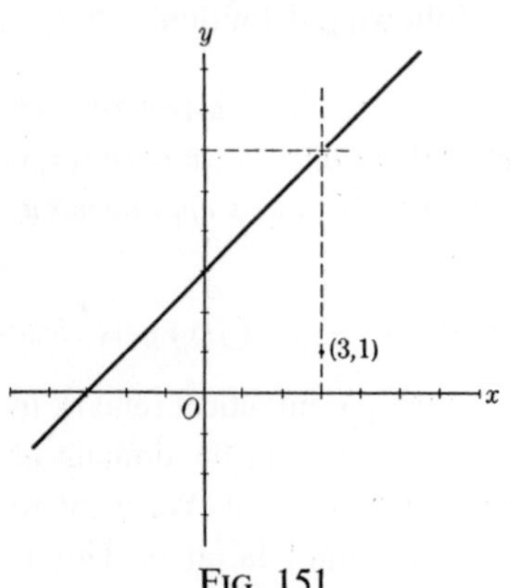

FIG. 151

These are examples of discontinuous functions. They suggest the following definition.

* **Definition.** *A single-valued function $f(x)$ is said to be* **continuous at $x = a$** *if:* (1) *$f(a)$ is defined;* (2) *$\lim_{x \to a} f(x)$ exists;* (3) *$\lim_{x \to a} f(x) = f(a)$. If any of these three conditions fails to be satisfied the function is called* **discontinuous at $x = a$.**

The third condition says that the limit of the function as x approaches a is the same as the value of the function at $x = a$.

In example 2, the function is discontinuous because condition (3) fails. In example 1, the function is discontinuous because condition (1) fails. The functions in Figs. 148 and 149 are discontinuous because condition (2) fails.

Intuitively, a *function is discontinuous if there is a break of some kind in its graph. A continuous function has an unbroken graph.*

To prove that a given function is continuous is often difficult. But it can be proved that the functions studied in elementary mathematics and its applications are all continuous except possibly for isolated values of x. *Thus polynomials are continuous for all values of x; and rational functions are continuous for all values of x except those for which the denominator becomes zero.* Assuming that these statements are correct we may use part (3) of our definition to find limits of continuous functions; for part (3) of the definition says that the limit of $f(x)$ as x approaches a can be found by substituting a for x in $f(x)$ as long as $f(x)$ is known to be continuous.

Example 3. $\lim_{x \to 0} (7 + 1000x + 10000x^2) = 7$. Notice that the magnitude of the coefficients of our polynomial has no effect. We have the table:

x	1	.1	.01	.001	.0001	.00001	···
$f(x)$	11007	207	18	8.01	7.1001	7.010001	···

* The formal definition may be omitted without disturbing the continuity of the chapter.

This table makes it intuitively clear that as $x \to 0$, $f(x) \to 7$. But since we know that a polynomial is continuous for all values of x, we could obtain this limit by merely substituting $x = 0$ in the polynomial.

Exercises

Evaluate the following limits:

1. $\lim_{x \to 2} (x^2 - 3)$. **2.** $\lim_{x \to 3} (3x^3 - 6x^2 + 8)$. **3.** $\lim_{x \to 3} \dfrac{x^2 - 9}{x + 5}$.

4. $\lim_{h \to 0} (3x + h)$. **5.** $\lim_{h \to 0} (3x^2 + 2hx + h^2)$. **6.** $\lim_{h \to 0} (h^2 + 3h)$.

Find the value of the expression $\lim_{h \to 0} \dfrac{f(x+h) - f(x)}{h}$, *where:*

7. $f(x) = x^2$. **8.** $f(x) = x^3$. **9.** $f(x) = 4x^2 + 3x - 1$.

10. $f(x) = 4x^3$. **11.** $f(x) = 1/x$. **12.** $f(x) = 3 - 4x - 3x^2$.

13. $f(x) = 1/x^2$. **14.** $f(x) = mx + p$. **15.** $f(x) = ax^2 + bx + c$.

★**16.** Prove each of the following theorems: if $f(x)$ and $g(x)$ have the same domains containing the real number a, and if $\lim_{x \to a} f(x) = F$ and $\lim_{x \to a} g(x) = G$, then

(*a*) $\lim_{x \to a} [f(x) + g(x)] = F + G$ (Hint: use exercise 20 section 119.)

(*b*) $\lim_{x \to a} [f(x) - g(x)] = F - G$ (Hint: use exercise 21 section 119.)

(*c*) $\lim_{x \to a} [f(x) \cdot g(x)] = F \cdot G$ (Hint: use exercise 22, section 119.)

(*d*) $\lim_{x \to a} \dfrac{f(x)}{g(x)} = \dfrac{F}{G}$ provided $G \neq O$ (Hint: use exercise 24, section 119.)

121. INFINITY; HOW CERTAIN FUNCTIONS VARY

Consider the function $y = 1/x$ (Fig. 152). It is not defined at $x = 0$. We see that if x takes successively the sequence of values .1, .01, .001, .0001, ..., $1/10^n$, ... then $f(x)$ takes the values 10, 100, 1000, 10,000, ..., 10^n, ... Similarly, if x takes the values $-.1, -.01, -.001, \ldots, -1/10^n, \ldots$, then $f(x)$ takes the values $-10, -100, -1000, \ldots, -10^n, \ldots$. Similarly, it is easy to see that if $x_1, x_2, x_3, \ldots, x_n, \ldots$ is any sequence of positive numbers approaching zero as a limit, then the terms of the sequence $f(x_1), f(x_2), f(x_3), \ldots, f(x_n), \ldots$ become ultimately larger than any pre-assigned positive number, no matter how large; and if $x_1, x_2, x_3, \ldots, x_n, \ldots$ is any sequence of negative numbers approaching zero as a limit, then the terms of the sequence $f(x_1), f(x_2), f(x_3), \ldots, f(x_n), \ldots$

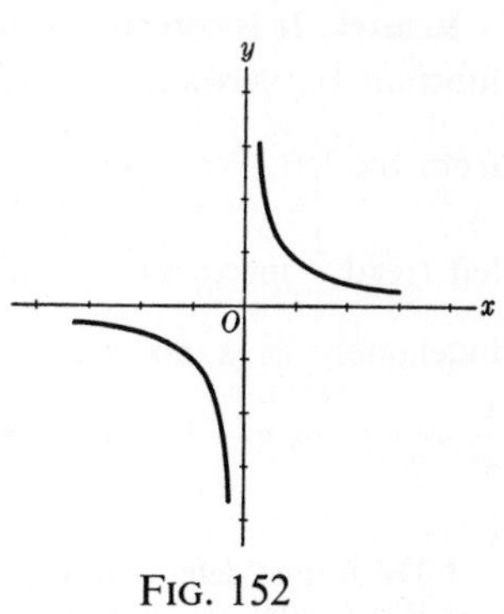

FIG. 152

become ultimately smaller than any preassigned negative number. In either case the absolute value $|f(x_n)|$ becomes greater than any preassigned positive number. This suggests the following definition.

* **Definition.** *If for every sequence $x_1, x_2 \ldots, x_n, \ldots \to a$ (all $x_n \neq a$) and any preassigned number H (no matter how large), there exists a corresponding term x_N of the sequence such that for all succeeding terms $x_m (m > N)$ we have*

$$|f(x_m)| > H, \tag{1}$$

then we say that the ***absolute value of $f(x)$ increases indefinitely as x approaches a.*** *In symbols we write $|f(x)| \uparrow$ as $x \to a$.*

Intuitively this means that the values of the function $f(x)$ get indefinitely large in absolute value as x gets near to a.

This is often written in the form $\lim_{x \to a} f(x) = \infty$ (read, the limit of $f(x)$ as x approaches a is infinity) or in the form $f(x) \to \infty$ as $x \to a$ (read, $f(x)$ becomes infinite as x approaches a). These symbols sometimes mislead the unwary student into thinking that there is a peculiar number, infinity, which is the limit of $f(x)$ as $x \to a$, or which is approached by $f(x)$ as x approaches a. Therefore we prefer to write $\left|\frac{1}{x}\right| \uparrow$ as $x \to 0$ instead of the usual $\lim_{x=0} \frac{1}{x} = \infty$. It would be even more misleading to write $\frac{1}{0} = \infty$, although some books do write it.† Of course, they use this notation to mean that $\left|\frac{1}{x}\right| \uparrow$ as $x \to 0$; they do not mean that ∞ is a number which you obtain by dividing 1 by 0. As we have seen $1/0$ is a meaningless symbol; and furthermore the symbol ∞ is not a number at all. "Infinity," in this sense, is merely a way of describing the manner in which certain functions vary.

Remark. It is sometimes desirable to distinguish between the manner in which the function $1/x$ varies as $x \to 0$ from the right and the behavior of the function as $x \to 0$ from the left. We write $\frac{1}{x}\uparrow$ as $x \to 0$ from the right, and $\frac{1}{x}\downarrow$ as $x \to 0$ from the left (read $\frac{1}{x}$ increases indefinitely as x approaches 0 from the right and $\frac{1}{x}$ decreases indefinitely as x approaches 0 from the left). This is often written in the form $\frac{1}{x} \to +\infty$ as $x \to 0$ from the right, and $\frac{1}{x} \to -\infty$ as $x \to 0$ from the left.

* The formal definition may be omitted without disturbing the continuity of the chapter.

† Historically, the statement $1/0 = \infty$ was actually taken literally. But we are now more familiar with the logical foundations of numbers than were many pioneers in the field.

Exercises

(*a*) *What can be said about the way in which the following functions vary as x approaches the indicated value?*

(*b*) *Draw a graph of each function for values of x near the value in question.*

1. $\dfrac{1}{x-2}$ as $x \to 2$.

2. $\dfrac{17}{2-x}$ as $x \to 2$.

3. $\dfrac{x^2+5x}{x-2}$ as $x \to 2$.

4. $\dfrac{2x^2-3x}{x^2-4}$ as $x \to 2$.

5. $1/x^2$ as $x \to 0$.

6. $-1/x^2$ as $x \to 0$.

122. TANGENTS

In high school, the tangent to a circle C at a given point P on C was defined as a line which meets the circle only at P. This definition is clearly unsuitable for other curves. For (Fig. 153), AB meets the curve only at A but is not

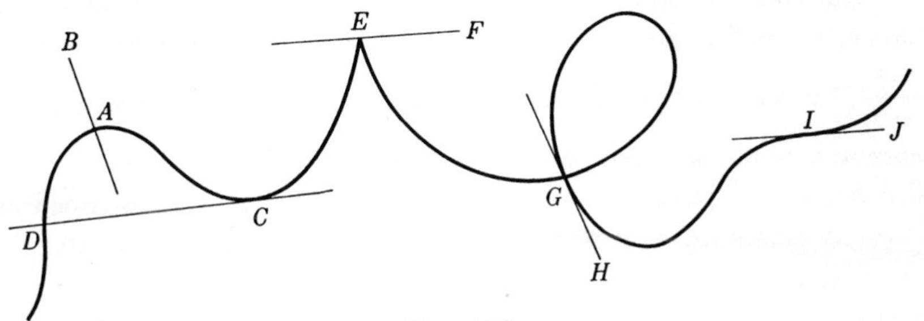

FIG. 153

what we would like to call a tangent; while CD is what we would like to call a tangent at C but meets the curve again at D. It will not do to say that a tangent at P is a line which does not "cross" the curve at P, for GH and IJ do cross the curve and are what we would like to call tangents, while EF does not cross the curve but is not what we would like to call a tangent. If one thinks of a curve as being generated by a moving particle, then we would like a tangent at a given point on the curve to be a straight line with the same "direction" as that in which the particle is moving at that point. A definition of tangent, corresponding to this intuitive idea, will involve the idea of limits. Let P be a point on our curve at which we would like to

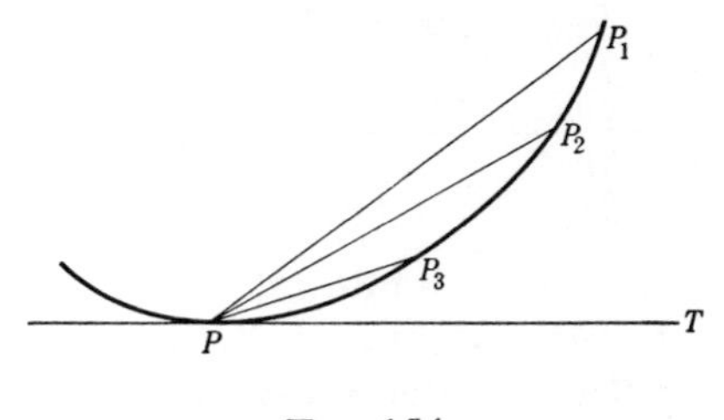

FIG. 154

define a tangent (Fig. 154). Let P_1 be a nearby point on the curve. Then PP_1 is a secant or chord. Now let $P_1, P_2, P_3, \ldots, P_n, \ldots$ be a sequence of points on the curve, all different from P, but approaching P as a limit.* Then we can conceive of the tangent PT at P as the "limiting position" of the sequence of secants $PP_1, PP_2, PP_3, \ldots, PP_n, \ldots$. Actually, since "limiting position" has not been defined precisely, it will be more convenient to define the slope of the tangent at P. This is sufficient† because if we know the coordinates of P and the slope of PT we can write the equation of PT (see section 95). Thus we shall define *the slope of the tangent at P as the limit of the slopes of the secants* PP_n as $P_n \to P$ (*if this limit exists*). Note that according to this definition, the "tangent" to a straight line at any point of the line is the line itself. This definition will be studied more closely in the next section.

123. THE DERIVATIVE OF A FUNCTION

Consider the function $y = f(x)$ at $x = x_1$. Let $y_1 = f(x_1)$. Take a nearby point (x_2, y_2) on the curve (Fig. 155); $y_2 = f(x_2)$. The slope of the secant P_1P_2 is $\dfrac{y_2 - y_1}{x_2 - x_1}$. Let $x_2 - x_1$ be called Δx, read "delta x," or the **difference in x** or the **change in x** or the **increment in x** or the **increase in x**. Similarly, let $y_2 - y_1$ be called Δy, or the **change in y**. (The symbol Δx is not to be understood as a number Δ multiplied by a number x; Δx stands for a single quantity which

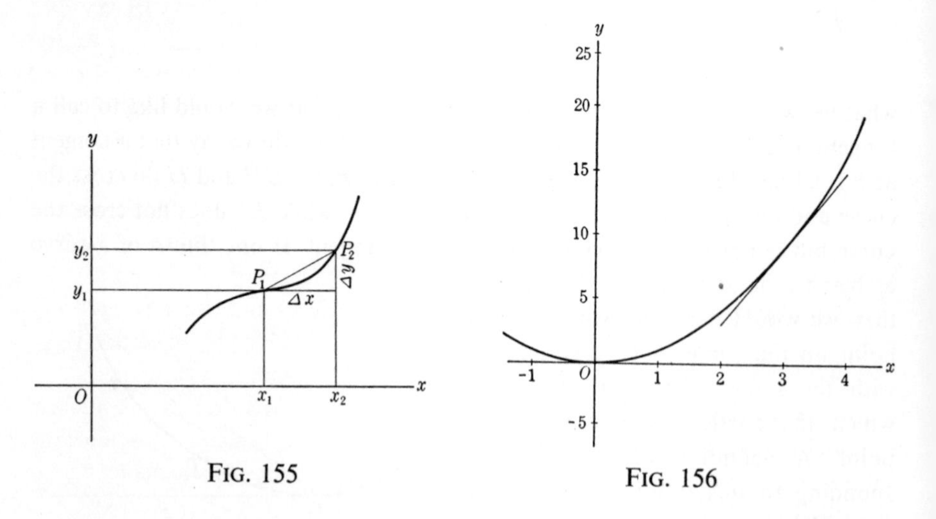

FIG. 155 FIG. 156

* This means that the distances $PP_1, PP_2, PP_3, \ldots, PP_n, \ldots$ approach zero as a limit.
† Except for vertical tangents which will not be discussed here.

happens to have a first and second name, just as you have.) Then the slope of the secant is $\Delta y/\Delta x$. As P_2 approaches P_1, x_2 approaches x_1, and $\Delta x \to 0$; similarly, $y_2 \to y_1$ and $\Delta y \to 0$. But it may happen that $\Delta y/\Delta x$ approaches a limit. (See example 1, section 120.) If this limit exists, it is called the **slope of the tangent at (x_1, y_1).**

Example. Consider the curve $y = x^2$. See Fig. 156. Let us find the slope of the tangent at $x_1 = 3$, $y_1 = 9$. Take a nearby value of x, say $x_2 = 3 + \Delta x$. Then for this value of x, $y_2 = (3 + \Delta x)^2 = 9 + 6 \cdot \Delta x + (\Delta x)^2$. Now Δy means, by definition, the difference between this value y_2 and the value $y_1 = 9$. Thus

$$\Delta y = 6 \cdot \Delta x + (\Delta x)^2. \tag{1}$$

Dividing both sides of (1) by Δx, we find that the slope of the secant is

$$\frac{\Delta y}{\Delta x} = 6 + \Delta x.$$

Therefore as $\Delta x \to 0$ we find that the slope of the tangent at (3,9) is

$$\lim_{\Delta x \to 0} \frac{\Delta y}{\Delta x} = 6.$$

It might be worth while to make a table for this example which will make the idea clear:

x_1	$x_2 = x_1 + \Delta x$	$\Delta x = x_2 - x_1$	y_1	$y_2 = y_1 + \Delta y = f(x_1 + \Delta x)$	$\Delta y = y_2 - y_1$	$\frac{\Delta y}{\Delta x}$
3	5	2	9	25	16	8
3	4	1	9	16	7	7
3	3.1	.1	9	9.61	.61	6.1
3	3.01	.01	9	9.0601	.0601	6.01
3	3.001	.001	9	9.006001	.006001	6.001

From this table it is intuitively clear that as Δx gets closer and closer to zero, Δy also approaches zero, but $\frac{\Delta y}{\Delta x}$ approaches 6.

It is usually possible to evaluate the slope of the tangent for all values of x at once. Consider the example $y = x^2$ again. Take any point (x,y) on the curve. Take a nearby value of x; call it $x + \Delta x$. The ordinate of the point on the curve corresponding to this abscissa is $(x + \Delta x)^2$; call it $y + \Delta y$. Thus

$$y + \Delta y = x^2 + 2x \cdot \Delta x + (\Delta x)^2. \tag{2}$$

But

(3) $$y = x^2.$$

Hence, subtracting (3) from (2), we have

(4) $$\Delta y = 2x \cdot \Delta x + (\Delta x)^2.$$

Therefore, dividing both sides of (4) by Δx, we have $\dfrac{\Delta y}{\Delta x} = 2x + \Delta x$, which is the slope of the secant joining (x,y) and $(x + \Delta x, y + \Delta y)$. Thus the slope of the tangent at (x,y) is $\lim\limits_{\Delta x \to 0} \dfrac{\Delta y}{\Delta x} = 2x$. This is true for any value of x. For example, for $x = 3$, the slope of the tangent is $2 \cdot 3 = 6$, as we saw before. Notice that the slope of the tangent to the curve $y = x^2$ at the point whose abscissa is x is $2x$. This is a new function of x, called the *derived function or derivative of the function* x^2. In general, we make the following definition.

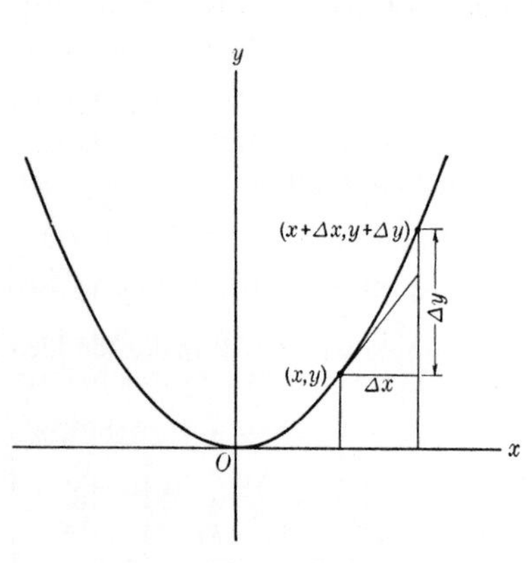

FIG. 157

Definition. *Consider the function $y = f(x)$. Let $y + \Delta y = f(x + \Delta x)$ for any increment Δx; then $\Delta y = f(x + \Delta x) - f(x)$. Now,*

$$\lim_{\Delta x \to 0} \frac{\Delta y}{\Delta x}$$

is a new function of x (provided this limit exists) called the ***derivative*** *or* ***derived function of f(x)***. *The derivative of the function $y = f(x)$ is denoted by dy/dx, read "the derivative of y with respect to x," or $\dfrac{d}{dx} f(x)$, read "the derivative of $f(x)$ with respect to x," or df/dx, read "the derivative of f with respect to x," or $f'(x)$, read "f prime of x," or "the derivative of $f(x)$," or simply y', read "y prime" or "the derivative of y." Briefly,*

$$\frac{dy}{dx} = \lim_{\Delta x \to 0} \frac{\Delta y}{\Delta x}.$$

Remark. We have assumed that the limit $\lim\limits_{\Delta x \to 0} \dfrac{\Delta y}{\Delta x}$ exists. Now

$$\frac{\Delta y}{\Delta x} = \frac{f(x + \Delta x) - f(x)}{\Delta x}$$

is, for a fixed x, a function of the independent variable Δx. We have seen that the limit of a function may not exist. But it can be proved that for the functions studied in elementary mathematics and its applications this limit always does exist, except possibly for isolated values of x.

The symbol dy/dx should not be thought of as the quotient of a quantity dy divided by a quantity dx. In particular, we cannot regard dx as meaning $\lim_{\Delta x \to 0} (\Delta x)$ and dy as meaning $\lim_{\Delta x \to 0} (\Delta y)$, since each of these limits is clearly zero and dy/dx would then become 0/0 which is undefined. Misinterpretations like this caused considerable trouble during the seventeenth and eighteenth centuries, since mathematicians, inspired by the tremendous success of the calculus in solving problems in both pure and applied mathematics, devoted their energies to developing the powerful methods of the subject and did not straighten out its logical foundations until the nineteenth century. Bishop Berkeley, in the eighteenth century, scoffed at derivatives as quotients of "the ghosts of departed quantities." This is reminiscent of the grinning Cheshire cat, in Lewis Carroll's *Alice in Wonderland*, who disappeared gradually, beginning with the end of his tail and working forward until nothing was left but the grin. However, it is not surprising, when viewed correctly, that two functions may each approach zero while their quotient approaches a value different from zero. For example, $\lim_{h \to 0} (6h) = 0$ and $\lim_{h \to 0} (3h) = 0$ but $\lim_{h \to 0} \left(\frac{6h}{3h}\right) = \frac{6}{3} = 2$. Berkeley wrote* that a person who can digest some of the concepts of the calculus "need not, methinks, be squeamish about any point in divinity." Berkeley's criticisms were not without foundation and helped to stimulate mathematicians to examine critically the logical foundations of the subject. For example, Berkeley asked "whether certain maxims do not pass current among analysts which are shocking to good sense? And whether the common assumption, that a finite quantity divided by nothing is infinite, be not of this number?" Thus Berkeley justly balked at the expression "$1/0 = \infty$" which was discussed in section 121. It was not until the nineteenth century that mathematicians began to avoid writing this misleading expression.

The process of finding the derivative of a given function is called **differentiation**. The study of derivatives is called the **differential calculus**. As we have already pointed out, *the value of the derivative $f'(x)$ at $x = x_1$ is the slope of the tangent to the curve $y = f(x)$ at (x_1, y_1) where $y_1 = f(x_1)$.*

* *The Analyst*, London, 1734.

Exercises

In each of the following exercises, (a) find the derivative of the given function; (b) find the slope of the tangent to the curve at the point where $x = 2$; (c) write the equation of the tangent to the curve at the point where $x = 2$; (d) plot the curve and the tangent line found in part (c):

1. $y = 3x^2$. **2.** $y = -2x^2$. **3.** $y = \frac{1}{2}x^2$.

4. $y = 3x^2 - 6x + 5$. **5.** $y = 2x^2 + 5$. **6.** $y = x^3$.

7. $y = 2x^2 - 3x + 5$. **8.** $y = 1/x$. **9.** $y = 1/x^2$.

10. $y = 2x$. **11.** $y = 2x + 3$. **12.** $y = x - 3$.

13. $y = x$. **14.** $y = \dfrac{1}{x-1}$. **15.** $y = \dfrac{1}{(x-1)^2}$.

16. Find the derivative of $y = mx + p$. Interpret graphically.

17. Find the derivative of $y = cx^2 + kx + a$.

124. INSTANTANEOUS RATE OF CHANGE

We have seen in section 110 that if $y = f(x)$, then the average rate of change of y with respect to x for the interval from x_1 to x_2 is the slope of the secant joining the points (x_1, y_1) and (x_2, y_2) of the curve $y = f(x)$. This average rate of change is $\Delta y/\Delta x$. If y varied with x at a uniform rate, then we might say that the rate of change at any instant is the same as the average rate for any interval, since all these average rates would be the same. But if y varies with x at a changing rate, what shall we mean by the rate of change of y with respect to x at a given value of x? For example, a falling body does not fall at a uniform speed but falls faster and faster as it falls. If s is the distance through which the body falls in t seconds, then s is a function of t and the "speed" with which the body falls is the rate of change of s with respect to t. What shall we mean by the speed of a falling body at a given instant (value of t)? Clearly, the average speed for a very small interval of time beginning with the given instant will be very close to what we want to mean by the instantaneous speed at that instant. This suggests the following definition.

Definition. *If $y = f(x)$, the* ***instantaneous rate of change of y with respect to x, at $x = x_1$****, is* $\lim_{\Delta x \to 0} \dfrac{\Delta y}{\Delta x}$, *or* $f'(x_1)$ where *$f'(x)$ is the derivative dy/dx of y with respect to x.*

Hence, an instantaneous rate corresponds graphically to the slope of a tangent, just as an average rate corresponds graphically to the slope of a secant.

Example. Consider the falling body problem. Here $s = 16t^2$ where s is the distance, measured in feet, through which the body falls in t seconds. What is the instantaneous speed of the falling body at the end of the first second? We have the following table:

t	$t + \Delta t$	Δt	s	$s + \Delta s = 16(t + \Delta t)^2$	Δs	$\frac{\Delta s}{\Delta t}$ = *average speed for the interval from t to t + Δt*
1	2	1	16	64	48	48
1	1.5	.5	16	36	20	40
1	1.1	.1	16	19.36	3.36	33.6
1	1.01	.01	16	16.3216	.3216	32.16
1	1.001	.001	16	16.032016	.032016	32.016

This table indicates that the average speed approaches 32 feet per second as a limit as $\Delta t \to 0$. This can be proved as follows. We have

$$s + \Delta s = 16(t + \Delta t)^2$$

or

$$s + \Delta s = 16t^2 + 32 \cdot t \cdot \Delta t + 16(\Delta t)^2.$$

Then

$$\Delta s = 32t \cdot \Delta t + 16(\Delta t)^2$$

and the average speed for the interval Δt is

$$\frac{\Delta s}{\Delta t} = 32t + 16\Delta t.$$

Hence, the instantaneous speed at the end of t seconds is

$$\lim_{\Delta t \to 0} \frac{\Delta s}{\Delta t} = 32t$$

or

$$\frac{ds}{dt} = 32t \text{ feet per second.}$$

At $t = 1$, this speed is 32 feet per second as suggested by the table.

The idea of an instantaneous rate of change is very useful in physics. Thus if a rectilinear motion (that is, motion in a straight line) is specified by giving the distance s from the starting point as a function of the time t, then ds/dt, is the **velocity** v. The rate of change of the velocity with respect to time, or dv/dt, is called the **acceleration.** In the above example, $v = 32t$. Hence, the acceleration of a falling body is dv/dt which may be calculated as follows:

$$v + \Delta v = 32(t + \Delta t) = 32t + 32 \cdot \Delta t$$

$$\Delta v = 32\Delta t$$

$$\frac{\Delta v}{\Delta t} = 32$$

$$\frac{dv}{dt} = \lim_{\Delta t \to 0} \frac{\Delta v}{\Delta t} = 32 \text{ feet per second per second.}$$

This is a constant and does not depend on the value of t; hence the acceleration of a falling body is 32 feet per second at any instant.

The problems of tangents and of instantaneous rates of change like velocity and acceleration were actually what led to the idea of the derivative of a function. Here again we see how the abstract idea of the derivative of a function may be applied to or interpreted in different concrete situations such as tangents in geometry or velocity and acceleration in physics. Newton was led to the invention of the differential calculus, or "method of fluxions" as he called it, because he was concerned with ideas like velocity and acceleration. Much of the importance and power of this calculus is due to the fact that it enables us to depart from static considerations and to study the dynamical problems of a changing, moving world.

Exercises

1. If a projectile is thrown straight up from the ground with an initial velocity of 96 feet per second, its height h above the ground is given by $h = 96t - 16t^2$ where h is measured in feet and t in seconds. (*a*) What is the velocity at $t = 1, 2, 3, 4$? (*b*) What is the acceleration at these times? (*c*) Interpret the plus and minus signs in your answers. (*d*) Draw a graph of this function from $t = 0$ to $t = 6$, plotting t on the horizontal axis and h on the vertical axis. Describe the motion of the projectile. (*e*) Is the graph of the motion a picture of the *path* of the projectile?

2. The distance s feet a ball rolled in a straight line down an inclined plane at the end of t seconds is given by $s = 4t^2$. (*a*) What is its average speed for the first two seconds? (*b*) What is its instantaneous speed at $t = 2$? (*c*) Find the acceleration at any instant.

3. A ball starts rolling up an inclined plane, moving in a straight line. Its distance from the starting point is given by $s = 100t - 10t^2$ where s is measured in feet and t in seconds. (*a*) Find expressions for the velocity and acceleration at any instant. (*b*) What is the velocity at $t = 5$? $t = 10$? $t = 15$?

4. The volume of a spherical balloon is given by $v = \frac{4}{3}\pi r^3$ where r is the radius and $\pi = 3.14 \ldots$. Suppose the balloon is being blown up. Find the rate of change of the volume with respect to the radius.

5. Find the rate of change of the area of a circle with respect to the radius, recalling that $A = \pi r^2$.

125. DIFFERENTIATION OF POLYNOMIALS

We have been differentiating each function considered by appealing directly to the definition of derivative. In this section we shall learn how to differentiate polynomials and certain other functions quickly.

Consider the function

$$y = x^n \tag{1}$$

where n is a natural number greater than one. Then $y + \Delta y = (x + \Delta x)^n$. By the binomial theorem, we find* that for any natural number $n > 1$,

$$y + \Delta y = (x + \Delta x)^n = x^n + nx^{n-1}\Delta x + \text{terms involving } \Delta x \text{ with an exponent of at least 2.} \tag{2}$$

Then, subtracting (1) from (2), we obtain

$$\Delta y = nx^{n-1}\Delta x + \text{terms involving } \Delta x \text{ with an exponent of at least 2.} \tag{3}$$

Hence, dividing both sides of (3) by Δx, we have

$$\frac{\Delta y}{\Delta x} = nx^{n-1} + \text{terms involving } \Delta x \text{ with an exponent of at least 1.}$$

Thus

$$\lim_{\Delta x \to 0} \frac{\Delta y}{\Delta x} = nx^{n-1}.$$

This proves the following theorem.

Theorem 1. *If $y = x^n$, where n is any natural number greater than one, then $dy/dx = nx^{n-1}$; that is, for $n > 1$,*

$$\frac{d}{dx}(x^n) = nx^{n-1}. \tag{4}$$

* The student should review section 74.

We have already seen (see exercise 13, section 123) that the derivative of x^1 with respect to x is 1. Hence (4) holds even for $n = 1$ since it says that the derivative of x^1 with respect to x is $1 \cdot x^0$ which *is* equal to 1. Hence *formula* (4) *is valid for all natural numbers n.*

Theorem 2. *Formula* (4) *is valid when n is any real number whatever, positive, negative, or zero.*

We shall not prove this here.

Example 1. The derivative of x^5 with respect to x is $5x^4$ by (4).

Example 2. Find the derivative of $1/x^2$. Now $1/x^2 = x^{-2}$. By (4), the derivative of x^{-2} is $-2x^{-3}$. Hence $\frac{d}{dx}(1/x^2) = -2/x^3$.

Theorem 3. *The derivative of a constant c with respect to x is zero.*

Proof. If $y = c$, then $y + \Delta y = c$ and hence $\Delta y = 0$. Therefore $\Delta y/\Delta x = 0$ and

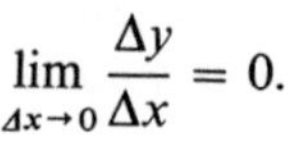

$$\lim_{\Delta x \to 0} \frac{\Delta y}{\Delta x} = 0.$$

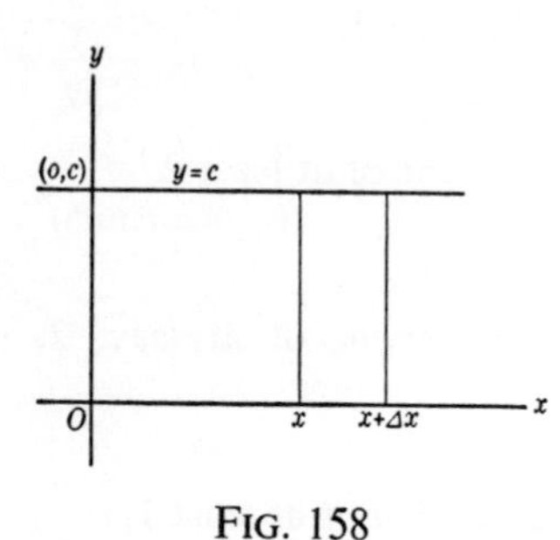

FIG. 158

Graphically, this means that the slope of the straight line $y = c$ is zero (that is, the line is horizontal) since the tangent to any straight line is the line itself.

We shall use the following theorems without proof.

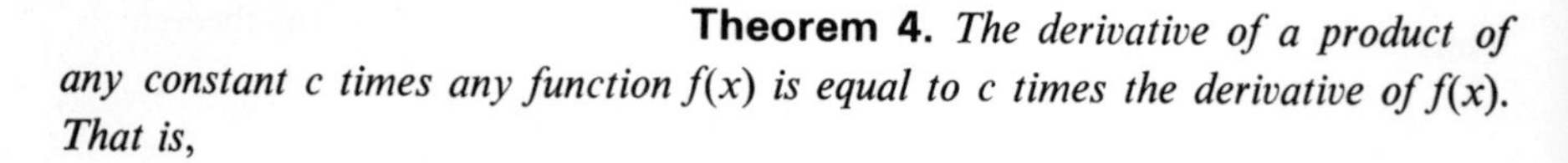

Theorem 4. *The derivative of a product of any constant c times any function f(x) is equal to c times the derivative of f(x). That is,*

$$\frac{d}{dx}[c \cdot f(x)] = c \cdot \frac{d}{dx} f(x). \tag{5}$$

Theorem 5. *The derivative of the sum of any two functions f(x) and g(x) is equal to the sum of their derivatives. That is,*

$$\frac{d}{dx}[f(x) + g(x)] = \frac{d}{dx} f(x) + \frac{d}{dx} g(x). \tag{6}$$

By using the above theorems, we can differentiate any polynomial and certain other functions as in the following examples.

Example 3. Differentiate the polynomial $6x^3 + 3x^2 + 5$. By theorem 5,

$$\frac{d}{dx}(6x^3 + 3x^2 + 5) = \frac{d}{dx}(6x^3) + \frac{d}{dx}(3x^2) + \frac{d}{dx}(5).$$

By theorem 4,

$$\frac{d}{dx}(6x^3) = 6\cdot\frac{d}{dx}(x^3) \quad\text{and}\quad \frac{d}{dx}(3x^2) = 3\cdot\frac{d}{dx}(x^2).$$

By theorem 3, $\frac{d}{dx}(5) = 0$. Hence,

$$\begin{aligned}\frac{d}{dx}(6x^3 + 3x^2 + 5) &= 6\cdot\frac{d}{dx}(x^3) + 3\cdot\frac{d}{dx}(x^2) + 0 \\ &= 6\cdot 3x^2 + 3\cdot 2x \qquad \text{(by theorem 1)} \\ &= 18x^2 + 6x.\end{aligned}$$

Example 4. Differentiate $\frac{3}{x^2} + \frac{4}{x^3}$. We have

$$\begin{aligned}\frac{d}{dx}\left(\frac{3}{x^2} + \frac{4}{x^3}\right) &= \frac{d}{dx}\left(3\cdot\frac{1}{x^2}\right) + \frac{d}{dx}\left(4\cdot\frac{1}{x^3}\right) \qquad \text{(by theorem 5)} \\ &= 3\cdot\frac{d}{dx}\left(\frac{1}{x^2}\right) + 4\cdot\frac{d}{dx}\left(\frac{1}{x^3}\right) \qquad \text{(by theorem 4)} \\ &= 3\cdot\frac{d}{dx}(x^{-2}) + 4\cdot\frac{d}{dx}(x^{-3}) \\ &= 3(-2)x^{-3} + 4(-3)x^{-4} \qquad \text{(by theorem 2)} \\ &= -6x^{-3} - 12x^{-4} = -\frac{6}{x^3} - \frac{12}{x^4}.\end{aligned}$$

Exercises

Differentiate each of the following functions by means of theorems 1–5 above:

1. $4x^3 + 6x^2$. **2.** $2x^3 + 5x^2 - 3x + 1$. **3.** $x^2 - 5x$.

4. $3x + 5$. **5.** $5x^4 + 2x^3 - 3x^2 - 4x - 5$. **6.** $\frac{3}{x^4} + \frac{2}{x^2}$.

7. $2x^3 + \frac{2}{x^3}$. **8.** $2x^2 + 5 + \frac{3}{x}$. **9.** $2x - 3 + \frac{4}{x^2}$.

In each of the following (a) find the slope of the tangent to the curve at the indicated point; (b) write the equation of the tangent to the curve at the indicated point; (c) plot the curve and the tangent found in part (b):

10. $y = x^2 - 5$ at the point for which $x = 2$.
11. $y = x^3$ at the point for which $x = 1$.
12. $y = x^3$ at the point for which $x = -\frac{1}{2}$.
13. $y = x^2 - 2x + 3$ at the point for which $x = 1$.
14. $y = 9 - x^2$ at the point for which $x = 3$.
15. $y = 9 - x^2$ at the point for which $x = -3$.
16. $y = 12/x$ at the point for which $x = 2$.
17. $y = 12/x$ at the point for which $x = -2$.
18. $y = 1/x^2$ at the point for which $x = 2$.
19. $y = 1/x^2$ at the point for which $x = -2$.
20. For what value of x is the tangent to the curve $y = x^2 - 4x + 5$ horizontal? Plot.
21. For what values of x are the tangents to the curve $y = \frac{1}{3}x^3 - \frac{1}{2}x^2 - 6x + 2$ horizontal? Plot.
22. (*a*) Differentiate x^2. (*b*) Differentiate x^3. (*c*) Differentiate x^5. (*d*) Is it true that the derivative of the product of two functions is equal to the product of their derivatives?
23. (*a*) Differentiate x^6. (*b*) Differentiate x^2. (*c*) Differentiate x^4. (*d*) Is it true that the derivative of the quotient of two functions is equal to the quotient of their derivatives?
24. A falling body traverses s feet in t seconds where $s = 16t^2$. (*a*) Find the velocity and acceleration at any instant; (*b*) at $t = 3$; (*c*) at $t = 4$.
25. (*a*) How fast does the volume of a cube change with respect to its edge x? (*b*) What is the rate of change of its surface area with respect to its edge x?
26. Prove theorem 4. **27.** Prove theorem 5.

126. MAXIMA AND MINIMA

Consider the curve $y = f(x)$ and let $f'(x)$ be the derivative of y with respect to x. Recall that $f'(x)$ is the slope of the tangent at the point whose abscissa is x. Let us consider how y changes as x goes from left to right (increases). If $f'(x)$ is positive, clearly y is rising at that point; if $f'(x)$ is negative, y is falling; if $f'(x) = 0$, the tangent is horizontal (Fig. 159). A value of x for which the tangent is horizontal is called a **critical value**. A point of the curve is called a **maximum** if it is higher than any nearby point and a **minimum** if it is lower than any nearby point. If (a,b) is a maximum point, the function $f(x)$ is said to have a **maximum value at $x = a$**. If (a,b) is a minimum point, the function $f(x)$ is said to have a **minimum value at $x = a$**. In any "smooth" curve, it is intuitively clear that at any maximum or minimum point, the curve has a horizontal tangent.

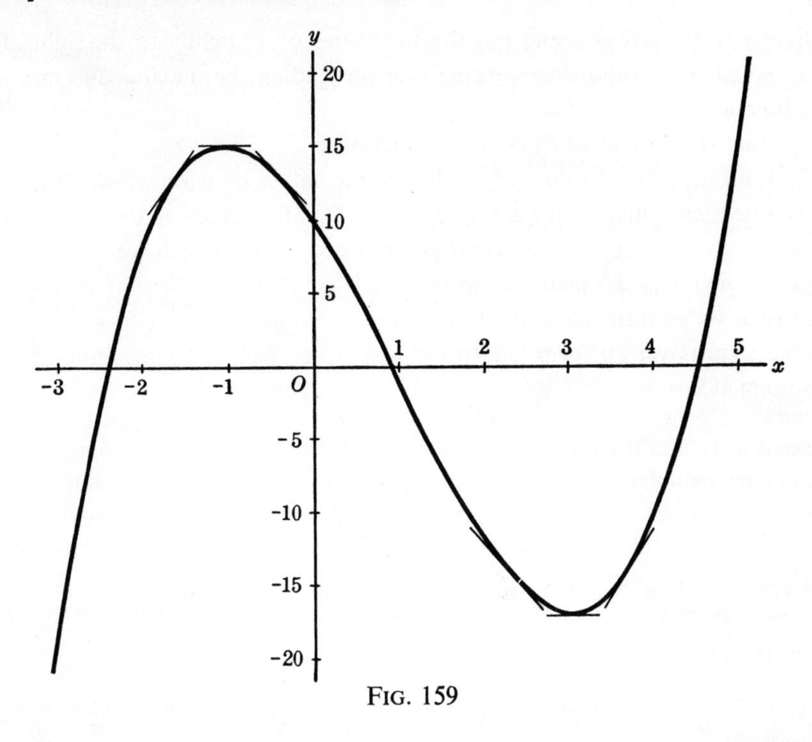

FIG. 159

(It can be proved that this is so for most functions studied in elementary mathematics. This is not so for curves with "corners" like that in the accompanying Fig. 160.) But the converse is not true; there are points (Fig. 161) which have a horizontal tangent and which are neither maxima nor minima. It is easy to see that a function $f(x)$ has a maximum at $x = a$ if $f'(x)$ is positive for values of x slightly less than a and negative for values of x slightly greater than a. Similarly, $f(x)$ has a minimum at $x = a$, if $f'(x)$ is negative for values of

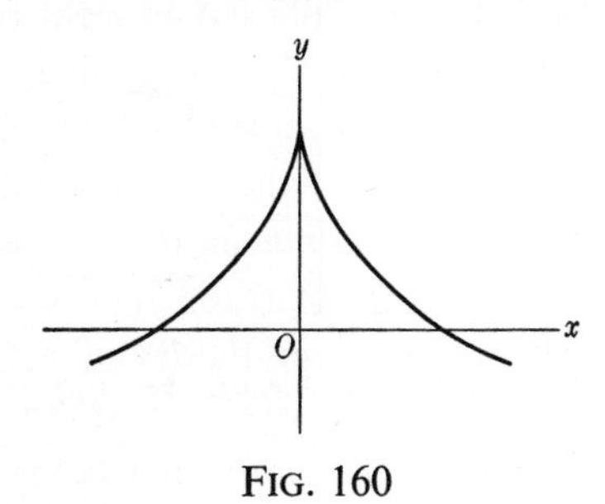

FIG. 160

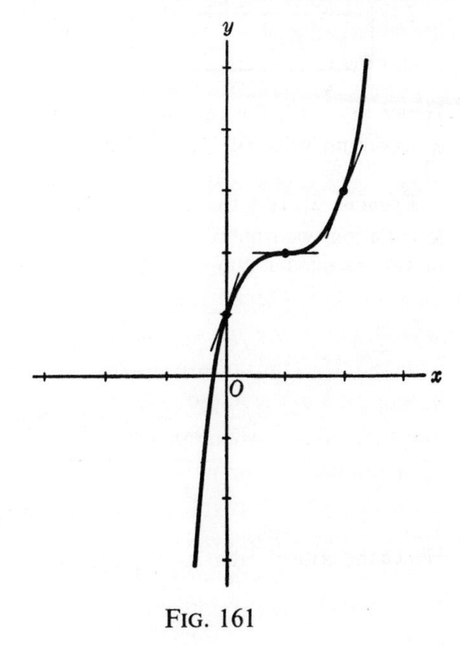

FIG. 161

x slightly to the left of a and positive for values of x slightly to the right of a. Thus we have the following working rule for finding the maxima and minima of a function:

(1) Find the derivative $f'(x)$ of the function.

(2) Find the critical values of x; that is, the values of x for which $f'(x) = 0$.

(3) For each critical value $x = a$, evaluate $f'(x)$ for values of x slightly to the left and right of a. If $f'(x)$ changes from positive to negative as we go from left to right, $f(x)$ has a maximum at $x = a$. If $f'(x)$ changes from negative to positive as we go from left to right, $f(x)$ has a minimum at $x = a$. If $f'(x)$ does not change sign as we go from left to right, $f(x)$ has neither a maximum nor a minimum at $x = a$.

Example 1. Test the curve $y = x^3 - 3x^2 - 9x + 10$ for maxima and minima. Differentiating, we obtain

$$\frac{dy}{dx} = f'(x) = 3x^2 - 6x - 9.$$

The critical values are obtained by solving the equation $3x^2 - 6x - 9 = 0$, or $x^2 - 2x - 3 = 0$, whose roots are $x = 3$ and $x = -1$. We may conveniently tabulate our work as follows:

x	2	3	4	-2	-1	0
$\frac{dy}{dx} = f'(x)$	neg.	0	pos.	pos.	0	neg.
$y = f(x)$		-17			15	

Hence at $x = 3$, the function y attains a minimum value of -17 and at $x = -1$ a maximum value of 15. See Fig. 159.

Example 2. Test the curve $y = x^3 - 3x^2 + 3x + 1$ for maxima and minima. Differentiating, we obtain $f'(x) = 3x^2 - 6x + 3$. Thus the only critical value is the root of $3x^2 - 6x + 3 = 0$, or $x^2 - 2x + 1 = 0$, or $x = 1$. We have

x	0	1	2
$\frac{dy}{dx} = f'(x)$	pos.	0	pos.
$y = f(x)$		2	

Hence the critical value $x = 1$ yields neither a maximum nor a minimum. See Fig. 161.

Remark. Note that a function may attain higher values than it does at a maximum value and lower values than it does at a minimum. For example, the function in example 1 attains the value 620 at $x = 10$; this is greater than the "maximum" value 15. These terms are used relative to sufficiently nearby points of the curve. Any peak in a mountain range is a maximum point even though it is not the highest peak of all. In the usual technical language, we are here finding "relative or local maxima and minima" rather than "absolute maxima and minima."

Exercises

Find the maxima and minima of the following curves and plot:

1. $y = x^2 - 6x + 2$.

2. $y = 6x - x^2 + 2$.

3. $y = 4x - x^2 + 3$.

4. $y = x^2 + 4x + 3$.

5. $y = 2x^3 - 9x^2 - 24x - 12$.

6. $y = \frac{1}{3}x^3 - \frac{1}{2}x^2 - 2x + 5$.

7. $y = x^3 - 6x^2 + 12x - 8$.

8. $y = \frac{1}{3}x^3 + \frac{1}{2}x^2 - 2x + 3$.

127. APPLIED MAXIMA AND MINIMA

Problems involving maxima and minima are obviously among the most important practical considerations that arise in applied mathematics. An engineer, manufacturer, or other practical worker tries to get a desired effect with the least effort, or the most efficient result with a given cost. Such problems often amount mathematically to the investigation of the maxima and minima of some function. From the conditions of the problem, we must first express the quantity in which we are interested as a function of one variable.

Example 1. A rectangular area is to be enclosed by 40 feet of fence. What should the dimensions of the rectangle be if we want the greatest possible area to be enclosed? What is the maximum area?

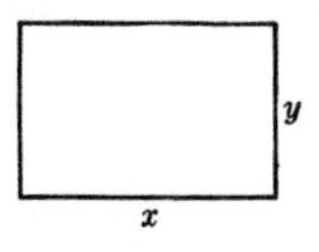

FIG. 162

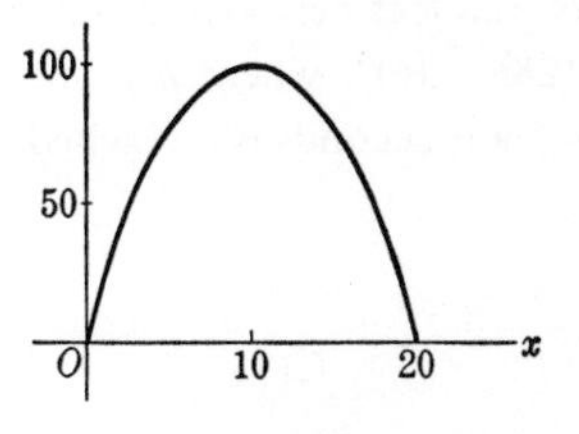

FIG. 163

Clearly, we might have many rectangles, 2 by 18, 3 by 17, 4 by 16, 4.5 by 15.5, etc., with different areas, all having the required perimeter, 40 feet. Let x and y be the length and width of any rectangle. Then $2x + 2y = 40$ by hypothesis. Hence $y = 20 - x$. Now the area A of the rectangle is given by $A = xy$, or, $A = x(20 - x)$, or $A = 20x - x^2$. It is this particular function of x of which we want the maximum value. Hence we find $dA/dx = 20 - 2x$. This derivative is zero only at $x = 10$. To the left of this critical value, say at $x = 9$, dA/dx is positive and to the right, say at $x = 11$, it is negative. Hence $x = 10$ gives a maximum. Thus the rectangle 10 by 10 has the greatest possible area, namely 100 square feet. It will be instructive to plot the graph of this function $A = 20x - x^2$ (Fig. 163) and to observe the graphical significance of the facts just discussed.

Example 2. An open box is to be made from a square piece of cardboard 12 inches on each side by cutting out equal squares from the corners and folding up the sides. How long should the edge of the cut-out square be in order to obtain a box of maximum volume? What is the maximum volume? See Fig. 164.

Let x be the length of the edge of the cut-out square. Then the volume of the box is given by $V = x(12 - 2x)^2 = 144x - 48x^2 + 4x^3$. This is the function of which we want the maximum value. We find $dV/dx = 144 - 96x + 12x^2$. The critical values of x are the roots of the equation

$$144 - 96x + 12x^2 = 0,$$

or
$$12 - 8x + x^2 = 0,$$

or
$$(x - 6)(x - 2) = 0,$$

or
$$x = 6, x = 2.$$

The critical value $x = 6$ need not be considered since, for this value, there would be no box at all. The value $x = 2$ gives a maximum since for $x = 1$, dV/dx is positive and for $x = 3$ it is negative. The box 2 by 8 by 8 has the maximum volume 128 cubic inches.

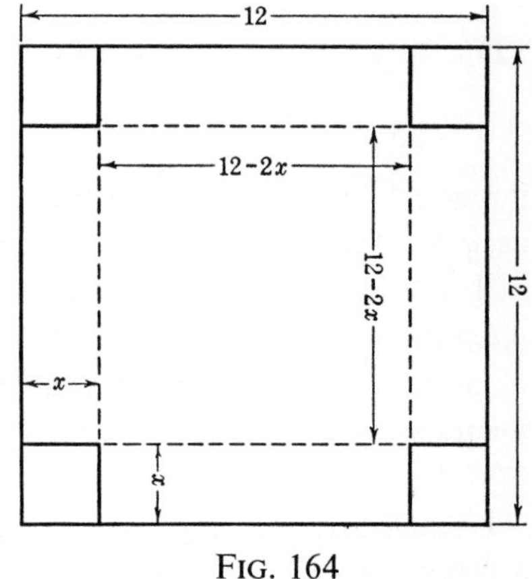

FIG. 164

Example 3. A projectile is thrown straight up from a height of 5 feet, at an initial velocity of 128 feet per second. Its height above the ground after t seconds is given by $h = 5 + 128t - 16t^2$, where h is measured in feet. What is its maximum height and after how many seconds is it reached? Differentiating, we obtain

$$\frac{dh}{dt} = 128 - 32t.$$

The only critical value is $t = 4$, which gives a maximum height of 261 feet.

Exercises

1. A rectangular area is to be enclosed by 100 feet of fence. Find the dimensions of the rectangle which will have the greatest area. What is the maximum area?

2. An open box is to be made of a square piece of tin 18 inches on each side by cutting out equal squares from the corners and folding up the sides. How long should the side of the cut-out square be in order to get a box with the greatest possible volume? What is the maximum volume?

3. A projectile is thrown straight up from the ground with an initial velocity of 96 feet per second. Its height after t seconds is given by $h = 96t - 16t^2$, where h is measured in feet. After how many seconds does the projectile reach its maximum height? What is the maximum height?

4. Find the dimensions of the rectangle with the smallest perimeter which has an area of 196 square feet. (Hint: make use of negative exponents.)

5. A closed box having a volume of 64 cubic feet is to have a square base. If the total area of the top, bottom, and four sides is to be minimum, find the dimensions of the box.

6. A closed box having a volume of 64 cubic feet is to have a square base. If the material for the top and bottom costs 16 cents per square foot and the material for the sides costs 2 cents per square foot, what should be the dimensions of the box in order to make the cost a minimum?

7. A projectile is thrown straight up from a height of 6 feet with an initial velocity of 192 feet per second. Its height after t seconds is given by $h = 6 + 192t - 16t^2$ where h is measured in feet. After how many seconds does the projectile reach its maximum height? What is the maximum height?

8. It is desired to fence off a rectangular field 3200 square yards in area along the straight bank of a river. No fence is needed along the river bank. What dimensions should the field have if the amount of fencing is to be a minimum?

9. A printed page is to contain 432 square centimeters of actual printed matter. There is to be a margin 4 centimeters wide along the sides and 3 centimeters wide along the top and bottom. What should be the dimensions of the page if the amount of paper used is to be a minimum?

10. An open box with a square base is to be made from 400 square inches of material. Find the dimensions of the box with maximum volume. What is the maximum volume?

11. An open box is to have a rectangular base twice as long as it is wide. If the box is to be made of 600 square inches of material, find the dimensions which will yield the maximum volume. What is the maximum volume?

12. If 400 people will attend a moving picture theater when the admission price is 30 cents and if the attendance decreases by 40 for each 10 cents added to the price, then what price of admission will yield the greatest gross receipts?

13. A telephone company can get 1000 subscribers at a monthly rate of \$5.00 each. It will get 100 more subscribers for each 10 cent decrease in the rate. What rate will yield the maximum gross monthly income and what will this income be?

14. For a box with square ends to be sent by parcel post, the sum of its length and girth (perimeter of a cross section) must not exceed 84 inches. Find the dimensions of the box with maximum volume that can be sent. What is maximum volume?

128. THE NUMBERS e and π

The study of derivatives, called the differential calculus, is based on the idea of limits as we have seen. This is not the only way that limits enter into mathematics. In fact, every irrational number may be considered as the limit of a sequence of rational numbers. Thus $\sqrt{2}$ is the limit of the sequence 1, 1.4, 1.41, 1.414, ..., and π is the limit of the sequence 3, 3.1, 3.14, 3.141, 3.1415, 3.14159, ...

An interesting and important irrational number called e arises from the compound interest law. If 1 dollar is invested at 100% interest compounded annually for one year, the amount at the end of the year is clearly 2 dollars. If the interest is compounded semi-annually, the amount is given by $A = 1(1 + \frac{1}{2})^2 = 2.25$ dollars. If it were compounded quarterly, the amount would be $A = (1 + \frac{1}{4})^4 = 2.441$ dollars, approximately. Clearly, the more often it is compounded, the greater the amount will be at the end of the year. How great can the amount become if we allow the interest to be compounded oftener and oftener, as every day or every minute or every tenth of a second? Intuition would probably lead us to expect a fortune, but the answer is, surprisingly enough, that the amount cannot surpass 2.72 dollars no matter how often the interest is compounded. This is so because $(1 + 1/n)^n$ is the amount obtained by compounding the interest n times during the year and it can be proved that

$$\lim_{n\uparrow} (1 + 1/n)^n = 2.71828 \ldots. \tag{1}$$

The number defined by (1) is called e and is used as the base of the so-called "natural" logarithms. We cannot prove (1) here but it can be made plausible by the following table:

n	1	2	4	10	100	1000	···
$(1+1/n)^n$	2	2.25	2.4414 ···	2.5937 ···	2.7048 ···	2.7169 ···	···

The irrational numbers e and π are perhaps the strangest members of number society. They enter into advanced mathematics in many curious and important ways.

The number $\pi = 3.14159265 \ldots$, approximately, is familiar to you but you have probably never learned how it may be calculated. Notice that $\pi \neq \frac{22}{7}$; the number $\frac{22}{7} = 3.142 \ldots$ and therefore gives the value of π correctly only as far as the hundredths place. It is interesting to note that, as far as we know, Euclid never calculated π. Euclid did prove the theorem that if A is the area of a circle of radius r and A' is the area of a circle of radius r', then $A/r^2 = A'/r'^2$. That is, the area of a circle divided by the square of the radius gives the same numerical result no matter how large or small a circle we take. This number A/r^2 may be called π for short; hence we have the familiar formula $A = \pi r^2$ for the area of any circle. Euclid, a pure mathematician, interested chiefly in the logical proof of his theorems, never estimated the value of π. Various crude estimates had been made before but no method, so far as we know, was developed for obtaining this value, possibly because there was no great practical need for it. For example, the Old Testament's estimate* of 3 for the value of π may have been good enough for the roughly circular ox-cartwheels of that era.† It would be hopelessly inadequate for the wheels of an automobile in which to ride comfortably on smooth roads. It remained for Archimedes, a brilliant mathematician and phycisist who lived in the century following Euclid, to develop such a method. It can be done in the following way. Take a circle of radius one; then π is exactly the area of the circle. Inscribe a square in the circle and circumscribe a square about it. Then it is easy to see (Fig. 165) that the area of the inscribed square is 2 and the area of the circumscribed square is 4. Thus $2 < \pi < 4$. This is a first approximation. Now we can double the number of sides. It is not hard to calculate‡ by the methods of elementary geometry that the area of the circumscribed regular 8-gon is 3.3137 ..., and the area of the inscribed regular 8-gon is 2.8284 .... Thus $2.8284 \ldots < \pi < 3.3137 \ldots$. If we continue to increase the number of sides, we get the results in the following table:

No. of sides	*Area of inscr. reg. polygon (approx).*	*Area of circum. reg. polygon (approx.)*	*Approximation of* π
4	2	4	
8	2.8284	3.3137	
16	3.0615	3.1826	3.+
32	3.1214	3.1517	3.1+
64	3.1365	3.1441	
128	3.1403	3.1422	3.14+
256	3.1413	3.1418	3.141+

* I Kings 7:23 and II Chron. 4:2.

† The ancient artisan probably worked by trial and error, making no use of theoretical computations. But modern industry could hardly do without a good approximation to π.

‡ The details are found in M. Richardson, *Plane and Spherical Trigonometry*, Macmillan, N. Y., 1950, section 65.

As we increase the number of sides, the area of the inscribed (or circumscribed) regular polygon approaches the area of the circle as a limit. In fact, the area of the circle may be defined as the limit of the area of the inscribed regular n-gon as n increases indefinitely. By taking n large enough we can approximate π as closely as we please. Archimedes carried this kind of process far enough to ascertain that $3\frac{10}{71} < \pi < 3\frac{1}{7}$, using a polygon of 96 sides. Archimedes' method is called the method of exhaustion, not because of what happens to its user, but because the growing inscribed regular polygon gradually exhausts the area of the circle. This method resembles and, indeed, contains the germ of the modern subject called integral calculus, which we shall take up briefly in the next sections.

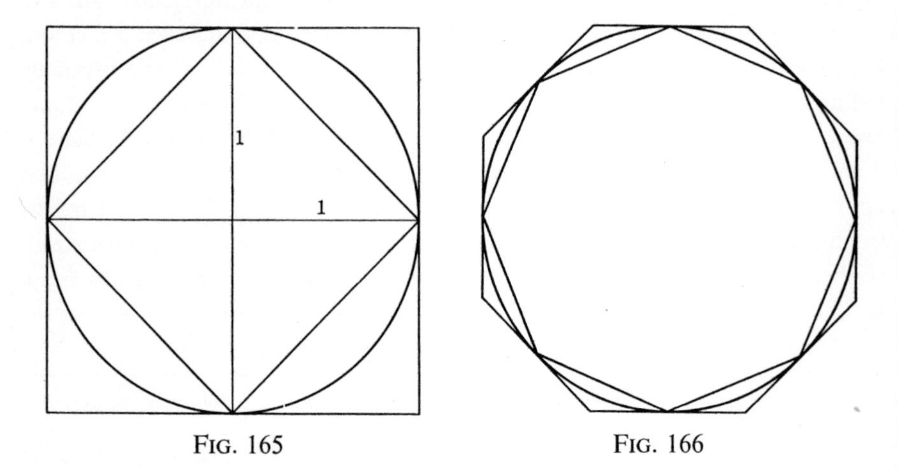

FIG. 165 FIG. 166

The idea of approximating a curved area by means of polygonal areas will be found again in modern form when we discuss the definite integral in sections 131 and 132.

Using electronic computers, π has been calculated to 100,000 decimal places.*

* D. Shanks and J. W. Wrench, Jr., *Mathematics of Computation*, vol. 16 (1962), pp. 76–99.

129. ANTI-DERIVATIVES

If a function has a constant value for all values of x, then its derivative is equal to zero. Conversely, it is plausible and true that if the derivative of a function is zero for all values of x, then the function is a constant, although we shall not prove this here. Thus if two functions $F(x)$ and $G(x)$ have the same derivative at every value of x, (that is, $F'(x) = G'(x)$ for every value of x), then their difference $G(x) - F(x) = C$, or $G(x) = F(x) + C$, where C is some constant, because the derivative of $G(x) - F(x)$ is $G'(x) - F'(x) = 0$ by hypothesis. Conversely, if $G(x) = F(x) + C$ where C is any constant, then we obtain $G'(x) = F'(x)$ by differentiating both sides, since the derivative of C is zero. We have the following theorem.

Theorem 1. *If two functions $F(x)$ and $G(x)$ have the same derivative, then $G(x) = F(x) + C$ where C is some constant, and conversely.*

Geometrically, this means that two curves $y = F(x)$ and $y = G(x)$ have parallel tangents for each value of x if and only if the ordinates of the two curves for each value of x have a constant difference (Fig. 167).

Definition. *If the derivative of $F(x)$ is $f(x)$ then $F(x)$ is called an* ***anti-derivative*** *of $f(x)$.*

By the above theorem, all the anti-derivatives of $f(x)$ are given by the expression $F(x) + C$ where C may be any constant whatever. Thus an anti-derivative of $f(x)$ is not uniquely determined but if $F(x)$ is any one of them, any other can be obtained by adding a suitable constant to $F(x)$. The expression $F(x) + C$, which represents all the anti-derivatives is called the **indefinite integral** of $f(x)$ and is often written as $\int f(x)\,dx$ (read, the indefinite integral of $f(x)$ with respect to x) for a reason which will appear shortly. The process of finding the anti-derivatives of a function is called **integrating** the function. By definition, we have

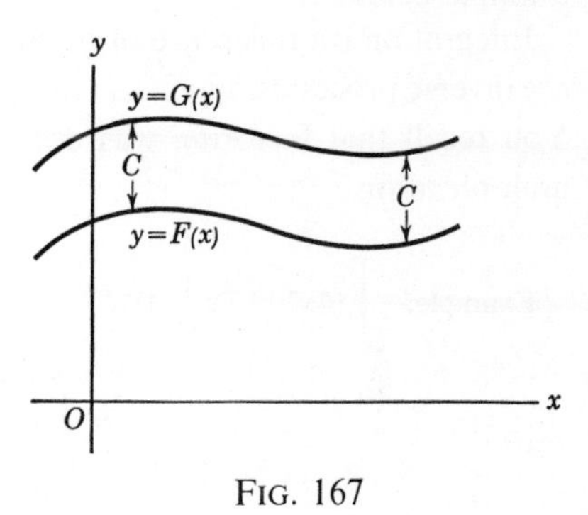

FIG. 167

$$\int f(x)\,dx = F(x) + C \text{ if and only if } F'(x) = f(x).$$

To integrate a polynomial is an easy matter if we recall the results of differentiation. For to ask for the indefinite integral of $f(x)$ is to ask, "What functions have $f(x)$ as their derivative?" That is, by definition, $\int f(x)\,dx = F(x) + C$, where C is any constant, if and only if $\frac{d}{dx} F(x) = f(x)$. For example,

$\int x^3\,dx = \frac{x^4}{4} + C$ since $\frac{d}{dx}\left(\frac{x^4}{4}\right) = x^3$. In general, if we differentiate $\frac{x^{n+1}}{n+1}$ we obtain $\frac{n+1}{n+1}x^n$ or x^n, where n is any natural number; hence,

(1) $$\int x^n\,dx = \frac{x^{n+1}}{n+1} + C \qquad \text{if } n \text{ is any natural number.}$$

Similarly, since $\frac{d}{dx}(kx) = k$, where k is a constant, we have

(2) $$\int k\,dx = kx + C.$$

We shall also use the following two theorems without proof:

(3) $$\int [f(x) + g(x)]\,dx = \int f(x)\,dx + \int g(x)\,dx,$$

(4) $$\int kf(x)\,dx = k\int f(x)\,dx, \quad \text{where } k \text{ is any constant.}$$

By means of (1), (2), (3), and (4), we can integrate any polynomial, as in the example below.

Integration (in this sense of finding the indefinite integral) and differentiation are inverse processes, much as multiplication and factoring are inverse processes. You recall that factoring was done essentially by remembering the results of multiplication.

Example. $\int (4x^3 + 3x + 4)\,dx$

$$= \int 4x^3\,dx + \int 3x\,dx + \int 4\,dx \qquad \text{by (3)}$$

$$= 4\int x^3\,dx + 3\int x\,dx + \int 4\,dx \qquad \text{by (4)}$$

$$= 4\cdot\frac{x^4}{4} + C_1 + 3\,\frac{x^2}{2} + C_2 + 4x + C_3 \qquad \text{by (1) and (2)}$$

$$= x^4 + \frac{3x^2}{2} + 4x + C,$$

denoting the sum of the constants $C_1 + C_2 + C_3$ by the single letter C. To check, we may differentiate our answer, obtaining the function we integrated, just as we checked factoring by multiplying the factors to obtain the original expression.

Exercises

Find the indefinite integral of each of the following functions and check:

1. $x + 3$. **2.** $3x^2 - 2x + 5$. **3.** 5. **4.** $6x^2 + 3x + 2$.
5. $9 - 6x^2$. **6.** $ax^2 + bx + c$. **7.** $ax + b$. **8.** $5x - 3$.
9. $96 - 32t$.
10. Prove: (*a*) formula (3); (*b*) formula (4).

130. THE CONSTANT OF INTEGRATION

The additive constant C which occurs in the indefinite integral may often be determined by the conditions of the problem.

Example 1. The slope of the tangent to a certain curve at any point (x,y) is equal to $x/2$. The curve passes through the point (2,4). Find the equation of the curve.

Let $y = F(x)$ be the equation of the curve. We have to find the function $F(x)$. The first sentence tells us that $F'(x) = dy/dx = x/2$. Since the derivative of $F(x)$ is $x/2$, $F(x)$ is an anti-derivative of $x/2$. Hence, integrating, we obtain $y = \frac{1}{4}x^2 + C$. The second sentence tells us that at $x = 2$, $y = 4$. Hence $4 = \frac{1}{4}\cdot 2^2 + C$ or $C = 3$. Thus $y = \frac{1}{4}x^2 + 3$ is the equation of the curve (Fig. 168). Other values of C would yield curves with parallel tangents, but not passing through the desired point.

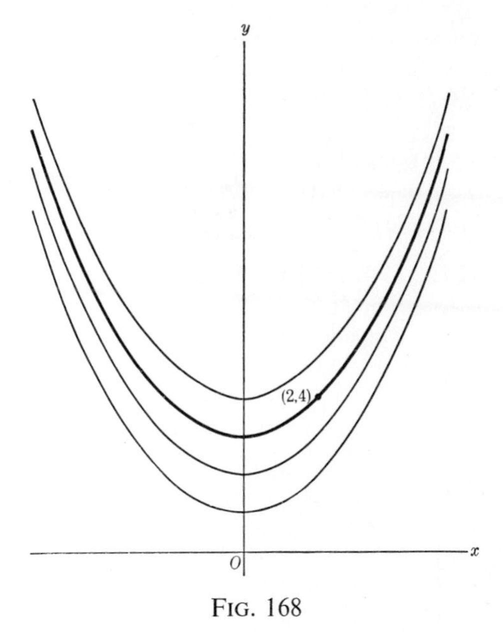

FIG. 168

Example 2. It is found by experiment that if a projectile is thrown directly upward, its acceleration is -32 feet per second per second. Let v denote the velocity of the projectile. By definition, acceleration $a = dv/dt$ or the rate of change of the velocity with respect to time. Hence $dv/dt = -32$. Integrating, we get $v = -32t + C$. Thus, at $t = 0$, $v = C$ or C is the initial velocity; call it v_0. Thus,

$$v = -32t + v_0. \tag{1}$$

Now if h is the height of the projectile, $v = dh/dt$ or the rate of change of the height with respect to time. Integrating (1) we get $h = -16t^2 + v_0 t + C_0$. At $t = 0$, $h = C_0$, or C_0 is the initial height; call it h_0. Hence

(2) $$h = -16t^2 + v_0t + h_0$$

gives the height as a function of t. For example, if a projectile is thrown straight up from a roof 30 feet high with an initial velocity of 100 feet per second, then its height, measured in feet, at the end of t seconds is given by $h = -16t^2 + 100t + 30$. Its velocity at the end of t seconds is given by $v = -32t + 100$.

Exercises

Find the equation of the curve whose tangent has the slope:

1. 3 at all values of x and passes through the point (2,7).
2. m at all values of x and passes through the point $(0,p)$.
3. $2x$ at all values of x and passes through the point (3,5).
4. $3x^2 + 4x + 1$ at all values of x and passes through the point (0,1).
5. $2x - 3$ at all values of x and passes through the point (1,3).

6. Find the function $h = F(t)$ whose derivative with respect to t is $128 - 32t$ and for which $h = 36$ when $t = 0$.

7. The acceleration of a falling body is 32 feet per second per second. With what velocity will a stone strike the ground if it is dropped from a roof 100 feet high?

8. If a stone is thrown straight down with an initial velocity of 80 feet per second, from a roof 96 feet high, with what velocity will it strike the ground?

9. A projectile is thrown straight up from the edge of a roof 64 feet high with an initial velocity of 48 feet per second. With what velocity will it strike the ground?

131. THE AREA UNDER A CURVE

Consider the curve $y = f(x)$ where $f(x)$ is a continuous single-valued function. Suppose the curve lies above the x-axis, for simplicity. By the **area under the curve between *a* and *b*** we mean the area enclosed by the curve, the x-axis, and the vertical lines $x = a$ and $x = b$. Thus $MNCD$ is the area A under the curve $y = f(x)$ between $x = a$ and $x = b$ (Fig. 169). But what can be meant by the area of a region with a curved boundary? A rectangle with base 3 feet and altitude 2 feet clearly has an area of 6 square feet since it contains two

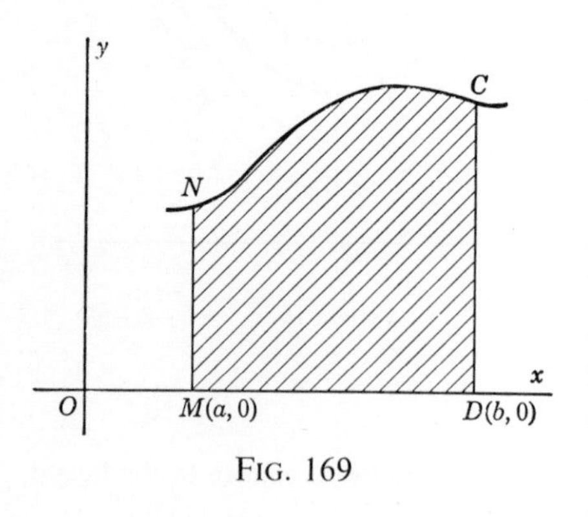

FIG. 169

rows of three 1-foot squares each (Fig. 170). Hence it is intuitively clear that the area of a rectangle (Fig. 171) of base b and altitude h is bh square units.* Since a parallelogram $ABCD$ (Fig. 172) of base b and altitude h, made of paper, can be converted into a rectangle of the same dimensions by snipping off right triangle ABF with scissors and putting it in position DCE, it is clear that the parallelogram has area bh as well. If a triangle ABD of base b and altitude h (Fig. 173) is placed next to a congruent copy CBD of itself along BD as common side, the resulting

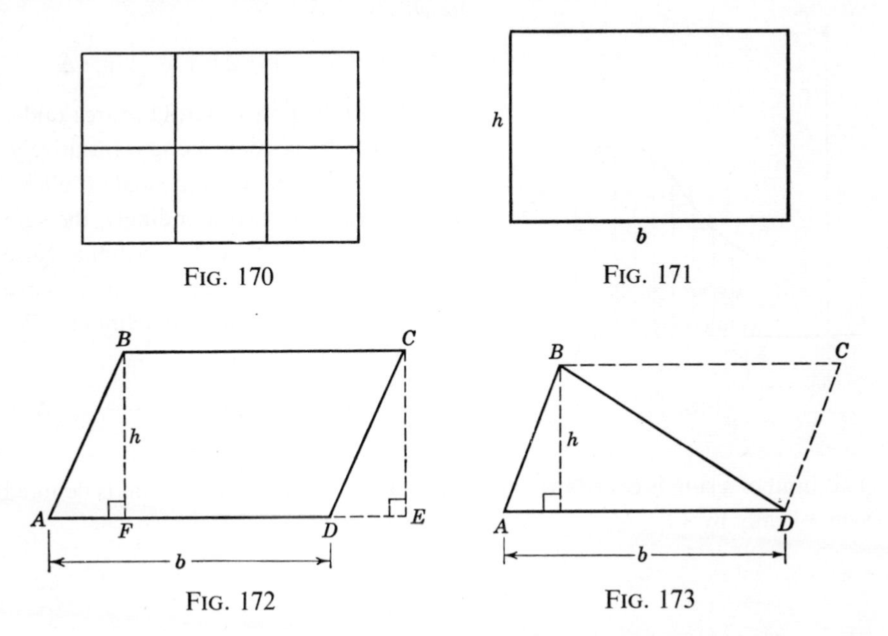

FIG. 170 FIG. 171

FIG. 172 FIG. 173

figure is a parallelogram of base b and altitude h. Since the triangle clearly has half the area of the parallelogram, the area of the triangle is $\frac{1}{2}bh$. Once this result is known, there is no difficulty in understanding the meaning of the area of any polygonal figure since any such can be decomposed into triangles by drawing suitable diagonals (Fig. 174). Ultimately, the area of any polygonal figure refers to the number of unit squares that can be fitted into it. But if a figure has a curved side, squares will not fit at all, and we need the idea of limit to *define* its area. Thus in the case of the circle, (section 128), we could *define* the area as the

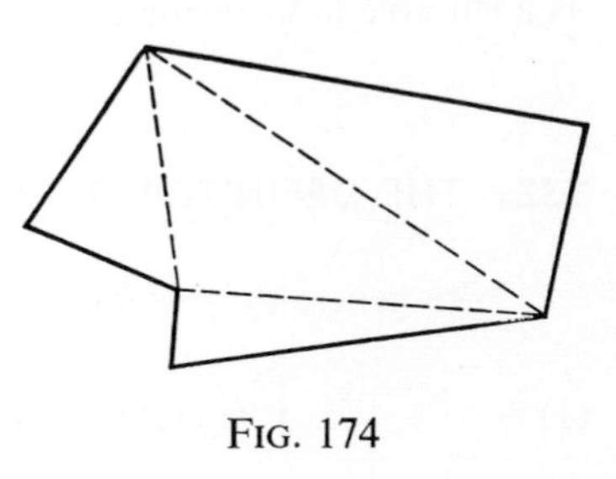

FIG. 174

* We neglect well-known and conquerable difficulties arising from irrational lengths or incommensurable sides. See section 30.

limit of the areas of the inscribed regular polygons as the number of sides increased indefinitely.

The area under the curve $y = f(x)$ between $x = a$ and $x = b$ (Fig. 169) can be considered in the following way. Divide the interval from a to b on the x-axis into n equal intervals of length Δx. Therefore, $n \cdot \Delta x = b - a$. Let $y_1, y_2, y_n, \ldots,$ be the values of y at the beginning of each of these small intervals, respectively. Then the area of the "staircase" (Fig. 175) composed of the resulting rectangles is

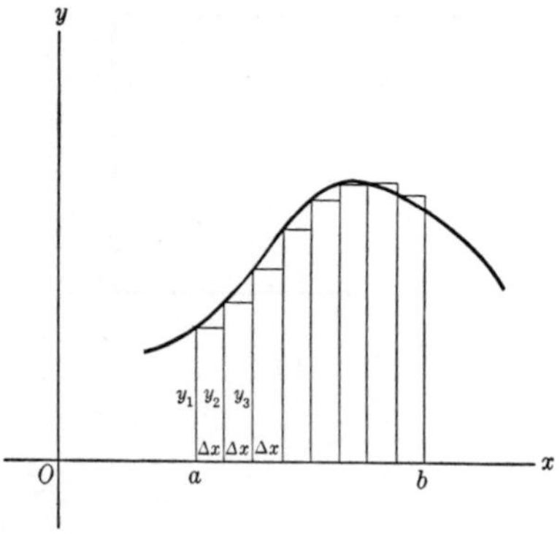

$$S = y_1 \cdot \Delta x + y_2 \cdot \Delta x + \cdots + y_n \cdot \Delta x.$$

Now this sum approximates the area under the curve if Δx is small enough. Intuitively, if we make Δx smaller and smaller, allowing n to increase correspondingly, the sum S approaches the area A as a limit. Note that since $\Delta x = (b - a)/n$, we must have $\Delta x \to 0$ when n increases indefinitely. We may *define* the area A as

FIG. 175

$$A = \lim_{\substack{\Delta x \to 0 \\ n \uparrow}} (y_1 \cdot \Delta x + y_2 \cdot \Delta x + \cdots + y_n \cdot \Delta x).$$

This limit of a sum is called the **definite integral of $f(x)$ from a to b** and is denoted symbolically by

$$\int_a^b f(x)\,dx.$$

The numbers a and b are called the **limits of integration**. The integral sign $\int$ comes from the idea of the definite integral as the limit of a sum; the sign is nothing but an elongated S. Thus the area of any curved figure can be defined as a suitable limit of the sum of rectangular areas.

132. THE DEFINITE INTEGRAL

In general, if $y = f(x)$, we define the **definite integral of $f(x)$ from a to b** as

$$(1) \qquad \int_a^b f(x)\,dx = \lim_{\substack{\Delta x \to 0 \\ n \uparrow}} (y_1 \cdot \Delta x + y_2 \cdot \Delta x + \cdots + y_n \cdot \Delta x),$$

as at the end of section 131. We shall sketch an argument connecting the definite integral with the anti-derivatives and indefinite integrals defined in section 129.

First it is intuitively clear that (Fig. 176)

$$\int_a^b f(x)\,dx + \int_b^c f(x)\,dx = \int_a^c f(x)\,dx. \tag{2}$$

It is also intuitively clear that for a continuous function $f(x)$, there exists at least one value $\bar{x}$, with $a \leqq \bar{x} \leqq b$, such that

$$\int_a^b f(x)\,dx = f(\bar{x})(b-a). \tag{3}$$

This means intuitively that the rectangle (Fig. 177) with altitude $f(\bar{x})$ and base

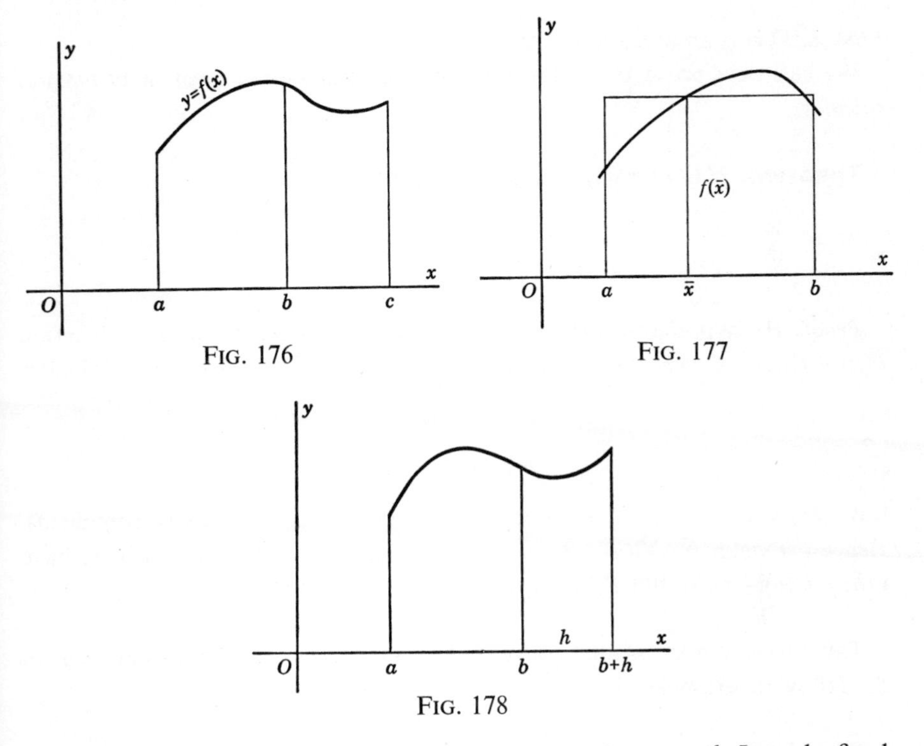

FIG. 176

FIG. 177

FIG. 178

$b - a$ has the same area as the area under the curve from a to b. Let a be fixed, and define the function $F(t)$ as

$$F(t) = \int_a^t f(x)\,dx. \tag{4}$$

Then (Fig. 178),

$$F(b+h) - F(b) = \int_a^{b+h} f(x)\,dx - \int_a^b f(x)\,dx = \int_b^{b+h} f(x)\,dx,$$

as one can see by transposing the term with the minus sign and using (2).

By (3) we can write

$$F(b+h) - F(b) = f(\bar{x})h \quad \text{where} \quad b \leqq \bar{x} \leqq b+h$$

or

$$\frac{F(b+h) - F(b)}{h} = f(\bar{x}).$$

As $h \to 0$, the left member approaches the derivative $F'(b)$ and the right member approaches $f(b)$ since $\bar{x}$ is pinned between b and $b+h$. Hence $F'(b) = f(b)$, or, writing x for b,

$$F'(x) = f(x). \tag{5}$$

That is, $F(x)$ is an anti-derivative of $f(x)$.

We can now prove the following so-called *fundamental theorem of integral calculus.*

Theorem. *If $G(x)$ is any anti-derivative of $f(x)$, then*

$$\int_a^b f(x)\,dx = G(b) - G(a).$$

Proof. By hypothesis $G'(x) = f(x)$. Hence $F'(x) - G'(x) = 0$, and therefore $F(x) - G(x) = C$ where C is a constant, or $F(x) = G(x) + C$. In particular.

$$F(b) = G(b) = C, \tag{6}$$

$$F(a) = G(a) + C. \tag{7}$$

But $F(a) = \int_a^a f(x)\,dx = 0$ (between $x = a$ and $x = a$, no area is contained). Hence (7) yields $0 = G(a) + C$, or $C = -G(a)$. Substituting this in (6), we have $F(b) = G(b) - G(a)$. But $F(b) = \int_a^b f(x)\,dx$. This proves the theorem.

This theorem may be used conveniently to calculate areas under curves as in the following example.

Example. Find the area under the parabola $y = \frac{1}{4}x^2 + 1$ between $x = 1$ and $x = 3$. The area desired is

$$\int_1^3 \left(\frac{1}{4}x^2 + 1\right) dx.$$

Now the indefinite integral $\int (\frac{1}{4}x^2 + 1)\,dx = \dfrac{x^3}{12} + x + C$. Hence the function $G(x) = \dfrac{x^3}{12} + x$ is an anti-derivative of $\frac{1}{4}x^2 + 1$. By the theorem above,

$$\int_1^3 \left(\frac{1}{4}x^2 + 1\right) dx = G(3) - G(1) = \frac{3^3}{12} + 3 - \left(\frac{1^3}{12} + 1\right) = \frac{25}{6}.$$

The idea of the definite integral as the limit of a sum of small quantities is the central idea of the **integral calculus** and is essential in many connections.

For example, the length of a curve can be defined as the limit of the length of an inscribed broken line; that is, the limit of a sum of chords as the number of chords becomes larger and the length of each chord becomes smaller (Fig. 179). Note that one cannot lightly pass off the definition of the length of a curve by saying that it is the "number of inches" in the curve. For to find the "number of inches" in a straight line we lay off a straight ruler along it; but no part of a

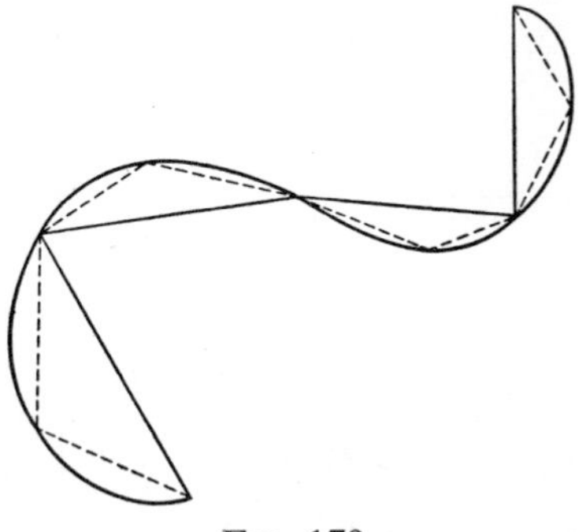

FIG. 179

curved line can be made to coincide exactly with a straight ruler. To speak of the length of a curved line as being the length of the straight line obtained by "bending" it until it is straight is equally futile. For you would want to bend it without stretching or contracting, which means that you want to bend it so that its "length" is unchanged during the process. But this definition presupposes that "length" has already been defined and would therefore be a circular definition.

Similarly, the volume of a curved solid may be defined as the limit of a sum of the volumes of thin slices as the number of slices becomes larger and each slice thinner (see section 133). These and many other geometrical and physical concepts may be defined as definite integrals and studied by means of the integral calculus.

Exercises

Find the area under the curve:

1. $y = 3x + 4$ from $x = 1$ to $x = 4$. Verify your answer by elementary geometry.

2. $y = 16 - 2x$ from $x = 1$ to $x = 4$. Verify your answer by elementary geometry.

3. $y = \frac{1}{2}x^2$ from $x = 1$ to $x = 4$.
4. $y = x^2 - x + 15$ from $x = 2$ to $x = 5$.
5. $y = 10 - x^2$ from $x = 0$ to $x = 3$.
6. (*a*) $y = 3x^2 + 4x$ from $x = 0$ to $x = 2$.
(*b*) $y = 4x^3 + 5$ from $x = 0$ to $x = 2$.

133. VOLUME OF A SOLID OF REVOLUTION

If the area $ABCD$ (Fig. 180) under a curve $y = f(x)$ in the plane is revolved in space about the x-axis, the resulting solid is called a **solid of revolution.**

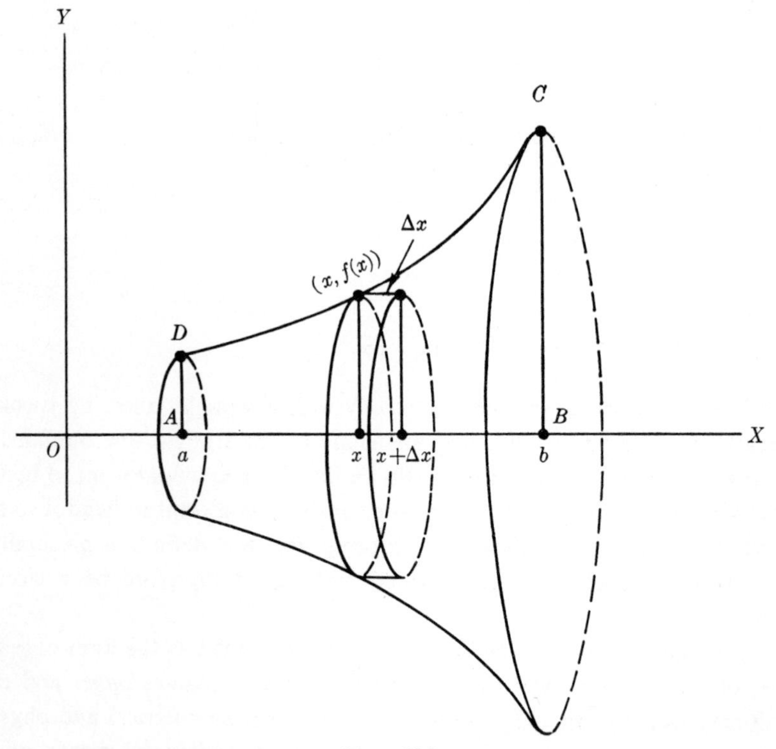

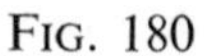
FIG. 180

If we partition the interval from a to b on the x-axis into subintervals of length Δx and replace the actual solid on a typical subinterval by a cylinder whose base is the circle in which a plane perpendicular to the x-axis at the left endpoint of our subinterval cuts the solid, then the sum of the volumes of these cylindrical slices clearly approximates the volume of the solid and the limit of this sum as

Δx approaches zero may be taken as the volume of the solid. Now *the volume of a right circular cylinder is known to be the area of its circular base* πr^2 *times its altitude* h. (This is plausible (Fig. 181) since each square foot of area in the circular base has a column of height h over it and this column has h cubic feet of volume; hence, the volume of the cylinder is $\pi r^2 h$.) Each cylindrical slice of our solid of revolution therefore has volume $\pi y^2 \Delta x$ or $\pi[f(x)]^2 \Delta x$. *The volume* V *of the solid is then the limit of the sum of such terms, or the definite integral*

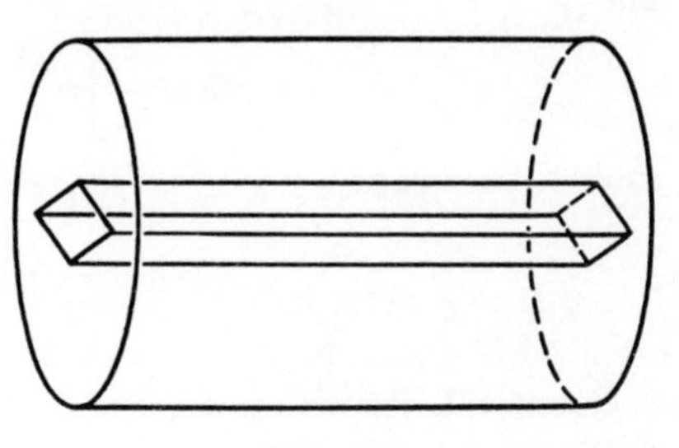

FIG. 181

$$V = \int_a^b \pi y^2 \, dx.$$

Example 1. Rotating the straight line $y = \dfrac{r}{h} x$ from $x = 0$ to $x = h$ about the x-axis generates a right circular cone of altitude h and radius of base r.

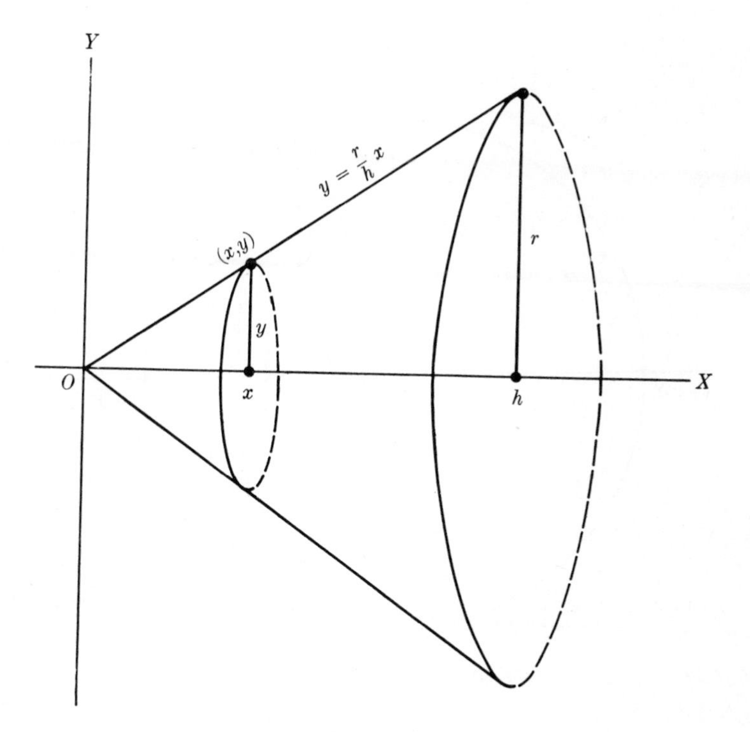

FIG. 182

The volume of such a cone is therefore

$$V = \int_0^h \pi y^2 \, dx = \int_0^h \pi \frac{r^2}{h^2} x^2 \, dx.$$

But

$$G(x) = \int \pi \frac{r^2}{h^2} x^2 \, dx = \pi \frac{r^2}{h^2} \frac{x^3}{3} + C,$$

so that the volume

$$V = G(h) - G(0) = \pi \frac{r^2}{h^2} \frac{h^3}{3} = \frac{\pi r^2 h}{3}.$$

Example 2. Revolving circle $x^2 + y^2 = r^2$ about the x-axis generates a sphere of radius r.

Its volume is therefore

$$\mathrm{V} = \int_{-r}^{r} \pi y^2 \, dx = \int_{-r}^{r} \pi (r^2 - x^2) \, dx.$$

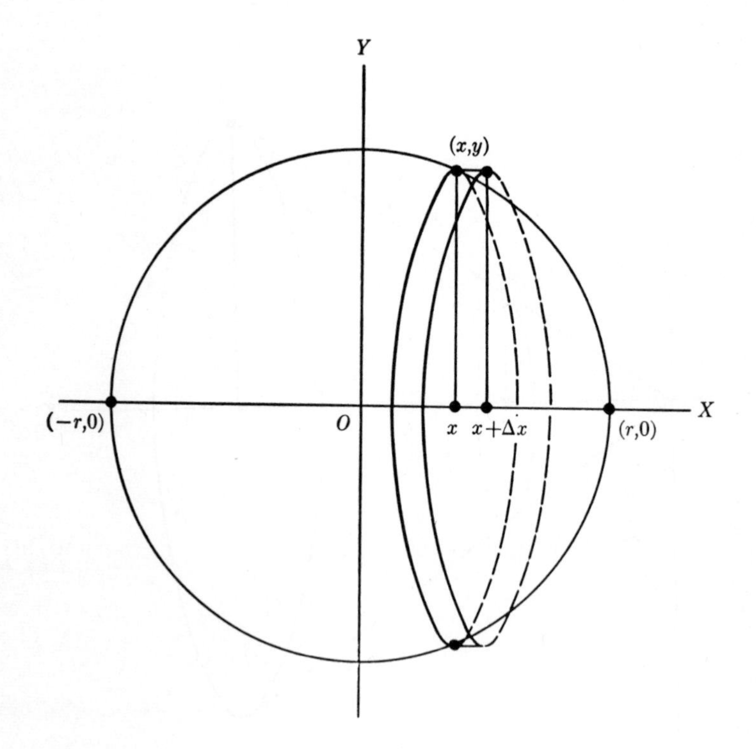

FIG. 183

But

$$G(x) = \int \pi(r^2 - x^2)\,dx = \pi r^2 x - \pi \frac{x^3}{3} + C.$$

Hence the volume is

$$V = G(r) - G(-r) = \pi r^3 - \pi \frac{r^3}{3} - \left(-\pi r^3 + \pi \frac{r^3}{3}\right) = \frac{4}{3}\pi r^3.$$

Exercises

Find the volume of the solid of revolution obtained by revolving each of the following curves about the x-axis:

1. $y = 6 - x$, from $x = 1$ to $x = 3$.
2. $y = 3x + 3$, from $x = 0$ to $x = 3$.
3. $y^2 = 4x$, from $x = 0$ to $x = 4$.
4. $y = x^2$, from $x = 0$ to $x = 5$.
5. $y = x^3$, from $x = 0$ to $x = 1$.
6. $\dfrac{x^2}{9} + \dfrac{y^2}{4} = 1$.
7. $\dfrac{x^2}{a^2} + \dfrac{y^2}{b^2} = 1$, where a and b are any positive numbers.

8. Explain why the volume generated by revolving a curve $x = f(y)$ from $y = y_1$ to $y = y_2$ about the y-axis is

$$\pi \int_{y_1}^{y_2} x^2\,dy = \pi \int_{y_1}^{y_2} [f(y)]^2\,dy.$$

Use the formula of exercise 8 *to find the volume of the solid of revolution obtained by revolving each of the following curves about the y-axis:*

9. $y = 6 - x$, from $y = 2$ to $y = 5$.
10. $y = 2x + 3$, from $y = 0$ to $y = 3$.
11. $y^2 = 4x$, from $y = 0$ to $y = 5$.
12. $y = x^2$, from $y = 0$ to $y = 10$.
13. The curve of exercise 6.
14. The curve of exercise 7.

134. INFINITE SERIES

The idea of limit enters elementary mathematics in another important way. Suppose we were to write the expression

$$\frac{1}{2} + \frac{1}{4} + \frac{1}{8} + \frac{1}{16} + \cdots + \frac{1}{2^n} + \cdots \tag{1}$$

where the three dots at the end indicate that the expression goes on forever. Such an expression is called an **infinite series**. What can this possibly mean? Surely it cannot mean that we are expected to spend the rest of our lives adding the successive terms to the partial sums already obtained. For, having thus mis-spent our lives we should obviously have to leave the task unfinished and curse our descendants with the burden of continuing; this little example might prove to be the ruin of the human race. What we do mean by the expression (1) is the following. Let s_n be the sum of the first n terms, where n is any natural number. Thus

$$s_1 = \tfrac{1}{2},\ s_2 = \tfrac{1}{2} + \tfrac{1}{4} = \tfrac{3}{4},\ s_3 = \tfrac{1}{2} + \tfrac{1}{4} + \tfrac{1}{8} = \tfrac{7}{8},\ s_4 = \tfrac{1}{2} + \tfrac{1}{4} + \tfrac{1}{8} + \tfrac{1}{16} = \tfrac{15}{16},$$

...; in general, we could prove that $s_n = \dfrac{2^n - 1}{2^n}$. If the sequence $s_1, s_2, \ldots, s_n, \ldots$ has a limit S we call S the *sum* of the infinite series (1). In this example

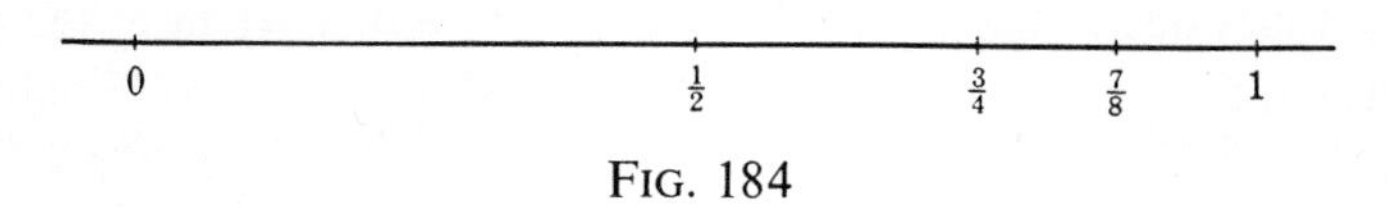

FIG. 184

$\lim\limits_{n\uparrow} s_n = 1$ and hence we write

$$\frac{1}{2} + \frac{1}{4} + \frac{1}{8} + \cdots + \frac{1}{2^n} + \cdots = 1.$$

The meaning of this statement involves the idea of limit. No matter how large a natural number n we take, the sum s_n of the first n terms is never equal to 1, but as n increases indefinitely, s_n approaches 1 as a limit. In general, given an infinite series

$$a_1 + a_2 + \cdots + a_n + \cdots$$

we say that the series has the **sum** S if the sequence of the partial sums

$$\begin{aligned} s_1 &= a_1 \\ s_2 &= a_1 + a_2 \\ s_3 &= a_1 + a_2 + a_3 \\ &\vdots \\ s_n &= a_1 + \cdots + a_n \\ &\vdots \end{aligned}$$

approaches S as a limit. If this happens the series is said to **converge**; if not, it is said to **diverge**.

Infinite series of the greatest practical value in mathematics and its applications. For example, if one wishes to calculate a good approximate value for a function which is difficult to compute directly, it is often possible to express the function as an infinite series and to approximate it by taking the sum of the first few terms. If a better approximation is desired, one can take the sum of a few more terms. This method is actually employed by mathematicians in the construction of tables, for example, of log x. Thus it can be shown that

$$\text{(2)}\qquad \log_e 2 = 1 - \frac{1}{2} + \frac{1}{3} - \frac{1}{4} + \frac{1}{5} + \cdots + \frac{(-1)^{n+1}}{n} + \cdots$$

$$\text{(3)}\qquad e = 2 + \frac{1}{2} + \frac{1}{3\cdot 2} + \frac{1}{4\cdot 3\cdot 2} + \frac{1}{5\cdot 4\cdot 3\cdot 2} + \frac{1}{6\cdot 5\cdot 4\cdot 3\cdot 2} + \cdots$$

and

$$\text{(4)}\qquad \pi = 4 - \frac{4}{3} + \frac{4}{5} - \frac{4}{7} + \frac{4}{9} - \frac{4}{11} + \frac{4}{13} - \cdots.$$

One can in fact decide how many terms one has to take to make the approximation accurate to the desired number of decimal places. Series (4) approaches its limit π so slowly that one would have to take a great many terms to get even the first few places of π. It is consequently virtually useless for the purpose of computing π. A better expression for this purpose is

$$\text{(5)}\qquad \pi = 16\left[\frac{1}{5} - \frac{1}{3\cdot 5^3} + \frac{1}{5\cdot 5^5} - \frac{1}{7\cdot 5^7} + - \cdots\right] - 4\left[\frac{1}{239} - \frac{1}{3\cdot 239^3} + \frac{1}{5\cdot 239^5} - + \cdots\right].$$

Besides the use of infinite series in the construction of tables of various sorts, they are of the greatest value to engineers, and others, in a great variety of practical situations. Their value in the development of pure mathematics is also immense.

The idea of limits disturbed the ancients, although a good logical treatment of them is of very recent date. For example, Zeno (fifth century B.C.) argued as follows. It a man has to reach a point a mile away, he cannot do it. For he first has to traverse the first half mile; then he would have to traverse the next quarter of a mile; then the next eighth of a mile, and so on. Thus he has to traverse an infinite succession of intervals. Zeno argued that to perform an infinite succession of acts should take an infinite length of time and therefore the man can never reach his goal. This "paradox" of Zeno has been the subject of much vague discussion. It is really not a paradox at all; one must simply realize that the "sum" of an infinite number of terms may very well be finite. In fact, if it takes the man 1 hour to walk a mile, he will walk the first half mile in a half hour, and so on. Therefore it will take him $\frac{1}{2} + \frac{1}{4} + \frac{1}{8} + \cdots + \frac{1}{2^n} + \cdots$ hours to walk a mile. Despite the fact that this is an infinite series, the sum is 1 hour.

The same mathematical situation was presented by Zeno in the form of the "paradox" of Achilles and the tortoise. Achilles, who could run 10 yards in 1 second, was to run a race with a tortoise, who could run only 5 yards in 1 second, but the tortoise was to have a handicap of 10 yards. Zeno asserted that Achilles could never catch the tortoise for the following reasons. By the time Achilles had run the 10 yards from his starting point A_1 to the point T_1 where the tortoise started, the tortoise would have run ahead 5 yards to T_2; by the time Achilles had run the 5 yards to T_2 the tortoise would no longer be there,

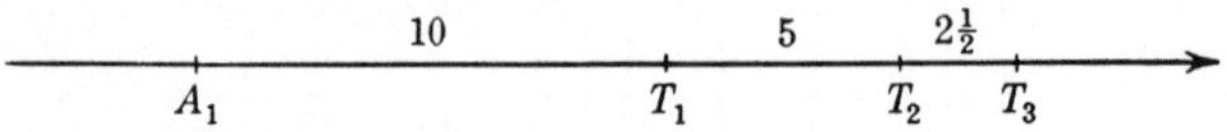

10 5 $2\frac{1}{2}$

A_1 T_1 T_2 T_3

FIG. 185

having run the $2\frac{1}{2}$ yards to T_3; and so on. Here again we have an infinite series, for Achilles requires 1 second to go from A_1 to T_1, $\frac{1}{2}$ second to go from T_1 to T_2, $\frac{1}{4}$ second to go from T_2 to T_3, and so on. Hence the time required by Achilles to catch the tortoise is the sum of the infinite series

$$1 + \frac{1}{2} + \frac{1}{4} + \cdots + \frac{1}{2^{n-1}} + \cdots$$

which is 2 seconds.

It should be said, in justice to Zeno, that he did not really believe anything so contrary to experience as the assertion that Achilles could not catch the tortoise. In fact, it is a simple problem in elementary algebra to find out how long it would take for Achilles to catch the tortoise. We leave this as an exercise for the student (see exercise 18 section 47). What Zeno was concerned about was locating the catch in his argument.

Exercises

1. Using the first five terms of series (2) calculate a four-place decimal approximation for $\log_e 2$.

2. Obtain a four-place decimal approximation for e from series (3) using (*a*) the first four terms; (*b*) the first five terms; (*c*) the first six terms.

3. Obtain a four-place decimal approximation for π from (5) using (*a*) the first two terms in each bracket; (*b*) the first three terms in each bracket.

★**4.** Prove that the geometric series

$$a + ar + ar^2 + \cdots + ar^{n-1} + \cdots$$

where $0 < r < 1$ converges to $a/(1-r)$. (Hint: use the results of example 2 and exercise 15, section 119, and the fact that the nth partial sum $s_n = (a - ar^n)/(1-r)$.)

★**5.** Show that a periodic decimal (like .27272727 ... for example) must represent a rational number. (Hint: use the result of exercise 4.)

135. CONCLUSION

Our discussion of calculus has been sketchy and intuitive because of the technical difficulty of discussing the subject logically. A strictly logical treatment is given in more advanced courses. Our purpose here was to introduce you to its most elementary ideas and to give you some hint of its practical importance and its power in applications to geometry and physics. The far reaching effects of the calculus in astronomy, physics, engineering, etc., can not be overemphasized. The calculus initiated a new era and may be said to mark a turning point in the history of mathematics and its applications.

References

Numbers refer to the bibliography at the back of the book.

Bell 16, 18, 19
Berkeley 27
Courant 57
Courant and Robbins 58
Dresden 65
Whitehead 206

12

Trigonometric Functions

136. INTRODUCTION

The word "trigonometry" means the study of the measurement of triangles. The student will doubtless recall that much of his high school course in plane geometry was devoted to the study of triangles. Why is the triangle given so much attention? It is easy to see that the triangle is the simplest possible figure, bounded by straight line segments, which is capable of enclosing an area; that is, the triangle is the simplest possible polygon. This would explain why it is studied early in geometry. But more important than its simplicity is the fact that every polygon can be split up into triangles by drawing suitable diagonals (Fig. 186). That is, the triangles are fundamental building blocks out of which we can make any polygon whatever. Or, to put it another way, we can measure any polygonal figure by splitting it into triangles and measuring each triangle. Therefore the study of surveying polygonal plots of land, etc., is reduced to the study of the triangle.

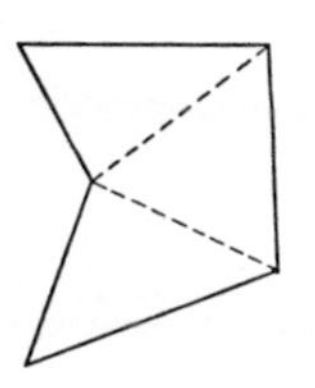

FIG. 186

An important class of functions, called the trigonometric functions, arises from the study of the measurement of triangles. Among their numerous applications, some of which will be mentioned below, is the remarkable achievement of the measurement of inaccessible distances, such as the heights of mountains, the distance from the earth to the moon, or the distance from a cannon to an enemy supply base; all of these are distances which it is either impossible or inadvisable to measure directly by the application of a tape measure. Their most elementary aspects go back to ancient times but many of their most interesting phases are of recent origin. We shall discuss both the elementary applications to surveying and the measurement of inaccessible distances and the more advanced applications to modern science.

137. ANGULAR MEASURE

Consider a line (extending indefinitely in both directions as opposed to a line-segment which has a definite length). Any point P on the line divides it into two parts, one on each "side" of the point. The set of all points on one side of the point P is called a **ray** or half-line. Thus P divides the line into two rays.

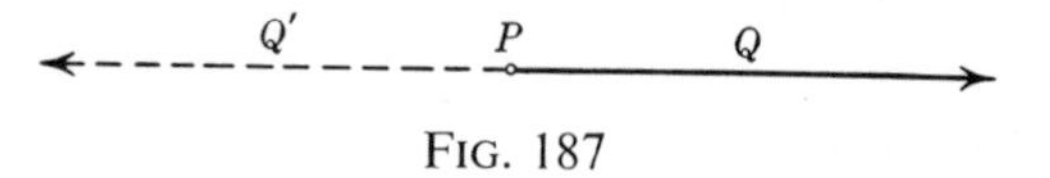

FIG. 187

PQ and PQ' (Fig. 187). The point P is called the **vertex** of each of these rays. The word "ray" is obviously suggested by light rays emanating from a source P. An **angle** is the figure consisting of (or, the set of points on) two rays having the same vertex (Fig. 188). We wish to associate with each angle a number called the measure of the angle. Intuitively, we want the measure of an angle to describe the smallest amount of rotation by which we can turn from the direction of one ray to the direction of the other. Perhaps the most obvious unit with which to measure the amount of rotation is a complete revolution; that is, the smallest actual rotation which brings you back to your initial direction (Fig. 189). But

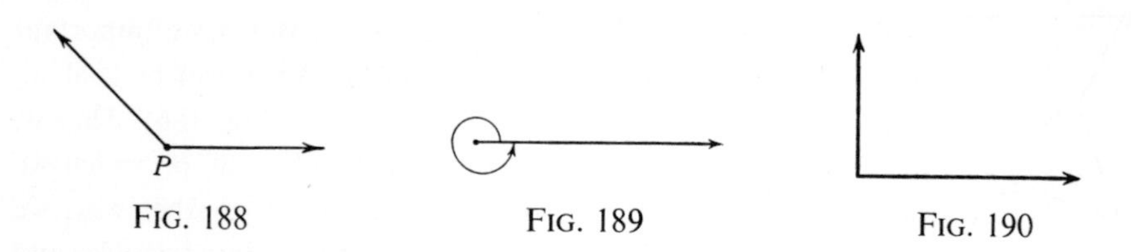

FIG. 188 FIG. 189 FIG. 190

this unit is so large that it is cumbersome. It is more usual to choose as the unit of angular measure the **degree**, which may be defined as one 360th of a complete revolution. Thus we associate with each angle a definite number called the **measure** of the angle, namely the smallest number of degrees required to rotate from the direction of one ray of the angle to the direction of the other ray. For example, the angle in Fig. 190 has a measure of $90°$ or $\frac{1}{4}$ of a complete revolution. The measure of an angle is a single-valued function of the angle, for to each angle there corresponds a unique number called its measure. *This function ranges between* $0°$ *and* $180°$ *only.*

One sixtieth of a degree is called a **minute**, and one sixtieth of a minute is called a **second**. The symbol $5° \, 3' \, 4''$ means 5 degrees, 3 minutes, and 4 seconds.

The **sexagesimal** or **degree system** of angular measure may have been used as far back as the time of the Babylonians (about two thousand years B.C. or perhaps earlier). It is sometimes said that they divided the circle into 360 equal parts because their year was taken as 360 days, but this is not certain. They probably knew that a chord equal in length to the radius could be laid off around the circle six times, thus inscribing a regular hexagon (Fig. 191), and they may have divded the central angle C into 60 equal parts because their notation for numbers was based on 60.

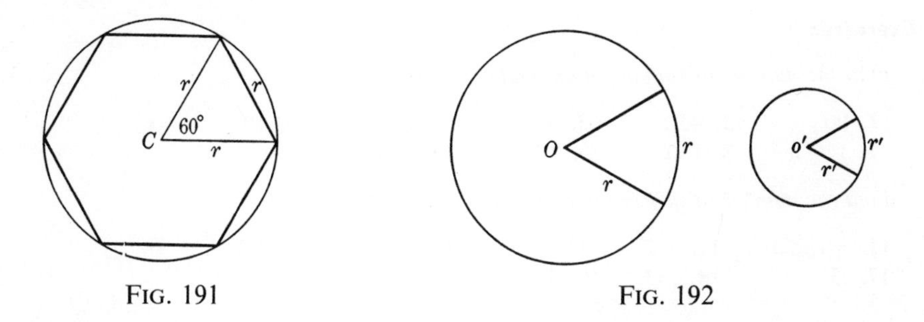

FIG. 191

FIG. 192

Another unit of angular measure was introduced in modern times for theoretical reasons (see remark 2, section 140). If an *arc* equal in length to the radius is laid off along the circumference of a circle, the angle formed at the center by the radii drawn to the extremities of this arc is uniquely determined; that is, if we did the same thing with any other circle, we would get an equal angle (angle $O =$ angle O' in Fig. 192). The smallest rotation by which we can turn from the direction of one ray of this angle to the direction of the other ray is called a **radian**. Measuring an angle according to the number of radians it contains is very convenient for certain purposes. Since the circumference of a circle is given by $C = 2\pi r$, the length of a semicircular arc is πr where r is the radius of the circle and $\pi = 3.14159265 \ldots$. Therefore an angular measure of 180° is equal to an angular measure of π radians; or

$$(1) \qquad 180^\circ = \pi \text{ radians.}$$

Dividing both sides of (1) by 180 we get

$$1^\circ = \pi/180 \text{ radians} = .01745 \ldots \text{ radians;}$$

dividing both sides of (1) instead by π we get

$$1 \text{ radian} = (180/\pi)^\circ = 57.295 \ldots^\circ.$$

This enables us to convert an angular measure from degrees to radians and conversely; just as the knowledge that 1 foot $= \frac{1}{3}$ yard and 1 yard $= 3$ feet enables us to convert a measure of length from feet to yards and vice versa. It is customary to use the symbol ° for degrees and to use no symbol at all when radians are meant. Thus an angular measure of 3° means 3 degrees while an angular measure of 3 means 3 radians.

It is customary to speak of an "angle" of 3° or an "angle" of 3 (radians) instead of an angle whose measure is 3° or 3. This abbreviated manner of speaking does no harm. Of course, the measure of an angle is only one of many functions that can be associated with an angle.

Exercises

Find the number of radians in an angle of:

1. 90°. **2.** 45°. **3.** 60°. **4.** 30°. **5.** 10°. **6.** 3°.
7. 120°. **8.** 150°. **9.** 18°. **10.** 135°.

Find the number of degrees in an angle of:

11. π radians. **12.** $\pi/2$. **13.** $\pi/6$. **14.** $\pi/9$. **15.** 1.5. **16.** 2.
17. .5. **18.** $\pi/5$. **19.** $3\pi/10$. **20.** $\pi/4$.

138. SIMILAR TRIANGLES

Two triangles ABC and $A'B'C'$ are called **similar** if their angles are respectively equal, that is, if $A = A'$, $B = B'$, and $C = C'$. Denoting the length of the side opposite angle A by a, and so on as in Fig. 193, we must recall the following important theorems of elementary geometry.

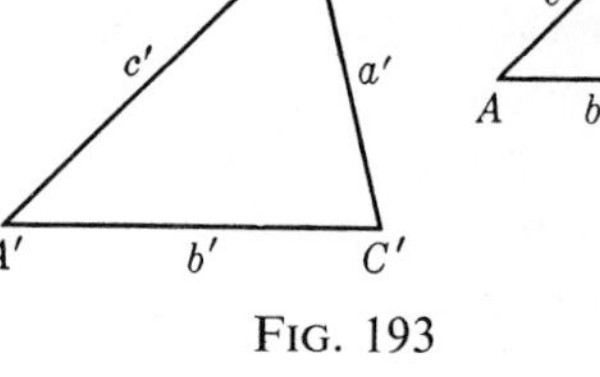

FIG. 193

Theorem 1. *If triangles ABC and A'B'C' are similar then* $a/b = a'/b'$, $b/c = b'/c'$, $a/c = a'/c'$.

Theorem 2. *The sum of the angles of any triangle is* 180°.

Corollary. *If two angles of one triangle are respectively equal to two angles of another triangle, then the triangles are similar.* (Why?)

Theorem 1 can be used to measure inaccessible distances. For example, the height of a vertical greased pole may be obtained as follows. Place a short stick perpendicular to the ground. Measure it, its shadow, and the shadow of the pole. Thus (Fig. 194) BC, AB, and $A'B'$ are known quantities. But since nearby sun's rays are parallel, for all practical purposes, angle A = angle A' and the triangles are therefore similar. (Why?) Hence $B'C'/A'B' = BC/AB$ or

$$B'C' = \frac{BC}{AB} \cdot A'B'.$$

For example, if the stick BC were 5 feet long, the stick's shadow AB were 3 feet long, and the pole's shadow $A'B'$ were 30 feet long, then the length $B'C'$ of the pole would be $\frac{5}{3} \cdot 30 = 50$ feet. Notice that we have not had to climb the greased pole with a tape measure. This method may have been used by Thales (about 600 B.C.), one of the earliest great Greek mathematicians, to calculate the height of an Egyptian pyramid, with the aid of his walking stick, to the consternation of the Egyptian priests.

Exercise. If a 5-foot pole, at right angles to the ground, casts a 3-foot shadow at the time when the shadow of an apartment house is 48 feet long, how high is the house?

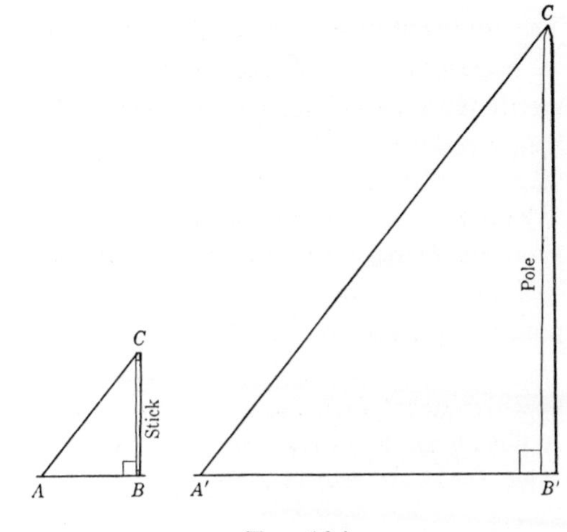

FIG. 194

139. THE TRIGONOMETRIC FUNCTIONS OF ACUTE ANGLES

An angle whose measure is greater than 0° but less than 90° is called **acute**. Consider a right triangle ABC with the right angle at C, lettered in the standard way, as in Fig. 195. Side c is called the **hypotenuse**, a is called **opposite to** A and **adjacent to** B, b is called **opposite to** B and **adjacent to** A. Any ratio of the lengths of two sides of the triangle, for example a/c, is a number which is completely determined by angle A alone and is independent of the size of the triangle. That is, if we took a larger or smaller right triangle $A'B'C'$ with $A = A'$ then $a'/c' = a/c$ since these triangles would be similar. Thus the number a/c is a function of the angle A; it is called the **sine** of A. Similarly, any other ratio of two of the sides depends only on the measure of angle A. There are six possible ratios that can be formed from the three sides of a right triangle. We give each of them a name by adopting the following definitions.

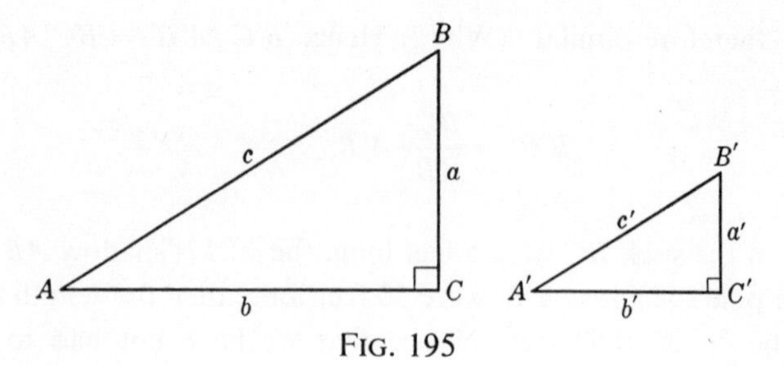

FIG. 195

Definitions.

$$\sin A = a/c = \text{opp.}/\text{hyp.} \qquad \csc A = c/a = \text{hyp.}/\text{opp.}$$
$$\cos A = b/c = \text{adj.}/\text{hyp.} \qquad \sec A = c/b = \text{hyp.}/\text{adj.}$$
$$\tan A = a/b = \text{opp.}/\text{adj.} \qquad \cot A = b/a = \text{adj.}/\text{opp.}$$

The abbreviations stand for **sine**, **cosine**, **tangent**, **cosecant**, **secant**, **cotangent**, of A, respectively. These queerly named functions of angle A are called **trigonometric functions** or **trigonometric ratios**. The origin of the names of the trigonometric functions will be discussed in section 144.

Example 1. Consider an isosceles right triangle (Fig. 196) whose leg is 1 unit long. From the Pythagorean theorem we find that $c^2 = 1^2 + 1^2$ or $c^2 = 2$; hence the hypotenuse is equal to $\sqrt{2}$. Thus $\sin 45° = \dfrac{1}{\sqrt{2}} = \dfrac{1}{\sqrt{2}} \cdot \dfrac{\sqrt{2}}{\sqrt{2}} = \dfrac{\sqrt{2}}{2} = \dfrac{1.414\cdots}{2} = .707\cdots$ approximately,* while $\tan 45° = 1$. If we took a different right triangle whose leg was 10 units long, the hypotenuse would have been $10\sqrt{2}$ and we would obtain the same values for sin 45°, etc. (Why?)

Example 2. Consider the equilateral triangle ABD whose side is 2 units long, bisected as in

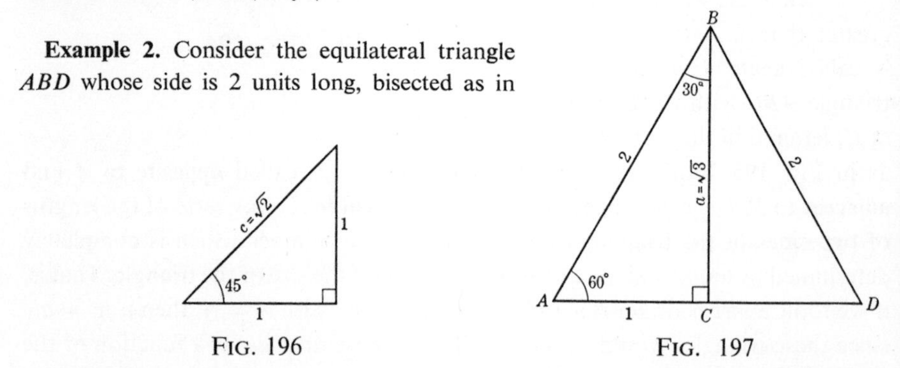

FIG. 196 FIG. 197

* The process by which we obtained $\sqrt{2}/2$ from $1/\sqrt{2}$ is called **rationalizing the denominator**. It was done for *the purpose of obtaining a decimal expression*, since it is easier to divide 1.414 . . . by 2 than to divide 1 by 1.414 . . . . For most purposes other than decimal evaluation, there is no reason to regard $\sqrt{2}/2$ as being "simpler" than $1/\sqrt{2}$. In what follows, we shall seldom rationalize denominators.

Fig. 197. Triangle ABC is called a 30°–60°–90° triangle. Clearly $AC = 1$ and from the Pythagorean theorem we find that $1^2 + a^2 = 2^2$; or $a^2 = 3$; hence $a = BC = \sqrt{3}$; hence $\sin 60° = \sqrt{3}/2 = 1.732 \cdots/2 = .866 \cdots$ approximately, $\sin 30° = \frac{1}{2} = .500$, etc.

Two different acute angles cannot have equal trigonometric functions. For suppose $\sin A = \sin A'$; that is $a/c = a'/c'$. Then it follows from a theorem of geometry that the two right triangles are similar and hence $A = A'$. Thus *an acute angle is uniquely determined if the value of one of its trigonometric functions is given.* In particular, given one trigonometric function of an acute angle, we can find the other five.

Example 3. Given the acute angle A with $\sin A = \frac{5}{13}$, find $\cos A$ (Fig. 198).

Since $\sin A = \frac{5}{13}$ we may place the angle A in a right triangle with $a = 5$ and $c = 13$. Then $5^2 + b^2 = 13^2$ or $b^2 = 169 - 25 = 144$. Hence $b = 12$. Therefore $\cos A = \frac{12}{13}$.

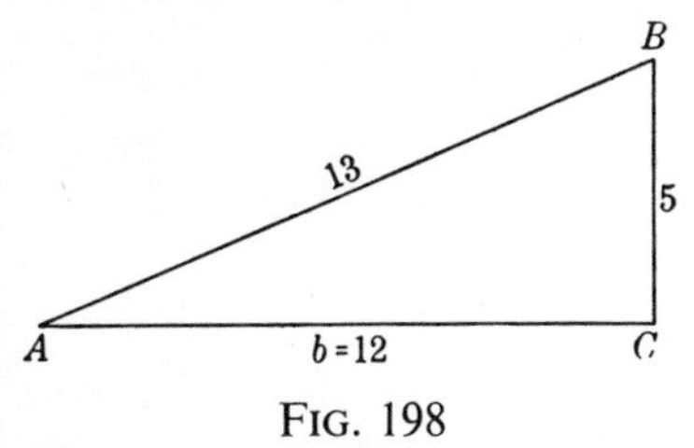

FIG. 198

If two trigonometric functions are such that the name of one can be obtained from the name of the other by prefixing or omitting the prefix "co-," we shall call them **co-functions**. For example, sine and cosine are co-functions. Let A and B be two **complementary** angles (that is, $A + B = 90°$) in a right triangle (Fig. 195). Since the side opposite A is adjacent to B, and vice versa, we have $\sin A = a/c = \cos B$, $\cos A = b/c = \sin B$, and so on. In general, we have the following theorem.

Theorem. *Any trigonometric function of an acute angle is equal to the co-function of its complement.*

Writing B as $90° - A$, this may be written as $\sin A = \cos (90° - A)$, $\tan A = \cot (90° - A)$, and so on.

Exercises

Find the values of the six trigonometric functions of an angle, in a right triangle, whose:

1. Opposite side is 3 and hypotenuse 5.
2. Adjacent side is 5 and hypotenuse 13.
3. Adjacent side is 12 and opposite 5.
4. Adjacent side is 3 and opposite 5.
5. Adjacent side is 5 and opposite 4.
6. Adjacent side is 3 and hypotenuse 4.
7. Adjacent side is 4 and opposite $\sqrt{3}$.

Find the values of the six trigonometric functions of:

8. 45°. **9.** 30°. **10.** 60°.

Find the number of degrees in the acute angle A if:

11. $\sin A = 1/\sqrt{2}$. **12.** $\tan A = 1/\sqrt{3}$. **13.** $\cos A = \frac{1}{2}$.
14. $\tan A = 1$. **15.** $\cos A = \sqrt{3}/2$. **16.** $\sin A = \sqrt{3}/2$.

Find all the trigonometric functions of the acute angle A given that:

17. $\sin A = \frac{6}{10}$. **18.** $\sin A = \frac{7}{25}$. **19.** $\cos A = \frac{5}{13}$.
20. $\sin A = \frac{15}{17}$ **21.** $\cos A = \frac{3}{4}$. **22.** $\tan A = \frac{5}{4}$.
23. $\tan A = \frac{4}{3}$. **24.** $\cos A = \frac{35}{37}$. **25.** $\tan A = \frac{5}{3}$.
26. $\csc A = \frac{4}{3}$. **27.** $\sec A = \frac{10}{8}$. **28.** $\cot A = \frac{4}{5}$.
29. $\sin A = .8$. **30.** $\cos A = .3$. **31.** $\tan A = 1.2$.
32. $\csc A = 1.2$. **33.** $\sec A = 1.4$. **34.** $\cot A = 1.3$.

35. If A and B are complementary angles and $\sin A = \frac{1}{3}$, find (*a*) $\cos B$; (*b*) $\cos A$; (*c*) $\sin B$.

36. If A and B are complementary angles, and $\sin A = \frac{3}{4}$, find all the trigonometric functions of both A and B.

37. If $\sin 27° = .454$, find $\cos 63°$.

38. If $\cot 41° = 1.15$, find $\tan 49°$.

39. If $\sec 44° = 1.39$, find $\csc 46°$.

140. APPLICATIONS

Suppose we observe that the shadow cast by a pole is 30 feet long at the instant when the **angle of elevation** of the sun (that is, the angle made by the sun's rays and the horizontal ground) is 38° (Fig. 199). How can we tell the height h of the pole? Clearly,

$$h/30 = \tan 38°$$

so that if we knew the value of tan 38° we could get $h = 30 \cdot \tan 38°$ without more ado. Thales obtained the value of this ratio from his walking stick and its shadow (section 138). But we would need no walking stick at all if we had a table giving the values of the trigonometric functions (or ratios) for various angles. Thus we see the utility of having a table of the trigonometric functions for acute angles. Such a table is found at the end of the book. From it we find that $\tan 38° = .7813$. Hence, $h = 23.44$ feet.

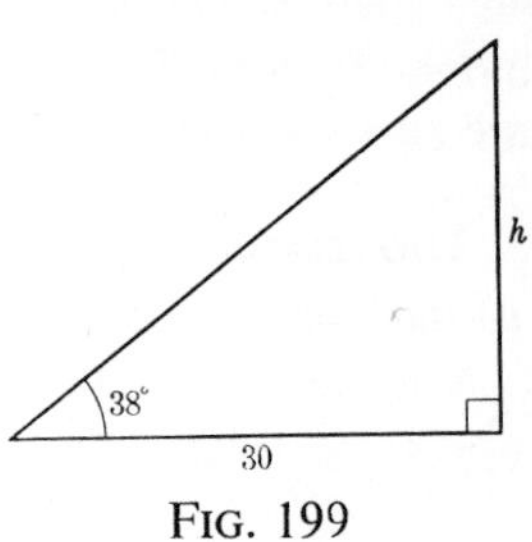

FIG. 199

One of the most important elementary applications of the trigonometric functions is to such problems of indirect measurement. Other applications are contained in the examples and exercises.

In reading the tables it must be understood that the headings at the top go with the angles at the left, while the headings at the bottom go with the angles at the right. This compact arrangement of the table is made possible by the theorem of section 139 on co-functions. For a glance at the table will show that sin 60°, for example, is located in the same place as cos 30°. This can be done because sin 60° = cos 30°, since 30° and 60° are complementary. Hence the trigonometric functions of angles of 1, 2 ..., 89 degrees can be arranged in 45 lines instead of 89 lines. Note that the line in the table giving the functions of 0° and 90° must be regarded as senseless at the moment because we have not yet defined the trigonometric functions of angles, like 0° and 90°, which are not acute. These will be defined in section 143.

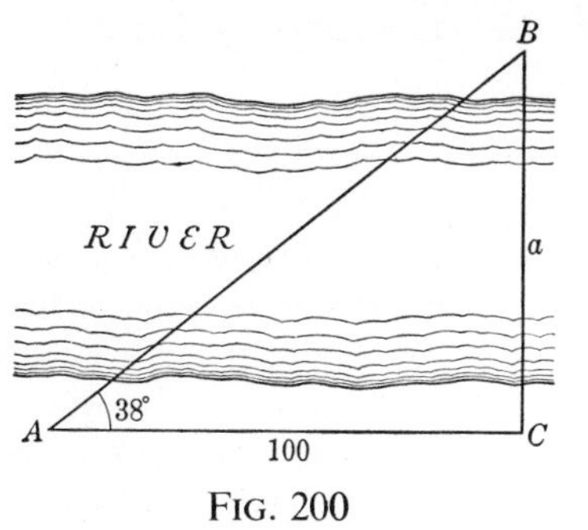

FIG. 200

Example 1. Find the distance BC across the river in Fig. 200 if $AC = 100$ feet and $A = 38°$ by direct observation.*

We are given the side adjacent to angle A and must find the side opposite angle A. Therefore we are concerned with the tangent of angle A. Clearly, $a/100 = \tan 38°$. Hence $a = 78.13$ feet. Notice that this distance is determined from data which can be obtained while remaining on one side of the river, as follows. We can stand at C with a transit pointing toward some object at B and turn it through 90°. An assistant finds a place A directly in the line of sight of the turned transit and marks the spot. Then AC is measured. Marking C we move the transit to A, point it toward B, and turn it until we sight C. We then read off the angle A from the transit.

A transit
FIG. 201

Example 2. If a 30-foot ladder is leaned against a window sill 20 feet high, what angle will the ladder make with the ground?

We are given the side opposite angle A and the hypotenuse (Fig. 202). Therefore we are concerned with the sine of angle A. Clearly, $\sin A = 20/30 = .6667$. From the table we find that the nearest value

* In practice, angles are measured by means of a *transit*, which is really nothing more than a glorified protractor with a spy-glass to aid the vision. A transit mounted on a tripod may be seen on any empty lot just before a building goes up.

to .6667 in the sine column is .6691, which is sin 42°. Hence we take $A = 42°$ as an approximate answer.

Example 3. If a projectile is fired at an angle A from the level of the ground its horizontal distance x and its height y at the end of t seconds are given by (Fig. 203)

$$x = v_0 t \cos A \tag{1}$$

$$y = v_0 t \sin A - 16t^2 \tag{2}$$

where v_0 is the initial velocity and distances are measured in feet. Suppose $A = 30°$, $v_0 = 160$ feet per second. Find the horizontal distance from the starting point to the point where the projectile will strike the ground.

Clearly, we want the value of x for which $y = 0$. Now from (2), $y = 0$ where $t(v_0 \sin A - 16t) = 0$ or at $t = 0$ and at $t = (v_0 \sin A)/16$. The first solution $t = 0$ corresponds to the starting point. The second solution is $t = 160(.5)/16 = 5$. Hence the projectile strikes the ground at the end of 5 seconds. From (1) this means that the distance $x = 160 \cdot 5(.866) = 692.8$ feet approximately.

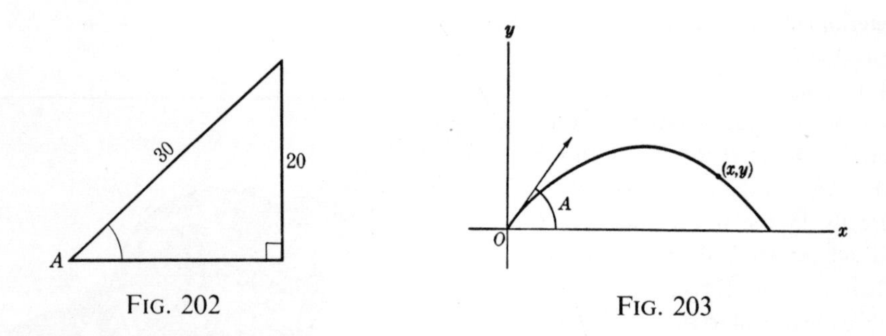

FIG. 202 FIG. 203

Remark 1. If more accurate approximations are desired we can use interpolation, more extensive tables, or both.

Remark 2. How are the tables constructed? A rough table could be made by direct methods. For example, to get cos 40° we might construct an angle of 40° with a protractor as accurately as we could; then we could form a right triangle, measure the adjacent side and hypotenuse as closely as possible, and divide one by the other. However, such a method would hardly be satisfactory except for rough work, for we could never be sure as to how accurate our results were; that is, we would never know how many decimal places in our results were really correct. A better method, which is actually used, is based on the following theorem, proved by the calculus. If x is the number of *radians* in the angle, then $\cos x$ is given by the infinite series

$$\cos x = 1 - \frac{x^2}{2} + \frac{x^4}{4 \cdot 3 \cdot 2} - \frac{x^6}{6 \cdot 5 \cdot 4 \cdot 3 \cdot 2} + \frac{x^8}{8 \cdot 7 \cdot 6 \cdot 5 \cdot 4 \cdot 3 \cdot 2} - \cdots.$$

Now $40° = .7$ radians, approximately. Hence,

$$\cos 40° = \cos .7 = 1 - \frac{(.7)^2}{2} + \frac{(.7)^4}{4\cdot 3\cdot 2} - \frac{(.7)^6}{6\cdot 5\cdot 4\cdot 3\cdot 2} + \cdots.$$

Taking the first three terms of this series we get $\cos 40° = .765$ approximately, which is correct as far as the hundredths place, as we see from the table. Similar infinite series for the other trigonometric functions may be found in text-books on the calculus. By this method we are able to calculate the trigonometric functions as accurately as we wish by taking enough terms of the infinite series. At each stage we can tell how large an error is committed by our approximation. Even with these modern methods, the labor involved in the calculation of tables is great, but the labor saved by having the tables is inestimable.

In the exercises in this chapter, angles will usually be found correct to the nearest degree and lengths correct to the nearest tenth. For a detailed discussion of accuracy, see Plane and Spherical Trigonometry, *cited in the references at the end of the chapter.*

Exercises

1. Find the height of a pole whose (horizontal) shadow is 85 feet long when the angle of elevation of the sun is 51°.

2. Find the length of the shadow of a pole 55 feet high when the angle of elevation of the sun is 51°.

3. A wire 50 feet long is stretched from the top of a 35-foot pole to the ground. What angle does the wire make with the pole?

4. A wire 50 feet long is stretched from the top of a pole to the ground making an angle of 58° with the pole. How high is the pole?

5. A wire is to be stretched from the top of a 50-foot pole to the ground making an angle of 48° with the ground. How long should the wire be?

6. A wire is stretched from the top of a pole to a point on the ground 50 feet from the base of the pole. If the angle between the wire and the ground is 42° what is the height of the pole?

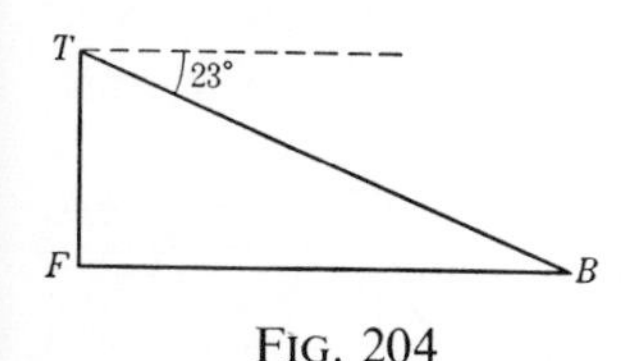

FIG. 204

7. From the top of a lighthouse 100 feet high the angle of depression* (Fig. 204) of a boat B is found to be 23°. How far from the foot F of the lighthouse, at sea level, is the boat?

8. Draw, with a protractor, an angle of 35° on graph paper. By measurement and long division, estimate the values of the trigonometric functions of 35°. Compare with the table.

9. A projectile is fired at an angle of 42° with the horizontal at an initial velocity of 144 feet per second. Using the formulas (1) and (2) of example 3 above, find: (*a*) the

* The angle between the line of sight and the horizontal.

distance of the point where the projectile strikes the ground from the starting point; (*b*) the maximum height reached by the projectile. (Hint: use the method of section 127 for part (*b*).)

10. A man drives 500 feet up a road whose inclination is 20°. How high above his starting level is he?

11. From a point opposite the middle of a battleship known to be 500 feet long, turned broadside, the angle subtended* by the ship is 6°. How far away is the battleship?

12. If the radius of the earth is 3960 miles, find the radius of the 42nd parallel (of latitude) (Fig. 205).

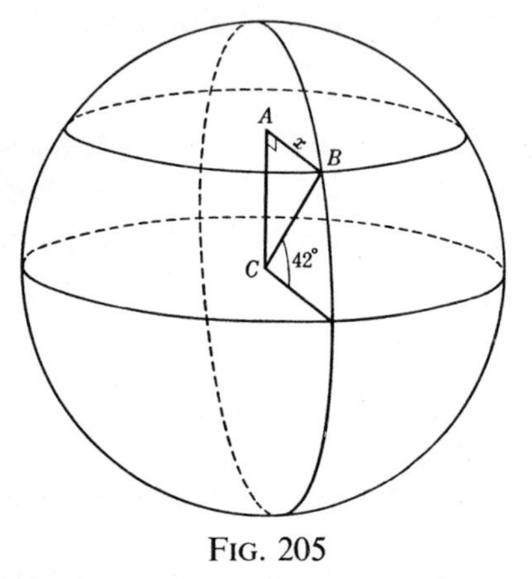

FIG. 205

13. Using the result of exercise 12, find the circumference of the 42nd parallel. How many miles do we cover if we traverse 36° of longitude along the 42nd parallel?

14. An observer in an airplane 3000 feet directly above a cannon finds that the angle of depression of an enemy supply base is 24°. Find the horizontal distance between the cannon and the supply base.

15. If the radius of the earth is 3960 miles and angle A (Fig. 206) is found to be 57′3″, find the distance between the center of the earth and the center of the moon. Suppose that $\sin 57'3'' = .01659$.

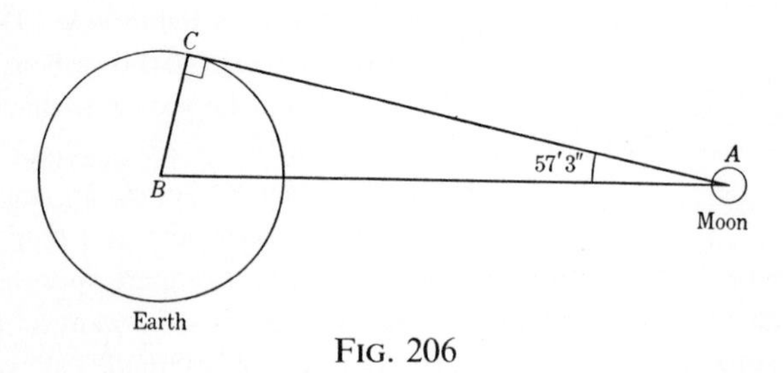

FIG. 206

* The angle **subtended** by an object at a point P is the angle between the lines of sight from P to the extremities of the object, as viewed from P.

16. An airplane is 1 mile above the ocean. How far away from it is the furthest visible point on the ocean (Fig. 207)? Suppose that the radius of the earth is 3960 miles. Use *both* the method of the text *and* the Pythagorean theorem and explain the discrepancy between the two answers.

17. Find the angle of elevation of the sun if a pole 50 feet long casts a horizontal shadow 22 feet long.

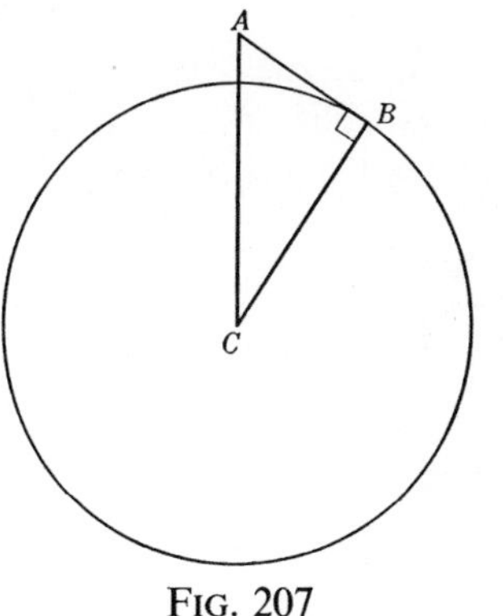

FIG. 207

141. VECTORS

Many physical quantities involve not only magnitude but direction as well. For example, to say that a force of 30 pounds is applied to an object does not specify the force completely; we need to know the direction in which the force is being applied. Velocities are also not completely described unless the direction is given. Such quantities, speaking loosely, are called **vectors**. A vector is conveniently represented by an arrow whose length corresponds to the magnitude and which points in the proper direction. Thus a force of 3 pounds applied in an easterly direction is represented graphically by an arrow 3 units long pointing east.

It is a well known result of experimental physics that if two forces $\overrightarrow{AC}$ and $\overrightarrow{AB}$ making an angle with each other are applied simultaneously, the resultant force is described with respect to both its magnitude and direction by the diagonal $\overrightarrow{AD}$ of a parallelogram as in Fig. 208. This is called the *parallelogram law for the composition of vectors*. Velocities also may be represented as vectors as may many other physical quantities. Vectors, like other parts of pure mathematics, may be applied to (and hence serve to unify) many different concrete physical interpretations.

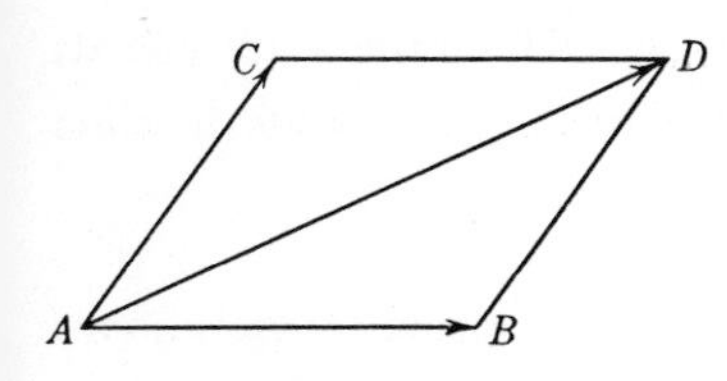

FIG. 208

The two given vectors are called **components**, and the diagonal vector is called the **sum** or **resultant**. We shall confine ourselves in this section to components which are at right angles to each other.

Example 1. A body is acted upon simultaneously by a force of 50 pounds due north, and a force of 120 pounds due east. Find the magnitude and direction of the resultant force. See Fig. 209.

By the Pythagorean theorem, $(AD)^2 = 50^2 + 120^2$; hence $AD = 130$. Clearly, $\tan x = 50/120 = .4167$. From the table of tangents we find $x = 23°$ approximately. Hence the resultant force is one of 130 pounds acting in a direction 23° north of east.

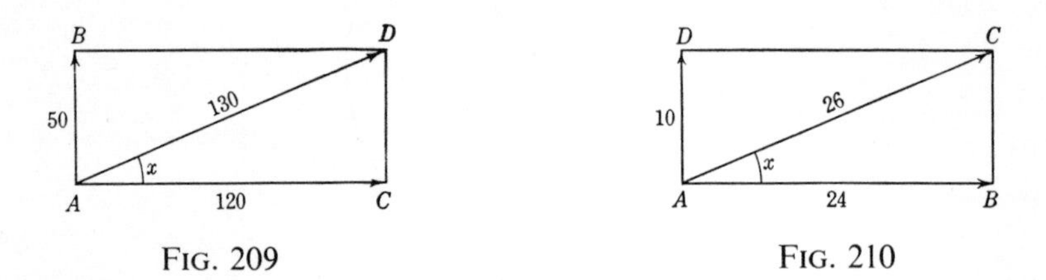

FIG. 209 FIG. 210

Example 2. A boat pointed east travels at the rate of 24 miles per hour under its own power and a wind blows it north at the rate of 10 miles per hour. Find the magnitude and direction of the velocity of the boat. See Fig. 210.

The resultant of the two given components is a velocity of 26 miles per hour, and $\cot x = 2.4$. From the table we find $x = 23°$ approximately. Hence the boat moves in a direction 23° north of east, with a speed of 26 miles per hour.

Example 3. A body weighing 100 pounds is on a plane inclined at an angle of 30° to the horizontal. What force must be applied to the body to keep it from sliding down the plane? Friction is to be neglected. See Fig. 211.

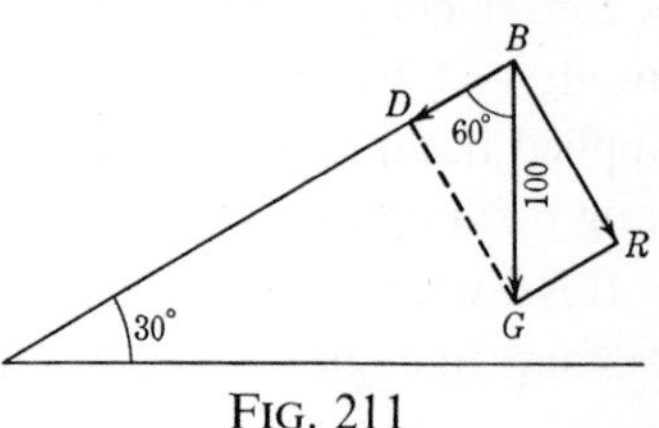

FIG. 211

The weight of the body means that the force of gravity acting on it is 100 pounds directed downward. We regard $\overrightarrow{BG}$ as the resultant of the two perpendicular forces $\overrightarrow{BD}$ and $\overrightarrow{BR}$. Clearly, $BD/100 = \cos 60°$ or $BD = 50$. Hence the force pushing the body downhill is 50 pounds in the direction $\overrightarrow{BD}$. Thus we must apply a force of 50 pounds in the opposite direction $\overrightarrow{DB}$.

Remark 1. A precise explanation of the concept of vector, explained loosely above may be given as follows. A **bound vector** $\overrightarrow{AB}$ is a directed line-segment. The bound vector $\overrightarrow{AB}$ has the **initial point** A and the **terminal point** B. Two bound vectors $\overrightarrow{AB}$ and $\overrightarrow{CD}$ are called **equivalent** if they are on the same or on parallel lines, and have equal lengths and similar sense.* For example, in Fig. 212, $\overrightarrow{AB}$, $\overrightarrow{CD}$, and $\overrightarrow{EF}$ are all equivalent. It is easily seen that the relation of equivalence defined here is indeed an equivalence relation (cf. section 11), i.e., it is reflexive, symmetric, and transitive. The equivalence classes determined by this relation are called **free vectors**. Thus, the free vector to which $\overrightarrow{AB}$ belongs, in Fig. 212, contains also the bound vectors $\overrightarrow{CD}$, $\overrightarrow{EF}$ and many others, and may be designated or represented by any one of them. To add two free vectors, say $\overrightarrow{PQ}$ and $\overrightarrow{RS}$ (Fig. 213), we select that member $\overrightarrow{QT}$ of the free vector $\overrightarrow{RS}$ whose initial point is the terminal point Q of $\overrightarrow{PQ}$ and take the free vector $\overrightarrow{PT}$ as the sum or resultant vector.

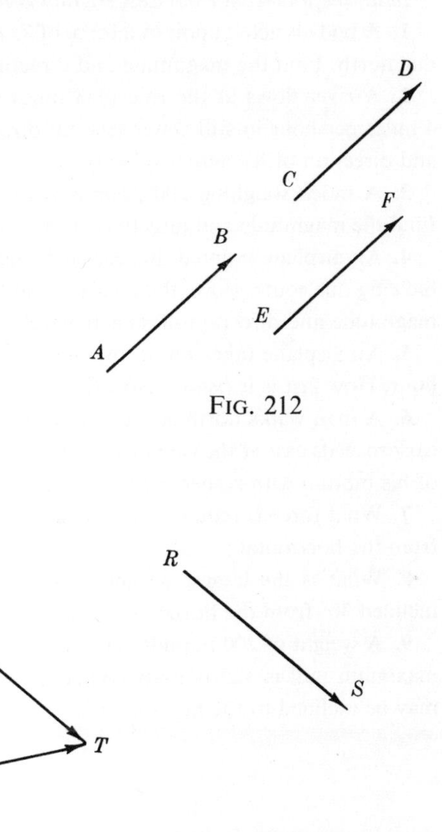

FIG. 212

FIG. 213

We include as a free vector also a zero-vector denoted by $\vec{0}$ determined when the initial point and terminal point coincide, forming a "line-segment" of length 0. Thus, if we add $\overrightarrow{PQ}$ to $\overrightarrow{QP}$ we get $\overrightarrow{PP}$ or $\vec{0}$.

Remark 2. Besides *bound vectors* and *free vectors* there are also *sliding-vectors* of use in physics in connection with "moments." Two bound vectors may be called **slide-equivalent** if they are on the same line and have the same length and sense. This relation is also an equivalence relation and its equivalence classes are called **sliding-vectors.** Thus, in Fig. 212, AB and CD belong to the same sliding vector but EF belongs to a different sliding vector. *When no adjective is used with the word vector, free vector is usually meant.*

* Two parallel lines are said to have the same direction but each line may be given two senses indicated by arrowheads. Thus, the line AB may have the sense from A toward B or the opposite sense from B towards A.

Exercises

In all the following exercises, friction is to be neglected.

1. A body is acted upon by a force of 75 pounds, due east, and a force of 100 pounds, due north. Find the magnitude and direction of the resultant force.

2. A river flows at the rate of 3 miles per hour. A man who rows at the rate of 4 miles per hour in still water sets out directly across the stream. Find the magnitude and direction of his actual velocity.

3. A block weighing 200 pounds is on a plane inclined at 45° to the horizontal. Find the magnitude and direction of the force needed to keep it from sliding downhill.

4. An airplane pointed due east is flying at the rate of 200 miles per hour. A wind blowing due south blows the airplane south at the rate of 30 miles per hour. Find the magnitude and direction of its actual velocity.

5. An airplane takes off at an angle of 5° while moving at the rate of 80 miles per hour. How fast is it rising? How fast is it moving forward (that is, horizontally)?

6. A man walks north across a railway car at the rate of 1 mile per hour while the car proceeds east at the rate of 10 miles per hour. What is the direction and magnitude of his motion with respect to the surface of the earth?

7. What force is required to drag a 2000-pound automobile up a ramp inclined 25° from the horizontal?

8. What is the largest weight which a man can keep from sliding down a ramp inclined 30° from the horizontal if he can exert a pull of 180 pounds?

9. A weight of 200 pounds is to be kept from sliding down a ramp by a man whose maximum pull is 125 pounds. What is the largest possible angle at which the ramp may be inclined to the horizontal?

142. DIRECTED ANGULAR MEASURE

One of the inconvenient features of our angular measures is that we cannot freely add or subtract them. For example, we cannot say that an angle whose measure is 100° plus an angle whose measure is 110° gives an angle whose measure is 210°, since no angular measure can be greater than 180° by our definition. Similarly, we cannot subtract an angular measure of 110° from an angular measure of 100° to get one of $-10°$ since "negative" angular measures have not been defined. However, for many purposes it is convenient to extend the notion of angular measure to allow for *directed* angular measures of any positive or negative number of degrees like $-960°$ or $+750°$, just as it is convenient to use directed numbers for coordinates. To do this we

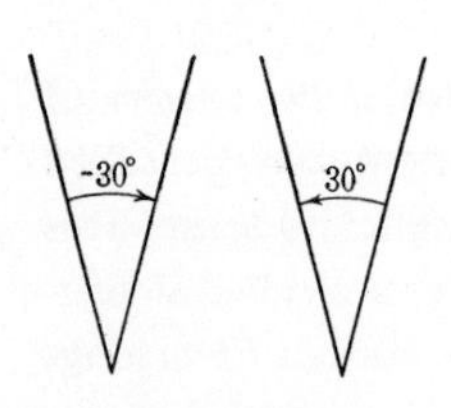

FIG. 214

agree that counterclockwise rotation shall be regarded as positive and clockwise rotation shall be regarded as negative. If we imagine the rotation beginning at one ray of an angle and ending at the other we shall call the first ray the **initial ray** and the other the **terminal ray**. Having decided which of the two rays of an angle is to be its initial ray, we shall mean by a **directed angular measure** of the given angle, with the given initial ray, the (directed) number of degrees in any rotation starting at the initial ray and ending at the terminal ray of the angle. The directed angular measure of an angle is still a function of the angle, with specified initial ray, but it is no longer a single-valued function, since the same angle may have different directed angular measures. For example, an angle, with specified initial ray, having a directed angular measure of 30°, also has the directed angular measures 390°, 750°, −330°, −690°, and so on, since rotating through 360° any number of times in either direction yields the same terminal ray. In fact, *if an angle (with specified initial ray) has a directed angular measure of x degrees, it also has all the directed angular measures given by $x + n \cdot 360$ degrees where n is any integer, positive, negative, or zero.* It is customary to speak of an *angle* of 390° or −330° instead of a directed angular measure of 390° or −330°. In the figure a curved arrow is used to indicate the amount and direction of the rotation.

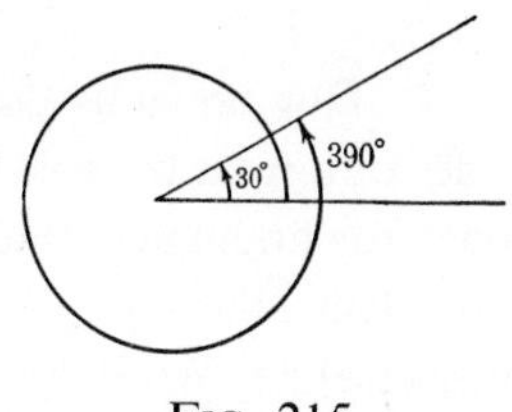

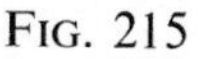
FIG. 215

Since all these directed angular measures correspond to the same angle, you may wonder why we bother to distinguish among them. But if you recall that our directed angular measure corresponds to the intuitive notion of rotation, you will see that there is a very practical distinction between +750° and −690°; if your car is parked near the edge of a cliff, you will be seriously concerned with the question of which of these rotations your wheels will make.

FIG. 216

Exercises

Name five other directed angular measures, three positive and two negative, possessed by an angle with the directed angular measure:

1. +10°. 2. −20°. **3.** 60°. 4. 160°. 5. 210°. 6. 310°.

143. TRIGONOMETRIC FUNCTIONS OF ANY ANGLE

Our previous definitions of the trigonometric functions in terms of the sides of a right triangle are clearly inapplicable to any angle other than an acute one; for an angle of 120°, say, cannot be put inside a right triangle. We shall now define the trigonometric functions of any angle (that is, any directed angular measure).

Definition. *Suppose any angle (with specified initial ray) has been given. Introduce an ordinary rectangular coordinate system into the plane with the origin at the vertex of angle A and the initial ray of angle A as the positive ray of the x-axis. Choose any point P whatever on the terminal ray of angle A, and let (x,y) be the coordinates of P and d its distance from the origin* (Fig. 217). *Then we define*

$$\begin{aligned} \sin A &= y/d = \text{ordinate/distance} \\ \cos A &= x/d = \text{abcissa/distance} \\ \tan A &= y/x = \text{ordinate/abscissa} \\ \csc A &= d/y = \text{distance/ordinate} \\ \sec A &= d/x = \text{distance/abscissa} \\ \cot A &= x/y = \text{abscissa/ordinate.} \end{aligned}$$

These quantities are really functions of the angle A alone. In particular, they do not depend on our choice of the point P; for if we chose a different point

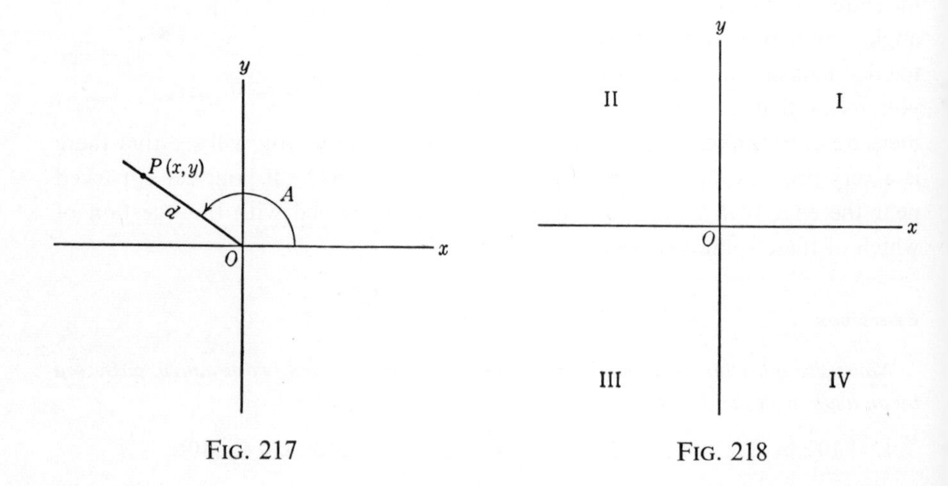

FIG. 217

FIG. 218

P' (x',y') on the terminal ray of A at a distance d' from the origin, it is clear that x' and y' would have the same signs as x and y, respectively, and, because of similar triangles, the ratios y'/d', x'/d', y'/x', etc., would be equal respectively to the ratios y/d, x/d, y/x, etc. Distance is always positive.

Clearly *any trigonometric function of an angle of $A°$ is equal to the same trigonometric function of any angle of $A + n \cdot 360$ degrees where n is any integer*, since all these angles have the same terminal ray. For example, $\sin 30° = \sin 390° = \sin(-330°)$.

After the coordinate system has been introduced, the plane is divided into four **quadrants**, which are always numbered as in Fig. 218. An angle is said to be "in" the quadrant in which its terminal ray lies. For positive acute angles, our new definitions yield the same results as those of section 139, since x and y are both positive for any point in the first quadrant and consequently are nothing more than the lengths of the sides adjacent and opposite to A, respectively. Therefore, no conflict arises between our old and new definitions. Our new definitions may be called "generalizations" of the old ones since they agree with the old ones for all angles to which the old ones may be applied (that is, acute angles) but are applicable to a wider class of angles.

Example 1. Find the cosine of the angle whose terminal ray passes through the point $P(-3,4)$. See Fig. 219.

The distance $d = PO$ is clearly 5 since, by the Pythagorean theorem, $d^2 = x^2 + y^2 = (-3)^2 + 4^2 = 25$. Thus $\cos A = -3/5$.

Example 2. Find the trigonometric functions of 210°. Clearly, if we choose a point P on the terminal ray whose distance from O is 2 units, the coordinates of P are

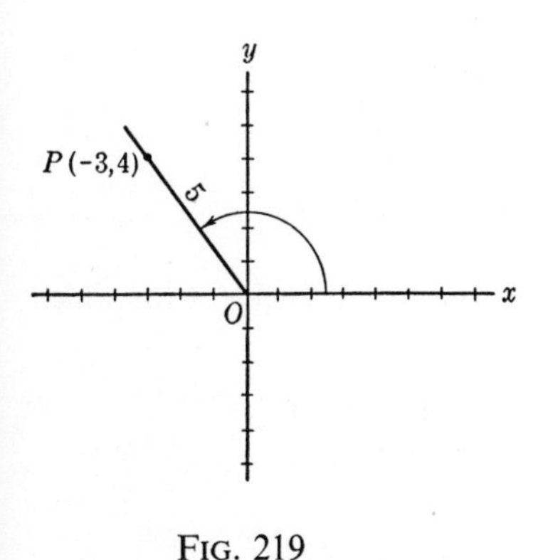

FIG. 219

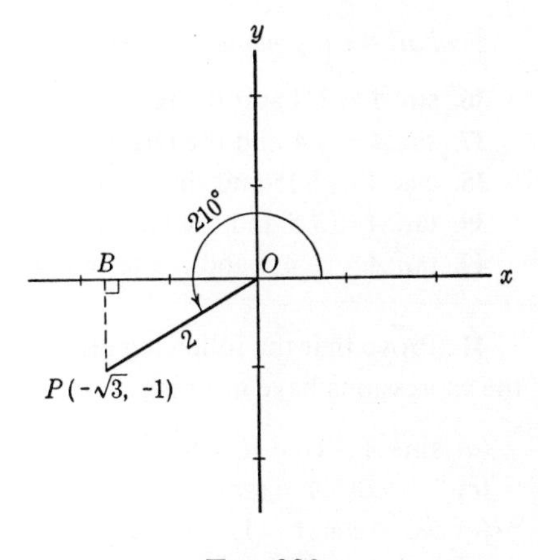

FIG. 220

$(-\sqrt{3},-1)$ since BPO is a 30°–60°–90° triangle. Hence (Fig. 220)

$\sin 210° = -1/2$ $\quad\csc 210° = -2$
$\cos 210° = -\sqrt{3}/2$ $\quad\sec 210° = -2/\sqrt{3}$
$\tan 210° = 1/\sqrt{3}$ $\quad\cot 210° = \sqrt{3}$.

Example 3. Find the trigonometric functions of 90°. Choose a point P on the terminal ray with coordinates (0,1). The distance d is then 1. Hence (Fig. 221)

$\sin 90° = 1$ $\quad\csc 90° = 1$
$\cos 90° = 0$ $\quad\sec 90°$ does not exist
$\tan 90°$ does not exist $\quad\cot 90° = 0$.

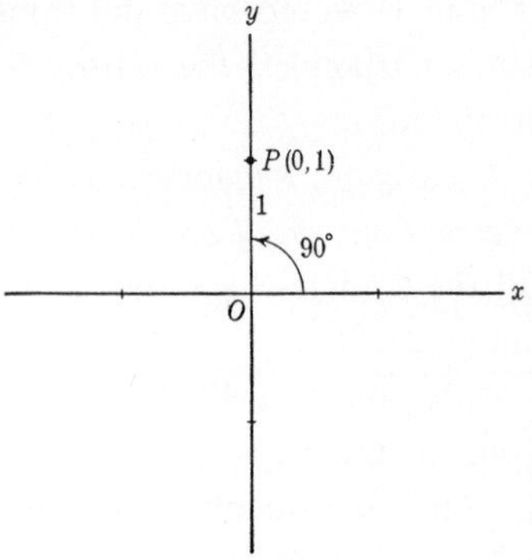

FIG. 221

Exercises

Find the trigonometric functions of an angle whose terminal ray contains the point:

1. (3,4). **2.** (−3,4). **3.** (−3,−4). **4.** (4,−5). **5.** (4,−3).
6. (0,−1). **7.** (1,0). **8.** (−1,0). **9.** (5,12). **10.** (−12,5).

Find the trigonometric functions of the following angles:

11. 30°. **12.** 150°. **13.** 240°. **14.** 330°. **15.** 510°.
16. −60°. **17.** −120°. **18.** −240°. **19.** −300°. **20.** −420°.
21. 45°. **22.** 135°. **23.** 225°. **24.** 315°. **25.** 765°.
26. 180°. **27.** 270°. **28.** 360°. **29.** 0°.

In which of the quadrants may angle A terminate if:

30. $\sin A > 0$. **31.** $\cos A < 0$. **32.** $\tan A > 0$.
33. $\csc A < 0$. **34.** $\sec A > 0$. **35.** $\cot A < 0$.

Find all the trigonometric functions of angle A if:

36. $\sin A = 3/4$ and the terminal ray of A is in quadrant I.
37. $\sin A = 3/4$ and the terminal ray of A is not in quadrant I.
38. $\cos A = 7/25$ and the terminal ray of A is not in quadrant I.
39. $\tan A = 3/5$ and the terminal ray of A is not in quadrant I.
40. $\tan A = -4/5$ and the terminal ray of A is not in quadrant II.

41. Prove that the following are identities, that is, true for all angles A for which the expressions have meaning:

(*a*) $\sin^2 A + \cos^2 A = 1$. (*b*) $1 + \tan^2 A = \sec^2 A$.
(*c*) $1 + \cot^2 A = \csc^2 A$. (*d*) $\tan A = \sin A/\cos A$.
(*e*) $\sec A \cos A = 1$. (*f*) $\sin A \csc A = 1$.
(*g*) $\cot A \tan A = 1$. (*h*) $\cot A = \cos A/\sin A$.

144. THE LINE-VALUES AND THE NAMES OF THE TRIGONOMETRIC FUNCTIONS

In the preceding section we agreed to *call* the ratio y/d by the name "sine of A." Needless to say, if we had wished to, we could have called it the "abracadabra of A." A student who is tempted to ask "How do we know that y/d *is* the sine of A?" is in the same class as the gushing lady who came up to a well-known astronomer after a public lecture, as gushing ladies do, to tell him how clear his talk was and how much she enjoyed it. She concluded by saying, "I understood how you found out the distances of the stars and all that, but there was one thing I didn't grasp. How did you ever find out their names?"

The choice of the names of the trigonometric functions is, logically, an arbitrary matter. But there does remain the historical or psychological question, "Why did we happen to choose these particular names rather than others?" Some light will be thrown on this question by examining the following geometric interpretation of the trigonometric functions.

Consider a circle of radius one unit with center at the origin, and let the positive ray of the x-axis lie along the initial ray of the angle A, as in the preceding section. Then (Fig. 222) draw tangents to the circle at Q and U. Let S be the point where the terminal ray of angle A meets the circle. Drop a perpendicular

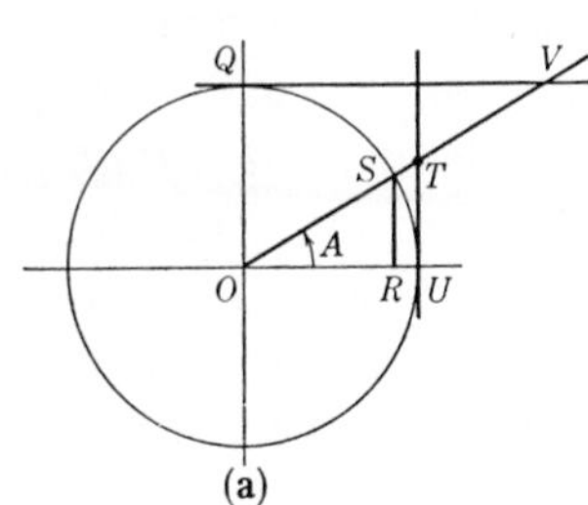

(a)

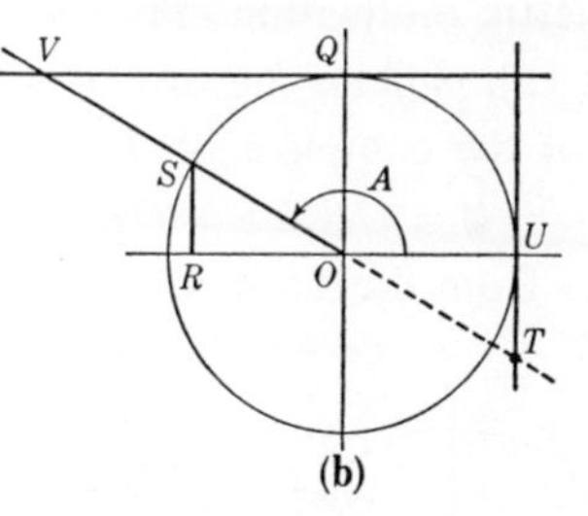

(b)

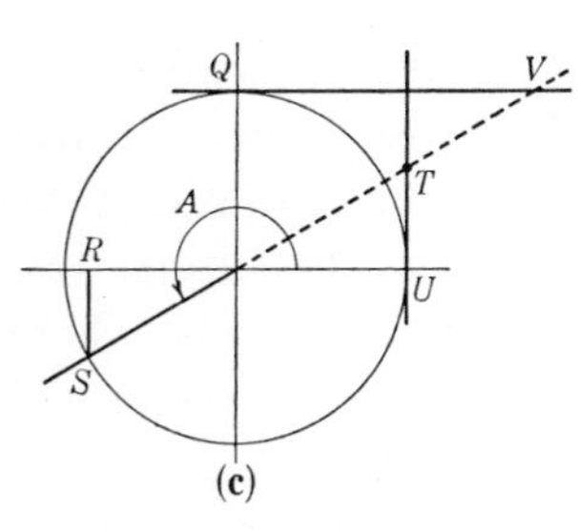

(c)

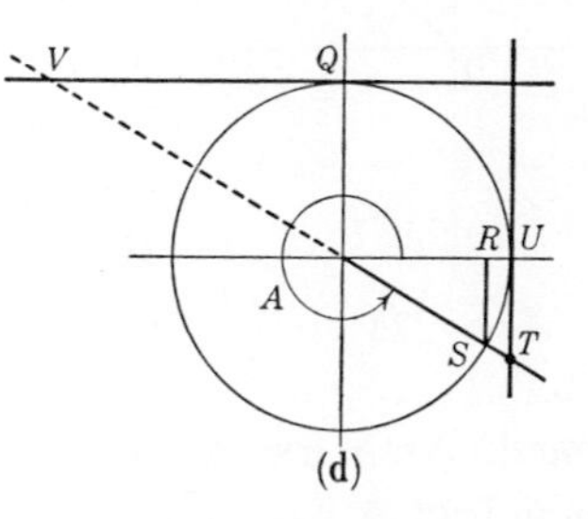

(d)

FIG. 222

from S to the x-axis meeting the x-axis at R. Produce the line OS until it meets the horizontal tangent line at V and the vertical tangent line at T. Let us agree that horizontal line-segments are to be counted positively or negatively according as they extend to the right or left of the y-axis; and that vertical line-segments are to be counted positively or negatively according as they extend up or down from the x-axis. Segments which have been obtained by producing the terminal ray backwards through O will be counted negatively. They are dotted in Fig. 222. Now let us consider the trigonometric functions of A.

Clearly, $OU = OQ = OS. = 1$ Taking account of our agreements as to signs, $\tan A = UT/OU = UT$. That is, the tangent of A is represented by the segment cut off by the terminal ray of A (produced if necessary) on the vertical tangent line.

In the same way, we have $\cot A = QV/OQ = QV$. That is, the cotangent of A is represented by the segment cut off by the terminal ray of A (produced if necessary) on the horizontal tangent line. It is, of course, the tangent of the complement of A.

Similarly, $\sec A = OT/OU = OT$. The name secant may have been suggested by the fact that the segment OT "cuts" the circle; the word "secant" comes from a Latin word which means "cutting."

Likewise, $\csc A = OV/OQ = OV$. This is, of course, the secant of the complement of A.

The names of the four functions considered so far have had fairly plausible geometric motivation. The case of sine and cosine is not so easily explained. If we can explain the origin of the name "sine," then "cosine" is simply the sine of the complement. Clearly, on Fig. 222, we have $\sin A = RS/OS = RS$ and $\cos A = OR/OS = OR$. But this scarcely explains the word sine, which comes from the Latin *sinus*, meaning fold, cavity, or bay. The fact is that the word sinus is due to a mistranslation, although historians are not agreed as to just what mistranslation was committed. Note (Fig. 223) that the sine of A is RS which is half the chord SS'. The ancients, however, were accustomed to use the entire chord SS' as the sine instead of the half-chord RS. Now, one plausible explanation of the origin of the word sinus is that the Hindu word for sine meant "bowstring," an idea clearly suggested by the figure of the chord SS' together with the arc SUS'; but because of similarity in sound, Arab translators confused their word for bowstring with a word meaning fold or bay, from which Latin translators got the word sinus.

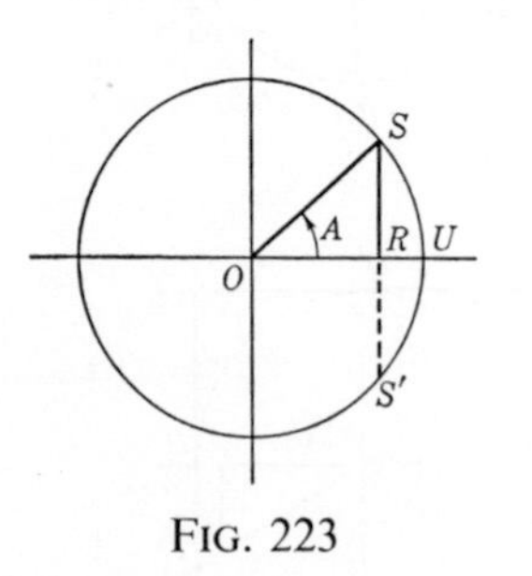

FIG. 223

145. REDUCTION FORMULAS

Since the table gives the values of the trigonometric functions for acute angles only, how can we look up the sine of 160°, say? Clearly, we have somehow to express the trigonometric functions of any angle in terms of the trigonometric functions of an acute angle (that is, an angle between 0° and 90°).

Case 1. If A terminates in quadrant I, there is an angular measure between 0° and 90° which can be looked up having the same terminal ray and therefore the same trigonometric functions. For example, $\sin 380° = \sin 20°$ which can be looked up. Hence $\sin 380° = .3420$.

Case 2. If A terminates in quadrant II, $180° - A$ terminates in quadrant I. For example, if $A = 160°$, $180° - A = 20°$. Choose a point (x,y) on the terminal ray of A at a distance d from the origin. Choose a point (x',y') on the terminal ray of $180° - A$ such that its distance from the origin is $d' = d$. Then clearly (Fig. 224), $y = y'$ and $x = -x'$. Hence,

$$\begin{aligned}
\sin A &= y/d = y'/d' = \sin (180° - A)\\
\cos A &= x/d = -x'/d' = -\cos (180° - A)\\
\tan A &= y/x = -y'/x' = -\tan (180° - A)\\
\csc A &= d/y = d'/y' = \csc (180° - A)\\
\sec A &= d/x = -d'/x' = -\sec (180° - A)\\
\cot A &= x/y = -x'/y' = -\cot (180° - A).
\end{aligned}$$

For example, $\sin 160° = \sin 20°$, $\cos 160° = -\cos 20°$, etc., and the functions of 20° can be looked up in the table. Hence $\sin 160° = .3420$, $\cos 160° = -.9397$, $\tan 160° = -.3640$, $\csc 160° = 2.924$, etc.

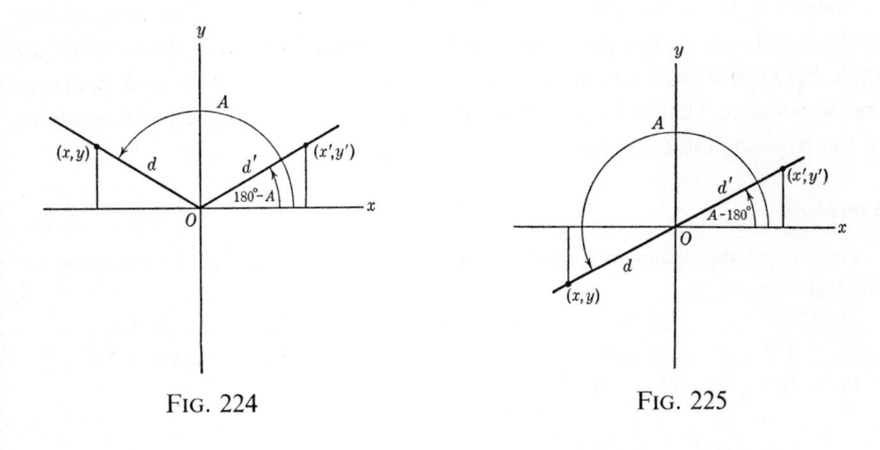

FIG. 224 FIG. 225

Case 3. If A terminates in quadrant III, then $A - 180°$ terminates in quadrant I. Choose points (x,y) and (x',y') on the terminal ray of A and $A - 180°$, respectively, such that $d = d'$ (Fig. 225). Then $x = -x'$, $y = -y'$. Hence,

$$\begin{aligned}
\sin A &= y/d = -y'/d' = -\sin (A - 180°)\\
\cos A &= x/d = -x'/d' = -\cos (A - 180°)\\
\tan A &= y/x = -y'/-x' = y'/x' = \tan (A - 180°)\\
\csc A &= d/y = -d'/y' = -\csc (A - 180°)\\
\sec A &= d/x = -d'/x' = -\sec (A - 180°)\\
\cot A &= x/y = -x'/-y' = x'/y' = \cot (A - 180°).
\end{aligned}$$

For example, $\sin 200° = -\sin 20°$, $\tan 200° = \tan 20°$. Hence, $\sin 200° = -.3420$, $\cos 200° = -.9397$, $\tan 200° = .3640$, $\csc 200° = -2.924$, etc.

Case 4. If A terminates in quadrant IV, then $-A$ terminates in quadrant I. Choose points (x,y) and (x',y') on the terminal rays of A and $-A$, respectively, such that $d = d'$ (Fig. 226). Then $x = x'$, $y = -y'$. Hence,

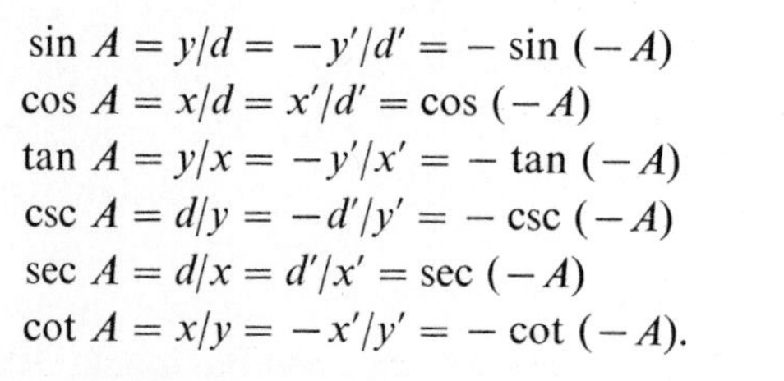

$$\begin{aligned}
\sin A &= y/d = -y'/d' = -\sin (-A)\\
\cos A &= x/d = x'/d' = \cos (-A)\\
\tan A &= y/x = -y'/x' = -\tan (-A)\\
\csc A &= d/y = -d'/y' = -\csc (-A)\\
\sec A &= d/x = d'/x' = \sec (-A)\\
\cot A &= x/y = -x'/y' = -\cot (-A).
\end{aligned}$$

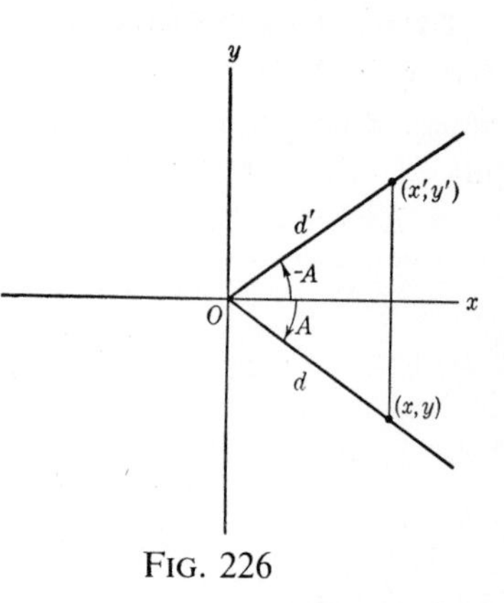

FIG. 226

For example, if $A = -20°$ then $-A = 20°$. Thus $\sin (-20°) = -\sin 20°$, $\cos (-20°) = \cos 20°$. Hence, $\sin (-20°) = -.3420$, $\cos (-20°) = .9397$.

The formulas obtained in this section are called **reduction formulas** because, by means of them, the problem of finding the trigonometric functions of any angle is reduced to the problem of finding the trigonometric functions of an angle between 0° and 90°, which may be looked up in the table, and prefixing the proper sign. That is, they enable us to get along with a table giving the values of the trigonometric functions for acute angles only.

Exercises

Find, using the reduction formulas and the tables, the values of the trigonometric functions of:

1. 170°. **2.** 195°. **3.** −10°. **4.** 340°. **5.** 530°.
6. −735°. **7.** 375°. **8.** 165°. **9.** 217°. **10.** 315°.
11. −165°. **12.** −303°.

13. Make a table giving the values of the trigonometric functions for 0°, 15°, 30°, 45°, 60°, ..., 360° (all angles 15° apart up to 360°).

Find angle A if:

14. $\sin A = .3907$, A not in quadrant I.
15. $\cos A = -.8387$, A between 0° and 180°.
16. $\sin A = 1/2$, A not in quadrant I.
17. $\cos A = -1/2$, A between 0° and 180°.
18. $\sin A = .8090$, A not in quadrant I.
19. $\cos A = -.8391$, A between 0° and 180°.
20. $\sin A = \sqrt{3}/2$, A not in quadrant I.
21. $\cos A = -\sqrt{3}/2$, A between 0° and 180°.
22. $\cos A = -\sqrt{2}/2$, A between 0° and 180°.
23. $\cos A = -.3420$, A between 0° and 180°.
24. $\tan A = 1$, A not in quadrant I.

146. THE SOLUTION OF OBLIQUE TRIANGLES

To find the height of a pole BC (Fig. 227), we have only to measure off any convenient distance AC from the foot of the pole, measure the angle A, and write $BC/AC = \tan A$. For example, if $AC = 100$ feet and $A = 38°$ then $BC = AC \tan A = 100(.7813) = 78.13$ feet. But to find the height h of a mountain we cannot proceed in the same way. To apply this method we should have to measure the distance AC (Fig. 228). But any attempt to measure directly the distance AC will obviously be sabotaged by the mountain. To circumvent the mountain's irritating obstructionist tactics, we proceed as follows. Measure angle A; suppose it is 30°. Move from A toward the mountain any convenient distance, say 1000 feet,* to D (Fig. 229). Measure angle BDC; suppose it is 70°. Clearly, if we only knew the distance $a = BD$ we would be able to find h from the relation $h/a = \sin 70°$. In the next section we shall develop a way of finding a from what we already know about the oblique† triangle ABD.

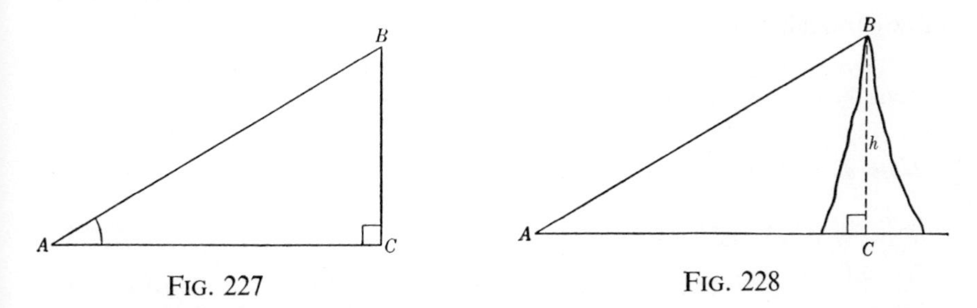

FIG. 227 FIG. 228

* The plain from A to D is assumed to be horizontal, as is usually the case—in textbooks.
† An **oblique triangle** is one which is not a right triangle.

Note that in triangle ABD we know two angles and the included side, since $\measuredangle A = 30°$, $AD = 1000$ feet, and $\measuredangle ADB$ is clearly 110° since it is supplementary to $\measuredangle BDC$. Now this is enough to determine or fix or specify the size and shape of the triangle completely, since, if any other triangle has two angles and the included side equal to 30°, 110°, and 1000 feet respectively, the second triangle must be congruent to the given triangle ABD. Since the size and shape of the triangle are determined by the data, we may reasonably expect to find the remaining sides and angles of triangle ABD.

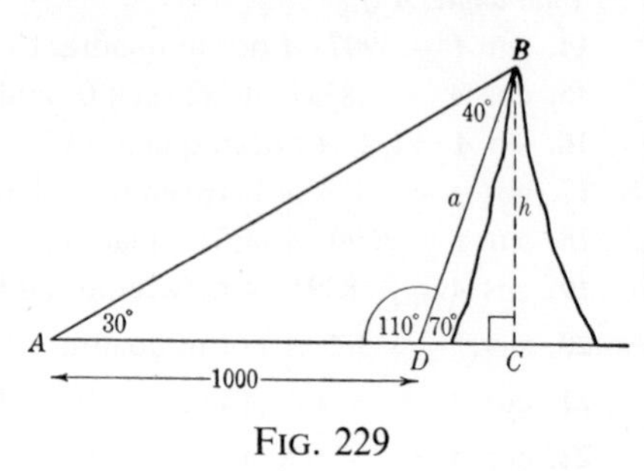

FIG. 229

In general, whenever we know enough about the sides and angles of a triangle to guarantee that any other triangle having the given measurements must be congruent to it, we shall expect to be able to compute the remaining sides and angles. From elementary geometry, we recall the following theorems about the congruence of triangles.

Two triangles are congruent if:

(1) two angles and the included side of one are equal respectively to two angles and the included side of the other;

(2) two sides and the included angle of one are equal respectively to two sides and the included angle of the other;

(3) three sides of one are equal respectively to three sides of the other.

Note that (1) can be modified to read "any two angles and one side" since if two angles of one triangle are equal to two angles of another triangle, then the third angles are equal. This is so because the sum of the angles of any triangle is 180°.

Hence, we shall expect to be able to calculate the remaining sides and angles of any triangle when we are given:

Case 1. any two angles and a side;

Case 2. two sides and the included angle;

Case 3. three sides.

To **solve** a triangle means to find the remaining sides and angles when some of them are known. In the next section we shall dispose of case 1 and in the following section of cases 2 and 3.

Exercise. The height h of the mountain in our illustrative example can be found by using two equations and two unknowns, without the easier method of the next section. Do it. (Hint: h is one unknown; let $k = DC$ be the other. Use triangles BCD and ABC, Fig. 229, to get two equations.)

147. THE LAW OF SINES

Consider any oblique triangle ABC. From B draw a perpendicular BD to AC. Either BD falls within the triangle ABC or not (Fig. 230).* We shall treat each case separately.

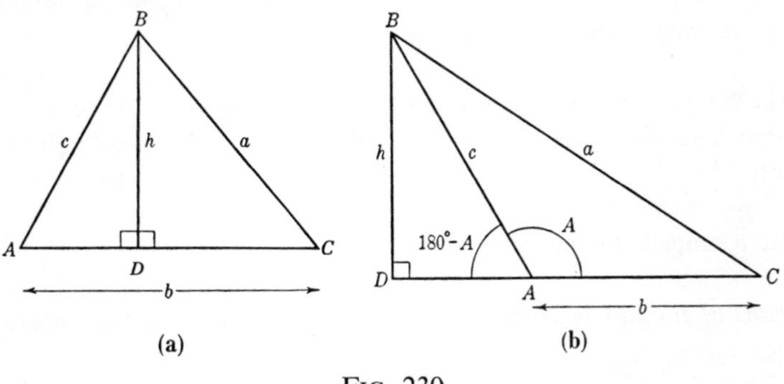

FIG. 230

Case (a). From right triangle ABD (Fig. 230*a*) we obtain $h/c = \sin A$ or

$$h = c \sin A. \tag{1}$$

From right triangle BDC we obtain $h/a = \sin C$ or

$$h = a \sin C. \tag{2}$$

From (1) and (2) we have

$$a \sin C = c \sin A.$$

Dividing both sides by $\sin A \sin C$, we obtain

$$\frac{a}{\sin A} = \frac{c}{\sin C}. \tag{3}$$

Case (b). From right triangle BDC (Fig. 230*b*) we obtain $h/a = \sin C$ or $h = a \sin C$ as before. From right triangle BDA we have $h/c = \sin (180° - A)$. But $\sin (180° - A) = \sin.\ A$ Hence $h/c = \sin A$ or $h = c \sin A$ as before. As in case (*a*) we obtain equation (3).

* The perpendicular BD cannot fall exactly along one side of the triangle ABC since ABC is oblique by hypothesis.

By dropping perpendiculars from A to BC instead of from B to AC we would obtain in the same fashion the equation

$$\frac{b}{\sin B} = \frac{c}{\sin C}. \tag{4}$$

From (3) and (4) we have the following theorem, known as the **law of sines.**

Theorem. *In any triangle.*

$$\frac{a}{\sin A} = \frac{b}{\sin B} = \frac{c}{\sin C}.$$

*Or, any side divided by the sine of the opposite angle is equal to any other side divided by the sine of **its** opposite angle.*

Remark. We have proved the theorem for oblique triangles. The reader can verify at once that it remains true even if one of the angles is 90°, recalling the fact that $\sin 90° = 1$.

Exercise. Complete the proof in all its details.

By means of the law of sines we can solve a triangle given two angles and one side.

Example 1. Given triangle ABC with $A = 40°$, $B = 80°$, and $a = 10$ feet. Then $C = 60!$. To find b we write $b/\sin B = a/\sin A$ or

$$\frac{b}{\sin 80°} = \frac{10}{\sin 40°}$$

or

$$b = \frac{10 \sin 80°}{\sin 40°} = \frac{10(.9848)}{.6428} = 15.3 \text{ feet approximately.}$$

To find c we would use similarly the relation $c/\sin C = a/\sin A$.

Example 2. Let us now complete the problem of finding the height of the mountain begun in section 146 (Fig. 229). Clearly, angle $ABD = 40°$. By the law of sines we have, from triangle ABD,

$$\frac{a}{\sin 30°} = \frac{1000}{\sin 40°}.$$

Hence

$$a = \frac{1000 \sin 30°}{\sin 40°} = \frac{1000(.5000)}{.6428}$$

$$= 777.8 \text{ feet approximately.}$$

Having found a we obtain from the right triangle BCD (Fig. 229) the relation $h/777.8 = \sin 70°$ or

$$h = 777.8 \sin 70° = 777.8(.9397)$$
$$= 731 \text{ feet approximately.}$$

Exercises

Solve the triangle ABC, given that:

1. $A = 42°$, $B = 73°$, $c = 15$ feet.
2. $B = 57°$, $C = 62°$, $c = 42$ feet.
3. $A = 103°$, $C = 48°$, $a = 25$ feet.
4. $A = 28°$, $B = 136°$, $c = 20$ feet.

5. To measure the length AB of a projected bridge across a canyon, a distance of 100 yards is measured from A to a point C and the angles BAC and ACB are found to be 82° and 43°, respectively. Find AB.

6. To measure the distance from a cannon C to an enemy fortification F, a distance of 1000 yards is measured from C to a point P, and the angles FCP and CPF are found to be 73° and 58°, respectively. Find CF.

7. From two observation points A and B, 5000 feet apart, on a straight road an airplane C is seen over the road between A and B. If at a given instant the angle of elevation of the airplane at A is 73°, and the angle of elevation of the airplane at B is 67°, find: (*a*) the distance of the airplane from A; (*b*) the distance of the airplane from B; (*c*) the airplane's altitude.

8. A ship S is observed from two points A and B on a straight beach, 1000 feet apart. If $\angle SAB = 86°$ and $\angle SBA = 63°$, find: (*a*) the distance SA; (*b*) the distance SB; (*c*) the distance of the ship from the shore.

9. To measure the height of a mountain, its angle of elevation from a point A on a level plain is found to be 34°. Proceeding toward the mountain, a distance $AB =$ 1000 feet is measured off. At B the angle of elevation of the mountain is found to be 58°. Find the height of the mountain.

10. Outline a method for finding the height of a tower located on the opposite bank of a river, without crossing the river. Invent your own numbers and solve.

148. THE LAW OF COSINES

Consider the oblique triangle ABC. Draw the line BD perpendicular to AC. Either BD falls within the triangle ABC or not (Fig. 231). (Since ABC is oblique BD cannot fall along one side of triangle ABC). We shall treat each case separately.

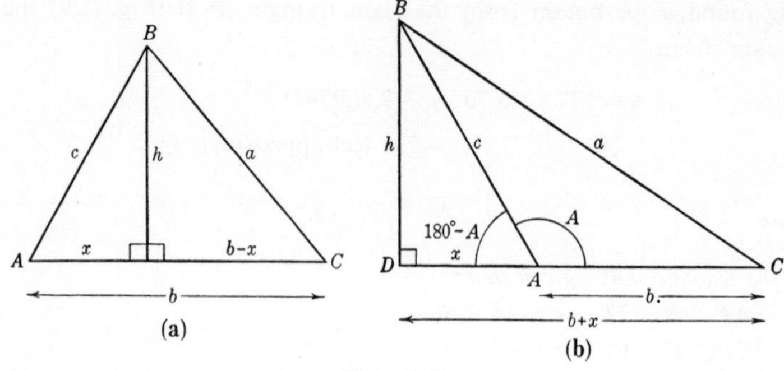

Fig. 231

Case (a). From right triangle ABD (Fig. 231(a)) we have $c^2 = x^2 + h^2$ or

(1) $$h^2 = c^2 - x^2.$$

From right triangle BDC we have $a^2 = (b - x)^2 + h^2$ or

(2) $$h^2 = a^2 - (b - x)^2.$$

From (1) and (2) we obtain

$$a^2 - (b - x)^2 = c^2 - x^2,$$

or

$$a^2 - b^2 + 2bx - x^2 = c^2 - x^2,$$

or

(3) $$a^2 = b^2 + c^2 - 2bx.$$

From right triangle ABD, we have $x/c = \cos A$, or

(4) $$x = c \cos A.$$

Substituting (4) in (3), we have

(5) $$a^2 = b^2 + c^2 - 2bc \cos A.$$

Case (b). From right triangle BDA (Fig. 231(b)) we have $c^2 = h^2 + x^2$, or

(6) $$h^2 = c^2 - x^2.$$

From right triangle BDC we have $a^2 = h^2 + (b + x)^2$ or

(7) $$h^2 = a^2 - (b + x)^2.$$

Hence,

$$a^2 - (b + x)^2 = c^2 - x^2,$$

or

$$a^2 - b^2 - 2bx - x^2 = c^2 - x^2,$$

or

(8) $$a^2 = b^2 + c^2 + 2bx.$$

From right triangle BDA, we have $x/c = \cos(180° - A)$ or $x = c \cos(180° - A)$. But $\cos(180° - A) = -\cos A$. Hence,

$$x = -c \cos A. \tag{9}$$

Substituting (9) in (8) we obtain (5), as before.

By dropping perpendiculars from A and C, respectively, we would get the remaining formulas in the following theorem, known as the **law of cosines.**

Theorem. *In any triangle ABC, we have*

$$a^2 = b^2 + c^2 - 2bc \cos A,$$
$$b^2 = a^2 + c^2 - 2ac \cos B,$$
$$c^2 = a^2 + b^2 - 2ab \cos C.$$

Or, the square of any side is equal to the sum of the squares of the other two sides minus twice their product times the cosine of the angle included between them.

Remark. We have proved the theorem for oblique triangles. But it is true for **right** triangles as well. For example, if in the last equation angle C were 90° we would have $c^2 = a^2 + b^2 - 2ab \cos 90°$. But $\cos 90° = 0$. Hence, $c^2 = a^2 + b^2$, which is nothing but the Pythagorean theorem. Therefore, the law of cosines may be said to be a generalization of the Pythagorean theorem, since it includes the Pythagorean theorem as a special case.

We may use the law of cosines to solve a triangle given three sides or given two sides and the included angle, as follows.

Example 1. Given triangle ABC with $a = 3$, $b = 5$, $c = 7$. Let us find angle C. We have

$$c^2 = a^2 + b^2 - 2\,ab \cos C.$$

Hence,

$$7^2 = 3^2 + 5^2 - 2 \cdot 3 \cdot 5 \cos C,$$

or

$$49 = 34 - 30 \cos C,$$

or

$$\cos C = -1/2 = -.5000.$$

Hence,

$$C = 120°.$$

Using the other formulas in our theorem similarly we would find angles B and A.

Example 2. Given triangle ABC with $c = 5$, $b = 3$, and $A = 120°$. Let us find a. We have,

$$a^2 = b^2 + c^2 - 2bc \cos A,$$

or

$$a^2 = 3^2 + 5^2 - 2\cdot 3\cdot 5 \cos 120^\circ$$
$$= 34 - 30(-1/2) = 49.$$

Therefore, $a = 7$. Now that we know all three sides the remaining angles may be found by the method of example 1.

Exercises

Solve the triangle ABC, given that:

1. $a = 20, b = 12, c = 28$.
2. $a = 35, b = 27, c = 24$.
3. $a = 15, b = 9, C = 120^\circ$.
4. $b = 20, c = 15, A = 57^\circ$.
5. $a = 42, c = 37, B = 79^\circ$.
6. $a = 15, b = 26, C = 132^\circ$.
7. $b = 12, c = 17, A = 123^\circ$.
8. $a = 38, c = 25, B = 108^\circ$.

9. A triangular plot of ground is 215 feet, 185 feet, and 125 feet, respectively, on its three sides. Find the three angles included between its sides. Find its area.

10. To find the length AB of a proposed tunnel through a mountain from point A to point B, a point C is found from which A and B are both visible. If $AC = 500$ feet, $BC = 350$ feet, and $\sphericalangle ACB = 76^\circ$, find AB.

11. To find the distance CT from a cannon C to a target T, invisible from C, an observer is stationed at a place P visible from both C and T. If $TP = 2000$ yards, $CP = 1500$ yards, and $\sphericalangle CPT = 84^\circ$, find CT.

12. A force of 12 pounds and a force of 17 pounds act on a body simultaneously. If the angle between their directions is 30°, find: (*a*) the magnitude of the resultant force; (*b*) the angle the resultant makes with each component.

13. Two forces of 30 pounds and 50 pounds, respectively, have an included angle of 60°. Find the magnitude of the resultant force and the angle it makes with each component.

14. A boat moves across a river in a direction 55° north of east with a speed of 10 miles per hour. The current of the river runs due east with a speed of 5 miles per hour. Find the speed of the boat in still water.

15. The distance from a boat B to two points A and C on the shore are known to be 500 yards and 400 yards, respectively. If angle ABC is 53°, find the distance AC.

16. To find the distance between two inaccessible points A and B, we select two observation points C and D, 100 yards apart, (Fig. 232) and measure angles p, q, r, s, t.* Suppose $p = 33^\circ, q = 42^\circ, r = 75^\circ$, $s = 37^\circ$, $t = 78^\circ$. Find AB. (Hint: From triangle BCD we can find BC. From triangle ACD we can find AC. Then from triangle ABC we can find AB.)

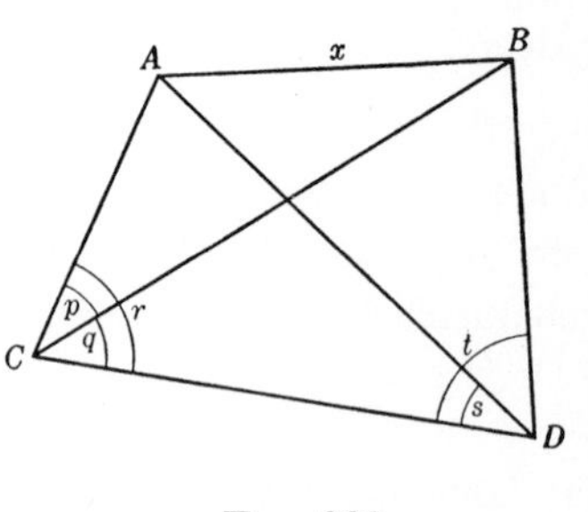

FIG. 232

* If A, B, C, D are in the same plane $r = p + q$. But our method is applicable even if they are not in the same plane.

149. THE GRAPHS OF THE TRIGONOMETRIC FUNCTIONS. PERIODICITY

With the help of section 145, we can draw the graph of the function $y = \sin x$,say, where x is the number of degrees. From the table, we can plot the point (x,y) where $y = \sin x$ for every angle 0°, 15°, 30°, 45°, 60°, 75°, 90° (Fig. 233). By means of the reduction formulas (see exercise 13, section 145) we can plot the points for all angles 15° apart from 90° to 360° in Fig. 234. Since $\sin x = \sin (x + n \cdot 360°)$, where n is any integer, the curve merely repeats itself in every interval of 360°.

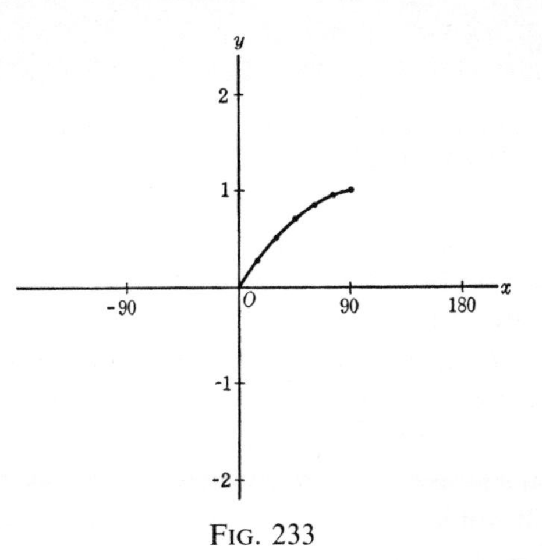

FIG. 233

The fact that $\sin x$ has the same value at intervals of 360° is expressed by saying that the function $y = \sin x$ is **periodic** (with period 360°). Periodic functions are extremely important in a large variety of physical applications. In fact, the earliest scientific observations made by the human race were doubtless certain periodic phenomena like the alternation of day and night, the cycle of the seasons, the recurrent phases of the moon, the recurrent patterns of stars in the sky, etc. Similarly, many modern scientific phenomena are periodic in character, like sound waves, the vibrations of a violin string, the oscillation of a

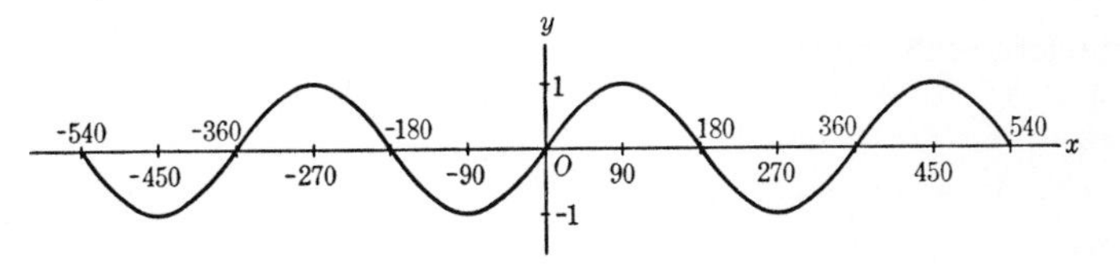

FIG. 234

pendulum, etc. The graph of $\sin x$ suggests wave motion, and in fact the trigonometric functions (which are the simplest of all periodic functions) are very useful in the description of such periodic phenomena.

The achievements of indirect measurement are quite remarkable, although they may seem pale beside such wonders as radio, television, etc. However, the student should remember that he now *understands* the more ancient miracles of trigonometrical indirect measurement, whereas he is doubtless merely *familiar* with the conveniences of the more modern miracles. The elementary applications

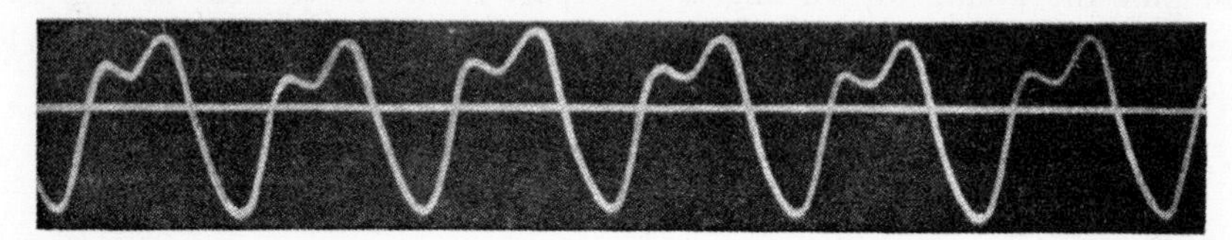

Photograph of a sound from a violin. An approximate equation of this graph is $y = 151 \sin x - 67 \cos x + 24 \sin 2x + 55 \cos 2x + 27 \sin 3x + 5 \cos 3x$.

FIG. 235

of the trigonometric functions to the measurement of inaccessible distances discussed in this chapter are interesting and important, but many of the most important and interesting applications of the trigonometric functions of more advanced character are due to the periodicity of these functions. Any book on the advanced physics of sound, light, mechanics, electromagnetics, etc., will be found to make frequent use of the trigonometric functions. For further work in trigonometry which will be useful for the student who goes on in mathematics beyond this book, see the reference to *Plane and Spherical Trigonometry*, below.

Exercises

Plot between 0° and 360° (using 15° intervals) the graph of each of the following. Choose different units on the x and y axes in some convenient manner.

1. $y = \cos x$. **2.** $y = \tan x$. **3.** $y = 2 \cos x$. **4.** $y = \cos 2x$.

5. $y = 2 \cos x + \cos 2x$. (Hint: use the tabulations of exercises 3 and 4.)

6. $y = \sin 2x + 2 \sin x$. **7.** $y = \sin x + \cos 2x$. **8.** $y = \cos x + \sin 2x$.

9. $y = 2 \sin x + \cos 2x$. **10.** $y = \sin x + 2 \cos 2x$.

References

Numbers refer to bibliography at the back of the book.

Jeans 99

Miller 133

Richardson 160

Whitehead 206

13

Probability and Statistics

150. INTRODUCTION

It is difficult to give a precise definition of statistics. Speaking loosely, statistics is concerned with coming to general conclusions, whose truth is more or less probable, concerning large classes of phenomena, by means of the study of large numbers of observations, and with making reasonable decisions in the face of uncertainty and incomplete information. It is therefore of the greatest importance in connection with the inductive logic of experimental methods. The use of statistical inference pervades the social and biological as well as the physical sciences. The insurance business, as well as other commercial affairs, makes essential use of statistics. The subject is based on the study of probability. The mathematical theory of probability had its beginning in correspondence between Fermat and Blaise Pascal (1623–1662) concerning certain questions about games of chance which were put to the puritanical Pascal by an aristocratic acquaintance with a penchant for gambling. Pascal, incidentally, was a child prodigy who displayed phenomenal talent in mathematics and by the age of 16 had done

Blaise Pascal
1623–1662, French

work of such calibre that Descartes is said to have refused to believe it was done by one so young. Pascal made noteworthy contributions to many branches of mathematics.

151. PROBABILITY

In everyday speech, the word "probable" is used in vague senses. For example, we say "it will probably rain tomorrow," "the Yankees will probably win the world series," "*A* probably murdered *B*," "the patient will probably recover," "Socrates probably existed." What meaning can be attached to the word "probability"?

Some philosophers have maintained that probability is merely a measure of belief. But since different people are notoriously capable of believing opposite statements with equal firmness, whose belief are we to measure? In fact, the same person may very well believe opposite statements at different times. Clearly, subjective theories of probability involve serious difficulties. We shall present here a more objective explanation which is scientifically useful.

We restrict our discussion to experiments which have a finite (limited) number of mutually exclusive possible outcomes which we shall term the **outcomes** or **possibilities** of the experiment.

Example 1. If a coin is tossed, we recognize two possible outcomes: head (H) or tail (T).

Example 2. If a single cubical die is thrown, we recognize six possible outcomes, namely, 1, 2, 3, 4, 5, or 6 facing up, respectively.

Example 3. If a penny and a nickel are tossed, we recognize four possible outcomes, namely, HH, HT, TH, TT, where the first letter of each pair represents the side of the penny and the second letter represents the side of the nickel which turns up.

Example 4. On the pictured dial with spinning pointer, the red sector occupies $\frac{1}{4}$ of the area; white, $\frac{1}{8}$; blue, $\frac{1}{8}$; and green, $\frac{1}{2}$. (If the pointer spins in the clockwise direction, we agree that the initial edge of each sector belongs to it while the terminal edge belongs to the next sector.) We recognize four outcomes: red, white, blue, green.

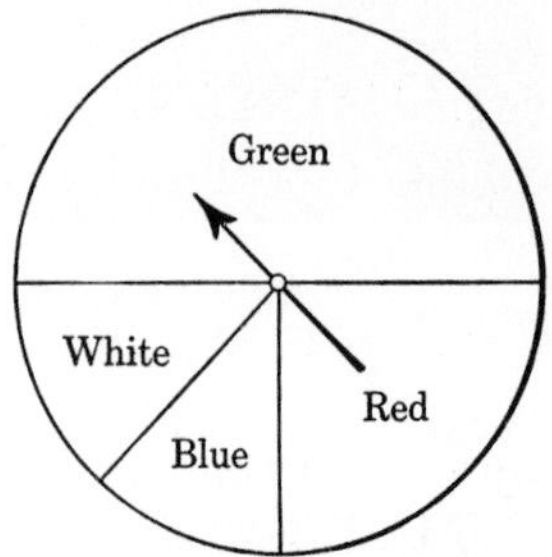

Whatever the particular experiment under discussion may be, let I represent the set of all possible outcomes. By an **event** E we shall mean any subset of this basic set*; that is, any set of possible outcomes is an event, including I itself and the empty set $\varnothing$. In example 1, heads is an event E; tails is another event E', the complement of E; heads or tails, that is, $E \cup E' = I$ itself is still another event. In example 2, throwing a six is an event E; throwing anything other than a six (abbreviated, not-six) is an event E' which is in fact the complement of the preceding event E; throwing an even number is another event F; throwing an odd number is the event F' complementary to the preceding event. In example 3, throwing exactly one head is an event E; throwing at least one head is another event F which contains the preceding event, $F \supset E$; throwing no head is the event F' complementary to the preceding event F. In example 4, pointing to red is an event E; pointing to a primary color is another event F, and $F \supset E$.

In the experiment of tossing a well-balanced coin, no reliable prediction can be made as to whether it will fall head or tail on any particular trial. However, in a long sequence of trials, great regularity is observed in the "percentage" or fractional part of the number of trials in which heads turns up. If $f(n)$ is the number of trials in which heads turns up in the first n trials, then this percentage or fractional part $f(n)/n$ is termed the **relative frequency** of heads in those n trials. For example, actual experiments with a coin might yield the following results:

n	10	20	50	100	1000	10,000	100,000	...
$f(n)$	4	13	23	52	493	5,023	50,117	...
$f(n)/n$	.4	.65	.46	.52	.493	.5023	.50117	...

Here it appears that the relative frequency is approaching 50% or $\frac{1}{2}$ as the number of trials increases.† Hence it seems plausible to *assign* the number $\frac{1}{2}$ as the "probability" of the outcome "heads" and to interpret this number as the limit which the relative frequency approaches as the number of trials increases. Practically, this is interpreted to mean that in a sufficiently long sequence (run) of trials, heads may be expected about half the time and hence tails about half the time. This can be accomplished by assigning equal numerical measures such as 1 and 1 (or 50 and 50) to the two possible outcomes H and T; in symbols, we write $m(H) = 1$, $m(T) = 1$. The **measure** of any event will be the sum of the measures of the outcomes in it. Thus in the present example, $m(I) = 1 + 1 = 2$.

* Section 64 should be reviewed at this point.

† In the language of Chapter 11, it appears that $\lim_{n\uparrow} \dfrac{f(n)}{n} = \frac{1}{2}$.

We always assign the measure 0 to the empty set $\varnothing$; in symbols, $m(\varnothing) = 0$. We could now define the **probability** $P(E)$ of any event E, in this experiment, as

$$P(E) = \frac{m(E)}{m(I)}.$$

Hence the probability of heads becomes

$$P(H) = \frac{m(H)}{m(I)} = \frac{1}{2},$$

i.e., this event happens 50% or half of the time, approximately. The probability of either heads or tails, that is, of the event $I = H \cup T$, is

$$P(I) = \frac{m(I)}{m(I)} = \frac{2}{2} = 1;$$

note that this event happens 100% or all of the time. The probability of neither heads nor tails, that is, of the empty set $\varnothing$, is

$$P(\varnothing) = \frac{m(\varnothing)}{m(I)} = \frac{0}{2} = 0;$$

note that this event happens 0% or none of the time.

Thus, *a certain event has probability 1, and an impossible event has probability 0; any probability is a number between 0 and 1* and indicates approximately the relative frequency to be expected in a long run of trials.

In any experiment, we may suppose that there is a natural measure* that can be assigned to the outcomes, and hence to all the events. This measure is to be approximately in proportion to the relative frequencies of the outcomes if experimental data are available, or it may be regarded merely as a plausible scientific hypcthesis, the usefulness of which is to be judged by the accuracy of its consequences or predictions. We frequently assume that all the outcomes have equal measures, that is, occur approximately with equal frequencies, or are equally likely. But in some situations this would not appear to be a reasonable hypothesis. Thus, a weighted coin, a loaded die, or the dial of example 4 ought plainly to have unequal measures assigned to the outcomes. In the case of example 4, the areas of the four sectors suggest themselves as appropriate measures; thus we would take $\frac{1}{4}, \frac{1}{8}, \frac{1}{8}, \frac{1}{2}$ or the proportional numbers 2, 1, 1, 4 as the measures of red, white, blue, and green, respectively. In any case the measures of the outcomes are to be interpreted as approximately proportional to the frequencies of their occurrence.

* Section 69 should be reviewed at this point.

As far as the pure mathematical theory or abstract mathematical science is concerned, the assignment of measures to the possible outcomes is entirely arbitrary, subject only to the following restrictions.

Whatever measures are assigned to the outcomes, we assume that they are non-negative real numbers, and that $m(\varnothing) = 0$, and we define the **measure of any event**, or set of outcomes, as the sum of the measures of the outcomes belonging to it. Denoting the measure of any event E by $m(E)$, we have the fundamental definition of our mathematical theory of probability.

Definition. *The* ***probability*** $P(E)$ *of any event* E *is given by*

$$P(E) = \frac{m(E)}{m(I)}.$$

It follows that $0 \leqq P(E) \leqq 1$, and that $P(I) = 1$ and $P(\varnothing) = 0$, and the interpretation is to be as in the example of the coin discussed above.

Unless otherwise stated we shall hereafter suppose that the outcomes are equally likely, so that the measure of an event may be taken as the number of outcomes contained in the event.

Examples. In example 2, the number of outcomes is 6, so that $m(I) = 6$. The event E of throwing an even number has 3 outcomes in it, so that $m(E) = 3$. Hence $P(E) = \frac{3}{6} = \frac{1}{2}$. The event F of throwing either a 4 or a 5 has 2 outcomes in it, so that $m(F) = 2$ and $P(F) = \frac{2}{6} = \frac{1}{3}$.

In example 3, the event E of obtaining at least one head has 3 outcomes in it, namely HH, HT, and TH, so that $m(E) = 3$. Since $m(I) = 4$, we have $P(E) = \frac{3}{4}$.

In example 4, we assign the measures 2, 1, 1, 4 to red, white, blue, green, respectively, as discussed above. If E is the event "red," then $m(E) = 2$, while $m(I) = 8$ so that $P(E) = \frac{1}{4}$. If F is the event "primary color," i.e., red or blue, then $m(F) = 3$ and $P(F) = \frac{3}{8}$.

If the possible outcomes are regarded as equally likely, and if t is the total number of possible outcomes in I, and s of these outcomes are in the event E, then $P(E) = s/t$. This is sometimes stated as follows: *if the possible outcomes are regarded as equally likely then the probability of success (i.e., being in* E*) is the number* s *of successful outcomes over the total number* t *of outcomes.*

Exercises

Assume equally likely outcomes unless otherwise stipulated.

1. Toss an actual coin 100 times and record the number of heads obtained in 10, 20, 30, ..., 100 tosses.

2. What is the probability of throwing a "six" with a single die?

3. What is the probability of throwing a total of "two" with a pair of dice?

4. What is the probability of throwing a total of "three" with a pair of dice? a total of "four"? a total of "seven"? Which is more probable, a total of "three" or a total of "seven"?

5. What is the probability of obtaining exactly one head in tossing two coins simultaneously? at least one head? exactly two heads? no heads?

6. Actually toss two coins 100 times and record the relative frequencies of 0, 1, 2 heads.

7. What is the probability of obtaining exactly 1 head in tossing three coins? two heads? three heads? no heads? at least one head? at least two heads?

8. What is the probability of obtaining exactly 0, 1, 2, 3, 4 heads in tossing 4 coins? at least one head? at least two heads? at least three heads?

9. What is the probability of picking a diamond from a pack of 52 ordinary playing cards? an ace? the ace of spades?

10. A loaded die is found to turn up the numbers 1, 2, 3, 4, 5, 6 with relative frequencies $\frac{1}{3}, \frac{1}{12}, \frac{1}{12}, \frac{1}{6}, \frac{1}{6}, \frac{1}{6}$. Using these numbers as measures of the outcomes, what is the probability of obtaining an odd number? an even number? a multiple of 3?

11. A loaded die is found to turn up the numbers 1, 2, 3, 4, 5, 6 with relative frequencies $\frac{1}{4}, \frac{1}{8}, \frac{1}{8}, \frac{1}{6}, \frac{1}{6}, \frac{1}{6}$. Using these numbers as measures of the outcomes, what is the probability of obtaining an odd number? an even number? a multiple of 3?

152. SOME THEOREMS ABOUT PROBABILITY

For any measure $m(E)$, we have, (compare section 69):

$$m(E) \geqq 0; \tag{1}$$

$$m(\varnothing) = 0; \tag{2}$$

$$m(E \cup F) = m(E) + m(F) - m(E \cap F); \tag{3}$$

$$\text{if } X \subset Y, \text{ then } m(X) \leqq m(Y). \tag{4}$$

Two events E and F are called **mutually exclusive** if no possible outcome belongs to both the sets E and F, i.e., if $E \cap F = \varnothing$. Hence (2) and (3) imply that *if E and F are mutually exclusive events, then*

$$m(E \cup F) = m(E) + m(F). \tag{5}$$

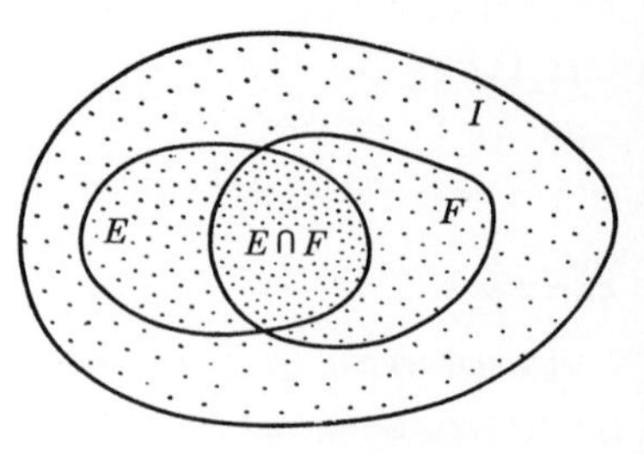

FIG. 236

Since E and the complementary event E' (sometimes read as "not-E") are mutually exclusive and $E \cup E' = I$, we have, from (5),

$$m(I) = m(E) + m(E'). \tag{6}$$

The event $E \cup F$ is sometimes read "E or F," and $E \cap F$ as "E and F." We can now prove some theorems about probability.

Theorem 1. *If E and F are any two events, then the probability of the event E or F is given by*

$$P(E \cup F) = P(E) + P(F) - P(E \cap F).$$

Proof. By definition, $P(E \cup F) = \dfrac{m(E \cup F)}{m(I)}$. By (3),

$$\begin{aligned} P(E \cup F) &= \frac{m(E) + m(F) - m(E \cap F)}{m(I)} \\ &= \frac{m(E)}{m(I)} + \frac{m(F)}{m(I)} - \frac{m(E \cap F)}{m(I)} \\ &= P(E) + P(F) - P(E \cap F). \end{aligned}$$

As a special case, we have the following.

Theorem 2. *If E and F are any two mutually exclusive events, then* $P(E \cup F) = P(E) + P(F)$.

Any finite number of events are called **mutually exclusive** if no pair of them has an outcome in common.

It is easily seen that theorem 2 extends to this situation.

Theorem 3. *If* $E_1, E_2, E_3, \ldots, E_k$ *are k mutually exclusive events, then*

$$P(E_1 \cup E_2 \cup E_3 \cup \cdots \cup E_k) = P(E_1) + P(E_2) + P(E_3) + \cdots + P(E_k).$$

Theorem 4. *If E is any event and E′ is the complementary event (not-E), then*

$$P(E) + P(E') = 1.$$

Proof. Since E and E' are mutually exclusive, and $E \cup E' = I$, theorem 2 implies

$$P(E) + P(E') = P(I).$$

But $P(I) = 1$.

Example 1. The probability that a king will be drawn in a single drawing from a deck of 52 playing cards is $\frac{4}{52} = \frac{1}{13}$. The probability of drawing a queen is also $\frac{1}{13}$. By theorem 2, the probability of drawing either a king or a queen is $\frac{1}{13} + \frac{1}{13} = \frac{2}{13}$.

Example 2. The probability of drawing a spade in a single drawing from a pack of 52 playing cards is $\frac{13}{52}$. The probability of drawing an ace is $\frac{4}{52}$. By theorem 1, the probability of drawing either a spade or an ace is $\frac{13}{52} + \frac{4}{52} - \frac{1}{52} = \frac{16}{52} = \frac{4}{13}$, since $\frac{1}{52}$ is the probability of drawing both an ace and a spade (the set $E \cap F$ consists of the ace of spades).

The student should now review carefully sections 69, 71, 72, and 73, which will be useful in working problems in probability.

Example. Three distinct English books and 3 distinct French books are placed at random on a bookshelf with room for 6 books. What is the probability that all books of the same language will be shelved together?

Solution. The total number of permutations of the 6 books is $6! = 720$. The number of permutations in which books of the same language are together is $3!3!2 = 72$. Hence the desired probability is $\frac{72}{720} = \frac{1}{10}$.

While we can never be sure that our assumptions (especially, the arbitrary assignment of measures to the outcomes) are really true in a concrete situation, nevertheless the theory of probability has been found to work very well in at least an approximate sense. The situation is quite the same as in the case of Euclidean geometry or Newtonian mechanics, or any other (applied) scientific theory (see Chapter 2, sections 8 and 9). We are simply faced again with the recurring distinction between pure mathematics and its application to reality. The ultimate test of the applicability of a theory to reality is whether or not it works. The theory of probability has been found to be of tremendous value in such diverse subjects as physical chemistry, statistical mechanics, heredity, biometrics, econometrics, the social sciences in general, the theory of gases, insurance, games of chance, experimental method in general, etc.

Exercises

Assume equally likely outcomes unless otherwise specified.

1. An urn contains 5 white, 3 black, and 2 red balls. In a single draw, find the probability of drawing: (*a*) a red ball; (*b*) a black ball; (*c*) either a white or a black ball.

2. In a single throw of a single die, find the probability of obtaining either a 2 or a 5.

3. In a single throw of a pair of dice, find the probability of obtaining a total of 11 or more.

4. In a single throw of a pair of dice, find the probability of obtaining a total of 4 or less.

5. If 6 different books are placed at random on a bookshelf with space for 6 books, find the probability that a certain 2 books will be next to each other.

6. If 6 people are seated at random in a row of 6 seats, find the probability that a certain 3 people will occupy adjacent seats.

7. A committee of 5 is chosen at random from a set of 8 men. Find the probability that: (*a*) a certain 2 men will both serve simultaneously on the committee; (*b*) a certain 2 men will not serve simultaneously on the committee; (*c*) a certain 2 men will both be off the committee.

8. If 4 boys and 4 girls are seated in a row of 8 seats at random, find the probability that: (*a*) all members of the same sex are in adjacent seats; (*b*) boys and girls alternate.

9. In a single throw of a single die, find the probability of throwing (*a*) an even number; (*b*) a multiple of 3; (*c*) either an even number or a multiple of 3.

10. In a single throw of the loaded die of exercise 10, section 151, find the probability of throwing (*a*) an even number; (*b*) a multiple of 3; (*c*) either an even number or a multiple of 3.

11. In a single throw of the loaded die of exercise 11, section 151, find the probability of throwing (*a*) an odd number; (*b*) a prime number; (*c*) either an odd or a prime number.

12. In drawing a single card from a deck of 52 playing cards find the probability of drawing either a heart or a face card (jack, queen, king).

13. A wheel of fortune is divided into sectors by means of radii. The area of the red sector is 30% of the total area; the yellow sector, 40%; the blue sector, 20%; the white sector, 10%. Using the area as a measure, find the probability that it will come to rest on (*a*) either red or blue; (*b*) not yellow; (*c*) a primary color.

14. A committee of 4 is chosen at random from a set of 4 Democrats and 3 Republicans. Find the probability that the committee will be composed of (*a*) exactly 2 Democrats and 2 Republicans; (*b*) at least two Democrats; (*c*) all Democrats.

15. Prove that if E, F, and G are any events, not necessarily mutually exclusive, then

$$P(E \cup F \cup G) = P(E) + P(F) + P(G) - P(E \cap F) - P(E \cap G) - P(F \cap G) + P(E \cap F \cap G).$$

(Hint: use exercise 6(*a*) of section 69.)

16. Using the formula of exercise 15, find the probability of drawing either a "spade" or a "face-card" or a "black card with value greater than 9" (face-cards are to be counted as greater than 9).

17. In a class of 100 students, 55 are females, 45 are blue-eyed, 40 are blonde, 25 are blonde females, 15 are blue-eyed blondes, 20 are blue-eyed females, and 5 are blue-eyed, blonde females. If their names are put on cards and shuffled thoroughly, and one card is drawn, find the probability that either a female or a blonde or a blue-eyed student will be drawn. (Hint: use the formula of exercise 15.)

18. A careless secretary drops 3 different letters, picks them up at random, and inserts them in the 3 envelopes. Find the probability that (*a*) none of the 3 goes to the right person; (*b*) at least one goes to the right person; (*c*) all go to the right persons; (*d*) at least one goes to a wrong person; (*e*) exactly one goes to a wrong person.

19. Answer the same questions as in exercise 18, assuming that there are 4 letters.

153. CONDITIONAL PROBABILITY. INDEPENDENT EVENTS. REPEATED TRIALS

In this section we discuss briefly some more complicated but useful concepts.

Example 1. Consider an urn containing 3 white balls and 1 black ball. The experiment is to consist of drawing 2 balls in succession from the urn. The first ball drawn is not to be replaced in the urn before the second is drawn. Find the probability that both balls drawn will be white.

Solution. Let E be the event that a white ball is obtained on the first drawing. Let F be the event that a white ball is obtained on the second drawing. If the white balls are designated by w_1, w_2, w_3 and the black ball by b, there are 12 (i.e., $4 \cdot 3$) different outcomes, or ordered pairs, in the basic set I, namely:

$$\begin{array}{cccc} (w_1,w_2) & (w_2,w_1) & (w_3,w_1) & (b,w_1) \\ (w_1,w_3) & (w_2,w_3) & (w_3,w_2) & (b,w_2) \\ (w_1,b) & (w_2,b) & (w_3,b) & (b,w_3). \end{array}$$

Assuming that these outcomes are equally likely, event E consists of the 9 outcomes listed in the first three columns, so that $P(E) = \frac{9}{12} = \frac{3}{4}$. We denote the probability of F assuming that E has already happened by the symbol $P(F|E)$, read "probability of F assuming E." In this example, $P(F|E)$ is the probability of a white ball on the second drawing, assuming that a white ball has already appeared on the first drawing. Hence, we are now dealing with E as the basic set and its measure $m(E)$ should be the denominator in the definition of probability, while only the measure $m(F \cap E)$ of the set of those outcomes in both F and E should appear as the numerator. Hence, $P(F|E) = m(F \cap E)/m(E) = \frac{6}{9} = \frac{2}{3}$. Intuitively, a white ball should appear on the first drawing 75% or $\frac{3}{4}$ of the times, and a second white ball should appear $66\frac{2}{3}$% or $\frac{2}{3}$ of *these* times. It follows that both F and E, i.e., 2 white balls in succession, should occur $\frac{2}{3}$ of $\frac{3}{4}$ of the times; that is, $P(F \cap E) = \frac{2}{3} \cdot \frac{3}{4} = \frac{1}{2}$. This can also be seen directly from the list of outcomes in I above, for $m(F \cap E) = 6$ and $m(I) = 12$ so that $P(F \cap E) = \frac{6}{12} = \frac{1}{2}$.

The probability $P(F|E)$ of F assuming E has already happened is called the **conditional probability of F assuming E.** In general, whatever measure is used for the outcomes, it is natural to define $P(F|E)$ by regarding E as the basic set of outcomes, so that $m(E)$ is the denominator and $m(F \cap E)$ the numerator. That is, we define

$$P(F|E) = \frac{m(F \cap E)}{m(E)}. \tag{1}$$

Hence,

$$P(E)P(F|E) = \frac{m(E)}{m(I)} \cdot \frac{m(F \cap E)}{m(E)}$$

$$= \frac{m(F \cap E)}{m(I)}$$

$$= P(F \cap E)$$

or

$$P(F \cap E) = P(E)P(F|E). \tag{2}$$

Two events are termed **independent** if the occurrence or non-occurrence of the first has no effect on the occurrence or non-occurrence of the second; in symbols $P(F) = P(F|E)$. If E and F are independent events then (2) becomes

$$P(F \cap E) = P(F)P(E). \tag{3}$$

More generally, a set of n events $\{E_1, E_2, \ldots, E_n\}$ is termed **independent** if, for every subset $\{E_i, E_j, \ldots, E_k\}$ of two or more of the n events, we have

$$P(E_i \cap E_j \cap \cdots \cap E_k) = P(E_i)P(E_j) \cdots P(E_k). \tag{4}$$

For example, to say that $\{E_1, E_2, E_3\}$ is an independent set of 3 events means that

$$P(E_1 \cap E_2) = P(E_1)P(E_2),$$

$$P(E_1 \cap E_3) = P(E_1)P(E_3),$$

$$P(E_2 \cap E_3) = P(E_2)P(E_3),$$

and

$$P(E_1 \cap E_2 \cap E_3) = P(E_1)P(E_2)P(E_3).$$

Example 2. The same as example 1, except that the first ball is to be replaced before the second ball is drawn. In this case, $P(E) = \frac{3}{4}$ as before, but $P(F|E) = P(F) = \frac{3}{4}$, since E and F are independent events. Hence $P(F \cap E) = P(F)P(E) = \frac{3}{4} \cdot \frac{3}{4} = \frac{9}{16}$. In this experiment there are 16 outcomes in I, namely,

$$\begin{matrix} (w_1,w_1) & (w_2,w_1) & (w_3,w_1) & (b,w_1) \\ (w_1,w_2) & (w_2,w_2) & (w_3,w_2) & (b,w_2) \\ (w_1,w_3) & (w_2,w_3) & (w_3,w_3) & (b,w_3) \\ (w_1,b) & (w_2,b) & (w_3,b) & (b,b) \end{matrix}$$

of which the event $F \cap E$ contains 9.

To say that an experiment is given repeated trials "under similar conditions" means that the successive trials are understood to be independent of each other. For such repeated trials we have the following theorem due to James Bernoulli (Swiss, 1654–1705).

Theorem 5. *If p is the probability that an event will occur in a single trial, then the probability that it will occur exactly r times out of n trials is $C(n,r)p^r q^{n-r}$ where $q = 1 - p$ is the probability that the event will fail to occur in a single trial.*

The probability that the event will occur in any particular set of r trials and fail in the remaining $n - r$ trials is exactly $p^r q^{n-r}$ by (4). But the particular set of r trials may be selected out of n trials in $C(n,r)$ ways which are mutually exclusive. Hence, by theorem 3 of section 152, we must add $C(n,r)$ terms each of which has the value $p^r q^{n-r}$. Therefore the probability desired is $C(n,r)p^r q^{n-r}$. This proves theorem 5.

Example 3. Find the probability of obtaining exactly two heads in tossing 5 coins. The probability of obtaining a head with any particular coin is $p = \frac{1}{2}$ and the probability of failing to obtain a head with any particular coin is $q = 1 - \frac{1}{2} = \frac{1}{2}$. Hence the probability in question is $C(5,2)(\frac{1}{2})^2(\frac{1}{2})^3 = \frac{5}{16}$.

Exercises

Assume equally likely outcomes unless otherwise stipulated.

1. What is the probability of throwing an ace twice in succession with a single die?

2. What is the probability of throwing a total of 18 with 3 dice?

3. What is the probability of drawing an ace from a pack of 52 cards four times in succession if: (*a*) each card is replaced in the pack after it is drawn? (*b*) no card is replaced after it is drawn?

4. A bag contains 6 white and 5 black balls. After drawing any ball it is to be replaced in the bag. What is the probability of drawing 2 white balls in succession? three black balls in succession?

5. The same as exercise 4 except that no ball is to be replaced after drawing.

6. What is the probability that an ace will turn up exactly once in 3 successive throws of a single die?

7. What is the probability that an ace will turn up exactly twice in 5 successive throws of a single die?

8. What is the probability that an ace will turn up at least once in 4 successive throws of a single die? (Hint: consider the probability of failure.)

9. If 10 coins are tossed in succession, what is the probability that (*a*) exactly 3 will be heads? (*b*) at least 3 will be heads?

10. If 10 coins are tossed, what is the probability that (*a*) exactly 8 will be heads? (*b*) at least 8 will be heads? (*c*) at most 8 will be heads?

11. If 5 dice are tossed what is the probability that (*a*) exactly 3 of them will turn up an ace? (*b*) at least 3 of them will turn up an ace? (*c*) at most 3 of them will turn up an ace?

12. What is the probability of drawing a hand consisting of the ace, king, queen, jack, and ten of diamonds in 5 successive draws from a pack of 52 cards?

13. What is the probability of throwing a total of seven with a pair of dice (*a*) 5 times in succession? (*b*) 10 times in succession? (*c*) is the probability in (*b*) half as great as that in (*a*)?

14. The probability that A will solve a problem is $\frac{3}{4}$. The probability that B will solve a problem is $\frac{4}{7}$. If both work on the problem independently, what is the probability that it will be solved?

15. A machine has two independent component parts, A and B. If either one breaks down, the machine breaks down. If the probability that A will break down within a year is $\frac{1}{5}$ and the probability that B will break down within a year is $\frac{1}{6}$, find the probability that the machine will break down within a year.

16. Two people A and B are to draw alternately 1 ball at a time from an urn containing 4 white and 2 black balls, drawn balls not being replaced. If A takes the first turn, find the probability that A will be the first to draw white.

17. In a "multiple-choice" test, each question is to be answered by selecting 1 of 5 different proposed answers, of which only 1 is correct. If there are ten questions on the test, find the probability that a completely ignorant student, guessing at random, will get: (*a*) exactly 6 correct; (*b*) at least 6 correct.

18. Under normal conditions 10% of a certain mass production item will be defective. In a certain sample of 10 units of this item, 4 of them are found to be defective. Find the probability that this happened by chance.

19. A coin is biased so that the probabilities of heads and tails are $\frac{3}{4}$ and $\frac{1}{4}$, respectively. A second coin is biased so that the probabilities of heads and tails are $\frac{2}{3}$ and $\frac{1}{3}$, respectively. If both coins are tossed, find the probability of (*a*) two heads; (*b*) exactly one head; (*c*) no head; (*d*) at most one head.

20. A loaded die is such that the probabilities of throwing 1, 2, 3, 4, 5, 6 are $\frac{1}{4}$, $\frac{1}{8}$, $\frac{1}{8}$, $\frac{1}{6}$, $\frac{1}{6}$, $\frac{1}{6}$, respectively. A second die is such that the probabilities of throwing 1, 2, 3, 4, 5, 6 are $\frac{1}{6}$, $\frac{1}{12}$, $\frac{1}{12}$, $\frac{1}{3}$, $\frac{1}{6}$, $\frac{1}{6}$. In a single throw of this pair of dice, find the probability of throwing (*a*) a total of 2; (*b*) a total of 3; (*c*) a total of 7.

21. If the first coin mentioned in exercise 19 is tossed 5 times, find the probability of obtaining exactly 3 heads.

22. If the first die mentioned in exercise 20 is thrown 6 times, find the probability of obtaining (*a*) exactly 2 aces; (*b*) at most 2 aces; (*c*) at least 5 twos.

154. STATISTICAL PROBABILITY

Probability as defined in section 151 is usually called **a priori probability**, because with this definition we may assign the measures of the outcomes before or without actually experimenting. A priori probability is of the greatest importance in both theoretical and practical work. However, it would hardly do for such things as life-expectancy in insurance. There is no a priori way in which one can say that a man, 40 years of age, in certain circumstances, has an $\frac{89}{100}$ chance of reaching the age of 50. For such matters, we take relative frequency as the tentative definition of probability. That is, we would collect data about a large number of men 40 years of age in similar circumstances and actually count the number who reach the age of 50. The total number n is the number of "trials" and the number $f(n)$ who live to the age of 50 is the number of "successes." The ratio $f(n)/n$ is called the **statistical probability** of success. Statistical probability is understood to be relative to some body of knowledge. With more data, the statistical probability might change. We could build up the theory of probability by taking $\lim_{n\uparrow} \frac{f(n)}{n}$ as the definition of the "true" probability, assuming that this limit exists. Then the successive statistical probabilities $f(n)/n$ as n increases are taken as approximations to the "true" probability. But in practical work we can never ascertain the value of this limit, since we are necessarily forced to use a finite value of n. If we make more trials so that the total number of trials is n' $(>n)$, then $f(n')/n'$ may be considered a better approximation of the "true" probability than $f(n)/n$. This is, in fact, what is done in connection with life-expectancy tables in insurance and other statistical data. When more trials are made or more data gathered the statistical probability, of life-expectancy for example, is changed if necessary. Statistical probability is called also **a posteriori**, **empirical**, or **experimental probability**.

It would be foolish to suppose that statistical probability is independent of assumptions because it is based on actual observation. We are still assuming among other things that the sequence $f(1)/1,\ f(2)/2,\ f(3)/3, \ldots, f(n)/n, \ldots$ approaches a limit as n increases indefinitely and that for a given "sufficiently large" value of n (whatever that may be) the fraction $f(n)/n$ is really a good approximation of this limit.

Example. Out of 100,000 10-year-old children, about 70,000 reach the age of 50 and about 58,000 reach the age of 60. On the basis of these data, we would say that the probability that (*a*) a 10-year-old will live to the age of 50 is $\frac{70}{100}$; (*b*) the probability that a 10-year-old will reach the age of 60 is $\frac{58}{100}$; and (*c*) the probability that a 50-year-old will reach the age of 60 is $\frac{58{,}000}{70{,}000}$ or nearly $\frac{83}{100}$. Needless to say, the assertion that a 50-year-old has, on the basis of these data, an 83% chance of reaching the age of 60 means absolutely nothing to any particular 50-year-old since it takes no account of his health or other circumstances. But the statement has a fairly reliable meaning for large groups, as may be seen from the soundness of the insurance business which is based upon just such principles of statistical probability.

Exercises

1. Of 100,000 10-year-olds, it is found that 74,000 reach the age of 45 and 65,000 reach the age of 55. Find the probability, on the basis of these data, that (*a*) a 10-year-old will reach the age of 45; (*b*) a 10-year-old will reach 55; (*c*) a 45-year-old will reach 55.

*155. A POWER INDEX IN POLITICAL STRUCTURES

Consider a business corporation in which stockholder A owns 51% of the stock, B holds 17%, and the rest is distributed among other stockholders. As usual, the policies of the corporation are to be determined by majority vote, each stock certificate carrying one vote. Under these circumstances it would be foolish to think that the number of votes a stockholder has is a good index of his power in the corporation. For example, it is nonsense to say that A has three times as much power as B on the grounds that $51 = 3 \cdot 17$. In fact A has all the power and B has none. We shall now discuss a better numerical index of power† of each member of a political structure such as those considered in section 70.

Suppose the members of the political structure are listed in a particular order as, $a_1, a_2, \ldots, a_n$. Consider the sets obtained by starting with the empty set and adding one member at a time in the given order, thus:

$$\emptyset \subset \{a_1\} \subset \{a_1,a_2\} \subset \{a_1,a_2,a_3\} \subset \cdots \subset \{a_1,a_2,\ldots, a_{p-1}\}$$
$$\subset \{a_1,a_2, \ldots, a_{p-1},a_p\} \subset \cdots \subset \{a_1, \ldots, a_n\}.$$

Suppose that the first one of these sets, reading from left to right, which is a winning coalition is $\{a_1,a_2, \ldots, a_p\}$. Then a_p is called the **pivot** of this arrangement $a_1, a_2, \ldots, a_n$ of the members. That is, $\{a_1,a_2, \ldots, a_{p-1}\}$, as well as all to its left, is a losing coalition while the addition of a_p to it makes it into a winning coalition. All sets to the right of $\{a_1,a_2, \ldots, a_p\}$, being supersets of it, are also winning.

By the **power index** of a member of a political structure we shall mean the probability of his being a pivot, regarding all arrangements of the members as equally likely.‡

Hence the power index of a member is the number of permutations of the members $a_1, \ldots, a_n$ of which he is the pivot, divided by the total number $n!$ of permutations of the members.

Example 1. In the political structures of examples 1 and 2 of section 70 the power index of each member is $\frac{1}{3}$. For example, in the six permutations ***abc***, ***acb***, ***bac***, ***bca***, ***cab***, ***cba***, the boldface letters indicate the occurrences of a pivot. Thus b's power index is $\frac{2}{6} = \frac{1}{3}$, as is a's and c's.

* This section may be omitted without disturbing the continuity.

† See L. S. Shapley and M. Shubik, A Method for Evaluating the Distribution of Power in a Committee System, *Amer. Pol. Sci. Rev.*, Vol. 48, 1954, pp. 787–792, and L. S. Shapley, A Value for N-person Games. *Annals of Mathematics* Study No. 28, Princeton 1953, pp. 307–317.

‡ The assumption that all arrangements are equally likely is made for convenience and may well be regarded as unrealistic. A realistic theory of the growth of coalitions remains to be desired.

Example 2. In the political structure of exercise 1, section 70, there are 24 permutations:

$$\begin{array}{cccc}
ab\boldsymbol{c}d & ba\boldsymbol{c}d & ca\boldsymbol{b}d & d\boldsymbol{a}bc \\
ab\boldsymbol{d}c & ba\boldsymbol{d}c & ca\boldsymbol{d}b & d\boldsymbol{a}cb \\
ac\boldsymbol{b}d & bc\boldsymbol{a}d & cb\boldsymbol{a}d & d\boldsymbol{b}ac \\
ac\boldsymbol{d}b & bc\boldsymbol{d}a & cb\boldsymbol{d}a & d\boldsymbol{b}ca \\
a\boldsymbol{d}bc & b\boldsymbol{d}ac & c\boldsymbol{d}ab & d\boldsymbol{c}ab \\
a\boldsymbol{d}cb & b\boldsymbol{d}ca & c\boldsymbol{d}ba & d\boldsymbol{c}ba.
\end{array}$$

Those with a boldface $\boldsymbol{a}$ indicate occurrences of a as a pivot. Thus a's power index is $\frac{4}{24} = \frac{1}{6}$, b's is $\frac{4}{24} = \frac{1}{6}$, c's is $\frac{4}{24} = \frac{1}{6}$, and d's is $\frac{12}{24} = \frac{1}{2}$.

Exercises

Find the power index of each member of the following political structures:

1. Exercise 2, section 70.

2. Exercise 3, section 70.

3. A committee of four members $\{a,b,c,d\}$, of which a is the chairman with power to break ties, with majority rule.

4. A committee of six members $\{a,b,c,d,e,f\}$, of which a has 3 votes and the other members have 1 vote each, with majority rule, if the chairman is a with the power to break ties.

5. Same as exercise 4, except that the chairman does not have power to break ties.

6. A corporation with three stockholders $\{a,b,c\}$ having 500, 490, and 10 shares, respectively, with majority rule, each share carrying a vote.

7. A political structure with a dictator, the other members therefore being dummies.

8. Explain why the sum of the power indices of all members is always 1.

*156. MATHEMATICAL EXPECTATION

If an experiment has n outcomes, the probabilities of which are $p_1, p_2, \ldots, p_n$, respectively, and if a person wins a reward of R_1 units of something, say dollars, if the first outcome occurs, a reward of R_2 if the second outcome occurs, and so on, then the amount

$$p_1R_1 + p_2R_2 + \cdots + p_nR_n$$

is termed his **mathematical expectation**. If he loses on a given outcome, his

* This section is needed only for section 158. Otherwise it may be omitted without disturbing the continuity.

"reward" may be a negative quantity. The mathematical expectation represents approximately his average winnings per trial in a sufficiently long sequence of trials. The situation is considered **fair** to the person if his expectation is zero.

Example 1. A man will win \$2.00 if he throws a 1, 2, 3, or 4 with a single die and will lose \$3.00 (win $-$\$3.00) if he throws a 5 or 6. His mathematical expectation is

$$\frac{1}{6}(2)+\frac{1}{6}(2)+\frac{1}{6}(2)+\frac{1}{6}(2)+\frac{1}{6}(-3)+\frac{1}{6}(-3)=\frac{2}{6}=\frac{1}{3}\text{ dollars.}$$

That is, in the long run he will win 1/3 dollars per trial. In a run of 600 trials he may expect to win about \$200.

If the probability of an event E is the fraction s/t, gamblers usually prefer to say that the **odds in favor** of the event are s to $t-s$, and the **odds against** the event are $t-s$ to s.

Example 2. The odds against throwing a six with a single throw of a die are 5 to 1.

Exercises

1. (*a*) If heads and tails are considered equally likely and a man wins \$1.00 if he throws heads and loses \$1.00 if he throws tails, what is his mathematical expectation?

(*b*) As in part (*a*), except that the coin is biased and heads and tails occur with probabilities $\frac{3}{4}$ and $\frac{1}{4}$, respectively.

2. A man wins \$2.00 if he throws either a total of 7 or a total of 11 with a pair of well-balanced dice and loses \$1.00 if he does not. (*a*) Find his mathematical expectation. (*b*) Find the odds against throwing either 7 or 11.

3. A wheel of fortune is divided by radii into red, white, blue, and yellow sectors with areas $\frac{3}{8}, \frac{2}{8}, \frac{2}{8}, \frac{1}{8}$, respectively. A man wins \$2.00 if it stops on red, \$1.00 if it stops on white, but loses \$3.00 if it stops on blue or yellow. Find his mathematical expectation.

4. A man wins a number of dollars equal to the number shown on a die if this number is odd but loses a number of dollars equal to the number shown on the die if this number is even. Find his mathematical expectation: (*a*) if the outcomes are equally likely; (*b*) if the numbers 1, 2, 3, 4, 5, 6 occur with probabilities $\frac{1}{4}, \frac{1}{8}, \frac{1}{8}, \frac{1}{12}, \frac{1}{12}, \frac{1}{3}$, respectively.

5. Find the odds against throwing either a total of 5 or a total of 8 with a pair of well-balanced dice.

6. If a man wins W dollars if an event occurs and loses L dollars if the event fails to occur, (*a*) what is his expectation if the odds in favor of the event are a to b? (*b*) In what ratio should W and L stand in order for the situation to be fair?

*157. THEORY OF GAMES OF STRATEGY

The preceding sections of this chapter make it clear that games of pure chance, such as dice, various card games, roulette, etc., can be analyzed by means of the theory of probability which dates back to the seventeenth century. What has been known since 1944† as the theory of games deals with games in which the players have the opportunity to make choices and use rational strategies such as chess, where no chance is involved, or bridge and poker, where a mixture of chance and strategy occurs. Since business, politics, and war are often colloquially called "games," it is not too surprising that this theory may have applications to these subjects. To be sure, in order to study any complicated aspect of reality, it is practically necessary to set up simplified mathematical models which abstract certain features of this reality and study them in isolation from other complicating features which may occur in reality. This procedure should not be taken as a portent of defeat, however, any more than in the case of Newton's replacement of the irregularly shaped earth by a single particle in the study of its planetary motion about the sun. The history of science has shown many times the wisdom of first studying simple models and, only after they are understood, passing to more complicated and realistic models which take into account more relevant factors. In this brief introduction, we shall be able to study only extremely simple parlor games, but the reader will find in the literature referred to in the references at the end of this chapter indications of more serious and, of course, more advanced work.

The central features common to business, war, politics, and parlor games, which this theory abstracts and takes as the object of its study, are the following: there are two or more players with conflicting interests who have certain freedom of choice in regard to some of the moves of the game but whose control over the progress of the game is at best partial and whose information as to the actual situation may be incomplete. Thus a player may choose his own actions within the rules of the game but not his opponents', nor those of chance, if any, such as the distribution of cards, or the fall of dice, and he may be ignorant of the cards in his opponents' possession. We then ask if there are "best" strategies for the players to adopt and, if so, how to determine them.

Games may be classified in various ways. First, if the number of players (or teams, or conflicting interests) is n, we speak of an ***n*-person game**. The theory

* This section is needed only for section 158. Otherwise it may be omitted without disturbing the continuity.

† A few isolated research papers appeared somewhat earlier but the great impetus in this field was provided by a notable book, *The Theory of Games and Economic Behavior*, by J. von Neumann and O. Morgenstern, Princeton University Press, Princeton, 1944.

increases in difficulty as n increases. For example, as soon as n becomes greater than 2, the possibility arises of two or more players forming coalitions and coordinating their strategies to the detriment of the other players, as certainly happens in business, politics, and war. The political structures studied in section 70 are sometimes called **simple n-person games.** *We shall, in this section and the next, study only 2-person games.* If whatever any player wins at the end of a game is lost by other players in the game, so that the sum of the payoffs (we speak of positive payoffs for winnings, negative payoffs for losses) to all the players is zero, then the game is called a **zero-sum game**. This is not the case in some economic "games" where goods may well be produced or consumed which were not in the game at first, or in war where goods are certainly destroyed, but it is usually the case in parlor games. We shall in this section and the next study only zero-sum, 2-person games and shall begin with a special class of these, namely, the so-called **matrix games** or **rectangular games**, in which each of the two players, named Mr. Roe and Mr. Collum or simply R and C, has only one move, to be made in ignorance of the other player's choice, in which he chooses one of a finite number of alternatives. When the two players reveal their choices, a predetermined table prescribes the payoffs to each. Since the game is to be zero-sum only the payoff to Mr. Roe need be listed, since if it is x units (of money or chips or whatever they are playing for), then the payoff to Mr. Collum must be $-x$.

A rectangular array of mn numbers, arranged in m rows and n columns, is called an $m \times n$ **matrix**. For example,

$$\begin{bmatrix} -5 & 3 & 1 & 20 \\ 5 & 5 & 4 & 6 \\ -4 & -2 & 0 & -3 \end{bmatrix} \tag{1}$$

is a 3×4 matrix, i.e., an array of 12 numbers arranged in 3 rows and 4 columns.

Example 1. Consider the following game. Mr. Roe chooses a number from the set $\{1,2,3\}$. Mr. Collum, in ignorance of Mr. Roe's choice, chooses a number from the set $\{1,2,3,4\}$. Their choices are then revealed, and if Mr. Roe has chosen 2, for example, and Mr. Collum has chosen 3, then Mr. Roe is paid by Mr. Collum the amount in the second row and third column of the matrix (1), namely \$4.00. If Mr. Roe chooses 1 and Mr. Collum chooses 1, then Mr. Roe is paid -5 by Mr. Collum, that is, Mr. Roe pays 5 to Mr. Collum. Briefly, (1) is termed the payoff matrix to Mr. Roe of this matrix game in which Mr. Roe chooses a row and Mr. Collum chooses a column, each in ignorance of the others' choice. The choice of a row is called a pure strategy for Mr. Roe, and the choice of a column is called a pure strategy for Mr. Collum.

We ask the question: *how can Mr. Roe and Mr. Collum play in order to guarantee themselves as much as possible no matter what choice the other player may make*? Each player assumes that the other is intelligent.

Mr. Roe would like to win 20, but he recognizes that, if he should pick row 1, Mr. Collum may well pick column 1, in which case Mr. Roe loses 5. Therefore, Mr. Roe argues as follows. If my choice is row 1, the worst that may happen is that Mr. Collum may pick column 1, and I lose 5. If my choice is row 2, the worst that can happen is that Mr. Collum may pick column 3 and I win 4. If my choice is row 3, the worst that can happen is that Mr. Collum may pick column 1 and I lose 4. Therefore, the safe choice for me is row 2, because then I must win 4 even if Mr. Collum makes the best possible choice for himself and I may even win more if Mr. Collum makes a poor choice. In short, Mr. Roe looks at the minimum payoff in each row (called the row minima) and chooses the row yielding the maximum of the row minima.

Similarly, Mr. Collum argues as follows. If my choice is column 1, Mr. Roe may pick row 2 and he wins 5. If my choice is column 2, Mr. Roe may pick row 2 and he wins 5. If my choice is column 3, Mr. Roe may pick row 2 and he wins 4. If my choice is column 4, Mr. Roe may pick row 1 and he wins 20. Therefore the safe choice for me is column 3 because it is then guaranteed that Mr. Roe can win no more than 4 even if he makes the best possible choice for himself and he may win even less (1 or 0) if he makes a poor choice. In short, Mr. Collum looks at the maximum payoff in each column (called the column maxima) and chooses the column yielding the minimum of the column maxima.

Thus in our example, Mr. Roe should choose row 2, and Mr. Collum should choose column 3, so that Mr. Roe assures himself of winning at least 4 and Mr. Collum guarantees that Mr. Roe wins no more than 4. The choice of row 2 is termed an *optimal pure strategy* for Mr. Roe, the choice of column 3 is termed an *optimal pure strategy* for Mr. Collum, and 4 is termed the *value* of the game.

Note that 4 in matrix (1) is the smallest number in its row and the greatest in its column; such a number is called a **saddle-value** and its position in the matrix (here, row 2, column 3) is called a **saddle-point** of the matrix. (This term is chosen because of the analogy with the point P on a saddle which is a maximum in one direction and minimum in another (Fig. 237).)

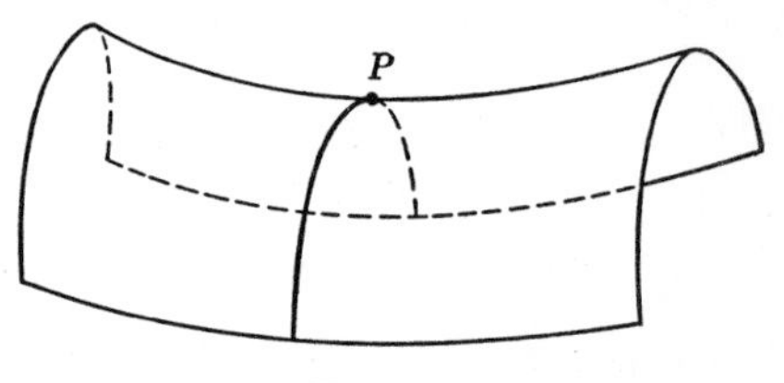

FIG. 237

In general, a **matrix game** is defined by a **payoff matrix**

$$\begin{bmatrix} a_{11} & a_{12} & a_{13} & \cdots & a_{1n} \\ a_{21} & a_{22} & a_{23} & \cdots & a_{2n} \\ a_{31} & a_{32} & a_{33} & \cdots & a_{3n} \\ \vdots & \vdots & \vdots & & \vdots \\ a_{m1} & a_{m2} & a_{m3} & \cdots & a_{mn} \end{bmatrix}$$

where a_{12} designates the number found in row 1 and column 2, and so on.* Mr. Roe chooses a row and Mr. Collum chooses a column, each in ignorance of

* For example, in the matrix (1) above, $a_{11} = -5$, $a_{13} = 1$, $a_{31} = -4$, $a_{34} = -3$, and so on.

the other's choice. The choice of a row is termed a **pure strategy** for Mr. Roe and the choice of a column is termed a **pure strategy** for Mr. Collum. If Mr. Roe chooses row i and Mr. Collum chooses column j, then Mr. Roe receives the payoff a_{ij} from Mr. Collum. We denote the largest number in the jth column by $c_j = \max_{1 \leqq i \leqq m} a_{ij}$ and it is called the jth **column maximum**. There is such a number for each $j = 1, 2, \ldots, n$. The smallest of these column maxima is denoted by $\min c_j = \min_{1 \leqq j \leqq n} (\max_{1 \leqq i \leqq m} a_{ij})$. Similarly, the smallest number in the ith row is denoted by $r_i = \min_{1 \leqq j \leqq n} a_{ij}$ and is called the ith **row minimum**. The largest of these row minima is denoted by $\max r_i = \max_{1 \leqq i \leqq m} (\min_{1 \leqq j \leqq n} a_{ij})$.

If there exists a number a_{st} in the matrix such that $a_{st} = \max r_i = \min c_j$, then the choice of the sth row is an **optimal pure strategy** for Mr. Roe and the choice of the tth column is an **optimal pure strategy** for Mr. Collum and the payoff a_{st} is termed the **value** of the game. As in the example above Mr. Roe can guarantee that he wins at least a_{st} by choosing the sth row, and Mr. Collum can guarantee that Mr. Roe wins no more than a_{st} by choosing the tth column. It can be proved that such optimal strategies exist if and only if a_{si} is a **saddle-value**, that is, if a_{st} is the smallest number in its row and the largest in its column.

The work of the example above might be conveniently arranged as follows.

R \ C	1	2	3	4	*Row minima*
1	−5	3	1	20	1
2	5	5	④	6	④
3	−4	−2	0	−3	−4
Col. maxima	5	5	④	20	

The row minima and column maxima are listed and it is observed that the maximum of the row minima is equal to the minimum of the column maxima and that both are attained by R's choosing row 2 and C's choosing column 3. Or, equivalently, one could inspect all numbers of the matrix and find that a saddle-value occurs in row 2, column 3.

Exercises

Find optimal pure strategies for both players and the value of the matrix game with payoff matrix (payoffs to player R*) given as follows:*

1. $\begin{bmatrix} 1 & 0 \\ 2 & -1 \end{bmatrix}$. **2.** $\begin{bmatrix} 2 & -2 & 0 \\ 4 & 3 & 1 \end{bmatrix}$. **3.** $\begin{bmatrix} 3 & -3 & 1 & -2 \\ -1 & 0 & 2 & 1 \\ 2 & 2 & 1 & 1 \end{bmatrix}$.

4. $\begin{bmatrix} 4 & 0 & -1 & 1 \\ 0 & 2 & -2 & 1 \\ -3 & 3 & -2 & 2 \end{bmatrix}.$

5. In war games between the Blue and Red armies, a battle is to take place at two mountain passes. Each army has 2 companies available to send to these passes. According to the rules, each commander may send either 2 companies to the first pass, 1 company to the first and 1 to the second, or 2 companies to the second pass. If the same number of companies appear at a given pass the score to each army is 0. If not, 1 point is awarded to the superior force for capturing a pass, and 1 point for each enemy company which is presumed captured if outnumbered at the pass. Should each commander divide his forces between the passes in the ratio 1:1 or 0:2? (Hint: the payoff matrix to Red is

Red \ *Blue*	0:2	1:1
0:2	0	1
1:1	−1	0

There is a saddle-value.)

★6. Prove that for any matrix, the maximum of the row minima is less than or equal to the minimum of the column maxima; in symbols,

$$\max r_i \leqq \min c_j.$$

(Hint: for any i and j, $r_i \leqq a_{ij} \leqq c_j$. Hence, $r_i \leqq \min c_j$. From this the theorem follows.)

★7. Prove that the maximum of the row minima is equal to the minimum of the column maxima if and only if there exists a saddle-value. (Hint: for a saddle-value a_{st} we have $a_{it} \leqq a_{st} \leqq a_{sj}$ for all i and j. Hence, $c_t \leqq a_{st} \leqq r_s$. Hence, $\min c_j \leqq c_t \leqq a_{st} \leqq r_s \leqq \max r_i$. This together with the result of exercise 6 implies that the max min is equal to the min max.

Conversely, suppose s such that $a_{sj_1} = r_s = \max r_i$ and t such that $a_{i_1t} = c_t = \min c_j$. Then the equality of max min and min max implies that $r_s = c_t$. Hence, $c_t \geqq a_{st}$ implies $r_s \geqq a_{st}$ which implies $a_{sj} \geqq a_{st}$ for all j. Similarly $r_s \leqq a_{st}$ implies $c_t \leqq a_{st}$ which implies $a_{it} \leqq a_{st}$ for all i. Hence, a_{st} is a saddle-value.)

*158. MIXED STRATEGIES

Simple examples show that not all matrix games have saddle-values and optimal strategies. For example, the game of matching pennies has none. In this game, players R and C each choose either head or tail in ignorance of the other

* This section may be omitted without disturbing the continuity.

player's choice. Suppose player R wins $1.00 if they both make the same choice and loses $1.00 if they make opposite choices. Then the payoff matrix to player R is

R \ C	*H*	*T*	*Row min.*
H	1	−1	−1
T	−1	1	−1
Col. max.	1	1	

and the maximum of the row minima is -1 while the minimum of the column maxima is 1. It is easily seen that no saddle-value exists.

How, then, should this game be played? Let us imagine it being played repeatedly a large number of times. Clearly, R must not always play the same pure strategy, say heads, for if he did, C would always play the opposite, tails, and win. Therefore, R must play heads some fraction x of the time and tails the rest or $1 - x$ of the time; in the language of probability, R must play H with probability x and T with probability $1 - x$. His mathematical expectation against pure strategy H for C would then be

$$1 \cdot x + (-1)(1 - x) = 2x - 1$$

while his expectation against pure strategy T for C will be

$$(-1)x + 1 \cdot (1 - x) = 1 - 2x.$$

If we graph the quantities $y = 2x - 1$ and $y = 1 - 2x$ on the same axes (Fig. 238) for x between 0 and 1, the only values probabilities can have, we see that for any value of x, the worst that R can expect on the average in the long run is the smaller of the two ordinates corresponding to this value of x on the graphs. R wishes to maximize this minimum ordinate and the graph shows that to do this R must choose x at the point of intersection of the two graphs, namely, $x = \frac{1}{2}$. Hence he should play H with probability $\frac{1}{2}$ and T with probability $1 - \frac{1}{2} = \frac{1}{2}$. A similar argument applies to player C with the same result. The expectation of both players is zero. We term the choice of rows for player R (columns for player C) the **pure strategies** for R (C), and a choice of probabilities or relative frequencies as $(\frac{1}{2}, \frac{1}{2})$ with which to play these pure strategies is termed a **mixed strategy**. Note that even the choice of the probabilities $(\frac{1}{2}, \frac{1}{2})$ for H and T is not sufficient unless H and T are played *at random* with these relative frequencies. For if player R should play H and T in a fixed pattern (as, for example, in alternation), then player C would soon learn this pattern and play the opposite. In order to insure randomness of play, some chance device with probability $\frac{1}{2}$ may be used to determine the next choice. In practice, players of this particular game toss the coin itself, since it is a chance device with probability $\frac{1}{2}$. In this way the correct frequencies are not only attained but the player himself does not know what he will call next and thus cannot be found out by the opposing player either by espionage or mind-reading. In this example, our theory therefore emerges with the same optimal mixed strategies which have been arrived at in practice by the long experience of the human race.

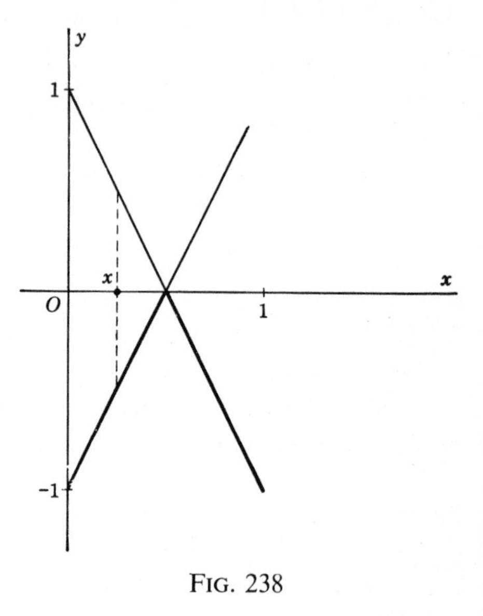

FIG. 238

A mixed strategy of player R which maximizes his minimum expectation against C's strategies is called **optimal** for R, and a mixed strategy of player C which minimizes R's maximum expectation against C's strategies is called **optimal** for C. It can be proved that with mixed strategies in a matrix game this maximum of minima is always equal to the minimum of maxima. This so-called **minimax principle** was first proved by von Neumann in 1928 and forms the basis for much of the elaborate theory of games which has been developed in recent years.

In general, in a matrix game with payoff matrix

$$\begin{bmatrix} a_{11} & a_{12} & \cdots & a_{1n} \\ a_{21} & a_{22} & \cdots & a_{2n} \\ \vdots & \vdots & & \vdots \\ a_{m1} & a_{m2} & \cdots & a_{mn} \end{bmatrix}$$

the choice of a row is a **pure strategy** for player R and the choice of a column is a **pure strategy** for player C. If there are optimal pure strategies (i.e., a saddle-value), then we need look no further. If there are no optimal pure strategies (i.e., no saddle-value), then we must look for optimal mixed strategies. The choice of probabilities $X = (x_1, x_2, \ldots, x_m)$ with $x_i \geqq 0$ and $x_1 + x_2 + \cdots + x_m = 1$ with which to play these rows is termed a **mixed strategy** for R; a choice of probabilities $U = (u_1, u_2, \ldots, u_n)$ with $u_i \geqq 0$ and $u_1 + u_2 + \cdots + u_n = 1$ with which to play the columns is termed a **mixed strategy** for C. The expectation of

R for the mixed strategy $(x_1, x_2, \ldots, x_m)$ against the jth pure strategy of C is

$$E(X, j) = x_1 a_{1j} + x_2 a_{2j} + \cdots + x_m a_{mj}.$$

A mixed strategy of R which maximizes the quantity $\min_{1 \leqq j \leqq n} E(X,j)$ is called an **optimal mixed strategy** for R.

The expectation of R for the mixed strategy $(u_1, \ldots, u_n)$ of C against the ith pure strategy of R is

$$E(i, U) = u_1 a_{i1} + u_2 a_{i2} + \cdots + u_n a_{in}.$$

A mixed strategy of C which minimizes the quantity $\max_{1 \leqq i \leqq m} E(i,U)$ is called an **optimal mixed strategy** for C. The basic **minimax theorem** of von Neumann can be stated as follows: *for any matrix game there exist optimal mixed strategies such that the minimum of* $\max_{1 \leqq i \leqq m} E(i,U)$, *for all possible U, is equal to the maximum of* $\min_{1 \leqq j \leqq n} E(X,j)$, *for all possible X, and this common value v is termed the* **value** *of the game.* Player R, by playing an optimal mixed strategy, can guarantee himself an expectation of at least v, and player C, by playing an optimal mixed strategy, can guarantee that R will have an expectation of no more than v.

A game is called **fair** if its value $v = 0$.

We must confine ourselves here to the simplest examples.

Example 1. *Modified matching pennies.* This game is the same as matching pennies except that the payoff matrix to player R is

$$\begin{array}{cc} & \begin{array}{cc} H & T \end{array} \\ \begin{array}{c} H \\ T \end{array} & \begin{bmatrix} 4 & -3 \\ -3 & 2 \end{bmatrix}. \end{array}$$

Solution. There is no saddle-value and hence no solution in pure strategies. Let a mixed strategy for R be $(x, 1-x)$. Then this expectation against pure strategy 1 or H for C is

$$E(X,1) = 4x - 3(1-x) = 7x - 3$$

while his expectation against pure strategy 2 or T for C is

$$E(X,2) = -3x + 2(1-x) = 2 - 5x.$$

Plotting the graphs of $y = 7x - 3$ and $y = 2 - 5x$ for $0 \leqq x \leqq 1$, we see (Fig. 239) that they intersect at $(\frac{5}{12}, -\frac{1}{12})$. Hence, by the same reasoning as in the case of matching pennies, an optimal strategy for R is to play heads with probability $x = \frac{5}{12}$ and tails with probability $1 - x = \frac{7}{12}$. His expectation is then $-\frac{1}{12}$. Similar reasoning shows that C should play heads and tails with the same relative frequencies. The value of the game is $-\frac{1}{12}$, and it is clearly not fair to R, although this might not have been anticipated intuitively, since the payoff matrix seems to suggest that he stands to win 6 or lose 6. With optimal mixed strategies for both players, R expects to lose $\frac{1}{12}$ per play in the long run.

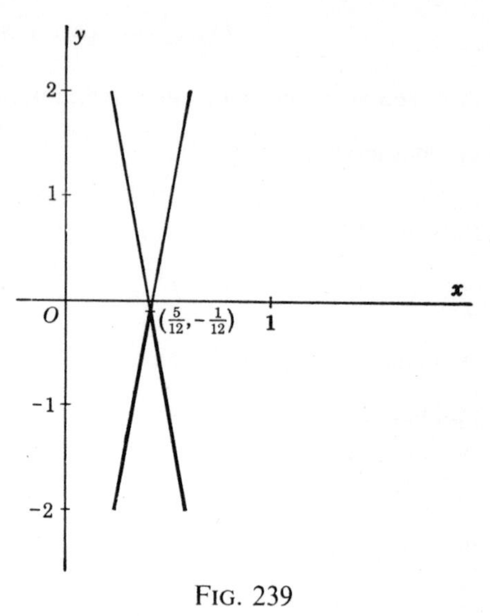

FIG. 239

Remark 1. The minimax principle assumes that we play for the reward exclusively and that every bit of reward matters to us. If you find fault with this and object that some people play for the pleasure of winning long shots or the excitement of gambling or for various other goals, your quarrel is not with our mathematics but with the scale of values attributed to the players. For further discussion of values or preferences, see section 194.

Remark 2. Matrix games have only one move for each player while most parlor games have many. To reduce the latter to the form of a matrix game it suffices to introduce the notion of *strategy*. Imagine a player R wishing to play but who, having to be elsewhere, must play through an agent or subordinate who can read but must not use his own judgment. The player may accomplish this by leaving his agent complete instructions as to the choices he wishes to make at each move under all possible circumstances that may arise. Such a set of instructions is called a *pure strategy*. Clearly, if the game has a finite number of moves with a finite number of alternative choices at each move, there will be only a finite, although perhaps very large, number of possible pure strategies. These will correspond to the rows of the matrix. Similarly, the pure strategies of player C will be finite in number and will correspond to the columns. Thus we arrive at a matrix game but perhaps with a very large matrix for which the elementary methods of solution used in this book will not suffice.

Remark 3. Since the expectation to R of mixed strategy X against mixed strategy Y of C is the weighted average

$$y_1E(X,1) + y_2E(X,2) + \cdots + y_nE(X,n)$$

which is $\geqq \min_{1 \leqq j \leqq n} (EX,j)$ (see exercise 17, section 28) it is sufficient to consider the pure strategies of C only in calculating the maximum of these minima. A similar remark holds for C.

Remark 4. The following economic game is not zero-sum and hence we give payoff matrices for R and C separately. Suppose the players are competitors who may sell their product either at a high price (H) or a low price (L). If they set different prices, low then captures the entire market, while if they both set the same price they split the market equally. Their profits per unit are given by the payoff matrices:

Payoff to Mr. Roe

$R \backslash C$	H	L
H	3	0
L	4	2

Payoff to Mr. Collum

$R \backslash C$	H	L
H	3	4
L	0	2

If they are forbidden to cooperate, they should each play strategy L since they dare not do otherwise. But if they do cooperate* and agree to fix the price at H, they both do better. Then coalitions like those of section 70 arise.

Exercises

Find optimal mixed strategies for both players and the value of each of the following games.

1. Payoff matrix $\begin{bmatrix} 1 & 0 \\ 0 & 2 \end{bmatrix}$.

2. Payoff matrix $\begin{bmatrix} 2 & -1 \\ -1 & 1 \end{bmatrix}$.

3. Player R has two cards, a black 1 and a red 4, and player C has two cards, a black 2 and a red 3. The players simultaneously play one of their cards. Player R wins if the colors match, C wins if they do not, and the amount won is the number of the winning card. The payoff matrix (payoffs to R) is therefore

	Black 2	Red 3
Black 1	1	−3
Red 4	−2	4

4. Player R has two cards, a black 2 and a red 7, and player C has a black 3 and a red 6. The game is otherwise as in exercise 3. Form the payoff matrix, and find optimal mixed strategies and the value.

* For a cooperative theory of games taking account of coalitions, see J. von Neumann and O. Morgenstern, *op. cit.* For a non-cooperative theory, see J. Nash, *Ann. of Math.*, Vol. 54, 1951, pp. 286–295.

5. Player R has a red 1, a black 1, and a red 2. Player C has a red 1, a black 1, and a black 2. The game is otherwise as in exercise 3, except that if the two 2's are played the payoff is 0. Verify that the payoff matrix is

$$\begin{array}{r} \\ \text{Red 1} \\ \text{Black 1} \\ \text{Red 2} \end{array} \begin{array}{c} \begin{array}{ccc} \text{Red 1} & \text{Black 1} & \text{Black 2} \end{array} \\ \begin{bmatrix} 1 & -1 & -2 \\ -1 & 1 & 1 \\ 2 & -1 & 0 \end{bmatrix} \end{array}$$

Find optimal mixed strategies and the value. (Hint: note that R should never play his red 1 since he does at least as well with the red 2. Similarly, C should never use his black 2. Thus the payoff matrix can be reduced to a 2×2 matrix

$$\begin{bmatrix} -1 & 1 \\ 2 & -1 \end{bmatrix}$$

which can be treated by means of the method used here.)

6. Payoff matrix $\begin{bmatrix} 4 & 1 & 5 \\ 2 & 3 & 6 \end{bmatrix}$.

7. Player R chooses one of the numbers $\{1,2\}$. Player C chooses one of the numbers $\{1,3\}$ simultaneously. If the sum of the two chosen numbers is odd, R wins; if the sum is even, C wins; the amount won is the sum of the chosen numbers. Write the payoff matrix and find optimal mixed strategies for both players and the value.

8. Payoff matrix $\begin{bmatrix} 0 & -2 & 4 \\ 2 & 1 & -2 \end{bmatrix}$.

*159. REDUCTION OF MATRIX GAMES TO LINEAR PROGRAMMING

We show that the solution of matrix games can be reduced to the solution of associated linear programming problems. First we note that if the same sufficiently large number k is added to all elements a_{ij} of the payoff matrix so that the new matrix has all elements $a'_{ij} = a_{ij} + k$ positive, then the value v' of the game with the new payoff matrix will be positive and $v' = v + k$, where v is the value of the original game. Furthermore, adding the same k to all payoffs obviously cannot alter the optimal strategies of either player at all. A mixed strategy for Mr. Roe is an ordered set $x_1, \ldots, x_m$ of probabilities for which the expectations are (dropping the primes for convenience)

$$(1) \qquad \begin{cases} x_1 a_{11} + x_2 a_{21} + \cdots + x_m a_{m1} \geqq w > 0 \\ x_1 a_{12} + x_2 a_{22} + \cdots + x_m a_{m2} \geqq w > 0 \\ \vdots \\ x_1 a_{1n} + x_2 a_{2n} + \cdots + x_m a_{mn} \geqq w > 0 \end{cases}$$

* May be omitted without disturbing the continuity.

where all $x_i \geqq 0$ and $x_1 + x_2 + \cdots + x_m = 1$. Mr. Roe wishes to maximize the value of w. Introducing new variables $u_1, u_2, \ldots, u_m$ where each $u_i = x_i/w$, we divide both members of each inequality in (1) by w, obtaining

$$\text{(2)} \qquad \begin{cases} u_1 a_{11} + u_2 a_{21} + \cdots + u_m a_{m1} \geqq 1 \\ u_1 a_{12} + u_2 a_{22} + \cdots + u_m a_{m2} \geqq 1 \\ \vdots \\ u_1 a_{1n} + u_2 a_{2n} + \cdots + u_m a_{mn} \geqq 1 \end{cases}$$

where each $u_i \geqq 0$ and $u_1 + u_2 + \cdots + u_m = 1/w$. Hence, if we minimize $u_1 + u_2 + \cdots + u_m$ we maximize w. But this is a familiar linear programming problem.

For example, let us find Mr. Roe's optimal strategy in the game of matching pennies, which has payoff matrix

$$\begin{bmatrix} 1 & -1 \\ -1 & 1 \end{bmatrix}.$$

We add $k = 2$ to each payoff obtaining the new matrix

$$\begin{bmatrix} 3 & 1 \\ 1 & 3 \end{bmatrix}.$$

The relations

$$\begin{cases} 3x_1 + 1x_2 \geqq w \\ 1x_1 + 3x_2 \geqq w \end{cases}, \quad x_1 \geqq 0, \quad x_2 \geqq 0, \quad x_1 + x_2 = 1$$

become, on introducing the new variables $u_1 = x_1/w$, $u_2 = x_2/w$,

$$\begin{cases} 3u_1 + u_2 \geqq 1 \\ u_1 + 3u_2 \geqq 1 \end{cases}, \quad u_1 \geqq 0, \quad u_2 \geqq 0, \quad u_1 + u_2 = 1/w.$$

We minimize $u_1 + u_2$ subject to the preceding inequalities by the methods of section 102 (see Fig. 240).

Solving the system of equations

$$\begin{cases} 3u_1 + u_2 = 1 \\ u_1 + 3u_2 = 1 \end{cases}$$

we get $u_1 = u_2 = \frac{1}{4}$, $u_1 + u_2 = 1/w = \frac{1}{2}$. Thus, the new game has value $w = 2$, and the original game has value $w - k = 2 - 2 = 0$. Further, $u_1 = x_1/w$ yields $\frac{1}{4} = x_1/2$ or $x_1 = \frac{1}{2}$, and similarly $x_2 = \frac{1}{2}$, so that Mr. Roe's optimal strategy is to play head and tail with probability $\frac{1}{2}$. The reader may similarly reduce the determination of Mr. Collum's optimal strategy to a linear programming problem which can then be solved.

This reduction indicates the importance of a systematic method of solving large scale linear programming problems. Such a method, called the *simplex method* is discussed in section 176.

Exercises

Solve the matrix games of section 158 by this method.

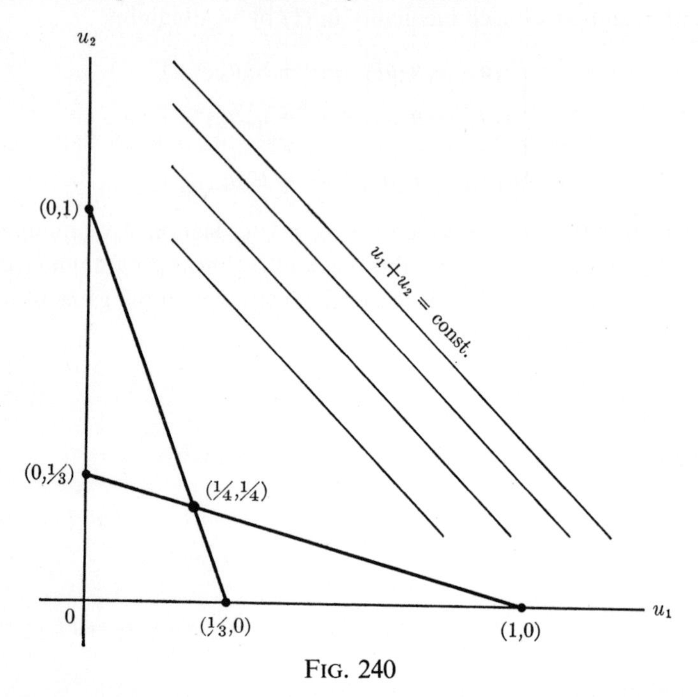

FIG. 240

160. STATISTICS

While we could go a little further into the study of probability and statistics here, we could not go very far without a more intensive study of certain technical parts of mathematics. In fact, many mistaken conclusions are drawn from statistical data by people whose mathematical training is insufficient. It is not because they make mistakes in calculation but because they often do not understand the mathematical (logical) basis for the formulas they use. If all the people who publish statements in newspapers and magazines, beginning with the words "Statistics prove ..." were laid end to end, there would probably be far less pseudo-scientific superstition among educated laymen. Abuses of this kind have led to the well-known classification of lies into 3 kinds: lies, worse lies, and statistics. This classification does not refer to statistics properly used. Although we cannot develop the theory of statistics logically in such a non-technical book as this, we can discuss some of its simpler ideas and point out some of the more glaring, cruder, elementary follies that are often committed. This we shall do in the remainder of the chapter.

161. ACCURACY

Many people who ought to know better make the mistake of thinking that a statistical report has a high degree of accuracy if its results are carried out to a great many decimal places. To see how ridiculous this notion is, let us consider the following experiment. Take a large tub of water and place seven empty pails on the floor, being careful to roll up the rug first. Now spill the water from the tub into the seven pails, giving each pail an equal share as nearly as you can. Suppose now you say that each pail contains roughly $\frac{1}{7}$ of a tub of water. This does not look very accurate. If, however, you divide 1 by 7 and get .142857 ... of a tub your report looks like a masterpiece of scientific accuracy, carried out to 6 decimal places. However, you could just as well have carried out the division of 1 by 7 to 18 decimal places, obtaining .142857142857142857 ... of a tub without improving the actual accuracy at all. You really know no more than you did when you said roughly $\frac{1}{7}$ of a tub. *Genuine accuracy depends on the accuracy of your data.* Thus in a table of logarithms or trigonometric functions, more decimal places really give more accuracy, but this is because of the source of the additional decimal places. The value of π is another example. The true value is $\pi = 3.14159265$ .... Taking more decimal places gives greater accuracy. But if you take $\pi = \frac{22}{7}$, roughly, you may get a decimal expression 3.14285 ... by division. Now if you take more than the first two decimal places from the latter expression, your increase in accuracy will be illusory because only the first two decimal places are correct. In fact, you will really be departing further and further from the true value given above. The italicized statement above was not appreciated by the visitor to the museum who said, "This fossil is 5,000,003 years old because when I was here 3 years ago the guide told me it was 5,000,000 years old." Nor is it understood by the trigonometry student who insists that the height of a mountain is 5,253.67952 feet.

162. INDEX NUMBERS

In making comparisons with respect to qualitative considerations, it is often convenient to sharpen vague comparisons by using numerical indices of some sort. Now numbers are used sometimes as direct measurements of quantitative characteristics and sometimes merely as identification labels or names; but in the case of qualitative comparisons they are usually used to indicate the relative order of the objects studied with respect to the given quality. Thus the intelligence quotient (I.Q.) of a person is essentially his score on a certain test.

Similarly, economists use various numerical scores or indices. Now in the interpretation of these scores, it must be remembered that we can usually use them only in so far as they place our specimens in an order. Thus if three people get I.Q.'s of 150, 100, and 75, respectively, we say that (as far as this test is concerned) the first is more intelligent than the second who is more intelligent than the third. But it is silly to say that the first is twice as intelligent as the third on the ground that $150 = 2 \cdot 75$. Similarly, to take an extremely simple case, if we arrange a class of boys according to size beginning with the smallest and assign to each one an index number indicating his place in line, we could not conclude that the boy with index number 20 is twice as tall as the boy with index number 10 merely because $20 = 2 \cdot 10$.

163. AVERAGES

In dealing with large collections of numbers (measurements or statistical data of any kind) it is often humanly impossible to draw quantitative conclusions about the group as a whole from the *entire* collection of individual numbers as they stand, simply because there are too many of them. Therefore, we would like somehow to describe the general quantitative characteristics of the entire group, at least in certain respects, by means of a few numbers. Two kinds of numbers are often used for this purpose. One kind, called *averages*, is for the purpose of describing the "central tendency" of the collection. Thus the collection of numbers 40, 45, 48, 50, 50, 50, 50, 50, 52, 55, 60, has the "average" 50; that is, 50 is the value about which the entire collection "centers." Another kind of numbers, called *measures of dispersion*, is for the purpose of describing how the numbers of the collection deviate from some average or central value. The collection of numbers 10, 30, 40, 50, 50, 50, 50, 50, 60, 70, 90, has the average 50 just as in the example above; but the numbers of this collection are dispersed very differently about this central value. We shall not discuss measures of dispersion in great detail here but shall examine more closely some of the measures which are often used as "averages." There are many such measures and we shall use different names for them to avoid the indefiniteness that usually accompanies the word "average."

The **arithmetic mean** of a set of n numbers $x_1, x_2, x_3, \ldots, x_n$ is their sum divided by their number; that is,

$$\frac{x_1 + x_2 + x_3 + \cdots + x_n}{n}.$$

Example 1. If a student gets marks of 70, 80, 90, 100 during the term, his "average" (arithmetic mean) is 85. Note that the arithmetic mean need not be one of his marks.

Example 2. A factory owner pays the following salaries:

Position	*No. of men*	*Weekly salary*
manager	1	$200
foremen	2	40
skilled workers	10	30
unskilled workers	11	20
apprentices	1	10

Clearly, the arithmetic mean of the numbers in the salary scale at the right, namely $\frac{200 + 40 + 30 + 20 + 10}{5} = 60$, would give a false impression of working conditions. Even the owner would doubtless be unwilling to say that the "average" salary paid in his factory is $60 per week. He might, however, say that the "average" salary is

$$\frac{1 \cdot 200 + 2 \cdot 40 + 10 \cdot 30 + 11 \cdot 20 + 1 \cdot 10}{25} = 32.40$$

or $32.40 per week. This is called the **weighted arithmetic mean** since each number in the salary scale is weighted according to its importance, the importance being measured by the number of people receiving that salary.

Example 3. A student receives a mark of 90 in a 5-credit course, 85 in a 4-credit course, and 65 in a 1-credit course. If his "average" were computed by the arithmetic mean, it would be $(90 + 85 + 65)/3 = 80$. But the student might be considered to have just cause for complaint. If the number of credits may be taken as indicating the relative importance of the courses, it would be fairer to use the weighted arithmetic mean which would give an average of

$$\frac{5 \cdot 90 + 4 \cdot 85 + 1 \cdot 65}{10} = 85.5.$$

The mathematical expectation (section 156) is the weighted arithmetic mean of the rewards, weighted in accordance with their probabilities of occurrence.

Arithmetic means have the property that they give great importance to extremely large or extremely small numbers. Thus, in example 2, if the owner announced that the average salary was the weighted arithmetic mean $32.40 per week, the labor union might object because the extremely large salary paid to the manager (who happened to be the owner's son-in-law) exerted an undue influence on the result. If the manager's salary is left out, the average (weighted arithmetic mean) salary is $25.42 per week.

In taking measurements in a laboratory experiment, it is natural to suppose that extremely wrong measurements do not occur. Thus, if a scientist takes a measurement a large number of times, obtaining only slightly different results each time, it is usual to regard the arithmetic mean of the various readings as the "most probable" value of the measurement. A great deal of useful statistical theory is based on this assumption.

The **mode** is the number, in a collection of numbers, which occurs most frequently, if such a number exists. In example 2, the modal salary is $20. The mode has the property that it is not influenced by isolated extreme values, like the manager's salary. But it has certain defects. For instance, the frequency with which various numbers occur may be the same or very much the same, so that the mode becomes meaningless or useless. For example, if a student gets marks of 90, 90, 80, 80, 75, 75, 65, 65, the frequency of each mark is 2 and there is no modal mark. Suppose a second student has marks of 100, 99, 98, 90, 90, 85, 85, 85, 65, 65, 65, 65. The modal value is 65 but it is hardly representative of the student's work. In fact, if the marks were classified by intervals of 10 the student's marks would have the following frequencies

interval	100–90	89–80	79–70	69–60
frequency	5	3	0	4

and the modal interval would be 100–90. If we used intervals of 5, however, we would have

interval	100–95	94–90	89–85	84–80	79–75	74–70	69–65
frequency	3	2	3	0	0	0	4

and the modal interval would be 69–65. Statements about "the average man" usually refer to the modal man.

If a collection of numbers is arranged in order of magnitude, the term in the middle position is called the **median**, if such a number exists. If the number of numbers in the collection is odd, the median always exists. If the number of numbers in the collection is even, there are *two* middle terms and we usually call the arithmetic mean of these two terms the median. Thus in the case of the first student just referred to, the median mark is 77.5. The second student has a median mark of 85. In example 2, the median salary is \$30. *All the various types of "averages" yield, in example 2, entirely different results.* It is possible that if the employer were announcing the "average" salary he would use the largest value while the labor union would announce the smallest value. Therefore, statements about "averages" must be carefully interpreted in the light of how the "average" was calculated and whether the type of average used was appropriate to the given situation.

There are other useful expressions which may be called averages. Suppose an investment dwindles in value to 20% of the original value during the first year and then dwindles during the second year to 80% of the value it had at the beginning of the second year. What steady rate of decrease would yield the same resulting value at the end of two years? If r is the steady rate, we would have $r \cdot r = \frac{20}{100} \cdot \frac{80}{100}$ or $r^2 = \frac{1600}{10000}$. Hence, $r = \sqrt{\frac{1600}{10000}} = \frac{40}{100} = 40\%$. This is called the geometric mean of the two given rates. In general, the **geometric mean** of two given quantities a and b is $\sqrt{ab}$. The **geometric mean** of n given quantities $x_1, x_2, \ldots, x_n$ is $\sqrt[n]{x_1 x_2 \ldots x_n}$.

The collection of numbers 10, 30, 40, 50, 50, 50, 50, 60, 70, 90 has the arithmetic mean 50. The collection of numbers 40, 45, 48, 49, 50, 50, 51, 52, 55, 60 also has the arithmetic mean 50. In fact the median and mode for each of these collections is also 50. Hence both exhibit the same "central tendency." That is, both collections center about the number 50. But clearly the numbers of the first collection are dispersed about the number 50 in quite a different manner from that in which those of the second collection are dispersed about the number 50. To describe such differences we use various "measures of dispersion" of which we shall mention only two here. Each number in the collection differs from the arithmetic mean by some amount, called its **deviation from the mean.** The deviations from the mean of the numbers in the first collection above are 40, 20, 10, 0, 0, 0, 0, 10, 20, 40. The arithmetic mean of these deviations is called the **average (or mean) deviation from the mean.** In this case it is 14. In the second collection above, the deviations from the mean are 10, 5, 2, 1, 0, 0, 1, 2, 5, 10. The average (mean) deviation from the mean in this case is 3.6. This indicates that the numbers in the second collection are not as widely dispersed about the mean value as those of the first collection.

Another widely used measure of dispersion is the **standard deviation**, defined as follows. If $x_1, x_2, \ldots, x_n$ are n values of x, and $\bar{x}$ is the arithmetic mean of these n values, then the standard deviation S_x is given by the formula

$$S_x = \sqrt{\frac{(x_1 - \bar{x})^2 + (x_2 - \bar{x})^2 + \cdots + (x_n - \bar{x})^2}{n}}$$

In the first collection above, we obtain $S_x = 20.5$, approximately, while in the second collection above, we obtain $S_x = 5.1$, approximately.

Exercises

1. A student's marks in 10 subjects are 95, 90, 85, 85, 85, 78, 77, 73, 72, 60.

(*a*) What is the arithmetic mean of his marks?
(*b*) What is the median mark?
(*c*) What is the modal mark?
(*d*) Using the intervals 95–100, 90–94, 85–89, ..., 60–64, what is the modal interval?
(*e*) Using the intervals 90–100, 80–89, 70–79, 60–69, what is the modal interval?
(*f*) If the first 5 marks are in major subjects counting 3 credits each and the last 5 are in minor subjects counting 1 credit each, find the weighted arithmetic mean, taking the number of credits as the measure of relative importance.
(*g*) Find the average (mean) deviation from the mean.
(*h*) Find the standard deviation.

2. The salaries in a certain firm are as follows:

Position	*No. of men*	*Weekly salary*
foremen	3	$50
skilled workers	20	40
unskilled workers	19	30
apprentices	8	10

Find (*a*) the modal salary; (*b*) the median salary; (*c*) the arithmetic mean of the salaries in the right-hand column; (*d*) the weighted arithmetic mean, the importance or weight of each salary being taken as the number of men receiving it.

3. A student's marks in 10 subjects are 98, 90, 93, 97, 85, 87, 88, 67, 70, 65. Using these data, answer the same questions as in exercise 1.

4. Prove that if a and b are any two positive numbers their arithmetic mean is greater than or equal to their geometric mean.

164. CORRELATION

Suppose we were to find that the marks of 10 students in intermediate algebra and trigonometry are as shown in the accompanying table. We might get the impression that there is some connexion or relation between the algebra marks $x_1, x_2, x_3 \ldots$ of these students and their trigonometry marks $y_1, y_2, y_3, \ldots$. Thus, we observe that, by and large, most of those who did well in algebra did well in trigonometry and most of those who did poorly in algebra did poorly in trigonometry. Of course the conclusion that a student's mark in trigonometry will be much like his mark in algebra is not justified if we apply it to some particular student. But it does seem as though there is some approximate relationship between the values of the variable x and the values of the variable y. It is

Student	x = *mark in int. alg.*	y = *mark in trig.*
1. Ames	$x_1 = 60$	$y_1 = 50$
2. Brown	$x_2 = 85$	$y_2 = 85$
3. Camp	$x_3 = 90$	$y_3 = 95$
4. Davis	$x_4 = 60$	$y_4 = 60$
5. Ellis	$x_5 = 60$	$y_5 = 55$
6. Fischer	$x_6 = 70$	$y_6 = 65$
7. Green	$x_7 = 75$	$y_7 = 85$
8. Harris	$x_8 = 70$	$y_8 = 60$
9. Irving	$x_9 = 70$	$y_9 = 75$
10. Jones	$x_{10} = 80$	$y_{10} = 90$

clear from the table that y is not a single-valued function of x, for the same value of x has associated with it many values of y. For example, the first, fourth, and fifth students all have $x = 60$ but they have different values of y. However, it does seem as though, in general, most of the values of y may be fairly well approximated by a single-valued function of x. Let us see what this means by plotting on a graph the points whose coordinates are (x_1, y_1), (x_2, y_2) (x_3, y_3), ... This gives us what is often called a **scatter diagram** (Fig. 241). These points are roughly clustered about a straight line (drawn on Fig. 241) although there are some stray points which are quite far from the line. Thus we would say that the values of y are fairly well approximated by a linear function of x; in technical terms, we say that the variable y has a high degree of **simple**

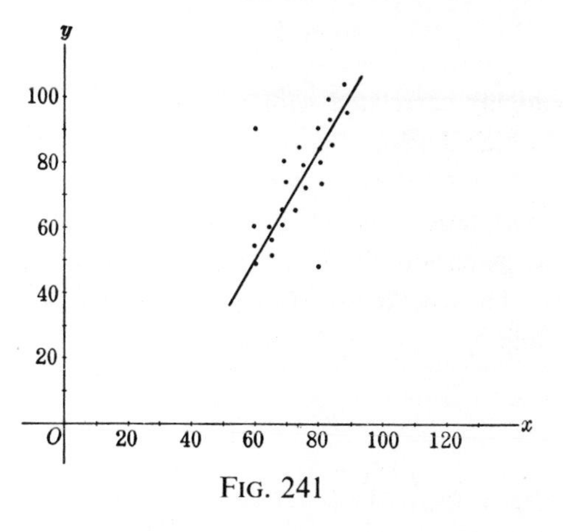

FIG. 241

correlation with the variable x. The case where the values of y are fairly well approximated by a linear function of x is also called **linear correlation** and it is possible to set up a certain expression called the **coefficient of correlation** which measures how closely the scatter diagram approximates a linear function. This coefficient is so constructed that it is positive if the y's generally increase as the x's increase (as in Fig. 241) and negative if the y's generally decrease as the x's increase (as in Fig. 242). If all the y's really lay along a straight line the correlation would be perfect. There are other types of correlation than the usual simple or linear type. The idea is that if the values of the variable y are, in general, fairly well approximated by a single-valued function of x, then y is said to be

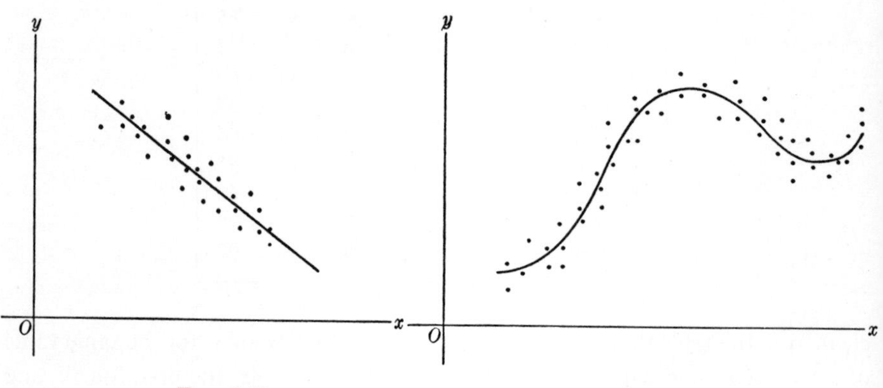

FIG. 242 FIG. 243

highly correlated with x. Thus Fig. 243 illustrates a scatter diagram exhibiting a high degree of correlation which is not of the linear type. We shall make no attempt to give a precise definition of correlation. We shall leave the idea of correlation on an intuitive level and hope that the sketchy, non-technical explanation given here conveys the idea to the reader, at least roughly.

The **coefficient of (linear) correlation** r of two sets of numbers $x_1, x_2, \ldots, x_n$ and $y_1, y_2, \ldots, y_n$ is given by

$$r = \frac{(x_1 - \bar{x})(y_1 - \bar{y}) + (x_2 - \bar{x})(y_2 - \bar{y}) + \cdots + (x_n - \bar{x})(y_n - \bar{y})}{\sqrt{(x_1 - \bar{x})^2 + \cdots + (x_n - \bar{x})^2} \cdot \sqrt{(y_1 - \bar{y})^2 + \cdots + (y_n - \bar{y})^2}}.$$

Example 1. If $x_1 = 1$, $x_2 = 2$, $x_3 = 3$ and $y_1 = 2$, $y_2 = 4$, $y_3 = 6$, then the formula yields $r = 1$, which indicates the fact that x and y are exactly related by a linear formula, namely, $y = 2x$.

Example 2. The marks of the 10 students, exhibited on page 453, in intermediate algebra and in trigonometry have a correlation coefficient of .92 or 92% approximately.

When two variables have a high degree of correlation, we might be inclined to suspect some genuine relationship between them. Thus in the case above, we might suspect that poor work in intermediate algebra often causes poor work in trigonometry. Such a conclusion must not be rashly drawn. A high degree of correlation may, indeed, be indicative of such a causal relationship, if supported by other evidence, but can never justify such a conclusion by itself. We might find that the annual numbers of births in Chicago have a high correlation with the corresponding annual numbers of storks observed in Central Asia, but we should be cautious about asserting that the high correlation implies a causal relationship. In the absence of additional evidence, such a correlation might well be accidental. To cite a somewhat different example, we might observe a high correlation between the daily numbers of people at nearby beach resorts and the corresponding daily numbers of people taking boat rides on the Hudson River. It would not be correct to say that, because these variables have a high correlation, one causes the other. Other evidence might indicate that both of these variables are dependent upon the weather. However, a high correlation may indicate the *possibility* of some causal relationship between the two variables, and it is often used for that purpose. But the causal relationship cannot be inferred from the correlation alone. For example, if we measure the lengths of an iron bar at various temperatures we might find that the length increases and decreases with the temperature. This might lead us to suspect that a change in temperature will cause a change in the length of the bar. Such methods are very much used in economics, biology, education, medicine, etc., and are very valuable tools in inductive reasoning by means of what is called the method of concomitant variation. But caution is necessary in drawing conclusions from statistical correlation. It is also possible to study correlation involving more than two variables.

Exercises

Find the coefficient of (linear) correlation of the following sets of numbers:

1.

x	1	3	7	11
y	5	7	17	25

2.

x	1	3	4	7
y	13	11	7	1

3.

x	1	11	12	20
y	1	2	100	101

4.

x	2	4	8	10	20
y	8	9	13	16	17

165. SAMPLING

Often statistical information about large numbers of people, say the population of the United States, is obtained by gathering data from a "representative sample" or "typical cross section" of the population. Naturally, the greatest care must be taken to insure that the sample shall really be "representative" or "typical" and not biased in some direction pertinent to the investigation in hand. Thus a poll on the desirability of Sunday Blue Laws might conceivably yield biased and different results if the sample of people questioned were chosen largely from the crowds emerging from the churches on Sunday or from the crowds emerging from a ball game on Sunday. A really "typical" sample should include the same proportion of people holding various views as is found in the entire population; that is, it should be truly representative. It is not easy to decide how to obtain a representative sample. The technique used by a certain commercial organization engaged in such polls is roughly to choose a small number of people in such a way that the proportion of Republicans, Democrats, and other political parties, the proportion of urban and rural residents, the proportion of old and young, the proportion of white and colored, the proportion of workers in various fields, the proportion of those living in various geographical divisions, and so on, are the same as in the entire population as revealed by the census. This method has enabled them to make very good predictions. The possibility must be borne in mind, however, that a sample which has shown itself to be typical or representative on one question may by chance be unrepresentative on another. Even with the most careful methods of sampling, conclusions cannot be regarded as certain. In any case, any such conclusions must be interpreted in the light of how the sample was chosen. It is worth noting that large numbers of individuals are not a necessity in obtaining a good sample. One individual may be sufficient if it is a truly representative individual. For example, a chemist is satisfied that a reaction will always take place under given conditions after having performed the experiment once, if he is fairly sure his samples have been typical or representative of the substances involved.

166. NORMAL FREQUENCY DISTRIBUTIONS

If we toss 3 coins there are 4 possible results: no heads, one head, two heads, or three heads. The a priori probability of these results would be $\frac{1}{8}$, $\frac{3}{8}$, $\frac{3}{8}$, $\frac{1}{8}$, respectively. These are the expected relative frequencies with which these results would occur if we made a large number of actual trials. We could represent this theoretical relative frequency distribution by a "step graph" as in Fig. 244. If we toss 4 coins, the a priori probabilities of 0, 1, 2, 3, 4 heads are respectively $\frac{1}{16}$, $\frac{4}{16}$, $\frac{6}{16}$, $\frac{4}{16}$, $\frac{1}{16}$. These theoretical frequencies would yield a step graph like that in Fig. 245. If we toss 6 coins, we get a step graph like that in Fig. 246. As the number of coins increases and the width of each rectangle in the step graph and the unit on the vertical axis are decreased accordingly (Fig. 247), the step graph approaches a smooth curve having the general shape

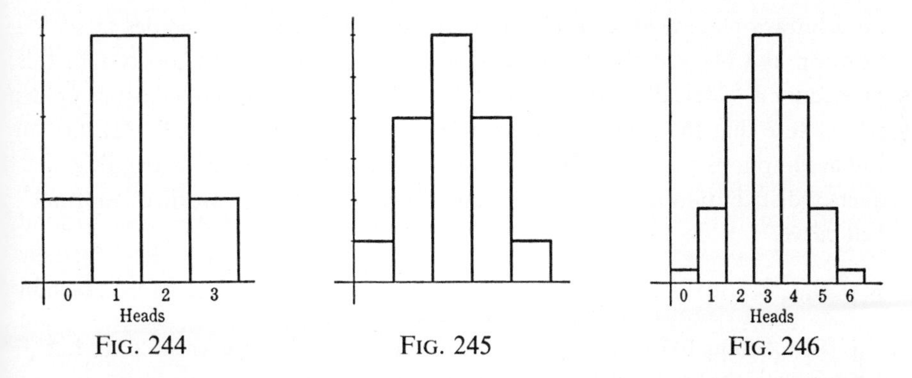

FIG. 244 FIG. 245 FIG. 246

of a bell (Fig. 248). It can be proved that this curve has an equation of the form $y = ce^{-hx^2}$ where c and h are constants and e is the number 2.71828 ... discussed in section 128. This is the so-called normal probability curve or normal frequency distribution. If we make a measurement in the laboratory a large number n of times and we assume (among other things) that the arithmetic mean of our readings is the most probable value, it can be shown that the frequency distribution of our errors will approach a curve of this shape as n increases, and that the

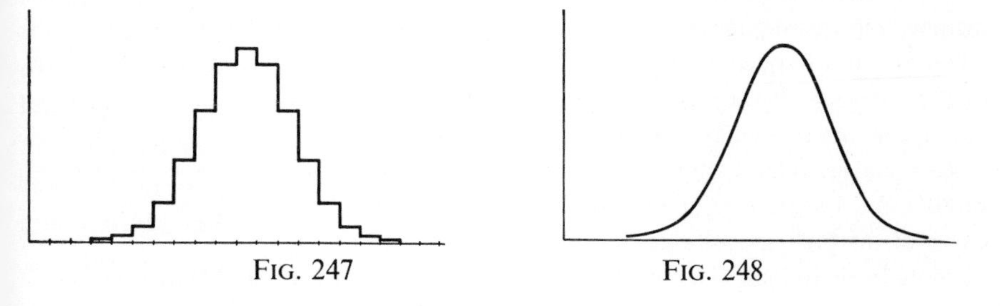
FIG. 247 FIG. 248

area under the curve for a small interval Δx will be proportional to the probability p that an error will be in that interval; that is, the area of this strip divided by the total area under the curve will be p. We cannot go into the details of this curve here except to say that the theorem that a frequency distribution will have approximately that shape is based on many assumptions. It is assumed that the number of cases is very large. It is assumed also that all deviations are due to chance and not to some special one-sided cause. It is silly to attempt to *force* any set of frequencies to fit this bell curve if they do not do so by themselves. For example, to arrange the marks of a class of 30 students so as to conform with the relative frequencies of a bell curve is sheer absurdity. Even if a "very large" number of measurements do not fit a bell curve we have no justification for trying to force them to fit the curve. For example, if a school desires to give 10% of its students a failing grade, 10% a grade of A, and so on, conforming with a bell curve, it certainly may do so; but it should be realized that this amounts to an arbitrary placement of levels of attainment for the various grades in such a position as will yield the desired frequencies. It is not correct to say that this procedure is "logically justified" by the mathematical theory of statistics unless one is sure that the concrete situation we are dealing with actually satisfies all the assumptions on which this part of the theory of statistics is based. A frequency distribution may well look quite different from the so-called "normal" bell curve.

Exercises

1. Toss 4 coins 100 times and compare the actual relative frequencies of 0, 1, 2, 3, 4 heads with the theoretical frequencies given in section 166. Make a step graph like that of Fig. 245 for the actually observed relative frequencies.

2. What would be the theoretical relative frequencies (a priori probabilities) for 0, 1, 2, 3, 4, 5 heads in tossing 5 coins simultaneously? Make a step graph for these probabilities. Actually toss 5 coins 100 times. Make a step graph for the observed relative frequencies.

3. A certain regiment has as a requirement for membership the stipulation that one must be at least 6 feet tall. If a frequency curve is made for the heights of the members of this regiment, the curve looks not like a bell curve but like that of Fig. 249. Why?

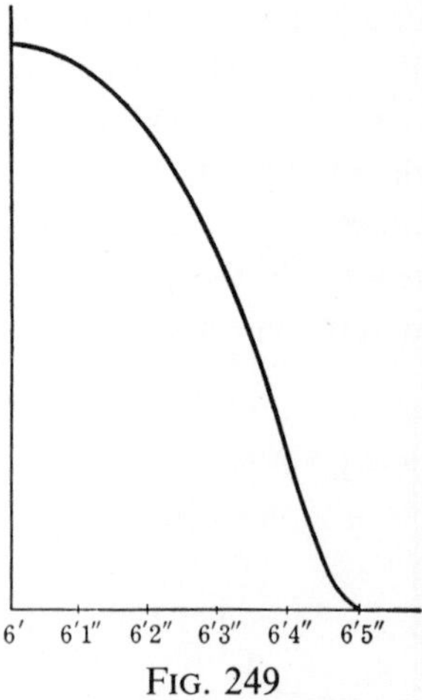

FIG. 249

4. A college requires for entrance an average mark of 80% for 4 years of high school. Would a frequency curve of the high school averages of its entering class be more likely to look like a bell curve or like the curve of Fig. 249? Why?

167. CURVE-FITTING

Suppose a definite number of observations are tabulated which relate two variables x and y. It is often desirable to approximate the functional relationship given by the table by some simple function like $y = f(x)$ where $f(x)$ is a polynomial, say. That is, plotting the points (x, y) given by the table, we want a curve $y = f(x)$ that approximately fits those points. Now, it is intuitively obvious that many different polynomials may approximate the plotted points (Fig. 250). Thus we might choose a straight line, (*aa*, Fig. 250), for the sake of simplicity, as the graph of the function to be used as an approximation to the plotted points. But a curve of degree 2 (*bb*, Fig. 250), 3 (*cc*, Fig. 250), or more might fit even better. In fact, even if we decide that a curve of some definite degree is to be used, there may be many of these which fit the plotted points very well. Thus fitting a curve to a finite number of observations should be accompanied by suitable

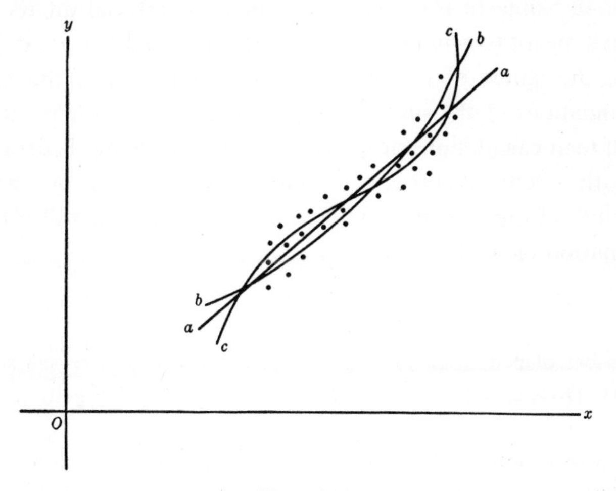

FIG. 250

caution and reservations, especially if the resulting curve or function is to be used for interpolation or extrapolation (prediction). (Compare sections 111 and 164.) Various devices* are studied in statistical theory, such as the "method of least squares," which are designed to minimize the error committed in fitting a curve of definite type to such data; that is, to choose that one of all curves of a definitely chosen degree which fits the data "best." But the logical basis for such

* See M. Richardson, *College Algebra*, Third edition, Prentice-Hall, Englewood Cliffs, N.J., 1966, for discussion of some methods of curve-fitting.

methods, as in the rest of statistics, has to be understood before the methods can be used intelligently. The ultimate test of the value of a fitted curve for the purposes of prediction is the test of experience. Just as in the case of a scientific theory, as long as the curve works well, we may use it; but, if it ceases to work, it must be abandoned or modified.

168. CONCLUSION

It must not be inferred from this chapter that the theory of statistics is worthless. It is, when properly used, an extremely important and useful branch of mathematics. It is of great value as an aid to the inductive reasoning used in experimental sciences, whether physical, chemical, biological, or social, and in making decisions, as we often must, in the face of uncertainty and incomplete information. Its value in insurance, and such commercial affairs, is obvious. What we have meant to point out is that statistical methods are easily misused, especially in the hands of people whose understanding of the mathematical (logical) foundations of the subject is not sufficient to enable them to interpret the results of their calculations properly. For this reason, our belief in statements beginning with "Statistics prove ..." must be conditioned by our knowledge of the reliability of the person who makes the statement, or still better, by first-hand examination of the facts.

Exercises

1. The number of people on relief in a certain town has increased steadily in the past few years. Does this mean that business has been steadily getting worse in that town?

2. The ratio of people on relief to the total population in a certain town has increased steadily in the past few years. Does *this* mean that business has been steadily getting worse in that town? Can you suggest another explanation?

3. The ratio of people convicted of crimes to the total population in a certain town has shown a marked rise in the past 50 years. Does this mean that there is more crime than formerly? Can you suggest another explanation?

4. A newspaper editorial says that business has been improving for the past few years because the annual increases in the number of unemployed have been steadily growing smaller. Criticize.

5. The number of people receiving treatments for neuroses has increased rapidly in the past 10 years. Does this mean that there are more neurotics now than formerly? Discuss.

References

Numbers refer to the bibliography at the back of the book.

Allen 2
Blackwell and Girshick 29
Boulding 33
Braithwaite 37
Bross 42
Burger 44
Bush and Mosteller 45
Chernoff and Moses 49
Churchman, Ackoff and Arnoff 51
Cohen and Nagel 55
Dantzig 61
Dorfman, Samuelson, and Solow 64
Dresher 66
Feller 72
Fry 80
Gale 81
Glicksman 87
Huff 96
Karlin 102
Kemeny, Snell, and Thompson 107
Luce and Raiffa 128
McDonald 131
McKinsey 132
Moroney 135
Morse and Kimball 136
Mosteller, Rourke, and Thomas 137
Ore 142
Peirce 146
Rapoport 153
Saaty 169
Sasieni, Yaspan, and Friedman 170
Schelling 172
Shubik 177, 178
Tucker 192
Vajda 195, 196, 197, 198
von Mises 199
von Neumann and Morgenstern 202
Wilks 211
Williams 212

14

Vectors and Matrices

169. SYSTEMS OF LINEAR EQUATIONS. PIVOT OPERATIONS

We begin with some general ideas which will be immediately followed by concrete examples. A system of m linear equations in n variables $x_1, x_2, \ldots, x_n$ may be written as

$$(1) \qquad \begin{cases} a_{11}x_1 + a_{12}x_2 + \cdots + a_{1j}x_j + \cdots + a_{1n}x_n = k_1 \\ a_{21}x_1 + a_{22}x_2 + \cdots + a_{2j}x_j + \cdots + a_{2n}x_n = k_2 \\ \quad\vdots \qquad\quad \vdots \qquad\qquad\quad \vdots \qquad\qquad\quad \vdots \qquad \vdots \\ a_{i1}x_1 + a_{i2}x_2 + \cdots + a_{ij}x_j + \cdots + a_{in}x_n = k_i \\ \quad\vdots \qquad\quad \vdots \qquad\qquad\quad \vdots \qquad\qquad\quad \vdots \qquad \vdots \\ a_{m1}x_1 + a_{m2}x_2 + \cdots + a_{mj}x_j + \cdots + a_{mn}x_n = k_m \end{cases},$$

where we will suppose that all numbers used are real.

We use subscripts to distinguish the variables $x_1, x_2, \ldots, x_n$ rather than different letters like $x, y, z, \ldots$ in order to deal with any number n of variables at once. The double subscripts attached to the coefficients a_{ij} signify that a_{ij} is the coefficient of the variable x_j in the ith equation. Thus, a_{21} is the coefficient of the first variable x_1 in the second equation.

An ordered n-tuple $[x_1, x_2, \ldots, x_n]$ of real numbers which satisfies all the equations of the system (1) is called a **solution** of the system. The totality of all solutions is termed the **solution-set** of the system. It is the intersection of the truth-sets of the propositional functions expressed by the individual equations of the system.

Another system of p equations in the same number n of variables

$$(2)\qquad \begin{cases} b_{11}x_1 + b_{12}x_2 + \cdots + b_{1j}x_j + \cdots + b_{1n}x_n = h_1 \\ b_{21}x_1 + b_{22}x_2 + \cdots + b_{2j}x_j + \cdots + b_{2n}x_n = h_2 \\ \vdots \\ b_{i1}x_1 + b_{i2}x_2 + \cdots + b_{ij}x_j + \cdots + b_{in}x_n = h_i \\ \vdots \\ b_{p1}x_1 + b_{p2}x_2 + \cdots + b_{pj}x_j + \cdots + b_{pn}x_n = h_p \end{cases}$$

is said to be **equivalent** to system (1) if they have the same solution-set. This is clearly an equivalence relation in the sense of section 12.

If the solution-set of a system (1) is not empty then the system is called **consistent** or **compatible**, otherwise **inconsistent** or **incompatible.**

We consider a single equation, such as the ith equation of (1):

$$(3)\qquad a_{i1}x_1 + a_{i2}x_2 + \cdots + a_{in}x_n = k_i.$$

It is termed a **trivial** equation if all the numbers

$$a_{i1} = a_{i2} = \cdots = a_{in} = k_i = 0.$$

A trivial equation is satisfied by *all* n-tuples $[x_1,x_2, \ldots,x_n]$ and so adjoining such an equation to or deleting such an equation from a system (1) produces an equivalent system.

Multiplying both sides of any equation of (1) by the same non-zero constant c does not affect the solution-set of this equation and hence of the system, since if equals are multiplied by equals the results are equal.

Replacing an equation by the sum of it and a multiple of some other equation, leaving all the remaining equations unaltered, has no effect on the solution-set. For the intersection S of the solution-sets of

$$(4)\qquad \begin{cases} a_{i1}x_1 + \cdots + a_{ij}x_j + \cdots + a_{in}x_n = k_i \\ a_{r1}x_1 + \cdots + a_{rj}x_j + \cdots + a_{rn}x_n = k_r \end{cases}$$

and the intersection S' of the solution-sets of

$$(5)\qquad \begin{cases} a_{i1}x_1 + \cdots + a_{ij}x_j + \cdots + a_{in}x_n = k_i \\ (a_{r1} + ca_{i1})x_1 + \cdots + (a_{rj} + ca_{ij})x_j + \cdots + (a_{rn} + ca_{in})x_n = k_r + ck_i \end{cases}$$

are the same. For, as noted above, the first equation of (4) has the same solution-set as

$$(6)\qquad ca_{i1}x_1 + \cdots + ca_{ij}x_j + \cdots + ca_{in}x_n = ck_i$$

so adjoining this equation (6) to or deleting it from the system (4) has no effect on the solution-set. But adding (6) to the second equation of (4) produces no change in the solution-set, since if equals are added to equals the results are equal. Hence, every solution of (4) is a solution of (5). That is, $S \subset S'$. But by adding $-c$ times the first equation of (5) to the second equation of (5), we return to system (4). Hence, $S' \subset S$. This means that the sets S and S' are equal.

Finally, rearranging the order of the equations in a system clearly has no effect on the solution-set.

Two systems (1) and (2) are called **row-equivalent** if one can be obtained from the other by a finite number of operations of the following kinds:

I. Adjoining or deleting a trivial equation.
II. Replacing an equation by a non-zero constant multiple of it.
III. Replacing an equation by the sum of itself and a constant multiple of another equation.
IV. Rearranging the order of the equations in the system.

The discussion above shows that *if two systems are row-equivalent then they are equivalent.* Clearly row-equivalence is an equivalence relation in the sense of section 12. Operations of types I–IV are called row operations.

If in any system (1), a variable x_j occurs with a non-zero coefficient a_{ij}, then we can multiply it by $1/a_{ij}$ and replace the system by a row-equivalent system in which this equation has the coefficient of x_j equal to 1. Then, by suitable operations of type III, we can make the coefficients of x_j in all other equations equal to 0. This operation is called a **pivot operation** with pivot element a_{ij}.

Example 1. The system

$$(7)\qquad \begin{cases} 2x_1 + 4x_2 + 6x_3 = 18 \\ 2x_1 - x_2 + 2x_3 = 11 \\ 3x_1 + 4x_2 - 2x_3 = -4 \end{cases}$$

becomes, by multiplying the first equation by $\frac{1}{2}$,

$$(8)\qquad \begin{cases} x_1 + 2x_2 + 3x_3 = 9 \\ 2x_1 - x_2 + 2x_3 = 11 \\ 3x_1 + 4x_2 - 2x_3 = -4. \end{cases}$$

Adding -2 times the first equation of (8) to the second, and then adding -3 times the first equation of (8) to the third, we get

$$(9)\qquad \begin{cases} x_1 + 2x_2 + 3x_3 = 9 \\ - 5x_2 - 4x_3 = -7 \\ - 2x_2 - 11x_3 = -31. \end{cases}$$

This completes a pivot operation with pivot element $a_{11} = 2$. This process can now be continued so that $1x_2$ stands alone in the second vertical column in some equation other than the first. For this we use pivot element $a_{32} = -2$ in (9). That is, we can first multiply the third equation by $-\frac{1}{2}$, obtaining

$$(10)\qquad \begin{cases} x_1 + 2x_2 + 3x_3 = 9 \\ \quad - 5x_2 - 4x_3 = -7 \\ \quad\quad x_2 + \frac{11}{2} x_3 = \frac{31}{2}. \end{cases}$$

Now adding -2 times the third equation to the first, and then adding 5 times the third equation to the second, we get

$$(11)\qquad \begin{cases} x_1 \quad - \quad 8x_3 = -22 \\ \quad\quad + \frac{47}{2} x_3 = \frac{141}{2} \\ \quad x_2 + \frac{11}{2} x_3 = \frac{31}{2}. \end{cases}$$

We now try to get x_3 to have the coefficient one in the second equation. For this we use pivot element $a_{23} = \frac{47}{2}$. That is, multiplying the second equation by $\frac{2}{47}$, we get

$$(12)\qquad \begin{cases} x_1 \quad - 8x_3 = -22 \\ \quad\quad\quad x_3 = \quad 3 \\ \quad x_2 + \frac{11}{2} x_3 = \frac{31}{2}. \end{cases}$$

Then, adding 8 times the second equation to the first, and then adding $-\frac{11}{2}$ times the second equation to the third, we get 0 as the coefficient of x_3 in the remaining equations, obtaining

$$(13)\qquad \begin{cases} x_1 \quad\quad\quad = \quad 2 \\ \quad\quad\quad x_3 = \quad 3 \\ \quad x_2 \quad\quad = -1. \end{cases}$$

Since this simple system is equivalent to the original system, we have solved the original system. The ordered triple [2, −1, 3] satisfies it and is the only solution.

In general we try to get as many of the unknowns as possible to stand alone in their columns with coefficient 1, each such unknown appearing in a different equation.

Example 2. The system

$$\begin{cases} x_1 + \ x_2 - 2x_3 = 3 \\ x_1 - 2x_2 + \ x_3 = 1 \end{cases}$$

becomes, by adding -1 times the first equation to the second,

$$\begin{cases} x_1 + \ x_2 - 2x_3 = 3 \\ \quad - 3x_2 + 3x_3 = -2. \end{cases}$$

By multiplying the second equation by $\frac{1}{3}$, we get

$$\begin{cases} x_1 + x_2 - 2x_3 = \quad 3 \\ \quad - x_2 + \ x_3 = -\frac{2}{3}. \end{cases}$$

By adding twice the second equation to the first, we get

$$\begin{cases} x_1 - x_2 \qquad = \frac{5}{3} \\ \quad - x_2 + x_3 = -\frac{2}{3} \end{cases}$$

or

$$\begin{cases} x_1 = \frac{5}{3} + x_2 \\ x_3 = -\frac{2}{3} + x_2, \end{cases}$$

which means that for any arbitrary value $x_2 = a$, the ordered triples $[x_1 = \frac{5}{3} + a, x_2 = a, x_3 = -\frac{2}{3} + a]$ satisfy the system. The solution set here is infinite. Thus, if $a = 0$, $x_1 = \frac{5}{3}, x_2 = 0, x_3 = -\frac{2}{3}$ is a solution; if $a = 7$, then $x_1 = \frac{5}{3} + 7, x_2 = 7, x_3 = -\frac{2}{3} + 7$ is a solution; and so on.

Example 3. The system

$$\begin{cases} x_1 + x_2 + x_3 = 6 \\ 2x_1 + 2x_2 + 2x_3 = 12 \end{cases}$$

becomes, by adding -2 times the first equation to the second,

$$\begin{cases} x_1 + x_2 + x_3 = 6 \\ \qquad\qquad 0 = 0. \end{cases}$$

Deleting the trivial equation, we have

$$x_1 = 6 - x_2 - x_3,$$

which means that for arbitrary values $x_2 = a$, $x_3 = b$, the triples $[x_1 = 6 - a - b, x_2 = a, x_3 = b]$ satisfy the system. The solution-set is infinite.

Example 4. The system

$$\begin{cases} x_1 + x_2 + x_3 = 6 \\ x_1 + x_2 + x_3 = 5 \end{cases}$$

becomes, by adding -1 times the first equation to the second,

$$\begin{cases} x_1 + x_2 + x_3 = 6 \\ \qquad\qquad 0 = -1. \end{cases}$$

Since no triple can satisfy this last equation, the system is inconsistent.

Any system can be reduced to a row-equivalent system by pivot operations such that as many variables as possible appear alone, with coefficient one, in their columns, each such variable appearing in a different equation, and all trivial equations being deleted. When this is done, as in the above examples, the resulting system is said to be in **reduced form** and a maximal set of different variables in different equations, each appearing alone in its column with coefficient one may be called a set of **basic variables**. If a self-contradictory equation, such as $0 = -1$ in example 4, appears in the reduced system, the system is inconsistent. If not, by transposing the non-basic variables to the right members, we are able to write an expression for all solution n-tuples of the system.

Remark. To save the clerical bother of copying the variables over and over during the pivot operations, one can detach the coefficients and work with the tableau of numbers, keeping them aligned in labeled columns. Thus, example 2 may be solved as follows

$$\begin{array}{ccc|c} x_1 & x_2 & x_3 & \\ \hline \textcircled{1} & 1 & -2 & 3 \\ 1 & -2 & 1 & 1 \end{array}.$$

We circle the pivot element $a_{11} = 1$ and add -1 times the first row to the second, obtaining

$$\begin{array}{ccc|c} 1 & 1 & -2 & 3 \\ 0 & -3 & \textcircled{3} & -2 \end{array}.$$

Multiplying the second row by $\frac{1}{3}$ to obtain a 1 instead of the circled 3 to pivot on, we get

$$\begin{array}{ccc|c} 1 & 1 & -2 & 3 \\ 0 & -1 & \textcircled{1} & -\frac{2}{3} \end{array}.$$

Pivoting on the circled element, we add twice the second row to the first, obtaining

$$\begin{array}{ccc|c} 1 & -1 & 0 & \frac{5}{3} \\ 0 & -1 & 1 & -\frac{2}{3} \end{array}$$

which is in reduced form. From this we read the solutions

$$\begin{cases} x_1 = \frac{5}{3} + x_2 \\ x_3 = -\frac{2}{3} + x_2 \end{cases}$$

as before.

Exercises

Use pivot operations to obtain a reduced equivalent system and thus find all solutions of each of the following systems.

1.–12. The systems of exercises 1–12, section 45.

13. $\begin{cases} x_1 + 2x_2 = 5 \\ 3x_1 + 6x_2 = 15. \end{cases}$

14. $\begin{cases} x_1 + 2x_2 + 3x_3 = 9 \\ 2x_1 - x_2 + 2x_3 = 11 \\ 3x_1 + 4x_2 - 2x_3 = -4. \end{cases}$

15. $\begin{cases} x_1 + x_2 = -4 \\ x_1 + x_3 = 1 \\ 3x_1 - x_2 + 2x_3 = 4. \end{cases}$

16. $\begin{cases} 2x_1 + 3x_2 + x_3 = 2 \\ 6x_1 + 6x_2 + 2x_3 = 5 \\ 12x_1 - 12x_2 - x_3 = 0. \end{cases}$

17. $\begin{cases} x_1 - x_2 + 2x_3 = 4 \\ 2x_1 + 3x_2 - x_3 = 5 \\ 3x_1 + 2x_2 + x_3 = 8. \end{cases}$

18. $\begin{cases} x_1 + 2x_2 + 3x_3 = 4 \\ 3x_1 - x_2 + 2x_3 = 2 \\ 5x_1 + 3x_2 + 8x_3 = 11. \end{cases}$

19. $\begin{cases} x_1 + x_2 = 7 \\ x_1 - x_2 = 3 \\ x_1 - 2x_2 = 1. \end{cases}$

20. $\begin{cases} x_1 + x_2 = 1 \\ x_1 - x_2 = 3 \\ 2x_1 - x_2 = 11. \end{cases}$

21. $\begin{cases} x_1 + 2x_2 + 3x_3 = 4 \\ 2x_1 + 4x_2 + 6x_3 = 7. \end{cases}$

22. $\begin{cases} x_1 + 2x_2 + 3x_3 = 4 \\ 2x_1 + 4x_2 + 6x_3 = 8. \end{cases}$

23. $\begin{cases} x_1 + x_2 - 4x_3 = 6 \\ x_1 - x_2 + 10x_3 = -2. \end{cases}$

24. $\begin{cases} x_1 + x_2 + x_3 = 0 \\ x_1 + 2x_2 + x_3 = 0 \\ 2x_1 + 3x_2 + 2x_3 = 0. \end{cases}$

25. $\begin{cases} 2x_1 + x_2 + x_3 = 0 \\ 3x_1 + 2x_2 + 4x_3 = 0 \\ x_1 - 2x_2 - 3x_3 = 0. \end{cases}$

26. $\begin{cases} x_1 - 2x_2 - 3x_3 = 2 \\ x_1 - 4x_2 - 13x_3 = 14 \\ -3x_1 + 5x_2 + 4x_3 = 0. \end{cases}$

27. $\begin{cases} 2x_1 + 3x_2 - x_3 + x_4 = 5 \\ 3x_1 + 4x_2 + 2x_4 = 9 \\ x_1 + x_2 + x_3 + x_4 = 4. \end{cases}$

28. $\begin{cases} x_1 + x_2 - x_3 - x_4 + 2x_5 = 1 \\ 2x_1 + 3x_2 - 4x_3 - 2x_4 + 3x_5 = 1 \\ 4x_1 + 5x_2 - 6x_3 - 4x_4 + 7x_5 = 3. \end{cases}$

29. $\begin{cases} x_1 + x_2 + x_3 + 3x_4 = 3 \\ 3x_1 + x_2 - x_3 = 0 \\ 2x_1 - 2x_2 - x_3 + 6x_4 = 4 \\ 4x_1 - x_2 - 2x_3 - 3x_4 = 0. \end{cases}$

30. $\begin{cases} x_1 - x_2 + x_3 - x_4 + x_5 = 1 \\ 2x_1 - x_2 + 3x_3 + 4x_5 = 2 \\ 3x_1 - 2x_2 + 2x_3 + x_4 + x_5 = 1 \\ x_1 + x_3 + 2x_4 + x_5 = 0. \end{cases}$

170. VECTORS

In section 141, it was pointed out that any vector in the plane or in three-dimensional space may be represented by a bound vector or directed line-segment with any initial point whatever. Let us select a representative line segment $\overrightarrow{OP}$ with initial point at the origin O. Then the coordinates of the terminal point P are called the **components** of the vector. In the plane, therefore, a vector may be represented by an ordered pair of real numbers $[x, y]$ or $[x_1, x_2]$, and in three-dimensional space by an ordered triple of real numbers $[x, y, z]$ or $[x_1, x_2, x_3]$. We extend this algebraic language to n-dimensional space, and call an ordered n-tuple of real numbers

$$X = [x_1, x_2, \ldots, x_n]$$

a **vector in *n*-dimensional space**, or an ***n*-vector**.

Two vectors $X = [x_1,x_2,\ldots,x_n]$ and $Y = [y_1,y_2,\ldots,y_n]$ are called **equal** if and only if $x_1 = y_1$, $x_2 = y_2,\ldots$, $x_n = y_n$, that is, corresponding components are equal.

By ***n*-dimensional space** R^n, we shall mean the set of all n-vectors.

In the plane R^2 it is clear from Fig. 251 that the resultant or sum of the two vectors $X = [x_1,x_2]$ and $Y = [y_1,y_2]$ is the vector $X + Y = [x_1 + y_1, x_2 + y_2]$ obtained by adding the first components of the two vectors to obtain the first component of the sum and similarly for the second components. In three-dimensional space R^3, it can also be proved that the resultant of the vectors $X = [x_1,x_2,x_3]$ and $Y = [y_1,y_2,y_3]$ is the vector $X + Y = [x_1 + y_1, x_2 + y_2, x_3 + y_3]$. Hence, we extend this idea to n-dimensional space and define the **sum** of two vectors $X = [x_1,x_2,\ldots,x_n]$ and $Y = [y_1,y_2,\ldots,y_n]$ as the vector $X + Y = [x_1 + y_1, x_2 + y_2,\ldots,x_n + y_n]$.

We define the **difference** $X - Y$ of the two n-vectors X and Y to be the n-vector Z such that $Y + Z = X$; it is easily seen that $Z = [x_1 - y_1, x_2 - y_2,\ldots, x_n - y_n]$.

In the plane, it is easily seen from Fig. 252 that a vector in the same direction and sense as X and 3 times as long has components $[3x_1,3x_2]$, each component of X being multiplied by 3. Similarly, a vector in the opposite sense and twice as long has components $[-2x_1,-2x_2]$, each component of X being multiplied by -2.

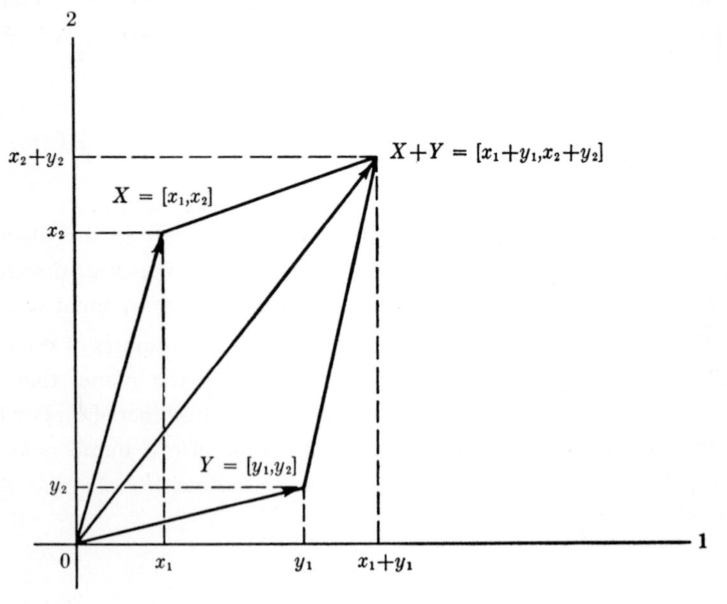

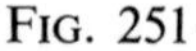
FIG. 251

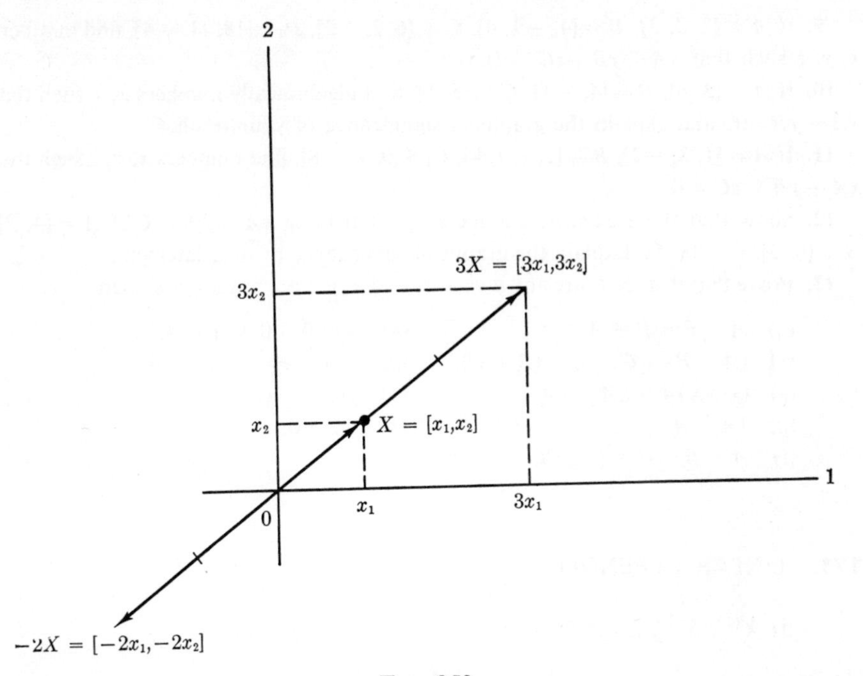

FIG. 252

A similar result can be proved for 3-dimensional space. Hence, we define the **product** of a vector in n-dimensional space $X = [x_1, x_2, \ldots, x_n]$ by a real number c to be the vector $cX = [cx_1, cx_2, \ldots, cx_n]$ obtained by multiplying each component by c. Clearly, $X - Y = X + (-1)Y$.

In the present chapter, we shall call the real numbers **scalars**, and shall denote them by small letters, while vectors will be denoted by capital letters. *The vector all of whose components are zeros, is denoted by* $0 = [0, 0, \ldots, 0]$.

Examples. In the plane, if the vectors X and Y are given by $X = [1,2]$, $Y = [-2,1]$, then $X + Y = [-1,3]$, $2X = [2,4]$, $3Y = [-6,3]$, $2X + 3Y = [-4,7]$.

Exercises

If $X = [3,5]$ *and* $Y = [2,-1]$, *find algebraically and picture graphically the vector:*

1. $X + Y$. **2.** $X - Y$. **3.** $2X$. **4.** $2X - 3Y$.

If $X = [1, 3, -2]$, $Y = [2, -1, 3]$, *and* $Z = [0, 0, 1]$, *find*

5. $X + Y + Z$. **6.** $3X - Y + 2Z$. **7.** $2X + (-1)Y + (-2)Z$.

8. If $A = [2, 3]$, $B = [-1, 4]$, $C = [7, -6]$, find algebraically numbers x and y such that $xA + yB = C$ and explain the graphical significance of your result.

9. If $A = [2, 2, 3]$, $B = [4, -1, 4]$, $C = [6, 2, -2]$, $D = [18, 11, -4]$, find numbers x, y, z such that $xA + yB + zC = D$.

10. If $A = [3, 6]$, $B = [4, -1]$, $C = [5, 1]$, find algebraically numbers x, y such that $xA + yB = C$ and explain the graphical significance of your result.

11. If $A = [1, 3, -2]$, $B = [2, -1, 4]$, $C = [0, 7, -8]$, find numbers x, y, z such that $xA + yB + zC = 0$.

12. Show that there exist no numbers x, y satisfying $xA + yB = C$ if $A = [4, 2]$, $B = [6, 3]$, $C = [8, 5]$. Explain the graphical significance of this statement.

13. Prove that if A, B, C are any n-vectors and x, y, z are any scalars, then

(*a*) $A + B = B + A$. (*b*) $A + 0 = 0 + A = A$.

(*c*) $(A + B) + C = A + (B + C)$. (*d*) $x(A + B) = xA + xB$.

(*e*) $(x + y)A = xA + yA$. (*f*) $y(zC) = (yz)C$.

(*g*) $1A = A$. (*h*) $0A = 0$.

(*i*) $A - B = A + (-1)B$.

171. LINEAR DEPENDENCE

If $X^{(1)}, X^{(2)}, \ldots, X^{(p)}$ are p n-vectors, then the vector

$$c_1X^{(1)} + c_2X^{(2)} + \cdots + c_pX^{(p)} \tag{1}$$

is called a **linear combination** of the vectors $X^{(1)}, X^{(2)}, \ldots, X^{(p)}$ with coefficients $c_1, c_2, \ldots, c_p$. If at least one of the numbers c_i is different from zero, the linear combination (1) is called **non-trivial**.

Example 1. In the plane ($n = 2$), let $X^{(1)} = [1,2]$ $X^{(2)} = [-2,1]$. Then $X^{(3)} = 2X^{(1)} + 3X^{(2)}$ is a linear combination of $X^{(1)}$ and $X^{(2)}$ with coefficients $c_1 = 2$, $c_2 = 3$. Here, $X^{(3)} = [-4,7]$.

If a non-empty set of p vectors $\{X^{(1)}, X^{(2)}, \ldots, X^{(p)}\}$ is such that there exists a non-trivial linear combination of them which is equal to the zero vector, the set is called **linearly dependent**. Otherwise, the set is termed **linearly independent**.

Example 2. In the plane R^2, the set of vectors $\{X^{(1)}, X^{(2)}, X^{(3)}\}$ given in example 1, is linearly dependent. For if $c_1 = 2$, $c_2 = 3$, and $c_3 = -1$, then the non-trivial linear combination $2X^{(1)} + 3X^{(2)} + (-1)X^{(3)}$ is equal to the zero-vector $0 = [0,0]$.

Remark. If two vectors are proportional, then they form a linearly dependent set. For example, the vectors $X^{(1)} = [1, 2]$ and $X^{(2)} = [3, 6]$ are proportional since $3X^{(1)} = X^{(2)}$; that is $\frac{3}{1} = \frac{6}{2} = 3$ or $3 = 3 \cdot 1$ and $6 = 3 \cdot 2$. But then $3X^{(1)} + (-1)X^{(2)}$ is equal to the zero vector $0 = [0,0]$. Hence, *linear dependence may be thought of as a generalization of the concept of proportionality.*

We can decide whether or not a set of vectors is linearly dependent by solving a system of linear equations.

Example 3. To decide whether or not the set of vectors $\{X^{(1)}, X^{(2)}, X^{(3)}\}$, where $X^{(1)} = [1, 0, 1]$, $X^{(2)} = [1, 2, 0]$, $X^{(3)} = [0, 1, 3]$, is linearly dependent let c_1, c_2, c_3 be unknowns and consider the vector equation $c_1X^{(1)} + c_2X^{(2)} + c_3X^{(3)} = 0$ or $c_1[1, 0, 1] + c_2[1, 2, 0] + c_3[0, 1, 3] = [0, 0, 0]$ which is the same as the system

$$\begin{cases} c_1 + c_2 = 0 \\ 2c_2 + c_3 = 0 \\ c_1 + 3c_3 = 0. \end{cases}$$

Solving this system, we get $c_1 = c_2 = c_3 = 0$ as the only solution. Hence, the given set of vectors is linearly independent.

Example 4. Decide whether the set of vectors $\{X^{(1)}, X^{(2)}, X^{(3)}\}$, where $X^{(1)} = [2, 0, 2]$, $X^{(2)} = [3, 0, 3]$, $X^{(3)} = [1, 1, 1]$, are linearly dependent or not. The vector equation

$$c_1[2, 0, 2] + c_2[3, 0, 3] + c_3[1, 1, 1] = [0, 0, 0]$$

is the same as the system

$$\begin{cases} 2c_1 + 3c_2 + c_3 = 0 \\ c_3 = 0 \\ 2c_1 + 3c_2 + c_3 = 0 \end{cases}$$

which reduces to

$$2c_1 + 3c_2 = 0$$

or

$$c_1 = -\tfrac{3}{2}c_2.$$

Hence, its solutions are all given by $c_1 = -\frac{3}{2}a$, $c_2 = a$, $c_3 = 0$, for arbitrary a. In particular, taking $a = 1$, for example,

$$-\tfrac{3}{2}X^{(1)} + X^{(2)} + 0 \cdot X^{(3)} = [0, 0, 0],$$

showing that the given set of vectors is linearly dependent.

Exercises

1. (*a*) If $X^{(1)} = [2, 0]$, $X^{(2)} = [0, 3]$, $X^{(3)} = [6, -6]$, show that the set $\{X^{(1)}, X^{(2)}, X^{(3)}\}$ is linearly dependent.

(*b*) Express each of $X^{(1)}$, $X^{(2)}$, $X^{(3)}$ as a linear combination of the other two.

(*c*) Show that every pair of these vectors is linearly independent.

2. If $X^{(1)} = [1, 0, 0]$, $X^{(2)} = [1, 2, 0]$, $X^{(3)} = [1, 2, 3]$, show that the set $\{X^{(1)}, X^{(2)}, X^{(3)}\}$ is linearly independent.

3. (*a*) If $X^{(1)} = [2, 4]$, $X^{(2)} = [3, 6]$, $X^{(3)} = [1, 5]$, show that the set $\{X^{(1)}, X^{(2)}, X^{(3)}\}$ is linearly dependent.

(*b*) Express each of $X^{(1)}$ and $X^{(2)}$ as a linear combination of the other two.

(*c*) Show that $X^{(3)}$ cannot be expressed as a linear combination of the other two, and explain the geometrical significance of this fact.

(*d*) Show that $\{X^{(1)}, X^{(3)}\}$ is a linearly independent set.

(*e*) Show that $\{X^{(2)}, X^{(3)}\}$ is a linearly independent set.

(*f*) Show that $\{X^{(1)}, X^{(2)}\}$ is a linearly dependent set.

4. If $X^{(1)} = [1, 2, 3]$, $X^{(2)} = [2, -1, 1]$, $X^{(3)} = [-1, 3, 1]$, show that the set $\{X^{(1)}, X^{(2)}, X^{(3)}\}$ is linearly dependent.

5. Show that any set of vectors $\{X^{(1)}, X^{(2)}, \ldots, X^{(k)}\}$ in R^n of which the zero-vector is a member (that is, some $X^{(i)} = 0$) is linearly dependent.

6. Show that if $\{X^{(1)}, X^{(2)}, \ldots, X^{(k)}\}$ is any linearly dependent set then there is at least one vector $X^{(i)}$ in the set which is expressible as a linear combination of the others, and conversely.

7. Show that any non-empty subset of a linearly independent set is linearly independent.

8. Show that any superset of a linearly dependent set is linearly dependent.

9. (*a*) Prove that if the set $\{X^{(1)}, X^{(2)}, \ldots, X^{(k)}\}$ is linearly independent and the set $\{X^{(1)}, X^{(2)}, \ldots, X^{(k)}, Y\}$ is linearly dependent, then Y is expressible as a linear combination of $X^{(1)}, X^{(2)}, \ldots, X^{(k)}$.

(*b*) Prove that under the same hypothesis as part (*a*), if $Y = c_1 X^{(1)} + c_2 X^{(2)} + \ldots + c_k X^{(k)}$ and also $Y = d_1 X^{(1)} + d_2 X^{(2)} + \ldots + d_k X^{(k)}$, then $c_1 = d_1$, $c_2 = d_2$, ..., $c_k = d_k$; that is, the linear expression is unique.

(*c*) Prove that if $\{X^{(1)}, X^{(2)}, \ldots, X^{(k)}\}$ is linearly independent and Y is not expressible as a linear combination of $X^{(1)}, X^{(2)}, \ldots, X^{(k)}$, then $\{X^{(1)}, X^{(2)}, \ldots, X^{(k)}, Y\}$ is linearly independent.

10. Prove that if any two of the vectors in the set $\{X^{(1)}, X^{(2)}, \ldots, X^{(k)}\}$ are equal (for example, $X^{(i)} = X^{(j)}$), then the set is linearly dependent.

★11. Discuss the geometric significance of a pair on non-zero vectors in R^2 being linearly dependent.

★12. Discuss the geometric significance of a triplet of non-zero vectors in R^3 being linearly dependent.

13. (*a*) Prove that in R^2 the unit vectors $E^{(1)} = [1, 0]$ and $E^{(2)} = [0, 1]$ constitute a linearly independent set.

(*b*) Express an arbitrary vector $A = [a_1, a_2]$ as a linear combination of $E^{(1)}$ and $E^{(2)}$.

14. (*a*) Prove that in R^3 the unit vectors $E^{(1)} = [1, 0, 0]$, $E^{(2)} = [0, 1, 0]$, $E^{(3)} = [0, 0, 1]$ constitute a linearly independent set.

(*b*) Express an arbitrary vector $A = [a_1, a_2, a_3]$ as a linear combination of $E^{(1)}$, $E^{(2)}$ and $E^{(3)}$.

172. BASIS AND DIMENSION

A subset $B = \{X^{(1)}, X^{(2)}, \ldots, X^{(n)}\}$ of vectors of a set S is said to be a **basis** for set S if B is linearly independent and if every vector of S can be expressed as a linear combination of the vectors of B. For example, in the plane, the unit vectors $E^{(1)} = [1,0]$ and $E^{(2)} = [0,1]$ form a basis (exercise 13, section 171).

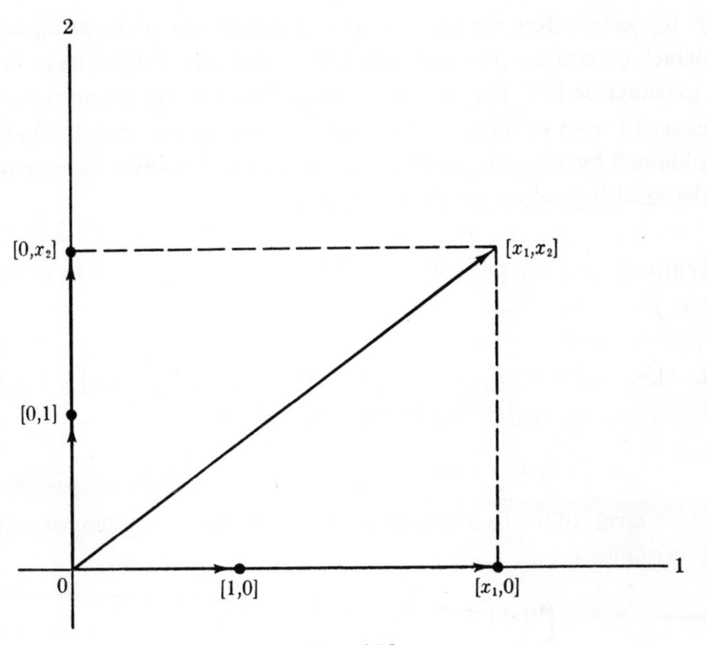

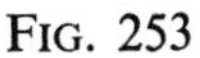
FIG. 253

Similarly, it can be shown that the **unit *n*-vectors**

$$
(1) \qquad \begin{cases} E^{(1)} = [1, 0, 0, \ldots, 0, 0] \\ E^{(2)} = [0, 1, 0, \ldots, 0, 0] \\ E^{(3)} = [0, 0, 1, \ldots, 0, 0] \\ \vdots \\ E^{(n)} = [0, 0, 0, \ldots, 0, 1], \end{cases}
$$

where the ith component of $E^{(i)}$ is 1 and the other $n - 1$ components are zeros, form a basis for R^n. (Exercise 1, below.)

The maximum number of elements in any linearly independent subset of S is called the **rank**, or **linear dimension** or, simply, the **dimension** of S.

A system of linear equations, such as (1) of section 169, is called a system of **homogeneous** linear equations if all the constant terms $k_1, \ldots, k_m$ are equal to zero.

Theorem 1. *Any system of m homogeneous equations in n variables with $m < n$ has a non-trivial solution, that is, a solution vector with at least one non-zero component.*

Proof. By section 169, we can use row operations to arrive at an equivalent system which is reduced. The number of basic variables cannot be more than m and hence must be less than n. Transposing the terms involving the non-basic variables to the right members of the equations, we see that non-trivial solutions can be obtained by assigning to any non-basic variables any non-zero value and taking the resulting values for the basic variables.

Theorem 2. *Any set $\{A^{(1)}, A^{(2)}, \ldots, A^{(n+1)}\}$ of $n+1$ vectors in R^n is linearly dependent.*

Proof. Let $A^{(1)} = [a_{11}, a_{12}, \ldots, a_{1n}]$, $A^{(2)} = [a_{21}, a_{22}, \ldots, a_{2n}], \ldots,$ $A^{(n+1)} = [a_{n+1,1}, a_{n+1,2}, \ldots, a_{n+1,n}]$. Consider the equation

$$c_1 A^{(1)} + c_2 A^{(2)} + \cdots + c_{n+1} A^{(n+1)} = 0.$$

Expressed in terms of the n components separately, this is a system of n equations in $n+1$ variables $c_1, \ldots, c_{n+1}$:

$$\begin{cases} a_{11}c_1 + a_{21}c_2 + \cdots + a_{n+1,1}c_{n+1} = 0 \\ a_{12}c_1 + a_{22}c_2 + \cdots + a_{n+1,2}c_{n+1} = 0 \\ \quad \vdots \qquad\quad \vdots \qquad\qquad\quad \vdots \\ a_{1n}c_1 + a_{2n}c_2 + \cdots + a_{n+1,n}c_{n+1} = 0. \end{cases}$$

By Theorem 1, this system has a non-trivial solution $[c_1, c_2, \ldots, c_{n+1}]$. This completes the proof.

Theorem 3. *The dimension of R^n is n.*

Proof. The set (1) of unit vectors is a basis (exercise 1, below) having n vectors. Thus, the dimension of R^n is $\geqq n$. But, by theorem 2, the dimension of R^n is $\leqq n$. Therefore, it is n. This proves the theorem.

Theorem 4. *Any basis of R^n has n vectors.*

Proof. Let $\{B^{(1)}, B^{(2)}, \ldots, B^{(k)}\}$ be any basis. By theorem 2, k cannot be more than n. Suppose k were less than n. Then, each vector $E^{(i)}$ of (1) is expressible as a linear combination of $B^{(1)}, B^{(2)}, \ldots, B^{(k)}$:

$$E^{(i)} = a_{i1}B^{(1)} + a_{i2}B^{(2)} + \cdots + a_{ik}B^{(k)} \qquad (i = 1, 2, \ldots, n).$$

Consider the linear combination

$$\begin{aligned} c_1E^{(1)} + c_2E^{(2)} + \cdots + c_nE^{(n)} &= c_1(a_{11}B^{(1)} + a_{12}B^{(2)} + \cdots + a_{1k}B^{(k)}) \\ &\quad + c_2(a_{21}B^{(1)} + a_{22}B^{(2)} + \cdots + a_{2k}B^{(k)}) \\ &\quad \cdots \\ &\quad + c_n(a_{n1}B^{(1)} + a_{n2}B^{(2)} + \cdots + a_{nk}B^{(k)}) \\ &= (c_1a_{11} + c_2a_{21} + \cdots + c_na_{n1})B^{(1)} \\ &\quad + (c_1a_{12} + c_2a_{22} + \cdots + c_na_{n2})B^{(2)} \\ &\quad \cdots \\ &\quad + (c_1a_{1k} + c_2a_{2k} + \cdots + c_na_{nk})B^{(k)}. \end{aligned} \tag{2}$$

By theorem 1, the system of k equations

$$\begin{cases} c_1a_{11} + c_2a_{21} + \cdots + c_na_{n1} = 0 \\ c_1a_{12} + c_2a_{22} + \cdots + c_na_{n2} = 0 \\ \cdots \\ c_1a_{1k} + c_2a_{2k} + \cdots + c_na_{nk} = 0 \end{cases}$$

has a non-trivial solution $[c_1, c_2, \ldots, c_n]$ since $k < n$. Hence, the vector equation

$$c_1E^{(1)} + c_2E^{(2)} + \cdots + c_nE^{(n)} = 0$$

has a non-trivial solution contrary to the linear independence of (1). Since k is not less than n and not more than n, we have $k = n$. This completes the proof.

Exercises

1. Show that the unit vectors $E^{(1)}, \ldots, E^{(n)}$ of R^n given in (1) constitute a basis for R^n.
2. Show that $A^{(1)} = [1, 2]$ and $A^{(2)} = [2, 1]$ constitute a basis for R^2.
3. Show that $A^{(1)} = [0, 1, 1]$, $A^{(2)} = [1, 0, 1]$, $A^{(3)} = [1, 1, 0]$ constitute a basis for R^3.
4. Show that if $\{A^{(1)}, A^{(2)}, A^{(3)}\}$ is a basis for R^3 so is $\{B^{(1)}, B^{(2)}, B^{(3)}\}$, where $B^{(1)} = A^{(2)} + A^{(3)}$, $B^{(2)} = A^{(3)} + A^{(1)}$ and $B^{(3)} = A^{(1)} + A^{(2)}$.
5. Prove that any set of more than n vectors in R^n is linearly dependent.
6. Prove that any linearly independent set of n vectors in R^n is a basis.
7. Prove that if $\{B^{(1)}, B^{(2)}, \ldots, B^{(n)}\}$ is any basis for R^n and if $A^{(1)} = a_1B^{(1)}$, $A^{(2)} = a_2B^{(2)}, \ldots, A^{(n)} = a_nB^{(n)}$, where $a_1, a_2, \ldots, a_n$ are any non-zero numbers, then $\{A^{(1)}, A^{(2)}, \ldots, A^{(n)}\}$ is a basis for R^n.

Find the dimension of each set of vectors:

8. {[1, 2], [2, 4], [3, 6]}.
9. {[2, 4, 6], [3, 6, 9], [1, 0, 1]}.
10. {[2, −1, 3], [−4, 2, −6], [−6, 3, −9]}.
11. {[1, 2, 3], [2, 3, 1], [−4, 1, −2]}.
12. {[1, 1, 1, 1], [1, 0, −1, 0], [0, 1, 1, −1], [2, 0, −1, −3]}.
13. {[1, 0, 1, 0], [0, 1, 1, 0], [1, 1, 0, 0], [2, 2, 2, 0]}.

173. INNER PRODUCT

If $X = [x_1, x_2, \ldots, x_n]$ and $Y = [y_1, y_2, \ldots, y_n]$ are two vectors of n components each, the real number $x_1 y_1 + x_2 y_2 + \ldots + x_n y_n$ is called the **inner product** of X and Y and is denoted by $X \cdot Y$. For example, if $X = [1,2,3]$ and $Y = [2,0,4]$, then $X \cdot Y = 1 \cdot 2 + 2 \cdot 0 + 3 \cdot 4 = 14$. Applications of this quantity are numerous. For example, if we purchase 3 different commodities, the first at a price of 1 dollar per unit, the second at a price of 2 dollars per unit, the third at a price of 3 dollars per unit, and if we buy 2 units of the first commodity, no units of the second, and 4 units of the third, then the total cost of our purchase is the inner product of [1,2,3] and [2,0,4] which is 14 dollars as seen above. In section 156, mathematical expectation was in fact the inner product of a "probability vector" $[p_1, p_2, p_3, \ldots, p_n]$ and a "reward vector" $[R_1, R_2, R_3, \ldots, R_n]$. A geometric interpretation will follow.

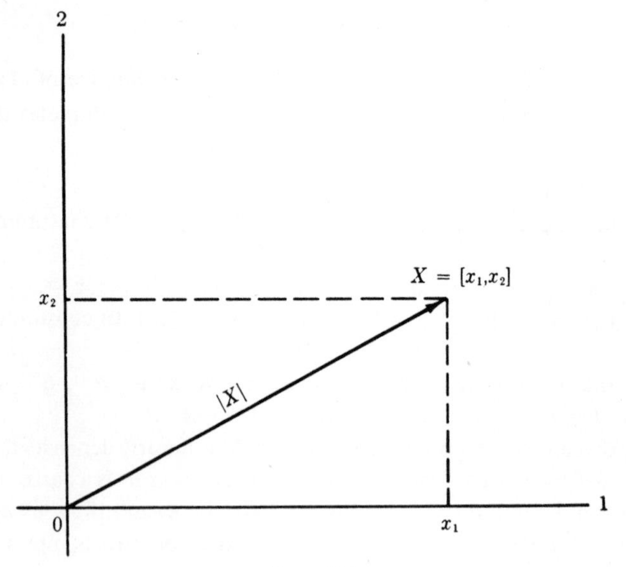

FIG. 254

In the plane, the length of a vector $X = [x_1,x_2]$ is the distance from the origin O to the point with rectangular coordinates $[x_1,x_2]$ or $\sqrt{x_1^2 + x_2^2}$. It is not difficult to prove that in three-dimensional space, the length of a vector $X = [x_1,x_2,x_3]$ is similarly $\sqrt{x_1^2 + x_2^2 + x_3^2}$. Hence we adopt the definition, for n-dimensional space, that the **length** of the vector $X = [x_1,x_2, \ldots,x_n]$ is

$$\sqrt{x_1^2 + x_2^2 + \cdots + x_n^2},$$

and will be denoted by $|X|$. In Fig. 255, it is easily seen that the vector $\overrightarrow{OZ}$ or $Z = [z_1,z_2,z_3]$, which is equivalent to the vector from Y to X, is the

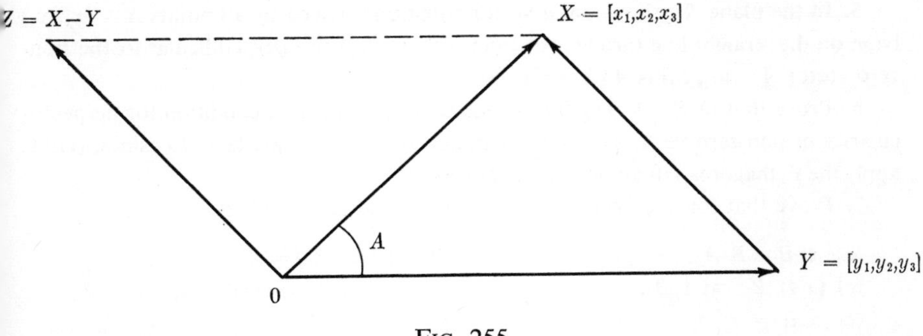

FIG. 255

difference $X - Y$ since, by vector addition $Y + (X - Y) = X$. Hence, the components of Z are in fact $z_1 = x_1 - y_1$, $z_2 = x_2 - y_2$, $z_3 = x_3 - y_3$. The law of cosines (section 148), then asserts that

$$|X - Y|^2 = |X|^2 + |Y|^2 - 2|X||Y| \cos A.$$

That is,

$$(x_1 - y_1)^2 + (x_2 - y_2)^2 + (x_3 - y_3)^2 = x_1^2 + x_2^2 + x_3^2 + y_1^2 + y_2^2 + y_3^2 - 2|X|\,|Y| \cos A.$$

Squaring the parentheses and simplifying the equation, we get $-2x_1y_1 - 2x_2y_2 - 2x_3y_3 = -2|X||Y| \cos A$, or dividing by -2,

$$X \cdot Y = |X||Y| \cos A.$$

In particular, *non-zero vectors X and Y are perpendicular* (*or orthogonal*) *if and only if $X \cdot Y = 0$.* Hence, for n dimensions we adopt the definition: two vectors X, Y are **perpendicular** (or **orthogonal**) if and only if $X \cdot Y = 0$.

Remark. The correlation coefficient (section 164) is nothing but the cosine of the angle between two vectors.

Exercises

1. Find the inner product of each pair of vectors and decide whether or not they are perpendicular:

(*a*) $[1, 2]$ and $[-2, 3]$. (*b*) $[-1, -3]$ and $[3, -1]$.
(*c*) $[2, -1, 4]$ and $[3, 5, -\frac{1}{4}]$. (*d*) $[4, 0, -3]$ and $[-\frac{3}{4}, 8, -1]$.

2. Show that for any non-zero vector X, the vector $Y = \frac{1}{|X|} X$ has unit length.

3. If $X = [6, 0]$ and $Y = [6, 6\sqrt{3}]$, find the length of each.

4. Find the cosine of the angle between the two vectors X and Y in exercise 3, and hence the angle.

5. In the plane R^2, show that a vector equation satisfied by all points $X = [x_1, x_2]$ lying on the straight line through the point $C = [c_1, c_2]$ and perpendicular to the non-zero vector $A = [a_1, a_2]$ is $A \cdot (X - C) = 0$.

6. Prove that in R^2, $X \cdot Y = 0$ is a necessary and sufficient condition for perpendicularity of non-zero vectors X and Y without appealing to the law of cosines. (Hint: apply the Pythagorean theorem and its converse.)

7. Prove that for any vectors A, B, C in R^n, and any numbers x, y:

(*a*) $A \cdot B = B \cdot A$. (*b*) $A \cdot (B + C) = A \cdot B + A \cdot C$.
(*c*) $(xA) \cdot B = x(A \cdot B)$. (*d*) $(xA) \cdot (yB) = (xy)(A \cdot B)$.
(*e*) $|xA| = |x||A|$. (*f*) $A \cdot A = |A|^2$.

8. Prove the statement of exercise 6 for vectors in R^3.

9. In R^3, show that a vector equation satisfied by all points $X = [x_1, x_2, x_3]$ lying on the plane through the point $C = [c_1, c_2, c_3]$ and perpendicular to the non-zero vector $A = [a_1, a_2, a_3]$ is $A \cdot (X - C) = 0$.

★**10.** Prove that in the plane R^2, the area K of the parallelogram $0XZY$ with vertices at $0 = [0, 0]$, $X = [x_1, x_2]$, $Y = [y_1, y_2]$, $Z = X + Y$ is given by:

(*a*) $K = |X||Y| \sin \measuredangle X0Y$.
(*b*) $K^2 = |X|^2|Y|^2 - (X \cdot Y)^2$.
(*c*) $K^2 = (x_1 y_2 - x_2 y_1)^2$.

174. MATRICES

A set of mn numbers arranged in a rectangular array

$$(1) \qquad A = \begin{bmatrix} a_{11} & a_{12} & \cdots & a_{1j} & \cdots & a_{1n} \\ a_{21} & a_{22} & \cdots & a_{2j} & \cdots & a_{2n} \\ \vdots & \vdots & & \vdots & & \vdots \\ a_{i1} & a_{i2} & \cdots & a_{ij} & \cdots & a_{in} \\ \vdots & \vdots & & \vdots & & \vdots \\ a_{m1} & a_{m2} & \cdots & a_{mj} & \cdots & a_{mn} \end{bmatrix}$$

of m (horizontal) rows and n (vertical) columns is called an m by n **matrix.** The matrix (1) may be denoted by the capital letter A or by a condensed symbol $[a_{ij}]$. *The symbol a_{ij} represents the element or number in the* ith *row and* jth *column of the matrix (1)*. The matrix (1) is said to be of **size** m by n. An n by n matrix is called a **square** matrix of **order** n.

A 1 by n matrix $[x_1,x_2, \ldots,x_n]$ may be called a **row-vector.** An m by 1 matrix

$$\begin{bmatrix} y_1 \\ y_2 \\ \vdots \\ y_m \end{bmatrix}$$

may be called a **column-vector.**

Definition 1. *Two matrices $A = [a_{ij}]$ and $B = [b_{ij}]$ of the same size are called* **equal** *if all corresponding elements a_{ij} and b_{ij} are equal.*

Definition 2. *Two matrices $A = [a_{ij}]$, $B = [b_{ij}]$ of the same size may be added by adding the elements in corresponding positions; that is, the* **sum** $A + B$ *is the matrix $C = [c_{ij}]$ of the same size for which every $c_{ij} = a_{ij} + b_{ij}$.*

For example,

$$\begin{bmatrix} 1 & 2 & 3 \\ -1 & 0 & 4 \end{bmatrix} + \begin{bmatrix} 2 & 0 & -1 \\ 3 & 1 & 2 \end{bmatrix} = \begin{bmatrix} 3 & 2 & 2 \\ 2 & 1 & 6 \end{bmatrix}.$$

Clearly, when this matrix addition is applied to two row-vectors (or two column-vectors), the result is the same as our earlier vector addition.

The row-vector $[a_{i1},a_{i2}, \ldots,a_{ij}, \ldots,a_{in}]$ consisting of the elements in the ith row of matrix A, given in formula (1), is called the ***i*th row-vector** of matrix A and will be denoted by A_i.

The column-vector

$$\begin{bmatrix} a_{1j} \\ a_{2j} \\ \vdots \\ a_{ij} \\ \vdots \\ a_{mj} \end{bmatrix}$$

consisting of the elements in the jth column of matrix A, given in formula (1), is called the ***j*th column-vector** of matrix A and will be denoted by $A^{(j)}$.

For example, in the 3 by 4 matrix

$$A = \begin{bmatrix} 1 & 0 & 2 & -1 \\ 2 & 1 & 0 & 3 \\ 4 & -1 & 0 & 0 \end{bmatrix}$$

the second row vector $A_2 = [2,1,0,3]$ and the third column-vector

$$A^{(3)} = \begin{bmatrix} 2 \\ 0 \\ 0 \end{bmatrix}.$$

We now give a useful definition of the product AB of two matrices, A and B, in that order, *provided the number of columns in A is the same as the number of rows in B.*

Definition 3. *If $A = [a_{ij}]$ is an m by n matrix and $B = [b_{ij}]$ is an n by p matrix, then the* **product** *$C = AB = [c_{ij}]$ is an m by p matrix in which the element c_{ij} in the* ith *row and* jth *column is the inner product of the* ith *row-vector A_i of A by the* jth *column-vector $B^{(j)}$ of B; that is,*

$$c_{ij} = A_i \cdot B^{(j)} = a_{i1}b_{1j} + a_{i2}b_{2j} + \cdots + a_{in}b_{nj}.$$

For example, if

$$A = \begin{bmatrix} 1 & 0 & 2 & -1 \\ 2 & 1 & 0 & 3 \\ 4 & -1 & 0 & 0 \end{bmatrix} \quad \text{and} \quad B = \begin{bmatrix} 1 & -1 \\ 2 & 0 \\ 3 & 1 \\ 4 & 0 \end{bmatrix},$$

then

$$c_{11} = A_1 \cdot B^{(1)} = 1 \cdot 1 + 0 \cdot 2 + 2 \cdot 3 + (-1) \cdot 4 = 3,$$

$$c_{21} = A_2 \cdot B^{(1)} = 2 \cdot 1 + 1 \cdot 2 + 0 \cdot 3 + 3 \cdot 4 = 16,$$

and so on. Thus, the reader may verify that

$$C = AB = \begin{bmatrix} 3 & 1 \\ 16 & -2 \\ 2 & -4 \end{bmatrix}.$$

Note that here BA is not even defined since the number of columns of B is not the same as the number of rows of A. Thus, there can be no commutative law for multiplication of matrices. Even when both AB and BA are defined they may be unequal. For example, if

$$A = \begin{bmatrix} 1 & 2 \\ 3 & 4 \end{bmatrix} \quad \text{and} \quad B = \begin{bmatrix} 1 & -1 \\ 2 & 0 \end{bmatrix}$$

then

$$AB = \begin{bmatrix} 5 & -1 \\ 11 & -3 \end{bmatrix} \quad \text{while} \quad BA = \begin{bmatrix} -2 & -2 \\ 2 & 4 \end{bmatrix}.$$

Definition 4. *The* **transpose** A^T *of an m by n matrix* $A = [a_{ij}]$ *is the n by m matrix* $A^T = B = [b_{ij}]$ *for which* $b_{ij} = a_{ji}$; *that is the* ith *row vector of A becomes the* ith *column-vector of* A^T *and the* jth *column-vector of A becomes the* jth *row vector of* A^T.

For example, if

$$A = \begin{bmatrix} 1 & 2 \\ 3 & 4 \\ 5 & 6 \end{bmatrix}$$

then

$$A^T = \begin{bmatrix} 1 & 3 & 5 \\ 2 & 4 & 6 \end{bmatrix}.$$

The system of equations (1) of section 169, can now be written in several more condensed notations.

If A is the m by n matrix

$$\begin{bmatrix} a_{11} & \cdots & a_{1n} \\ \vdots & & \vdots \\ a_{m1} & \cdots & a_{mn} \end{bmatrix}$$

of coefficients of the variables, X is the column-vector

$$\begin{bmatrix} x_1 \\ x_2 \\ \vdots \\ x_n \end{bmatrix},$$

and K is the column-vector

$$\begin{bmatrix} k_1 \\ k_2 \\ \vdots \\ k_m \end{bmatrix},$$

then the system (1) of section 169 can be written as

$$\begin{cases} A_1 \cdot X = k_1 \\ A_2 \cdot X = k_2 \\ \quad\vdots \\ A_m \cdot X = k_m, \end{cases}$$

or as

$$x_1A^{(1)} + x_2A^{(2)} + \cdots + x_nA^{(n)} = K,$$

or, most simply, as

$$AX = K.$$

For example, the system

$$\begin{cases} 2x_1 + 3x_2 + 4x_3 = 5 \\ x_1 - x_2 + x_3 = 7 \end{cases}$$

can be written as

$$\begin{cases} [2, 3, 4]\cdot\begin{bmatrix} x_1 \\ x_2 \\ x_3 \end{bmatrix} = 5 \\ [1, -1, 1]\cdot\begin{bmatrix} x_1 \\ x_2 \\ x_3 \end{bmatrix} = 7, \end{cases}$$

or as

$$x_1\begin{bmatrix} 2 \\ 1 \end{bmatrix} + x_2\begin{bmatrix} 3 \\ -1 \end{bmatrix} + x_3\begin{bmatrix} 4 \\ 1 \end{bmatrix} = \begin{bmatrix} 5 \\ 7 \end{bmatrix},$$

or, most simply, as

$$\begin{bmatrix} 2 & 3 & 4 \\ 1 & -1 & 1 \end{bmatrix}\begin{bmatrix} x_1 \\ x_2 \\ x_3 \end{bmatrix} = \begin{bmatrix} 5 \\ 7 \end{bmatrix}.$$

The square n by n matrix

$$I = \begin{bmatrix} 1 & 0 & 0 & \dots & 0 \\ 0 & 1 & 0 & \dots & 0 \\ 0 & 0 & 1 & \dots & 0 \\ \cdots & \cdots & \cdots & \cdots & \cdots \\ 0 & 0 & 0 & \dots & 1 \end{bmatrix}$$

which has the unit vectors $E^{(1)}, E^{(2)}, \dots, E^{(n)}$ as its row-vectors and column-vectors, has the property that if A is any n by n matrix, we have

$$IA = A \quad \text{and} \quad AI = A$$

The reader should prove this. Thus the matrix I, called the **identity matrix**, has a property analogous to the number 1 in the algebra of numbers. A matrix B which has the property that $AB = I$ and $BA = I$ is called the **inverse** of A and is denoted by A^{-1}. Thus,

$$AA^{-1} = A^{-1}A = I.$$

Not every square matrix has an inverse (see exercises).

Let 0 denote the matrix of any size all of whose elements are zeros. Let the **product** cA of any matrix $A = [a_{ij}]$ by a scalar (number) c be the matrix $B = [b_{ij}]$, where $b_{ij} = ca_{ij}$. If X and Y are matrices of the same size, let $X - Y = X + (-1)Y$.

Remark 1. A matrix may be defined rigorously without referring to any particular notational arrangement on the page. If I_m is the set $\{1, 2, ..., m\}$ of the first m natural numbers and I_n is the set $\{1, 2, ..., n\}$, then the cartesian product $I_m \times I_n$ is the set of all ordered pairs (i,j) with $i \in I_m$, $j \in I_n$. A **matrix** A with real elements is then a function or mapping from $I_m \times I_n$ to the set R^1 of all real numbers. The functional value $A(i,j)$ is merely denoted by a_{ij}, and in the usual notation is the element written in the ith row and jth column.

Remark 2. We have already used matrices as payoff matrices of matrix games (section 157). Other applications will be suggested in what follows.

Exercises

In each of the following, find $A + B$ and AB, if possible:

1. $A = \begin{bmatrix} 1 & 2 \\ 3 & 4 \end{bmatrix}, B = \begin{bmatrix} 2 & -1 \\ 0 & 3 \end{bmatrix}$,

2. $A = \begin{bmatrix} 2 & 1 \\ -1 & 0 \end{bmatrix}, B = \begin{bmatrix} 0 & 3 \\ 2 & -1 \end{bmatrix}$.

3. $A = \begin{bmatrix} 1 & 2 & -1 \\ 3 & 0 & 2 \end{bmatrix}, B = \begin{bmatrix} 2 & 0 \\ 4 & -1 \\ 1 & -2 \end{bmatrix}$,

4. $A = \begin{bmatrix} 2 & 1 & 3 \\ -1 & 2 & 1 \end{bmatrix}, B = \begin{bmatrix} -1 & 3 & 4 \\ 5 & 2 & 0 \end{bmatrix}$.

5. $A = \begin{bmatrix} 1 & 2 & 3 \\ -1 & 0 & 2 \\ 2 & 1 & 0 \end{bmatrix}, B = \begin{bmatrix} 2 \\ 1 \\ -1 \end{bmatrix}$.

6. $A = [1,2,3], B = \begin{bmatrix} 2 & 0 & -1 \\ 0 & 0 & 1 \\ -1 & 2 & 1 \end{bmatrix}$.

7. $A = \begin{bmatrix} 1 & 0 & 0 \\ 2 & -1 & 0 \\ 1 & 2 & 3 \end{bmatrix}, B = \begin{bmatrix} 1 & 0 & 1 \\ 0 & 2 & 3 \\ 0 & 0 & -1 \end{bmatrix}$.

8. $A = \begin{bmatrix} 1 & 2 & -1 \\ 0 & 0 & 1 \\ 2 & 1 & -3 \end{bmatrix}, B = \begin{bmatrix} 1 & 2 \\ 2 & -1 \\ 3 & 4 \end{bmatrix}$.

9. Find BA in exercise 1.

10. Find BA in exercise 2.

11. Find BA in exercise 3.

12. Find BA in exercise 7.

13. Find $A + B^T$ in exercise 3.

14. Find B^TA in exercise 4.

15. If $A = [a_1, a_2, ..., a_n]$ and $B = [b_1, b_2, ..., b_n]^T$, find AB and BA.

16. For arbitrary 2 by 2 matrices A, B, C, verify that

(*a*) $A + B = B + A$.

(*b*) $(A + B) + C = A + (B + C)$.

(*c*) $(AB)^T = B^TA^T$.

(*d*) $(A^T)^T = A$.

(*e*) $(AB)C = A(BC)$.

★(*f*) If A^{-1} and B^{-1} both exist, then $(AB)^{-1} = B^{-1}A^{-1}$.

(*g*) $A(B + C) = AB + AC$.

(*h*) $(B + C)A = BA + CA$.

(*i*) If A has an inverse A^{-1}, then $(A^{-1})^{-1} = A$.

(*j*) If A has an inverse, then it has only one inverse; that is, if $AB = BA = I$ and $AC = CA = I$, then $B = C$.

(*k*) If

$$A = \begin{bmatrix} a_{11} & a_{12} \\ a_{21} & a_{22} \end{bmatrix},$$

then A^{-1} exists if and only if $a_{11}a_{22} - a_{21}a_{12} \neq 0$.

***17.** Verify parts *a–j* of exercise 16 for any matrices for which the expressions involved have significance.

18. If A, B, C are matrices of the same size, and if c, d are any scalars (numbers), then prove that

(*a*) $A - A = 0$. (*b*) $A(B - C) = AB - AC$.
(*c*) $(B - C)A = BA - CA$. (*d*) $c(A + B) = cA + cB$.
(*e*) $(c + d)A = cA + dA$. (*f*) $c(dA) = (cd)A$.
(*g*) $A + 0 = 0 + A = A$.

175. THE ADJACENCY MATRIX OF A NETWORK

A directed network (section 81) can be specified completely by a matrix whose elements are 0's or 1's, called the **adjacency matrix** $A = [a_{ij}]$ which has one row and one column labeled to correspond with each vertex of the network, where $a_{ij} = 1$ if there exists an arc from vertex i to vertex j, and $a_{ij} = 0$ if not. For example, the network of Fig. 256 has the adjacency matrix where the ith row and ith column correspond to the vertex labeled i ($i = 1,2,3,4$):

$$A = \begin{bmatrix} 0 & 1 & 1 & 1 \\ 0 & 0 & 1 & 1 \\ 1 & 0 & 0 & 1 \\ 0 & 0 & 1 & 0 \end{bmatrix}.$$

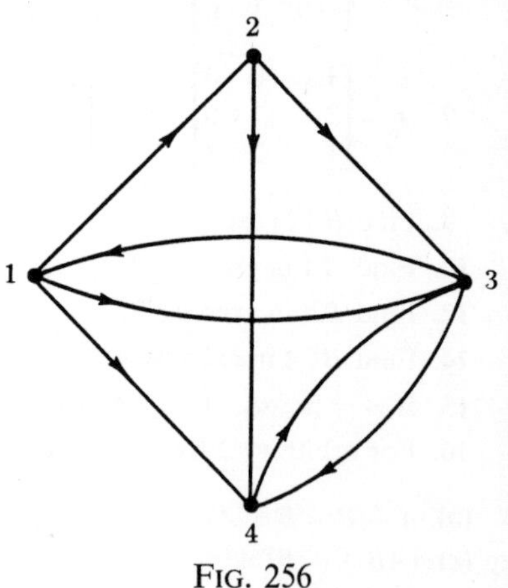

FIG. 256

Clearly, given the matrix A, the directed network could be reconstructed from it.

Suppose this network to be the graph of a binary relation R, where $i\,R\,j$ shall mean "individual i can communicate directly with individual j." That is, the set of vertices represents a society of four individuals 1, 2, 3, 4 and an arc goes from i to j if and only if $i\,R\,j$ (i can communicate directly with j). We observe that the element S_{14} of the matrix $S = AA = A^2$ is the inner product $A_1 \cdot A^{(4)}$ of the first row-vector of A with the fourth column-vector of A, or

$$(1) \qquad a_{11}a_{14} + a_{12}a_{24} + a_{13}a_{34} + a_{14}a_{44} = 0 \cdot 1 + 1 \cdot 1 + 1 \cdot 1 + 1 \cdot 0 = 2$$

which is the number of different two-stage communications possible from 1 to 4. Clearly, one of the four terms in (1) will be $=1$ if and only if both factors in it are $=1$, otherwise it will be $=0$. Thus, the second and third terms in (1) are $=1$ because either individual 2 or individual 3 can be used as an intermediary for a two-stage communication from 1 to 4. Thus, in general, *the elements of* $AA = A^2$ *give a tabulation of the numbers of possible two-stage communications.*

We consider a communications relation R (i.e. any binary relation) which is

(a) **irreflexive** (that is, $i\,R\,i$ for no individual i),

(b) **connex** (that is, for every pair of distinct individuals i and j, either $i\,R\,j$ or $j\,R\,i$).

The relation of Fig. 256 is such a relation. We prove the following well-known but unobvious theorem about such relations.

Theorem. *In any irreflexive, connex communication relation with n individuals, there exists at least one individual who can communicate with every other individual in either 1 or 2 stages.*

Proof. From what has been said above it is clear that it suffices to prove that, A being the adjacency matrix of the relation, there exists at least one row-vector C_i of the matrix $C = A + A^2$ with all elements different from zero except possibly the element c_{ii}. We prove this in two parts.

(a) If individual i cannot communicate with individual j ($j \neq i$) in either 1 or 2 stages, then j can communicate in 1 stage with at least one more person than can i. That is, if $a_{ij} = 0$ and $c_{ij} = A_i \cdot A^{(j)} = 0$, then $a_{j1} + a_{j2} + \cdots + a_{jn} > a_{i1} + a_{i2} + \cdots + a_{in}$. For, by connexity, $a_{ij} = 0$ implies $a_{ji} = 1$. Now $A_i \cdot A^{(j)} = 0$ implies that if $a_{ik} = 1$, then $a_{jk} = 1$; for $a_{ik} = 1$ implies $a_{ki} = 0$ since their product must be 0, so that we must have $a_{ik} = 1$ by connexity. But $a_{ii} = 0$ by irreflexiveness, while $a_{ji} = 1$ as already proved above. Hence

$$a_{j1} + a_{j2} + \cdots + a_{jn} \geqq (a_{i1} + a_{i2} + \cdots + a_{in}) + 1.$$

(b) Now let m be an individual for whom the sum of the elements in the mth row $c_{m1} + c_{m2} + \cdots + c_{mn}$ has the greatest value of all the rows. Then m can communicate with all other individuals in 1 or 2 stages. For if not, part (a) assures us that there would exist another row with a greater sum which would contradict the fact that m yields the maximum sum.

Exercises

1. Calculate the matrices A^2 and $A + A^2$ for the example in the text, and follow through the details of the proof above for this example.

2. (*a*) Draw the directed graph whose adjacency matrix is

$$A = \begin{bmatrix} 0 & 1 & 0 & 0 \\ 1 & 0 & 1 & 1 \\ 1 & 0 & 0 & 1 \\ 1 & 0 & 0 & 0 \end{bmatrix}.$$

(*b*) Calculate A^2 and $A + A^2$.

(*c*) Is this a connex, irreflexive relation?

(*d*) Which individual who can communicate with every one else in one or two stages is selected by the method of the theorem?

(*e*) Which other individuals, if any, can communicate with every one else in one or two stages?

(*f*) How many two-stage communications are possible from individual 2 to individual 1? Which element of A^2 indicates this?

3. Answer the questions of exercise 2 for the adjacency matrix

$$A = \begin{bmatrix} 0 & 1 & 0 & 0 & 1 \\ 0 & 0 & 0 & 1 & 1 \\ 1 & 1 & 0 & 0 & 0 \\ 1 & 0 & 1 & 0 & 1 \\ 0 & 0 & 1 & 0 & 0 \end{bmatrix}.$$

4. In a directed network without loops the **out-degree** $d_o(j)$ of the jth vertex is the sum of the elements in the jth row of the adjacency matrix A, and the **in-degree** $d_i(j)$ is the sum of the elements in the jth column of A. Show that if there are V vertices and E arcs in the network, then:

(*a*) $d_o(1) + d_o(2) + \cdots + d_o(V) = E.$

(*b*) $d_i(1) + d_i(2) + \cdots + d_i(V) = E.$

(*c*) Since the degree $d(j)$ of the jth vertex is $d(j) = d_o(j) + d_i(j)$, this implies that $d(1) + d(2) + \cdots + d(V) = 2E$ (cf. exercise 1, section 81).

5. Explain why the number of 3-stage communications between individual i and individual j in a binary relation, interpreted as communication as in the discussion above, is equal to the element in the ith row and jth column of $A^3 = AAA$, where A is the adjacency matrix.

6. Let the vertices of a directed network represent persons named 1, 2, ..., n and let the network have an arc directed from vertex x to vertex y if x likes y. Let A be the adjacency matrix and A^T its transpose, and let $AA^T = M = [m_{ij}]$ and $A^TA = N = [n_{ij}]$. Show that: (*a*) m_{ij} is the number of persons liked by both i and j; (*b*) n_{ij} is the number of persons who like both i and j.

176. THE SIMPLEX METHOD FOR LINEAR PROGRAMMING PROBLEMS

It has been pointed out that the solution of matrix games can be reduced to linear programming problems (section 159), and that a systematic method of solving large scale linear programming problems is desirable. Such a method, called the **simplex method** was devised by G. Dantzig in the 1940's. We illustrate this method by using it to solve the mousetrap problem of section 102. The problem is to find non-negative values of x and y satisfying the inequalities

$$(1) \qquad \begin{cases} 2x + 4y \leqq 12 \\ 4x + 2y \leqq 12 \end{cases}$$

and maximizing $P = 3x + 5y$. We convert (1) into a system of equations by introducing so-called **slack variables** u and v, so that the problem becomes that of finding non-negative values of x, y, u, and v satisfying the equations

$$(2) \qquad \begin{cases} 2x + 4y + u \qquad\qquad = 12 \\ 4x + 2y \qquad + v \qquad = 12 \\ -3x - 5y \qquad\qquad + P = 0 \end{cases}$$

and maximizing $P = 3x + 5y + 0u + 0v$. Detaching the coefficients, we have

(3)

x	y	u	v	P	constants
2	④	1	0	0	12
4	2	0	1	0	12
−3	−5	0	0	1	0

Note that the column-vectors consisting of the coefficients of u, v, P are the unit vectors forming a basis for 3-dimensional space. We have previously called such variables *basic variables* (section 169). A solution of the system (2) or (3) which yields non-zero values only for basic variables is called a **basic feasible solution**. It can be proved that if a linear programming problem has any feasible (or optimal) solution at all then it has a basic feasible (or optimal) solution. A basic feasible solution is easily read off from (2) or (3), namely, $u = 12$, $v = 12$, $x = 0$, $y = 0$, $P = 0$. But it is clear that a better feasible solution might be found. Since every increase in the value of y increases P by 5 times as much, let us try to keep the value of x fixed and increase y. Since we are using $x = 0$, the first two equations of (2) require that $u = 12 - 4y$ and $v = 12 - 2y$. We cannot increase y by too much since u and v are also required to be non-negative. In order to keep v non-negative, y must not be higher than 6. But in order to keep u non-negative y must not be higher than 4. Hence, we try to put y into a new basic feasible solution and to remove u. Thus, we pivot on the 4 which was therefore circled in (3). Dividing the first equation of (2) or (3) by 4 and subtracting suitable multiples of the resulting equation from the others, we get

x	y	u	v	P	constants
$\frac{1}{2}$	1	$\frac{1}{4}$	0	0	3
③	0	$-\frac{1}{2}$	1	0	6
$-\frac{1}{2}$	0	$\frac{5}{4}$	0	1	15

A basic feasible solution for this (equivalent) system of equations is easily read off, namely, $x = 0$, $y = 3$, $u = 0$, $v = 6$, $P = 15$. But this can be improved further as can be seen from the fact that there is still a negative coefficient in the third line. Thus, we wish to introduce x into the basic feasible solution and this is done by pivoting on the circled 3. We obtain

x	y	u	v	P	constants
0	1	$\frac{1}{3}$	$-\frac{1}{6}$	0	2
1	0	$-\frac{1}{6}$	$\frac{1}{3}$	0	2
0	0	$\frac{7}{6}$	$\frac{1}{6}$	1	16

from which the basic feasible solution $x = 2$, $y = 2$, $u = 0$, $v = 0$, $P = 16$ is easily read off. But *since there are no more negative coefficients in the third line, this must be an optimal solution.*

For a minimum problem, there are additional steps to be taken. Consider the problem of finding non-negative values of x and y satisfying the inequalities

$$(4) \qquad \begin{cases} 2x + y \geqq 4 \\ x + 3y \geqq 7 \end{cases}$$

and minimizing $Q = x + y$. First, to minimize Q is the same as to maximize $-Q$. Introducing slack variables u and v as before, we must find non-negative values of x, y, u, and v satisfying the equations

$$(5) \qquad \begin{cases} 2x + y - u & & = 4 \\ x + 3y & - v & = 7 \\ x + y & & + (-Q) = 0 \end{cases}$$

and maximizing $(-Q)$. In the previous example, we were able to start with an obvious basic feasible solution because the slack variables appeared with $+1$ as coefficient, thus providing unit vectors in the last three columns of the tabulation to the left of the equals sign. But now there is no obvious basic feasible solution because the coefficients of the slack variables are -1. We overcome this difficulty by introducing further **artificial non-negative variables** a and b so that the constraint equations become

$$\begin{cases} 2x + y - u \quad + a \quad = 4 \\ x + 3y \quad - v \quad + b = 7 \end{cases}$$

and we maximize $M = (-Q) - L(a + b)$, where L is a sufficiently large positive number so that M could never be maximum if either a or b are not zero. The new artificial problem is now to find non-negative values of x, y, u, v, a, and b satisfying

$$\begin{cases} 2x + y - u \quad + a \quad = 4 \\ x + 3y \quad - v \quad + b \quad = 7 \\ x + y \quad + La + Lb + M = 0 \end{cases} \tag{6}$$

and maximizing M. The appropriate pivot operations are indicated below.

x	y	u	v	a	b	M	constants
2	1	-1	0	①	0	0	4
1	3	0	-1	0	1	0	7
1	1	0	0	L	L	1	0

An obvious basic feasible solution has $a = 4$, $b = 7$, but, since L is so large, we know that a and b cannot occur in an optimal solution, so we first remove a and b from the expression for M by pivoting on the 1's in their columns in turn. That is, multiplying the first line by $-L$ and adding the product to the third line, we get

2	1	-1	0	1	0	0	4
1	3	0	-1	0	①	0	7
$1-2L$	$1-L$	L	0	0	L	1	$-4L$

Now multiplying the second line by $-L$ and adding to the third line, we get

2	1	-1	0	1	0	0	4
1	③	0	-1	0	1	0	7
$1-3L$	$1-4L$	L	L	0	0	1	$-11L$

A basic feasible solution is now $a = 4$, $b = 7$, $x = y = u = v = 0$, $P = -11L$, but this can be improved since there are negative coefficients in the third line. The most negative entry is $1 - 4L$, so we would like to increase y. Now $y + a = 4$, $3y + b = 7$ if all other values in the basic feasible solution are held fixed. If a is to be non-negative, y can be no bigger than 4. If b is to be non-negative, y can be no bigger than $\frac{7}{3}$. Hence, we pivot on the circled 3, obtaining

$\textcircled{\frac{5}{3}}$	0	-1	$\frac{1}{3}$	1	$-\frac{1}{3}$	0	$\frac{5}{3}$
$\frac{1}{3}$	1	0	$\frac{1}{3}$	0	$\frac{1}{3}$	0	$\frac{7}{3}$
$\frac{2}{3}-\frac{5}{3}L$	0	L	$\frac{1}{3}-\frac{1}{3}L$	0	$\frac{4}{3}L-\frac{1}{3}$	1	$-\frac{7}{3}-\frac{5}{3}L$

Since L is large, $\frac{2}{3} - \frac{5}{3}L$ is still a negative coefficient in the expression for M, so that M can be improved by putting x into the solution. Thus, we pivot on the circled $\frac{5}{3}$, obtaining

1	0	$-\frac{3}{5}$	$\frac{1}{5}$	$\frac{3}{5}$	$-\frac{1}{5}$	0	1
0	1	$\frac{1}{5}$	$-\frac{6}{15}$	$-\frac{1}{5}$	$\frac{6}{15}$	0	2
0	0	$\frac{2}{5}$	$\frac{1}{5}$	$L-\frac{2}{5}$	$L-\frac{1}{5}$	1	-3

The absence of negative coefficients in the third line shows that the basic feasible solution $x = 1$, $y = 2$, $u = v = a = b = 0$, $M = -3$ is optimal. Since $M = -3$, $Q = 3$ is the minimum value of Q.

The simplex method is an example of a **finite algorithm**, i.e., a finite process which must produce an answer to the problem if an answer exists.

The calculations of the simplex method are such that they can be performed by an electronic computer. We have dealt only with cases where a basic feasible solution is easily found. Further discussion of the theory of the simplex method and details of considerations omitted here are found in the references.

Exercises

1. Solve problems 1–3, 5–9 of section 102 by the simplex method.

2. Solve problems 1–8 of section 158 by converting the game problems into linear programming problems as in section 159 and solving these by the simplex method.

177. MARKOV CHAINS

In section 153 we dealt with probabilities of repeated independent trials. If the probability of a later trial is influenced by the outcome of some or all of the earlier trials, the situation is much more complicated. We consider a situation in which *every trial after the first is influenced by the outcome of the one immediately preceding it and no others*. Then, assuming a finite number of possible outcomes or states labeled 1, 2, 3, ..., n, we assume that there are constant conditional probabilities p_{ij} that the jth state will occur next, assuming that the ith state has just occurred. These are called **transition probabilities** and the square n by n matrix $M = [p_{ij}]$ is called the **matrix of transition probabilities**. Such a situation is termed a **Markov chain**.

Example. Suppose a first urn contains 2 balls and a second urn contains 4 balls. Of the 6 balls, 2 are white and 4 are black. One ball is simultaneously chosen from each urn and placed in the other urn. By the "state" of the system is meant the number of black balls in the first urn, which may be 0, 1, or 2. Then the matrix M of transition probabilities is

	0	1	2
0	0	1	0
1	$\frac{1}{8}$	$\frac{1}{2}$	$\frac{3}{8}$
2	0	$\frac{1}{2}$	$\frac{1}{2}$.

The sum of the elements in each row of the transition matrix is always 1. A matrix of non-negative numbers whose rows all have the sum one is termed a **stochastic** matrix.

We ask now for the probabilities that the experiment will be in state j after two stages, assuming it is now in state i. Since the probability that it passes from i to k and then from k to j is clearly $p_{ik}p_{kj}$, our answer is

$$p_{i1}p_{1j} + p_{i2}p_{2j} + p_{i3}p_{3j} + \cdots + p_{in}p_{nj} \tag{1}$$

since any of the states might be the intermediate one. This, however, is the inner product of the ith row-vector of M with the jth column-vector of M, or simply the element in the ith row and jth column of $MM = M^2$. Clearly, the matrix M^3 yields the corresponding probabilities after 3 stages, and so on.

If we determine the starting state by a chance device with fixed probabilities $p_1, p_2, \ldots, p_n$ for the n states respectively, then by a similar argument, the probabilities of being in jth state after one stage are

$$p_1p_{1j} + p_2p_{2j} + p_3p_{3j} + \cdots + p_np_{nj}.$$

Denoting by P the probability vector $[p_1, p_2, \ldots, p_n]$, these probabilities are clearly given by the vector PM. Similarly, the probabilities of being in the various states after n stages are given by PM^n.

Markov chains, and more general processes, are studied in some of the references. They have been fruitfully applied to problems in physics, engineering, psychological learning theory, genetics, etc.

Exercises

1. A Markov chain with two states has the matrix of transition probabilities

$$M = \begin{bmatrix} \frac{1}{3} & \frac{2}{3} \\ 1 & 0 \end{bmatrix}.$$

(*a*) Calculate M^2.

(*b*) Find the probability that the second state will occur after two steps if the process starts in the first state.

(*c*) If the process starts in states one and two with probabilities $P = [\frac{3}{4}, \frac{1}{4}]$ respectively, find the probabilities that it will be in states one and two respectively after one step.

(*d*) The same as (*c*), after two steps.

2. Answer the same questions as in exercise 1 if

$$M = \begin{bmatrix} \frac{1}{2} & \frac{1}{2} \\ \frac{1}{4} & \frac{3}{4} \end{bmatrix}.$$

3. For the example in the text of this section:

(*a*) Calculate M^2.

(*b*) If the initial states (0, 1, or 2) are chosen with probabilities $[\frac{1}{3}, \frac{2}{3}, 0]$ respectively what are the probabilities of states 0, 1, or 2, respectively, after one step?

(*c*) The same question as (*b*), but after two steps.

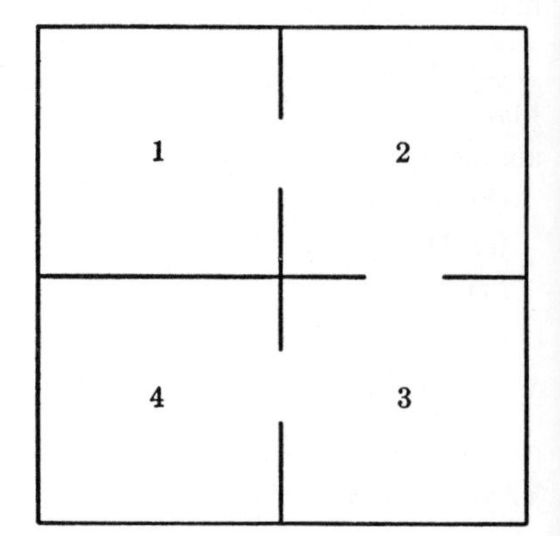

4. If a mouse in the accompanying maze is in one of the four states (cells), he will proceed to an adjacent state (cell) with the following transition probabilities

$$\begin{bmatrix} 0 & 1 & 0 & 0 \\ \frac{1}{2} & 0 & \frac{1}{2} & 0 \\ 0 & \frac{1}{3} & 0 & \frac{2}{3} \\ 0 & 0 & 0 & 1 \end{bmatrix}.$$

For example if he is in cell 2 he will go either to 1 or 3 with probability $\frac{1}{2}$, and so on.

(*a*) Calculate M^2.

(*b*) Calculate M^3.

(*c*) If he is placed in cell 1 what is the probability that he will be in cell 3 after 2 stages?

(*d*) In cell 4 after 3 stages?

(*e*) If he is placed in cell 3 what is the probability that he will be in cell 4 after 2 steps?

(*f*) After 3 steps?

5. Prove that the product of two stochastic matrices is a stochastic matrix. (Hint: try it first for 2 by 2 matrices, and perhaps for 3 by 3 matrices before attempting the general n by n case.)

6. A **probability vector** is a vector of non-negative components whose sum is 1. Show that the product of a probability vector and a stochastic matrix is a probability vector.

7. Using the results of exercises 5 and 6, show that if P is a probability vector and M is a stochastic matrix then M^n is a stochastic matrix and PM^n is a probability vector for any natural number n.

8. Show that independent trials with two states (outcomes) with probabilities p and $q = 1 - p$ is a special case of a Markov chain with matrix of transition probabilities

$$M = \begin{bmatrix} p & q \\ p & q \end{bmatrix}.$$

Show that $M = M^2 = \cdots = M^k$ for any natural number k.

9. The same as exercise 8 for independent trials with n states (outcomes) with probabilities $p_1, p_2, \ldots, p_n$ with $p_1 + p_2 + \cdots + p_n = 1$.

10. A probability vector P is called fixed or stationary for the Markov chain with matrix M of transition probabilities if $PM = P$.

(*a*) Show that then $PM^2 = P$ and $PM^n = P$ for any natural number n. Thus, if the Markov process begins with initial probabilities given by $P = [p_1, p_2, \ldots, p_n]$, the probabilities of the various states at any stage are still given by P.

(*b*) If M is the matrix of exercise 1, find such a fixed probability vector P.

(*c*) The same, if M is the matrix of exercise 2.

(*d*) The same, if

$$M = \begin{bmatrix} \frac{1}{3} & \frac{2}{3} \\ \frac{1}{2} & \frac{1}{2} \end{bmatrix}.$$

178. THE INVERSE OF A SQUARE MATRIX

If A is a square n by n matrix, we term the **inverse** of A a square n by n matrix B such that $BA = AB = I$, if such a matrix B exists. It is easily seen that if an inverse of A exists, there is only one (exercise 11). The inverse of A is denoted by A^{-1}. If A^{-1} exists, A is called **non-singular** or **invertible**.

Theorem 1. *If A^{-1} exists, then the system of equations*

$$AX + IY = 0 \tag{1}$$

can be solved for X, obtaining

$$IX + BY = 0 \tag{2}$$

no matter what given vector Y is.

Proof. Multiplying both members of equation (1) by A^{-1}, we obtain $A^{-1}AX + A^{-1}IY = A^{-1}0$ which reduces to (2), where $B = A^{-1}$.

Lemma. *If $M = [m_{ij}]$ is an n by n square matrix such that $MX = 0$ for all vectors X, then $M = 0$; that is, all $m_{ij} = 0$.*

Proof. Substituting for X in turn the n unit vectors E_i, we find at once that all $m_{ij} = 0$.

This lemma enables us to prove the following converse of theorem 1.

Theorem 2. *If (1) can be solved for (2) for all Y, then $B = A^{-1}$.*

Proof. Substituting (2) in (1), we get $AIX + IY = A(-BY) + IY = (I - AB)Y = 0$ for all Y. By the lemma, $I - AB = 0$ or $AB = I$. The row operations used in obtaining (2) from (1) can be reversed to get (1) from (2) no matter what X is. Hence, we may substitute (1) in (2), obtaining $IX + B(-AX) = (I - BA)X = 0$. By the lemma, $I - BA = 0$ or $BA = I$. Hence, $B = A^{-1}$.

These theorems provide a convenient way to calculate the inverse of an n by n matrix A, if it exists. Write the matrix $[A,I]$ as

$$\left[\begin{array}{ccc|ccccc} a_{11} & \cdots & a_{1n} & 1 & 0 & 0 & \cdots & 0 \\ a_{21} & \cdots & a_{2n} & 0 & 1 & 0 & \cdots & 0 \\ \cdots & \cdots & \cdots & \cdots & \cdots & \cdots & \cdots & \cdots \\ a_{n1} & \cdots & a_{nn} & 0 & 0 & 0 & \cdots & 1 \end{array}\right]$$

and perform on the entire matrix those row operations designed to reduce the left half of the matrix to I. Then the resulting matrix in the right half is A^{-1}.

Example. Find the inverse of

$$A = \begin{bmatrix} 1 & 0 & 1 \\ 2 & 3 & 1 \\ 1 & 3 & 2 \end{bmatrix}.$$

Solution. We write

$$\left[\begin{array}{ccc|ccc} 1 & 0 & 1 & 1 & 0 & 0 \\ 2 & 3 & 1 & 0 & 1 & 0 \\ 1 & 3 & 2 & 0 & 0 & 1 \end{array}\right]$$

and add -2 times the first row to the second row, and add -1 times the first row to the third row, obtaining

$$\left[\begin{array}{ccc|ccc} 1 & 0 & 1 & 1 & 0 & 0 \\ 0 & 3 & -1 & -2 & 1 & 0 \\ 0 & 3 & 1 & -1 & 0 & 1 \end{array}\right].$$

Multiply the second row by $\frac{1}{3}$, obtaining

$$\left[\begin{array}{ccc|ccc} 1 & 0 & 1 & 1 & 0 & 0 \\ 0 & 1 & -\frac{1}{3} & -\frac{2}{3} & \frac{1}{3} & 0 \\ 0 & 3 & 1 & -1 & 0 & 1 \end{array}\right].$$

Add -3 times the second row to the third row, obtaining

$$\left[\begin{array}{ccc|ccc} 1 & 0 & 1 & 1 & 0 & 0 \\ 0 & 1 & -\frac{1}{3} & -\frac{2}{3} & \frac{1}{3} & 0 \\ 0 & 0 & 2 & 1 & -1 & 1 \end{array}\right].$$

Multiply the third row by $\frac{1}{2}$, obtaining

$$\left[\begin{array}{ccc|ccc} 1 & 0 & 1 & 1 & 0 & 0 \\ 0 & 1 & -\frac{1}{3} & -\frac{2}{3} & \frac{1}{3} & 0 \\ 0 & 0 & 1 & \frac{1}{2} & -\frac{1}{2} & \frac{1}{2} \end{array}\right].$$

Add -1 times the third row to the first row, and add $\frac{1}{3}$ times the third row to the second row, obtaining

$$\left[\begin{array}{ccc|ccc} 1 & 0 & 0 & \frac{1}{2} & \frac{1}{2} & -\frac{1}{2} \\ 0 & 1 & 0 & -\frac{1}{2} & \frac{1}{6} & \frac{1}{6} \\ 0 & 0 & 1 & \frac{1}{2} & -\frac{1}{2} & \frac{1}{2} \end{array}\right].$$

$$\text{Hence } A^{-1} = \begin{bmatrix} \frac{1}{2} & \frac{1}{2} & -\frac{1}{2} \\ -\frac{1}{2} & \frac{1}{6} & \frac{1}{6} \\ \frac{1}{2} & -\frac{1}{2} & \frac{1}{2} \end{bmatrix}$$

To check, calculate AA^{-1} and $A^{-1}A$ to see if they are I.

Remark. If A has an inverse, a system of n linear equations in n unknowns $x_1, \ldots, x_n$, $AX = Y$ can be solved by calculating A^{-1} above and multiplying by it, for $A^{-1}AX = A^{-1}Y$, or $X = A^{-1}Y$.

Exercises

Find the inverse of each matrix, and check:

1. $\begin{bmatrix} 4 & 3 \\ 3 & 2 \end{bmatrix}$. **2.** $\begin{bmatrix} 5 & 3 \\ 3 & 2 \end{bmatrix}$. **3.** $\begin{bmatrix} 4 & 1 \\ 2 & 3 \end{bmatrix}$. **4.** $\begin{bmatrix} 3 & 0 \\ 2 & 1 \end{bmatrix}$.

5. $\begin{bmatrix} 1 & 0 & 0 \\ 2 & 2 & 0 \\ 3 & 3 & 3 \end{bmatrix}$. **6.** $\begin{bmatrix} 1 & 2 & -2 \\ -1 & 3 & 0 \\ 0 & -2 & 1 \end{bmatrix}$. **7.** $\begin{bmatrix} 2 & 1 & 3 \\ -1 & 0 & 4 \\ 1 & 1 & 2 \end{bmatrix}$.

8. $\begin{bmatrix} 2 & 0 & 3 \\ 0 & 1 & 2 \\ 0 & 0 & 1 \end{bmatrix}$. **9.** $\begin{bmatrix} 1 & 0 & 3 & 2 \\ 2 & -2 & 2 & -1 \\ 3 & 0 & 1 & -2 \\ 4 & 0 & 1 & 1 \end{bmatrix}$. **10.** $\begin{bmatrix} 1 & 0 & 0 & 0 \\ 2 & 2 & 0 & 0 \\ 1 & 2 & 3 & 0 \\ -1 & 0 & 0 & 1 \end{bmatrix}$.

11. Prove that if B and C are both inverses of the square matrix A then $B = C$.

12. Prove that if the square matrix A has an inverse A^{-1} then so does A^{-1} and $(A^{-1})^{-1} = A$.

13. Prove that if A and B are invertible square matrices of the same order, then $(AB)^{-1} = B^{-1}A^{-1}$.

179. CONCLUSION

The subject of vectors and matrices is an important one in both pure and applied mathematics. Matrices enter into algebra, geometry, analysis, graph theory, topology, and many other parts of pure mathematics. They find application in physics, engineering, electrical circuit theory, economics, psychology, sociometry, etc. In fact, their study is one of the principle needs of students of mathematical applications in the social sciences as well as in the physical sciences.

References

Numbers refer to the bibliography at the back of the book.

Abbott 1
Allen 2
Ashby 9
Avondo-Bodino 11
Baumol 14
Berge 24
Birkhoff and MacLane 28
Burger 44
Bush and Mosteller 45
Dantzig 61
Ficken 73
Flament 76
Ford and Fulkerson 77
Gale 81
Glicksman 87
Hadley 88, 89
Harary, Norman, and Cartwright 91
Jaeger 98
Karlin 102
Kemeny and Snell 105, 106
Luce and Raiffa 128
Manning 129
McCoy 130
McKinsey 132
Ore 143, 145
Spivey 183
Tucker 192
Vajda 195, 196, 197, 198

15

Natural Numbers and Mathematical Induction

180. POSTULATES FOR THE NATURAL NUMBERS

In section 32, we showed that the algebra of real numbers could be considered as an abstract mathematical science based on certain postulates in which "real number" was an undefined term. In Chapters 3 and 4, we indicated how the various kinds of numbers could be defined and studied on the basis of the natural numbers alone. Thus in sections 15 and 16, we assumed that we knew what was meant by "natural number" and assumed such things as the addition tables and the associative, commutative, and distributive laws, which we regarded as being derived from experience, and in section 19 we defined fractions in terms of natural numbers. Now in any abstract logical system we are necessarily forced to base everything on unproved postulates and undefined terms. Thus, we might convert our work in Chapters 3 and 4 into an abstract mathematical science by taking "natural number" as an undefined term and taking as postulates essentially what we assumed there. But such a treatment would not seem elegant to a mathematician. For both aesthetic and logical reasons, we would like to assume as little as possible. In Chapter 3 we assumed many things that we could have proved. For example, we could have proved as theorems the addition and multiplication tables if we had begun with the postulates given in the present section, which are due to G. Peano (1858–1932, Italian). This would push the foundation of our algebra still further back to a more primitive level (more primitive in a logical sense, more sophisticated in a psychological sense).

Let us recall that the choice of undefined terms and unproved postulates, on which we base our abstract mathematical science, is largely suggested by experience. Now our experience with counting suggests that every natural number has a successor, that is, the next natural number in order of magnitude. For example, the successor of 3 would be 4. (Note that we could not say this for all fractions; for example, there is no next fraction in order of magnitude after $\frac{1}{2}$.) Thus Peano begins his abstract mathematical science by taking as undefined terms the terms "natural number," "successor," and "1." He then bases the whole system on five postulates or assumptions. The first two are:

P_1. *1 is a natural number.*

P_2. *If x is any natural number, there is, corresponding to it, another natural number called the successor of x, denoted by x'.*

Using these two postulates alone we can proceed as follows. By P_1, 1 is a natural number. By P_2, 1 must have a successor $1'$. Call $1'$ by the name 2. Now 2 is a natural number, and by P_2, it must have a successor $2'$. Call $2'$ by the name 3. And so on.

Notice that these postulates have other concrete interpretations besides the one we are thinking of. For example, suppose we let the undefined terms "natural number" and "successor of" mean "person" and "mother of," respectively, and let "1" mean "yourself." Then P_1 says "you are a person." P_2 says "if x is any person, there is, corresponding to that person, another person called the mother of x."*

The next of Peano's postulates is:

P_3. *1 is not the successor of any natural number.*

This means intuitively that 1 is the *first* of the natural numbers. The next axiom is:

P_4. *If $x' = y'$, then $x = y$.*

Intuitively this means that if two natural numbers are known to have the same successor, they must be equal to each other. Or, to put it another way, two different natural numbers cannot have the same successor. Or, two different natural numbers must have different successors. Note that this postulate is not satisfied by the mother-person interpretation above, for two different persons may have the same mother. The last axiom, called the **axiom of mathematical induction** requires very careful reading:

* A somewhat stilted version of the familiar Mother's Day slogan: "Everybody has a mother."

P_5. ***If*** *S is any set of natural numbers which is known to have the following two properties:*

(*1*) *The natural number 1 is in the set S,*

(*2*) *If any natural number k is in the set S, then the successor k′ of k must also be in the set S,*

then *all natural numbers are in the set S.*

This postulate seems very plausible. For if 1 is in S, then hypothesis (2) says that $1'$ or 2 is in S. Then, since 2 is in S, (2) says that $2'$ or 3 is in S. And so on. The reason that we have to take P_5 as an assumption is precisely because of the words "and so on." We cannot very well go on so, for very long, because life is too short and the succession of natural numbers goes on forever. Thus if we kept on with the argument we just started we might, in 3 score and 10 years, get to the point of saying that since 2,345,678,901 is in S, (2) says that $2{,}345{,}678{,}901'$ or 2,345,678,902 is in S. But still we could not assert that *all* natural numbers are in S. However, this assertion does seem plausible; hence we take it as our assumption P_5.

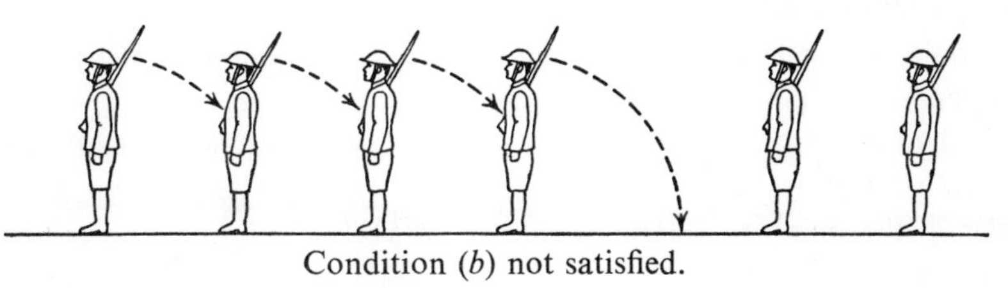

Condition (*b*) not satisfied.
FIG. 257

The postulate P_5 may be understood intuitively by the following analogy. Consider an endless single file of tin soldiers beginning somewhere and continuing forever. Suppose we want to make sure that *all* these soldiers fall. It wouldn't do to knock down the first soldier, then knock down the second, and so on, because we could in this way dispose of only a finite (limited) number of soldiers and this is an *endless* file of soldiers. However, we would be sure they would all fall if we could be sure of two things:

(*a*) the first soldier is knocked down;

(*b*) the soldiers are so spaced that, if any soldier falls, he automatically knocks over the next soldier (his successor).

Condition (*a*) corresponds to (1) in P_5 and condition (*b*) to (2) in P_5. In the case of the tin soldiers, let S be the set of all tin soldiers who must fall. Hence P_5 may be paraphrased to read: *if S* is a set of tin soldiers which is known to have the properties:

(1) the first soldier is in the set S,

(2) if any soldier is in the set S, then his successor (the next soldier) must also be in the set S,

then all the soldiers are in the set S.

If we were to base our study of natural numbers on Peano's postulates alone, we would have to define what we mean by addition and multiplication, since nothing is said about these operations in the postulates and they were not taken as undefined terms. Thus we might define $k + 1 = k'$, the successor of k; $k + 2 = (k + 1)'$, the successor of $k + 1$; $k + 3 = (k + 2)'$, the successor of $k + 2$; and so on, where k is any natural number. We would have to prove then, as theorems, that $2 + 2 = 4$, and the rest of the addition table. For example, we could prove $2 + 2 = 4$ as follows. By the definition of addition suggested above, $2 + 2 = (2 + 1)'$, the successor of $2 + 1$. But $2 + 1 = 2' = 3$. Hence, by substitution, $2 + 2 = 3' = 4$. Similarly, $3 + 2 = (3 + 1)' = (3')' = 4' = 5$. And so on. We would have to prove, also, the associative, commutative, and distributive laws, etc., all of which we assumed in Chapter 3. This can be done, but we shall not attempt it here.

Peano's postulates are essentially an abstract formulation of the process of counting.

We shall now turn to an important use of P_5, the postulate of mathematical induction, which was considered to be perhaps the most basic axiom of mathematics in the opinion of Henri Poincaré (1854–1912), one of the greatest of modern mathematicians.

181. MATHEMATICAL INDUCTION

Notice that P_5 provides us with a criterion for deciding whether a given set S of natural numbers contains *all* natural numbers. If we can somehow prove that the given set S actually has the properties (1) and (2) of P_5, then the axiom asserts that S contains all natural numbers. This criterion may be used to prove theorems like the following. The method of proof is called **mathematical induction**.

Example 1. Prove that if n is any natural number whatever, the formula

$$(A) \qquad 2 + 4 + 6 + 8 + \cdots + 2n = n(n + 1)$$

is correct.

First let us see what the theorem asserts. On the left we have the sum of the first n even numbers. The first even number is $2 \cdot 1$; the second even number is $2 \cdot 2$; the third even number is $2 \cdot 3$; the fourth even number is $2 \cdot 4$; the nth even number is $2n$. The theorem then asserts that the sum of the first n even numbers is exactly $n(n+1)$ no matter what natural number n is. For example, it asserts that the sum of the first 50 even numbers is $50 \cdot 51 = 2550$. Hence, the theorem makes an infinite number of assertions, one assertion corresponding to each value of n.

For example, the theorem says that:

for $n = 1$, $\quad 2 = 1(1 + 1)$;
for $n = 2$, $\quad 2 + 4 = 2(2 + 1)$;
for $n = 3$, $\quad 2 + 4 + 6 = 3(3 + 1)$;
for $n = 4$, $\quad 2 + 4 + 6 + 8 = 4(4 + 1)$;
for $n = 5$, $\quad 2 + 4 + 6 + 8 + 10 = 5(5 + 1)$;

and so on. The five statements above can be verified directly by arithmetic. But saying "and so on" is begging the question, or simply assuming that things do go on as we wish. We cannot prove that this formula works for *all* natural numbers n by merely going on to verify it for one natural number after another because neither we nor our posterity can live to finish the job. Instead of futilely going on with our direct verification of the formula for particular values of n, we use axiom P_5, as follows.

Let S be the set of all those natural numbers for which the theorem is true. We have already verified by direct arithmetical calculation that 1 is in the set S; this is condition (1) of P_5. That is, the formula is true for the value $n = 1$. Let us now prove that condition (2) of P_5 is satisfied. Condition (2) says that *if* k is a natural number for which (A) is true (that is, if k is in S), *then* $k + 1$ is also a natural number for which the theorem is true (that is, $k + 1$ is in S). We must prove the following theorem.

Hypothesis. $2 + 4 + 6 + \cdots + 2k = k(k + 1)$

Conclusion. $2 + 4 + 6 + \cdots + 2k + 2(k + 1) = (k + 1)(k + 1 + 1)$
$= (k + 1)(k + 2) = k^2 + 3k + 2.$

The hypothesis is what the formula asserts for the value $n = k$; it is obtained by substituting $n = k$ in the proposed formula (A). The conclusion is what the formula asserts for the value $n = k + 1$; it is obtained by subsituting $n = k + 1$ in the proposed formula (A). We have to show that if the hypothesis is a true statement, then so must the conclusion be a true statement. That is, it is the formula (A) which is on trial. We have to show that if (A) tells the truth for $n = k$, then it also tells the truth when $n = k + 1$.

Proof. By hypothesis,

$$2 + 4 + 6 + \cdots + 2k = k(k + 1).$$

The left side is the sum of the first k terms of the sequence of even numbers. But the left side of the conclusion is the sum of the first $k+1$ terms of the sequence of even numbers. It is this latter sum about which we must prove something. Hence, it is natural to add to both sides of our hypothesis the $(k+1)$th or next term of the sequence; that is, the $(k+1)$th even number $2(k+1)$. We may add $2(k+1)$ to both sides, since if equals are added to equals the results are equal. Thus, we obtain

$$2+4+6+\cdots+2k+2(k+1)=k(k+1)+2(k+1)=k^2+3k+2,$$

which is precisely the right side of our conclusion. This is what we had to prove.

Since we have verified conditions (1) and (2) of P_5, it follows that *all* natural numbers are in the set S of natural numbers for which the formula (A) is true. That is, formula (A) is true for all natural numbers n.

The work may be arranged conveniently as in the following example.

Example 2. Prove that $3+6+9+12+\cdots+3n=3n(n+1)/2$ for any natural number n.

Proof. Let S be the set of natural numbers for which the theorem is true.

Part I. The set S contains 1, because for $n=1$, the theorem asserts that $3=3\cdot 1(1+1)/2=3$, which is true.

Part II. If the set S contains any natural number k, then it also contains $k+1$.

Hypothesis. $3+6+9+12+\cdots+3k=\dfrac{3k(k+1)}{2}$.

Conclusion. $3+6+9+12+\cdots+3k+3(k+1)$

$$=\frac{3(k+1)(k+1+1)}{2}=\frac{3(k+1)(k+2)}{2}$$

$$=\frac{3k^2+9k+6}{2}.$$

Proof. By hypothesis, $3+6+9+12+\cdots+3k=3k(k+1)/2$. We may add the $(k+1)$th term, $3(k+1)$, to both sides, since if equals are added to equals the results are equal. Thus we obtain

$$3+6+9+12+\cdots+3k+3(k+1)$$

$$=\frac{3k(k+1)}{2}+3(k+1)$$

$$=\frac{3k(k+1)+2\cdot 3(k+1)}{2}=\frac{3k^2+9k+6}{2}$$

which is the same as the right side of our conclusion. This proves the proposition of Part II.

Since we have verified the conditions (1) and (2) of P_5, it follows from P_5 that *all* natural numbers are in the set S of natural numbers for which the theorem is true.

Remark 1. It is *necessary* to verify *both* conditions (1) and (2). From the example of the tin soldiers it is intuitively clear that both conditions are necessary. Knocking down the first soldier will not accomplish the fall of all the soldiers unless they are properly spaced so that the kth soldier knocks over the $(k+1)$th soldier as he falls. Similarly, having them properly spaced does us no good unless the first soldier is actually knocked down. We give two algebraic examples to show that both conditions are necessary.

(*A*) The (false) formula $2+4+6+\cdots+2n = n(n+1)+10$ will satisfy condition (2) but not condition (1). For if k were a number for which the formula were true, $k+1$ would have to be one, too. For the proposition of Part II would proceed as follows.

Hypothesis. $2+4+6+\cdots+2k = k(k+1)+10.$

Conclusion.

$$\begin{aligned} 2+4+6+\cdots+2k+2(k+1) &= (k+1)(k+1+1)+10 \\ &= (k+1)(k+2)+10 \\ &= k^2+3k+12. \end{aligned}$$

Proof. If $2+4+6+\cdots+2k = k(k+1)+10$, we may add $2(k+1)$ to both sides obtaining

$$\begin{aligned} 2+4+6+\cdots+2k+2(k+1) &= k(k+1)+2(k+1)+10 \\ &= k^2+3k+12, \end{aligned}$$

which verifies condition (2).

But $n=1$ does not make the formula true, since for $n=1$, the formula says that

$$2 = 1(1+1)+10 = 12.$$

Thus condition (1) is not satisfied.

(*B*) The (false) formula $2+4+6+\cdots+2n = n(n+1)+(n-1)$ is true for $n=1$. But it is not true for $n=2$. If we tried to verify condition (2) it would not work. Let us try it.

Hypothesis.

$$2+4+6+\cdots+2k = k(k+1)+(k-1) = k^2+2k-1.$$

Conclusion.

$$\begin{aligned} 2+4+6+\cdots+2(k+1) &= (k+1)(k+1+1)+(k+1)-1 \\ &= k^2+4k+2. \end{aligned}$$

Proof. By hypothesis, $2+4+6+\cdots+2k=k^2+2k-1$. Adding $2(k+1)$ to both sides, we get

$$2+4+6+\cdots+2(k+1)=k^2+2k-1+2(k+1)=k^2+4k+1$$

which is *not* the same as the right side of the conclusion. Hence, Part II of the proof does not go through.

Remark 2. It is important to distinguish between inductive logic as used in the experimental sciences and mathematical induction which belongs to deductive logic. In experimental science we might test a proposed formula, like that of example 1, by verifying it directly for $n=1, 2, 3, \cdots$, and so on up to some arbitrary number. If it worked for the first few numbers we might conclude that it was probably true for all numbers. If it worked for the first 100 numbers, we would consider it more probably true. If it worked for the first 1000 numbers we would consider its truth for all natural numbers extremely probable. But this would not be the same as asserting that it is certain. In fact, it is easy to write a formula which is true for the first 5 or 100 or 1000 numbers and false thereafter. For example, we have proved that the formula

$$2+4+6+\cdots+2n=n(n+1)$$

is true for all natural numbers n. Now suppose we alter the right member by writing

$$2+4+6+\cdots+2n=n(n+1)+(n-1)(n-2)(n-3)(n-4)(n-5).$$

Then for $n=1, 2, 3, 4, 5$, this latter formula is correct since the added term will be zero for these values of n. But for $n=6, 7, 8, \cdots$, and so on the latter formula will be wrong because the added term will no longer be zero and the right member will therefore no longer yield the correct result. For example, for $n=6$ the right member yields 162 instead of the correct sum 42. In the same way

$$2+4+6+\cdots+2n=n(n+1)+(n-1)(n-2)\cdots(n-1000)$$

would yield the correct result for all values of n from $n=1$ to $n=1000$ but will be wrong thereafter. This shows that 1000 or 1,000,000 verifications cannot prove that the formula is true for *all* natural numbers n. Hence the need for the axiom of mathematical induction P_5. A proof by mathematical induction is not an argument of inductive logic, as in experimental science, but is an argument of deductive logic based on axiom P_5.

Remark 3. When we write a sequence of terms like

$$2, 4, 6, \ldots, 2n, \ldots$$

the term $2n$ is called the **general term** or the ***n*th term** because, for $n=1$, $2n=2$; for $n=2$, $2n=4$; for $n=3$, $2n=6$; and so on. On many psychological "intelligence" tests people are asked to write the next term of a sequence whose first few terms are given. Thus a typical question would be:

"Write the next term of the sequence 2, 4, 6, 8, 10, 12, ..." Now, the answer ex-expected is 14 which is obtained by assuming that the general term is $2n$ as is suggested by the first 6 terms which are given. But the general term might just as well have been

$$2n + (n-1)(n-2)(n-3)(n-4)(n-5)(n-6)$$

in which case the first 6 terms would have been exactly the given ones while for $n = 7$ we would have not 14 but $14 + 6 \cdot 5 \cdot 4 \cdot 3 \cdot 2 \cdot 1 = 734$. The general term might also have been

$$2n + (n-1)(n-3)(n-3)(n-4)(n-5)(n-6) \cdot f(n)$$

where $f(n)$ is any polynomial, say, in n. A person of exceptional intelligence who was able to perceive that there is no logical reason to suppose that $2n$ is the general term would be at a loss to answer this question on the "intelligence" test, and he might be ranked as a moron, at least as far as this question is concerned. For the question has no logical answer and is really a problem, not in reasoning, but in clairvoyance, for we must guess which of the many possible general terms the examiner is thinking of.*

Remark 4. While the development of the natural numbers on the basis of axioms P_1–P_5 is due to Peano, (late in the nineteenth century), the idea of proving theorems by mathematical induction can be traced, in some form, back to the sixteenth century. Note that by mathematical induction we prove an infinite number of assertions, in a short space.

Remark 5. It is not hard to show that if we verify the truth of any formula for any particular natural number, (for example, 4) and then verify the second condition of our axiom of mathematical induction, then we have proved the truth of the formula for all natural numbers beginning with the particular one started with (in our example, for 4, 5, 6, and so on).

Exercises

Write (a) the 5-th term; (b) the 75-th term; (c) the k-th term; (d) the $(k + 1)$-th term; (e) the $(k + 6)$-th term, of the sequence whose n-th term is:

1. $4n$. **2.** $5n$. **3.** $2n - 1$. **4.** $\dfrac{1}{n(n+1)}$. **5.** $3n$. **6.** $n(n + 1)$.

(a) In each of the following exercises verify the correctness of the given formula for $n = 1, 2, 3, 4, 5$. (b) Does the work in part (a) suffice to establish the correctness of

* E. T. Bell in his *Men of Mathematics* writes that "... when Poincaré was acknowledged as the foremost mathematician and leading popularizer of science of his time he submitted to the Binet tests and made such a disgraceful showing that, had he been judged as a child instead of as the famous mathematician he was, he would have been rated—by the tests—as an imbecile."

the given formula for all natural numbers n? Explain. (c) *Prove by mathematical induction that the given* formula is correct for all natural numbers n.*

7. $4+8+12+16+\cdots+4n=2n(n+1)$.

8. $5+10+15+20+\cdots+5n=\dfrac{5n(n+1)}{2}$.

9. $1+2+3+4+\cdots+n=\dfrac{n(n+1)}{2}$.

10. $6+12+18+24+\cdots+6n=3n(n+1)$.

11. $1+3+5+7+\cdots+(2n-1)=n^2$.

12. $\dfrac{1}{1\cdot 2}+\dfrac{1}{2\cdot 3}+\dfrac{1}{3\cdot 4}+\dfrac{1}{4\cdot 5}+\cdots+\dfrac{1}{n(n+1)}=\dfrac{n}{n+1}$.

13. $1\cdot 2+2\cdot 3+3\cdot 4+4\cdot 5+\cdots+n(n+1)=\dfrac{n(n+1)(n+2)}{3}$.

14. $1^2+2^2+3^2+4^2+\cdots+n^2=\dfrac{n(n+1)(2n+1)}{6}$.

15. $1^3+2^3+3^3+4^3+\cdots+n^3=\dfrac{n^2(n+1)^2}{4}$.

16. $3+3^2+3^3+3^4+\cdots+3^n=\dfrac{3^{n+1}-3}{2}$.

* Note that while we here prove that the *given* formula is correct we give no hint as to how the right member of the formula was discovered. The formula of exercise 11 might be guessed from the following arrangement of pebbles.

$1=1^2$ $1+3=2^2$ $1+3+5=3^2$ $1+3+5+7=4^2$

Similarly, the formula of exercise 9 might have been discovered from the following arrangement of pebbles.

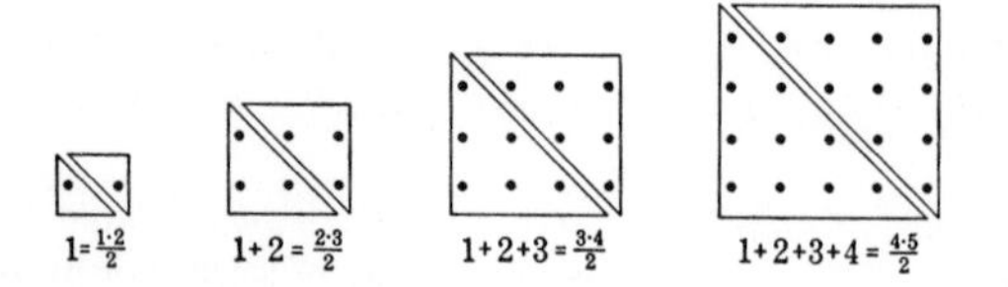

However, the general problem of finding an expression for the sum of n terms of a given sequence is a very difficult one.

17. Prove by mathematical induction that the sum of the "geometric progression"

$$a + ar + ar^2 + \cdots + ar^{n-1} = \frac{a - ar^n}{1 - r}, \qquad (r \neq 1)$$

for all natural numbers n.

18. Prove by mathematical induction that the sum of the "arithmetic progression"

$$a + (a + d) + (a + 2d) + \cdots + (a + [n - 1]d) = \frac{n(2a + [n - 1]d)}{2},$$

for all natural numbers n.

19. Prove by mathematical induction that for $n = 4, 5, 6, 7, \ldots$, and so on, $2^n < n!$. (Hint: see remark 5.)

20. Prove by mathematical induction that $(ab)^n = a^n b^n$ for all natural numbers n.

★21. Prove by mathematical induction that $C(2,2) + C(3,2) + C(4,2) + \cdots + C(n + 1,2) = C(n + 2,3)$, for all natural numbers n.

★22. Prove by mathematical induction that $x - y$ is a factor of $x^n - y^n$ for all natural numbers n. (Hint: $x^{k+1} - y^{k+1} = (x^{k+1} - xy^k) + (xy^k - y^{k+1})$.)

182. CONCLUSION

We have been discussing the study of natural numbers on the basis of Peano's postulates. These axioms push the unproved propositions or postulates we start with much further back than the postulates we used in Chapter 3. Thus on the basis of Peano's postulates we can prove as theorems the tables of addition and multiplication, and the associative, commutative, and distributive laws, which we took as assumptions in Chapter 3. But, in Peano's postulates we still take "natural number" as an undefined term. Hence Peano's abstract mathematical science may be given other concrete interpretations than the one we were thinking of. For example, if the undefined term "natural number" is interpreted to mean "even number," and "successor" to mean "next even number" and "1" to mean the first even number or "2," then all of Peano's postulates are satisfied. Or, if "natural number" is taken to mean "fraction of the form $1/n$" and "1" to mean "1/1" and "successor of $1/k$" to mean "$1/(k + 1)$," then all of Peano's postulates are satisfied. The fact that all arithmetic and algebra can be built up with "natural number" left undefined is not surprising. In fact, a calculating machine is capable of doing arithmetic, but it certainly doesn't know what "number" means. It is, however, constructed so as to obey all the formal rules of numbers, which is all that matters so far as pure mathematics is concerned. In Chapter 16, we shall push the process of definition back further and shall define number in terms of more primitive notions.

References

Numbers refer to the bibliography at the back of the book.

Poincaré 148 Russell 163

16

Cardinal Numbers, Finite and Transfinite

183. THE CARDINAL NUMBER OF A SET

In section 69, we defined **finite set** and **the number of elements in a finite set**. We shall here extend the latter idea to sets which are not necessarily finite. Consider the class of all sets equivalent to a given set S; for example, the set of all trios or triplets of things. We might conceive of "number" as some property common to all the sets in the class of equivalent sets. Thus "three" might be thought of as some property common to all trios or triplets like the set of letters A, B, C, or the set of people Smith, Jones, and Brown, or the three Muses, or the three little pigs, or the set of wheels on a tricycle, or the set of balls in front of a pawnshop. Now this idea of "three" as an abstract property belonging to all these different sets of objects is somewhat vague. In fact, all these trios might conceivably have more than one property in common; for example, they might all be considered to have the property of "existence." It would be nicer to be able to say exactly what the number "three" is, instead of referring to a vague common property. This can actually be done. There is one simple specific property that every trio has, namely, the property of belonging to the class of all sets equivalent to itself. Moreover, no non-trio has this property. Thus we might even more simply say that the number "three" *is* the class of all sets equivalent to the set consisting of Smith, Jones, and Brown. Any set belonging to this class is said to *have* (*or more properly, to belong to*) *the number "three."* Thus we are led to the following general definitions.

Definition 1. *Any two sets are said to* **have the same number** (*more properly, belong to the same number*) *if and only if they are equivalent* (*that is, if and only if their elements can be placed in one-to-one correspondence*).

Definition 2. *The* ***number of a set*** *S (or the number of elements in a set S) is the class of all sets equivalent to the set S. A number thus defined is usually called a* ***cardinal number***.*

The notion of equivalence is an equivalence relation, in the sense of section 12, and the cardinal numbers are the equivalence classes which the relation determines.

For our own convenience, we invent names for those numbers to which we wish to refer frequently. For example, the cardinal number of any set equivalent to the set consisting of Smith, Jones, and Brown is called "three." The cardinal number of any set equivalent to the set of fingers on one hand is called "five." However, to determine that two sets have the same number, it is not necessary to know what the number of either is called. It suffices to know that the two sets can be placed in one-to-one correspondence. Thus, if every seat in a theatre is occupied and there is no one standing, we know that the number of seats is the same as the number of people, even if we do not know what this number is called. Our definition 1 corresponds precisely to our intuitive notion of number. In fact, when we count on our fingers we are merely placing some set of objects in one-to-one correspondence with some set of fingers. If the cardinal number is small enough to be in common use we usually invent a name for it to make reference to it easier. Thus the number denoted symbolically by 10^9 or 1,000,000,000 is called a billion. On the other hand, the number 10^{100} (or, "one" with a hundred zeros after it) is much larger than anything in common use even in governmental finance. In fact, it is larger than the number of electrons in the entire universe, which, according to Eddington, is about 10^{79}. However, in order to refer to this number conveniently, it has been named a "googol," the name having been invented by a child. The much larger number $10^{(10^{100})}$ or 10 raised to the googol power (a "one" with a googol zeros after it) has been called† a "googolplex."

184. TRANSFINITE CARDINAL NUMBERS. THE WHOLE AND ITS PARTS

A set B is called a **subset** or **part** of the set A if every element (member) of B is also an element of A. According to this definition the set A is a "part" of itself. *If B is part of A and A is also part of B, then A and B are the same set.*

* If definition 2 gives you mental indigestion at first, don't let it worry you. The idea of definition 1 is more important than that of definition 2 and much easier to digest.

† See E. Kasner and J. Newman, *Mathematics and the Imagination*, Simon & Schuster, N. Y. 1940.

In other words, if any element of the set A is called an "a" and any element of the set B is called a "b," then the statement "B is part of A" may be worded as "all b's are a's." Similarly, "A is part of B" means "all a's are b's." If all a's are b's *and* all b's are a's, then the sets A and B are identical. However, if B is part of A and there exists at least one element of A which is not an element of B, then B is called a **proper part** or a **proper subset** of A. That is, a proper part is a part which is not the whole thing.

Consider the set A of *all* natural numbers $1, 2, 3, \ldots, n, \ldots$, and the set B of all natural numbers greater than 10. The set B is a proper part of A since the numbers 1, 2, 3, 4, 5, 6, 7, 8, 9, 10 are in A but not in B. Nevertheless, we can place the sets A and B in one-to-one correspondence by pairing off their elements as follows: let any natural number x in A correspond to the number $x + 10$ in B. Thus,

$$\begin{array}{cccccc} 1, & 2, & 3, & 4, \ldots, & n & , \ldots \\ \updownarrow & \updownarrow & \updownarrow & \updownarrow & \updownarrow & \\ 11, & 12, & 13, & 14, \ldots, & n+10, & \ldots. \end{array}$$

The double arrow is read "corresponds to." Hence the sets A and B are equivalent, or have the same cardinal number.

Consider the set C of all even natural numbers $2, 4, 6, \ldots, 2n, \ldots$. The set C is equivalent to A since they can be placed in one-to-one correspondence by allowing any natural number x in A to correspond to $2x$ in C, as follows:

$$\begin{array}{cccccc} 1, & 2, & 3, & 4, \ldots, & n, & \ldots \\ \updownarrow & \updownarrow & \updownarrow & \updownarrow & \updownarrow & \\ 2, & 4, & 6, & 8, \ldots, & 2n, & \ldots. \end{array}$$

Hence C has the same cardinal number as A, in spite of the fact that the set C is a proper part of the set A.

Consider the set D of all odd natural numbers $1, 3, 5, \ldots, 2n - 1, \ldots$. The set D is equivalent to A since they can be placed in one-to-one correspondence by allowing the natural number x in A to correspond to the odd number $2x - 1$ in D, as follows:

$$\begin{array}{cccccc} 1, & 2, & 3, & 4, \ldots, & n & , \ldots \\ \updownarrow & \updownarrow & \updownarrow & \updownarrow & \updownarrow & \\ 1, & 3, & 5, & 7, \ldots, & 2n-1, & \ldots. \end{array}$$

Hence D has the same cardinal number as A, although the set D is a proper part of the set A.

We have shown that the set A has the same number of elements (or is equivalent to, or has the same cardinal number) as the sets B, C, and D, each of which is a proper part of A. This shows that the number of elements in a proper part of a set may be quite the same as the number of elements in the whole set. This is at first surprising since it seems to upset violently the notion (once considered self-evident) that the whole is greater than any of its parts.

Another illustration is the following. Consider a 12-inch line-segment AB and a 6-inch line-segment CD placed as in Fig. 258. Let E be the point where AC and BD intersect. Then let P be any point on AB. The line PE intersects CD in exactly one point P'. Conversely, if Q is any point on CD, the line QE intersects AB in exactly one point Q'. Thus the points of AB can be placed in one-to-one correspondence with the points of CD simply by letting any point P on AB correspond to the point P' on CD where the line PE meets CD. Hence the number of points on the 12-inch line-segment AB is exactly the same as the number of points on the 6-inch line-segment CD. On the other hand, the

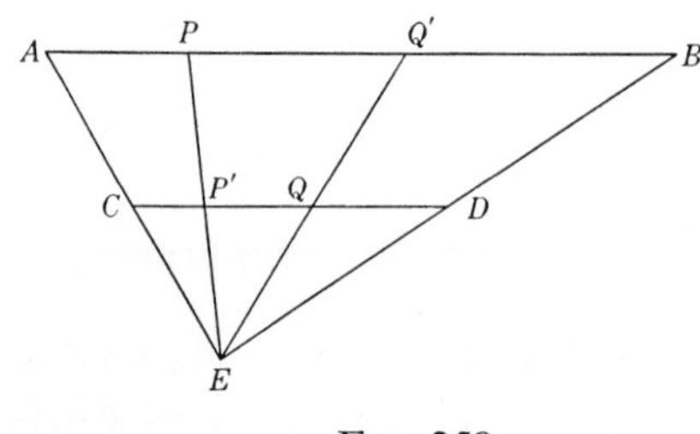

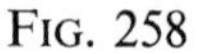
FIG. 258

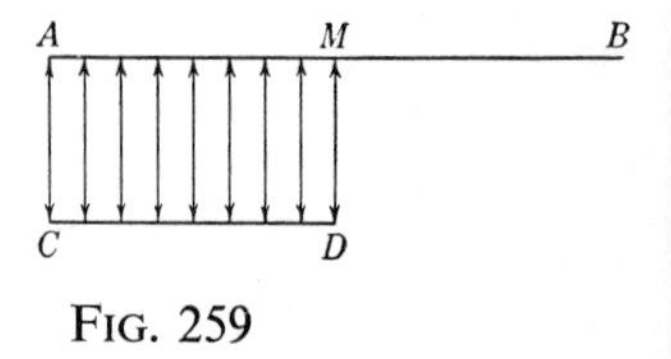

FIG. 259

number of points on CD is the same as the number of points on half of AB, as can be seen by setting up a correspondence between AM (M being the midpoint of AB) and CD by means of perpendiculars as in Fig. 259. Since the number of points on AB is the same as the number of points on CD and the number of points on CD is the same as the number of points on half of AB, it follows that the number of points on AB is the same as the number of points on half of AB. In the same way it can be shown that the number of points on any line-segment is the same as the number of points on any other line-segment, regardless of their lengths. There are just as many points on a line-segment 1 inch long as on one stretching from here to the star Arcturus.

This illustration also seems to do violence to the notion that the whole is greater than any of its parts. Note, however, that we are talking about the number of points in the line-segment, not its length. It is true that the cardinal number of a set may be the same as the cardinal number of a proper subset or part. However, this cannot happen with finite sets, that is, intuitively speaking, with sets that can be counted out at a steady rate of speed in a limited time. So far as finite quantities, or lengths, areas, angles, and other magnitudes used in the elementary applications of mathematics are concerned, " the whole is greater than any of its (proper) parts" remains valid. In fact, it can be proved that *a set is* ***infinite*** *if and only if it is equivalent to a proper part of itself.*

Definition 1. *The cardinal number of an infinite set is called a* ***transfinite*** *cardinal number. The cardinal number of a finite set is called a* ***finite*** *cardinal number.*

Remark. To say that the number of elements in a set is infinite is quite different from saying that it is a very large finite number. Thus 10^{100} and $10^{(10^{100})}$ are staggeringly large finite numbers but they are finite. Neither should the idea of infinite or transfinite numbers discussed here be confused with the idea of "infinity" which we discussed in connection with sequences, limits, and functions in section 121.

The cardinal number of any set equivalent to the set of all natural numbers is denoted by $\aleph_0$ (read, "aleph-null") after G. Cantor (1845–1918) who first studied transfinite numbers systematically. The cardinal number of the set of all points on the line-segment AB is denoted by $\aleph$ (read, "aleph"). Both are transfinite cardinal numbers. It can be shown that $\aleph_0$ is not the same as $\aleph$. In fact, there are many different transfinite cardinals which can be studied systematically.

An arithmetic of transfinite numbers can be worked out. For example, we shall define the "sum" of two cardinal numbers, finite or transfinite, as follows. Let x be the cardinal number of a set X and let y be the cardinal number of a set Y.

Georg Cantor
1845–1918, German

Definition 2. *If the sets X and Y have no element in common, then by the* ***sum*** *$x + y$ of the two cardinal numbers x and y we shall mean the cardinal number of the set consisting of all the elements of the set X and all the elements of the set Y together.*

In other words, the sum of the cardinal numbers of two sets is defined to be the cardinal number of the set composed of all the elements of the two sets taken together, *provided the two given sets have no element in common.* The reason for this latter restrictive proviso becomes obvious when you consider the following simple example. Let X be the set consisting of Ames and Brown and let Y be the set consisting of Camp, Davis, and Earl. Then the sum of the cardinal number of set X (2) and the cardinal number of the set Y (3) is the cardinal number of the set consisting of Ames, Brown, Camp, Davis, and Earl together (5). But if the set Y were composed of Brown, Camp, and Davis we would not say that the sum of 2 and 3 is the cardinal number of the set composed of Ames, Brown, Camp and Davis. Briefly, the sum of the cardinal number of X and the cardinal number of Y is the cardinal number of $X \cup Y$ if $X \cap Y = \varnothing$.

Let us apply this natural definition of the sum of two cardinal numbers to transfinite numbers.

Example 1. The set A of all natural numbers has the cardinal number $\aleph_0$. As we showed above, the set C of all even natural numbers has the same cardinal number $\aleph_0$ and the set D of all odd natural numbers also has the cardinal number $\aleph_0$. But the set A of all natural numbers has for its elements all the elements of the sets C and D together; and the sets C and D clearly have no element in common. Hence the sum of the cardinal number of C plus the cardinal number of D is the cardinal number of A, or

$$\aleph_0 + \aleph_0 = \aleph_0.$$

Example 2. Let E be the set of numbers 1, 2, 3, 4, 5, 6, 7, 8, 9, 10. The cardinal number of the set E is 10. The set B of all natural numbers greater than 10 has the cardinal number $\aleph_0$ as shown above. But all the elements of the sets B and E together constitute the set A of all natural numbers; and the sets E and B have no element in common. Hence

$$\aleph_0 + 10 = \aleph_0.$$

These are only two of the many surprising statements that arise in the arithmetic of transfinite numbers.

Another surprising result is the fact that there are just as many natural numbers as there are positive fractions, despite the fact that the positive fractions are densely distributed on the line while the natural numbers are spaced apart at intervals of one unit. (See section 30.) This may be seen by arranging the fractions in the order indicated by the arrow in Fig. 260 as follows:

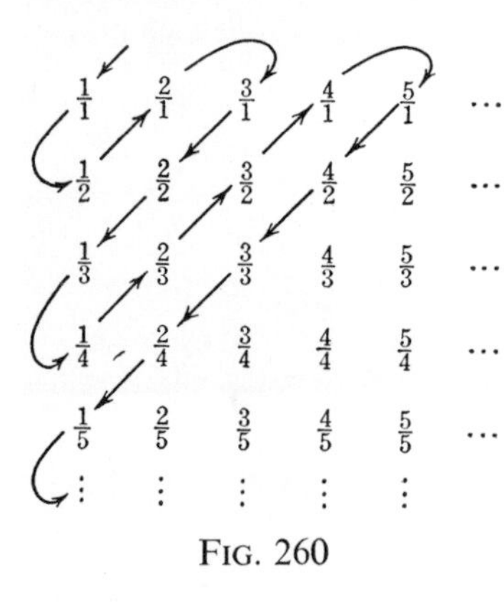

FIG. 260

$$\begin{array}{cccccccccccc} \frac{1}{1}, & \frac{1}{2}, & \frac{2}{1}, & \frac{3}{1}, & \frac{2}{2}, & \frac{1}{3}, & \frac{1}{4}, & \frac{2}{3}, & \frac{3}{2}, & \frac{4}{1}, & \frac{5}{1}, & \dots \\ \updownarrow & \updownarrow & \updownarrow & \updownarrow & \updownarrow & \updownarrow & \updownarrow & \updownarrow & \updownarrow & \updownarrow & \updownarrow & \\ 1, & 2, & 3, & 4, & 5, & 6, & 7, & 8, & 9, & 10, & 11, & \dots . \end{array}$$

In this way we are able to place the set of all positive fractions in one-to-one correspondence with the set of all natural numbers. Hence the cardinal number of the set of all positive fractions is $\aleph_0$, just as is the cardinal number of the set of all natural numbers. Of course, the set of all natural numbers is a proper subset of the set of all positive fractions.

In section 11, we defined the Cartesian product $A \times B$ of two sets A and B as the class of ordered pairs (a,b), where a is any element of A and b any element of B. Since a positive fraction a/b is an ordered pair which could be written as (a,b), the same diagonal method of enumeration (Fig. 260) shows that if A is the set of all natural numbers, then the set of fractions $A \times A$ has the same cardinal number as A.

Definition 3. *The **product** of the cardinal number of a set A and the cardinal number of a set B is the cardinal number of their Cartesian product $A \times B$.*

Thus, we see that $\aleph_0 \cdot \aleph_0 = \aleph_0$.

The subject of infinity has been difficult since ancient times. Cantor made the first extensive assault upon it that could be called successful, although others (Galileo, for example) had had glimmerings of his ideas before. Cantor was led to the study of transfinite numbers by his researches in connection with functions and real numbers. His work provided a new foundation for much of mathematics and stirred up many controversies which are not yet settled.

Exercises

1. Show that the set of all square integers 1, 4, 9, 16, 25, ..., n^2, ... has the cardinal number $\aleph_0$.

2. Show that the set of all positive fractions with numerator 1 has the cardinal number $\aleph_0$.

3. Show that the set of points on the hypotenuse of a right triangle is equivalent to the set of points on the shorter leg of the triangle.

4. Show that $\aleph_0 + 3 = \aleph_0$.

5. Show that $\aleph_0 + 7 = \aleph_0$.

6. Show that $\aleph_0 \cdot 2 = \aleph_0$.

185. THE FINITE CARDINAL NUMBERS

We pointed out in Chapter 15 that, in Peano's postulates for the natural numbers, the term "natural number" was an undefined term. Suppose we now interpret the term "natural number" as meaning "finite cardinal number." Let us consider a set consisting of a single object. Its cardinal number may be called 1. In Peano's system the term "successor" was undefined. Let us now interpret the term "successor" as follows. Consider any finite set A of objects. Let the cardinal number of A be denoted by a. Let us consider a set B consisting of a single object *not* belonging to A. Now consider the set consisting of all the elements of A together with the element of B. The cardinal number of this set is called the successor of a or $a + 1$. With these concrete interpretations for the undefined terms in Peano's abstract system, we could now prove that all his postulates are satisfied. This will not be done here. While Peano's postulates describe abstractly "the process of counting," the finite cardinal numbers provide a concrete interpretation of Peano's abstract mathematical science which really has to do with the "number of objects in a set" as we think of this phrase intuitively. Our definition of cardinal number involves the concepts of "set" of objects and "one-to-one correspondence," both of which are very primitive intuitive ideas which will not be further analyzed here.

References

Numbers refer to the bibliography at the back of the book.

Bell 20
Breuer 38
Cantor 48
Dantzig 62
Gamow 83
Halmos 90
Hausdorff 92
Kamke 101
Kasner and Newman 103
Lieber 120
Newman 140
Russell 163
Wilder 210
Zippin 218

17

Euclidean and Non-Euclidean Geometry

186. INTRODUCTION

In Chapter 2, section 8, we pointed out that Euclidean geometry, considered as a branch of pure mathematics, was an abstract mathematical science. We took as undefined terms the words point and line (and others), and we assumed many unproved propositions or postulates such as the following.

Postulate 1. *Given any two distinct points, there is at least one line containing them.*

Postulate 2. *Given any two distinct points, there is at most one line containing them.*

These two postulates are sometimes quoted together as "two points determine exactly one line." From these two postulates alone we can deduce a theorem.

Theorem 1. *Two distinct lines have at most one point in common.*

Proof. Let l and m be any two distinct lines. Either l and m have more than one point in common or they have not. Suppose they have more than one point in common; that is, suppose the theorem were false. Then there would be two distinct points, P and Q, say, each of which is on both lines. Then by postulate 2, l and m must be the same line, since there can be at most one line through P and Q. This contradicts the hypothesis that they are distinct. Since our supposition leads to a false conclusion, it must be false. Therefore, the only remaining possibility is that l and m do not have more than one point in common. This is what we had to prove.

This theorem tells us that any two distinct lines have either no point or one point in common. We now make the following definition.

Definition. *If two distinct lines in the same plane have no point in common, they are called* ***parallel*** *to each other.*

In other words, two lines are called parallel if they do not meet.*

Notice that theorem 1 does not tell us whether there *are* any parallel lines at all. In Euclidean geometry we proceed to make the following **Euclidean parallel postulate**.

Postulate 3. *Given a line l and a point P not on l, there exists one and only one line m through P which is parallel to l.*

Many other postulates are made in Euclidean geometry besides these three but we shall not trouble to list them here. The important thing is that, having given a complete list of postulates, it is possible to deduce all the theorems by pure logic without ascribing any meaning to the undefined terms like "point" and "line" just as was done with the simple arguments in section 5, Chapter 2. In fact, "point" and "line" might equally well be called "mumbo" and "jumbo," respectively, to emphasize that they may be regarded as completely undefined terms. As we saw in section 105, these undefined terms are susceptible of more than one concrete interpretation; thus "point" may be interpreted either as a dot or as a pair of real numbers. But in deducing theorems we need not have any concrete interpretation in mind. In particular, no reference to diagrams need be made.

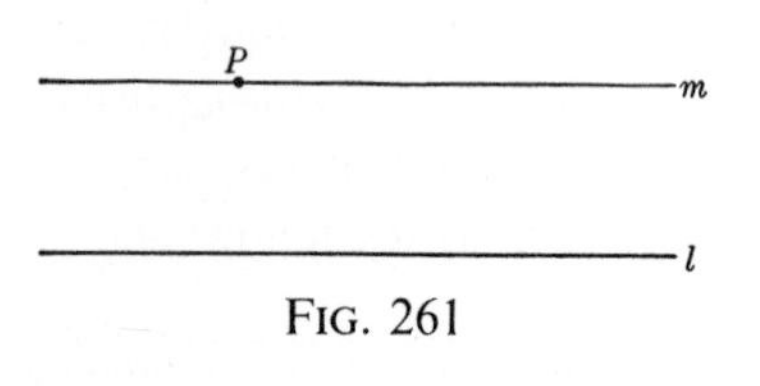

FIG. 261

Exercise. Rewrite postulates 1 and 2 and theorem 1 and its proof, using mumbo and jumbo instead of the words point and line, respectively.

If one thinks of Euclidean plane geometry as referring to diagrams, then one is dealing with Euclidean geometry not as an abstract mathematical science, but as a concrete interpretation or application to the real world where the undefined

* It follows from this definition that any statement about parallel lines "meeting" at "infinity" or at any other forsaken place is sheer nonsense of the most self-contradictory sort, since it would mean that "lines which never meet, meet at infinity." Despite the fact that such statements are as silly as the statement "two railroads which never meet, meet in Chicago," they are often made. There are, in fact, other systems of geometry in which such statements have a sense when properly understood.

terms point and line are interpreted as referring to the dots and streaks drawn on paper. We have already remarked, in section 8, Chapter 2, that when we make this concrete interpretation of Euclidean geometry we can no longer be sure that our postulates are true statements concerning these objects. The idea that these postulates are self-evident truths derived from our physical experience does not hold water. If the undefined terms point and line are taken to mean dot and streak, respectively, then even postulate 2 is no longer true except in an approximate sense, as may be seen by looking at a diagram with a magnifying glass (Fig. 262), although intuitively it seems as though there would be only one streak through two dots if you could only make the dots and streaks thin enough (you can't). In fact, the Greeks probably thought of points and lines as "idealized" dots and streaks, whatever they may be. Thus Euclid and nearly everybody else for 2000 years after him probably thought of these postulates as self-evident truths about these "idealized" points and lines and they regarded Euclidean geometry as an absolutely true description of physical space. Fortunately, however, many people regarded the parallel postulate as being somewhat less self-evident than the others. This is natural because the parallel postulate asserts that certain lines will not meet no matter how far they are produced. Now, if you wish to regard your axioms as self-evident truths derived from our physical experience, you can hardly say that you have any experience about lines which are produced indefinitely far. Our experience is confined to a very small portion of what we imagine to be the real world. Therefore, many people did not like to regard the parallel postulate as self-evident even though they were content to regard the other postulates as self-evident. There is some evidence that Euclid himself was reluctant to assume the parallel postulate and postponed its use as long as he could, using proofs which did not involve it as far as he could. Since the parallel postulate was not regarded as a self-evident truth in good standing, it was natural to try to prove it as a theorem on the basis of the other postulates. If it could be proved as a theorem, there would be no need to assume it and the whole question of its self-evidence would disappear, since it would then be true automatically by virtue of being a logical consequence of the other self-evidently true postulates. Therefore, for about 2000 years, attempts were made to prove the parallel postulate on the basis of the other postulates, but without success. The history of these attempts is interesting but can hardly be gone into here. The question was definitely settled in the nineteenth century when Lobachevski (1793–1856), a Russian, J. Bolyai (1802–1860), a Hungarian, and Gauss (1777–1855), independently of each other, established definitely that the parallel postulate

FIG. 262

could not be proved on the basis of the other postulates. That is, they showed that it is entirely independent of the other postulates.

How they showed this is an interesting story. Essentially their method was this. If the Euclidean parallel postulate can be proved on the strength of the other postulates, then the other postulates together with a postulate that flatly contradicts the Euclidean parallel postulate must lead ultimately to a contradiction. To be precise, suppose all of Euclidean geometry can be deduced from 16 postulates, of which the 16th is the Euclidean parallel postulate. Now if the 16th statement can actually be deduced from the first 15 then a new logical system based on the first 15 and a new 16th which contradicts the Euclidean parallel postulate must be inconsistent, that is, must lead to a contradiction. For the new system would contain among its theorems the Euclidean parallel postulate, as a consequence of the first 15 assumptions, and this would contradict our new 16th postulate. That is, an abstract mathematical science based on all the other postulates of Euclidean geometry together with a postulate which contradicts the Euclidean parallel postulate would have to be inconsistent. What Lobachevski did was to assume, *instead* of Euclid's parallel postulate, the following postulate.

Nicholaus Ivanovich Lobachevski
1793–1856, Russian

Lobachevskian Parallel Postulate. *Given a line l and a point P not on l, there exist at least two lines through P parallel to l.*

This postulate was assumed together with *all* the *other* postulates of Euclid. The resulting abstract mathematical science is usually called **Lobachevskian plane geometry** (or hyperbolic geometry) because Lobachevski was the one who developed this geometry to the greatest extent. It is one of the many forms of **non-Euclidean geometry**. As remarked above, Lobachevski established the independence of the parallel postulate by showing that this Lobachevskian geometry is not inconsistent, that is, does not lead to a contradiction. How this is done will now be described. We confine ourselves to plane geometry.

187. A EUCLIDEAN MODEL FOR LOBACHEVSKIAN GEOMETRY

We shall show that the abstract mathematical science called Lobachevskian geometry can be given a concrete interpretation in a part of the Euclidean plane. Take a definite circle, as small or as large as you please, in the Euclidean plane. By the *Lobachevskian plane* we shall mean the interior of this circle. Let us now interpret the undefined term "point" in Lobachevski's system as meaning a Euclidean point interior to this circle. Let us interpret the undefined term "line" in Lobachevski's system as meaning that part of a Euclidean line which is contained within the circle. Then, it is easy to verify that, when the undefined terms point and line are given these concrete interpretations, all of Lobachevski's postulates are satisfied, including *his* parallel postulate (Fig. 263). This shows that his abstract mathematical science is consistent; more precisely, it shows that if Lobachevski's geometry involves any inconsistencies or contradictions, then so does Euclid's, since we have a model or concrete interpretation of the Lobachevskian "plane" within the Euclidean "plane." That is, any contradictory statements in Lobachevskian geometry would yield corresponding contradictory statements concerning figures within a circle in Euclidean geometry. What is really established is that *Lobachevskian geometry is as consistent as Euclidean.* As far as logical consistency is concerned, there is no reason to prefer Euclid's geometry to Lobachevski's. The question of how *any* abstract mathematical science can be proven absolutely consistent is a very deep problem; it is obviously not easy to prove that no contradiction will *ever* appear among the logical consequences of a set of postulates no matter how many theorems are deduced. We return to this question in Chapter 18. In any case, if we grant that Euclidean geometry is consistent, then so is Lobachevskian.

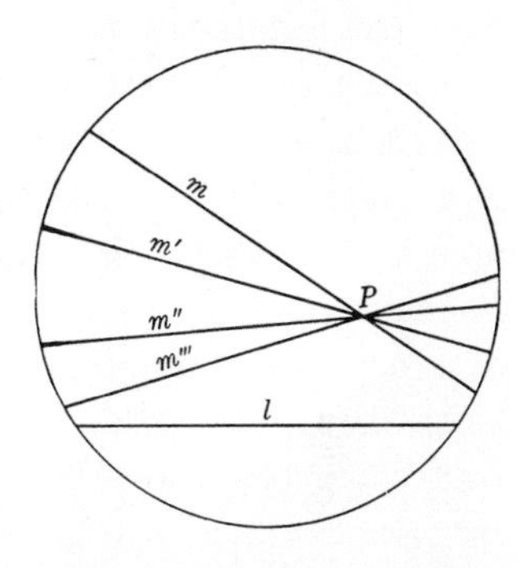

None of the "lines" m, m', m'', m''' have any "points" in common with the "line" l; that is, they are all "parallel" to l.

FIG. 263

However, the reader may now object that while Lobachevskian geometry may be a logically self-consistent system, it is not at all clear that it lends itself to practical application to the real world. Let us examine this question.

Since Lobachevski's geometry differs from Euclid's only with respect to the parallel postulate, all theorems whose proofs do not depend on the parallel postulate will be quite the same in both geometries. But we should expect theorems which depend on the parallel postulate to differ. For example, in

Euclidean geometry we can prove that the sum of the angles of a triangle is exactly 180°, while in Lobachevski's geometry we can prove that the sum of the angles of a triangle is less than 180°. (How this can be proved will be indicated in section 188.) The reader may now ask: "Does not this allow us to say that Lobachevskian geometry does not apply to the real world? For if we measure the angles of a triangle their sum will be 180°." To dispose of this question we have only to remind the reader that all physical measurements are at best approximate and that we could not tell by measurement whether the sum of the angles of the triangle is 180° or 179.99999999876° (or, for that matter, 180.0000002°). Thus this test does not enable us to say that Lobachevskian geometry does not apply to the real world.

It can also be proved that, in Lobachevskian geometry, the sum of the angles of a triangle depends on the area of the triangle, differing from 180° more and more as the area becomes larger. But even this does not enable us to assert that Lobachevskian geometry is inapplicable to the real world, for small and large have only comparative and not absolute meanings. For example, 1,000,000 is large compared to .0001 but 1,000,000 is small compared to 10^{100}; and .0001 is large compared to .000000000001. If we measured what we felt was a very large triangle, like a triangle joining three distant stars, and found the sum of the angles to be indistinguishably close to 180°, we could not conclude that Lobachevskian geometry does not provide an accurate description of the real world. For it might well be that our complete observational experience with the real world, large though it may seem to us, is confined to a region so small that within it the discrepancies between Lobachevskian and Euclidean geometry are still too small to measure.

It must not be supposed that the interior of a circle is the only possible concrete interpretation of Lobachevskian geometry. The whole point is that the actual universe, so far as we can tell, may be a concrete interpretation of Lobachevskian geometry. The interior of the circle was introduced merely to establish that Lobachevskian geometry is just as logically consistent as Euclidean since concrete objects in Euclidean geometry satisfy the Lobachevskian postulates. In particular, it must not be inferred from the circle-interior model of Lobachevskian geometry that the length of a line is limited in Lobachevskian geometry. This model is only one possible picture or map of Lobachevskian geometry and one must not read from it more than is intended; just as one must not conclude from a map of the United States that the state of Kansas has an area of less than 3 square inches and is uniformly pink in color. In fact, some geographical maps (Mercator maps, in which meridians of longitude appear as vertical straight lines and parallels of latitude as horizontal straight lines) do not even preserve the relative proportions of distances or areas.

On the other hand, the entire universe might be contained within a large sphere, so that any physical "plane" would be actually contained within a large circle, whose radius may be supposed to be larger than the range of our actual experience. Of course we are used to imagining the universe as extending indefinitely but this is merely a habit of thought and not a logical necessity. In fact, Poincaré suggested the possibility that we might be convinced that the world were unlimited in extent even though it were really limited. His argument is essentially this. Suppose the world were contained in a limited sphere, but that we ourselves, and all other material bodies, shrank as we approached the boundary in such a way that we could never reach it. Then we would think that the world were limitless in extent. Furthermore, we could never detect our own shrinkage because our measuring rods would shrink in proportion.

Jules Henri Poincaré
1854–1912, French

To summarize, the discrepancies between the theorems of Euclidean and Lobachevskian geometry may be smaller than we are able to measure, so that for practical applications there is no choice between them. In practical work we prefer Euclidean geometry because it is more familiar and because it is easier to handle.

188. PROOFS OF SOME THEOREMS IN LOBACHEVSKIAN GEOMETRY

We shall sketch a proof, in Lobachevskian geometry, of the theorem that the sum of the angles of any triangle is less than 180°. This will be a fairly easy (though long) job to do because Lobachevskian geometry is very much like Euclidean, since it differs *only* in so far as the parallel postulate is concerned. Therefore all the theorems of Euclidean geometry whose proofs do not involve the parallel postulate are also correct theorems in Lobachevskian geometry.

Hence, we shall not bother to prove many such theorems here, but we shall assume you are familiar with them from your study of Euclidean geometry in high school. *Until we say otherwise explicitly, all the following theorems are based only on those postulates which are common to Euclidean and Lobachevskian geometry; that is, they involve neither the Euclidean nor the Lobachevskian parallel postulate and therefore are correct theorems in both geometries.* Such propositions as "vertical angles are equal," and others, will be used without proving them here.

Remark. It will be necessary to recall that the statement

(1) "if A is true, then B is true"

does not imply the statement

(2) "If A is not true, then B is not true"

nor does (1) imply the statement

(3) "If B is true, then A is true."

(3) is called the converse of (1). (2) and (3) are equivalent. (2) and (3) may be incorrect even though (1) is correct. Likewise (2) and (3) may be correct even though (1) is not.

Exercise. Make up a simple example to illustrate each of these points.

We shall not prove theorems 1 and 2.

Theorem 1. *Two triangles are congruent if two sides and the included angle of one are equal, respectively, to two sides and the included angle of the other.*

Corollary 1(*a*). *The base angles of an isosceles triangle are equal.*

Proof. Draw the angle bisector BD of the vertex angle (Fig. 264). Then $AB = BC$ by hypothesis, $p = q$, and $BD = BD$. Therefore, triangles ABD and BCD are congruent, by theorem 1. Hence $A = C$, since corresponding parts of congruent triangles are equal.

Theorem 2. *At least one perpendicular can be drawn to a given line l from a given point P, whether P is on l or not.*

We can now prove the following theorems.

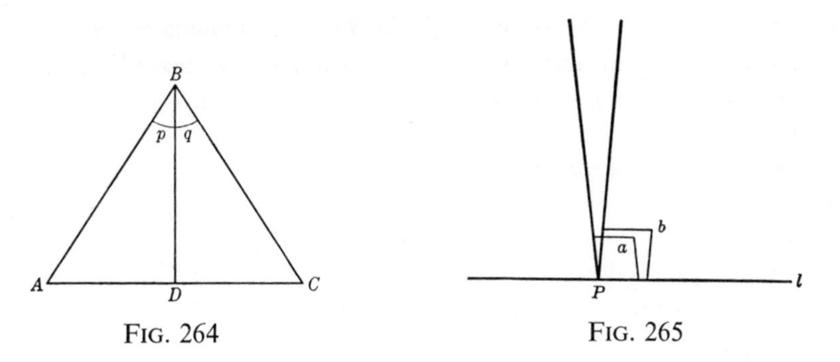

FIG. 264

FIG. 265

Theorem 3. *If the point P is on the line l, only one perpendicular can be drawn to l at P.*

Proof. If there were two, then angle a and angle b (Fig. 265) would be right angles. But $a > b$, since the whole is greater than any of its parts, which is a contradiction since all right angles are equal. Hence there can be only one perpendicular at P.

Theorem 4. *An exterior angle of a triangle ABC is greater than either remote interior angle.*

Proof. We prove first that the exterior angle DCB is greater than angle B (Fig. 266). Let M be the midpoint of BC. Thus $BM = MC$. Extend AM its

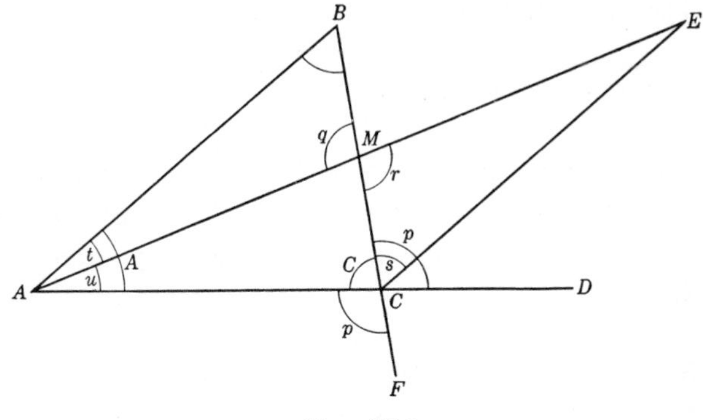

FIG. 266

own length to E, so that $AM = ME$. Angle $q =$ angle r, since vertical angles are equal. Therefore triangles ABM and CEM are congruent by theorem 1. Hence angle $B =$ angle s because corresponding parts of congruent triangles are equal. Now, the exterior angle p ($\sphericalangle DCB$) is greater than angle s, since the whole is greater than any of its parts. Hence angle DCB is greater than angle B. To prove that $\measuredangle DCB$ or $\measuredangle ACF$ is greater than $\measuredangle A$, we would start by taking the midpoint of AC and proceed in the same way.

Exercise. Prove the last statement in detail.

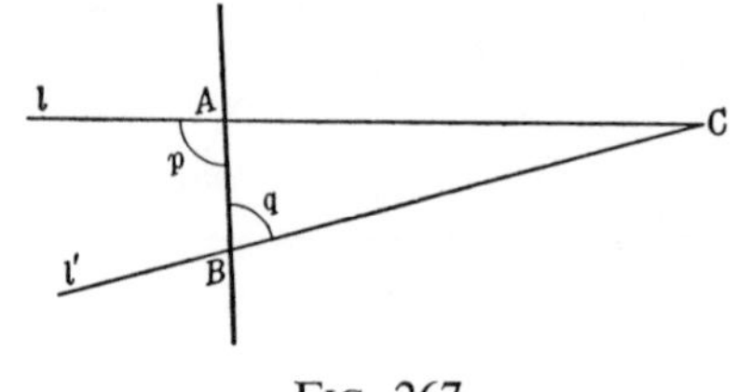

FIG. 267

Corollary 4(*a*). *If two alternate interior angles made by a transversal to two lines are equal, then the lines are parallel.*

Proof. Let angle p = angle q (Fig. 267). Either the lines are parallel or not. Suppose the lines were not parallel. Then they would meet at some point C (Fig. 267). Then $p > q$ by theorem 4, contradicting the hypothesis that $p = q$. Since our supposition leads to a false conclusion, it is false. Hence the lines are parallel.

The converse of corollary 4(*a*) cannot be proved without the Euclidean parallel postulate; it is not true in Lobachevskian geometry.

Theorem 5. *The sum of any* **two** *angles of a triangle ABC is less than 180°.*

Proof. Consider the exterior angle p ($\measuredangle BCD$) at C (Fig. 266). By theorem 4, $p > B$ and $p > A$. Now $p + C = 180°$ since their sum is a straight angle. Hence $B + C < 180°$ and $A + C < 180°$. To prove $A + B < 180°$, use an exterior angle at A and proceed similarly.

Exercise. Prove the last statement in detail.

By the **angle-sum of a triangle** we mean the sum of its three interior angles. (We must not assume that this angle-sum is 180° because the proof of that theorem in Euclidean geometry depends on the parallel postulate which we are not assuming here.)

Theorem 6. *Let A be any angle of a triangle ABC. Then there is another triangle one of whose angles $\leqq A/2$ and whose angle-sum is equal to the angle-sum of triangle ABC.*

Proof. Suppose the given triangle ABC is that of Fig. 266. As in the proof of theorem 4, we have triangle ABM congruent to triangle ECM. Then $t = E$, $B = s$, $C = C$. Hence $E + u + (C + s) = (t + u) + C + B$, by substitution, or

$E + u + \measuredangle ACE = A + C + B$. Thus the triangle ACE has the same angle-sum as triangle ABC. Now since $t + u = A$ either t or u must be $\leqq A/2$, since if both were $> A/2$ their sum would be $> A$. But $t = E$. Hence either E or u must be $\leqq A/2$. Thus triangle ACE satisfies the requirements of the theorem. This completes the proof.

We must now point out the arithmetic fact that if A is any positive real number, no matter how large, and h is any positive number, no matter how small, then there exists a natural number n such that $A/2^n < h$. That is, no matter how small h is, there exists a definite term in the sequence $A/2$, $A/4$, $A/8$, $A/16$, ..., $A/2^n$, ... which is smaller than h. For example, suppose $A = 200$ and h is $\frac{1}{10}$. Then the sequence is 100, 50, 25, 12.5, 6.75, 3.375, 1.6875, .84375, .421875, .2109375, .10546875, .052734375, ... The last term we wrote is less than $\frac{1}{10}$. Clearly, if we divide any given number by 2 often enough, we can make the result as small as we please.

Theorem 7. *The angle-sum of any triangle is not greater than 180°. That is, if ABC is any triangle, then* $A + B + C \leqq 180°$.

Proof. Either the theorem is correct or not. Suppose the theorem were not correct. Then we would have $A + B + C > 180°$, or $A + B + C = 180° + h°$, where h is some positive number; for example, we might have $A + B + C = 180° + 1°$ or $181°$. By theorem 6, there is another triangle T_1 one of whose angles A_1 is $\leqq A/2$ and which has the same angle-sum as triangle ABC. Applying theorem 6 now to triangle T_1, there is another triangle T_2 one of whose angles A_2 is $\leqq A_1/2 \leqq A/2^2$ and which has the same angle-sum as triangle ABC. This argument can be repeated as often as we please. After n such steps we obtain a triangle T_n one of whose angles $A_n \leqq A/2^n$ and which has the same angle-sum as triangle ABC. Now, by the remark above, there exists a natural number n, such that $A/2^n < h°$. For such a value of n, one of the angles in triangle T_n is less than $h°$. But the sum of the other two angles of the triangle T_n must be less than 180° by theorem 5. Hence the angle-sum of triangle T_n must be less than $180° + h°$, contradicting the supposition that it is equal to $180° + h°$. Therefore our supposition is false. Hence the theorem is correct. This completes the proof.

Theorem 8. *An exterior angle of a triangle is greater than or equal to the sum of the remote interior angles.*

Proof. By theorem 7, $A + B + C \leqq 180°$. Subtracting C from both sides we obtain $A + B \leqq 180° - C$. But (Fig. 268) $p = 180° - C$. Hence, by substitution, $A + B \leqq p$, or $p \geqq A + B$ which was to be proved.

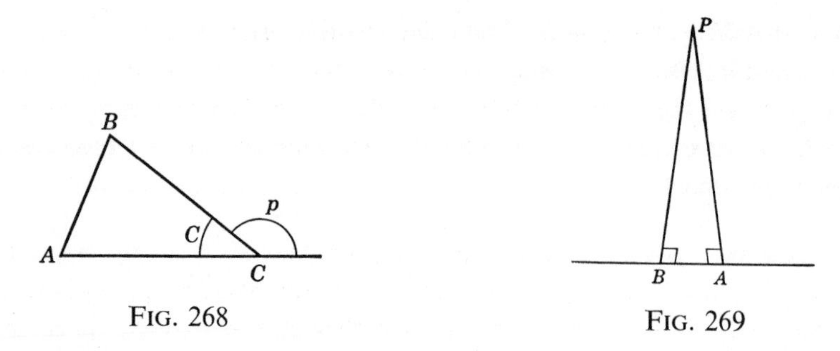

FIG. 268 FIG. 269

Theorem 9. *If the point P is not on the line l, then only one perpendicular can be drawn from P to l.* (Compare theorem 3.)

Proof. If there were two perpendiculars then the angle-sum of triangle PAB (Fig. 269) would be more than 180° contrary to theorem 7.

Definition. *By the* **angle-sum** *of a quadrilateral is meant the sum of its four interior angles,*

Theorem 10. *The angle-sum of any quadrilateral is $\leqq 360°$.*

Proof. Let $ABCD$ be any quadrilateral. Draw a diagonal lying within the quadrilateral, say AC (Fig. 270). Now $p + B + r \leqq 180°$ and $q + D + s \leqq 180°$ by theorem 7. Hence $(p + q) + B + (r + s) + D \leqq 360°$ or $A + B + C + D \leqq 360°$. This completes the proof.

Theorem 7 does not tell us whether or not there *are* any triangles whose angle sum is 180°. The next few theorems will be based on the hypothesis that there is (at least) *one* such triangle. Of course, there may not really be any, as far as we know at this moment. That does not stop us from investigating what *would* take place *if* there *were* one.

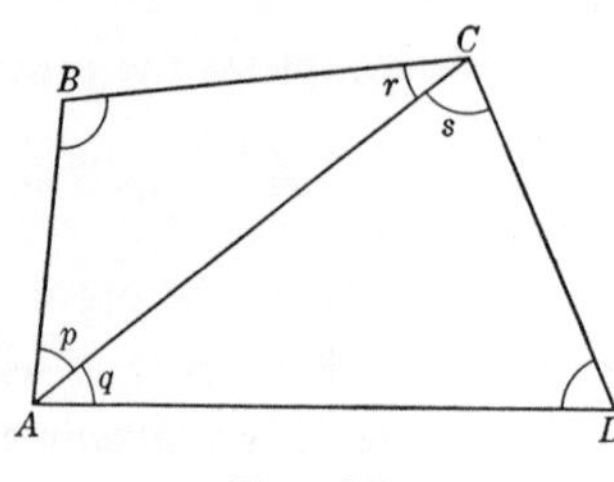

FIG. 270

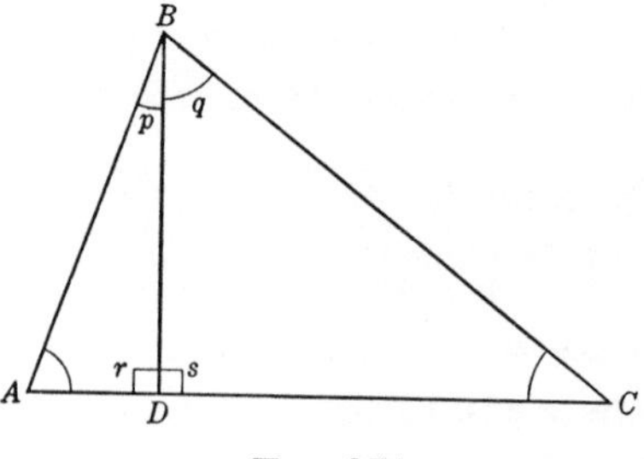

FIG. 271

Theorem 11. *If there exists* **one** *triangle whose angle-sum is 180°, then there exists a right triangle whose angle-sum is 180°.*

Proof. Suppose ABC is the triangle with angle-sum 180°, whose existence is assumed in our hypothesis. Then (Fig. 271) we can draw the perpendicular from some vertex, say B, to the opposite side. Now $p + q = B$. Hence, by hypothesis, $A + C + (p + q) = 180°$. Now $r = s = 90°$. Hence, we obtain $A + C + (p + q) + r + s = 360°$; or $(A + p + r) + (q + s + C) = 360°$. Now, if one of these parentheses were less than half of 360° the other would have to be more than half of 360°. But each parenthesis is the angle-sum of one of the triangles ABD or BCD and therefore cannot be more than 180° by theorem 7. Hence, neither of these triangles can have an angle-sum less than 180°. But the angle-sum of any triangle is either less than or equal to 180°. Hence ABD and BCD are right triangles whose angle-sums = 180°. This completes the proof.

Definition. *A quadrilateral with four right angles is called a* **quadrirectangle.**

Notice that if three of the angles of the quadrilateral are right angles, we may *not* conclude that the fourth is a right angle, since the sum of the angles of a quadrilateral may be less than 360°, as far as we know. In fact, we don't know whether or not there *are any* quadrirectangles.

Theorem 12. *If there exists* **one** *triangle whose angle-sum is 180°, then there exists a quadrirectangle.*

Proof. By theorem 11, there exists a right triangle XYZ whose angle-sum is 180°. Construct a congruent right triangle (as in Fig. 272) on the other side of YZ with right angle at U. Then $a = c$, $b = d$. But

(1) $$a + b = 90°$$

and

(2) $$c + d = 90°$$

since $X + a + b = 180°$ and $U + c + d = 180°$. Substituting d for b in (1) we get $a + d = 90°$ or $Y = 90°$. Substituting b for d in (2) we get $c + b = 90°$ or $Z = 90°$. Therefore $XYUZ$ is a quadrirectangle. This completes the proof.

Theorem 13. *If $ABCD$ is a quadrirectangle and (Fig. 273) if at any point E on AD we construct EF perpendicular to AD, then $ABFE$ is a quadrirectangle.*

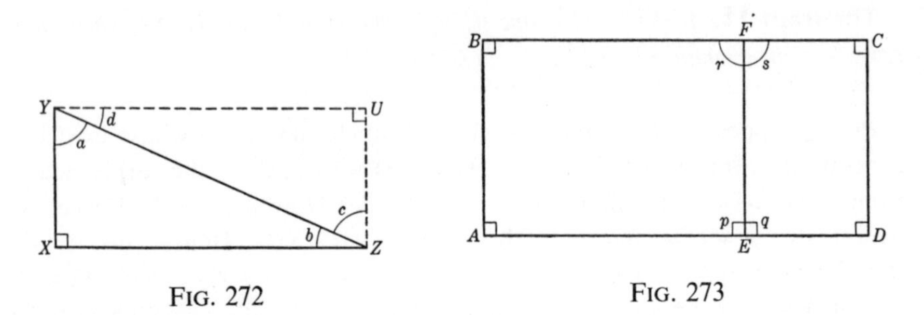

FIG. 272

FIG. 273

Proof. Now, we have $p + q = 180°$, and $r + s = 180°$, although we do not know at present whether or not r and s are right angles. By hypothesis, $A + B + C + D = 360°$. Hence $A + B + C + D + p + q + r + s = 720°$. Or, $(A + B + r + p) + (s + q + C + D) = 720°$. Now, if one of these parentheses were less than half of 720° the other would have to be more than half of 720°. But each parenthesis is the angle-sum of a quadrilateral and, by theorem 10, cannot be more than 360°. Hence each of them is exactly 360°. Therefore $r = 90°$, which completes the proof.

Intuitively, this theorem provides a way of snipping off a smaller quadrirectangle from a larger one.

Theorem 14. *If ABCD is a quadrirectangle and if a quadrirectangle CDEF is constructed on the other side of CD, the resulting figure ABFE is a quadrirectangle (Fig. 274).*

Proof. Since p and q are right angles, BCF is a straight line. Similarly, ADE is a straight line. Therefore $ABFE$ *is* a quadrilateral. The rest is obvious.

Intuitively, this means that when we put together two quadrirectangles on a common side, we get a larger quadrirectangle.

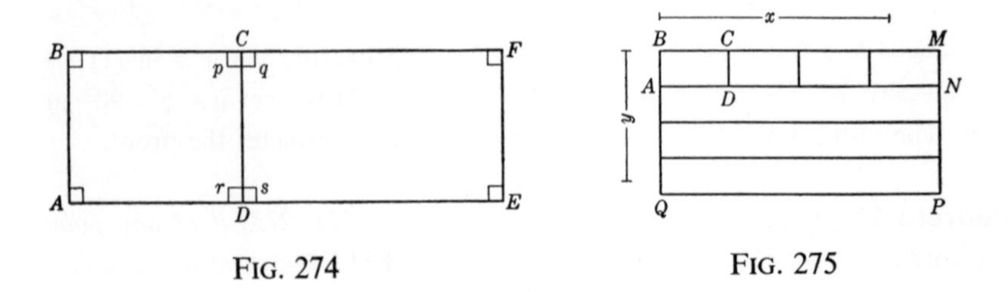

FIG. 274

FIG. 275

Theorem 15. *If there exists* **one** *triangle whose angle-sum is 180°, then we can construct a quadrirectangle whose base and altitude* are greater than any given lengths x and y.*

Proof. By theorem 12, there is *one* quadrirectangle $ABCD$. If this quadrirectangle happens to be large enough, we have nothing further to do; but its base and altitude may be much smaller than the given line-segments. In that case we can duplicate it by theorem 14 as many times as necessary (as in Fig. 275) to make the base of the resulting quadrirectangle $ABMN$ larger than the given length x. Then by theorem 14, we may duplicate $ABMN$ as many times as necessary (Fig. 275) to make the altitude of the resulting quadrirectangle $BMPQ$ greater than the given length y.

Theorem 16. *If there exists* **one** *triangle whose angle-sum is 180°, then we can construct a quadrirectangle whose base and altitude have exactly any given lengths b and a.*

Proof. By theorem 15, we can construct a quadrirectangle $ABCD$ whose base and altitude are greater than b and a, respectively. Lay off $AE = b$ on AD. Construct EF perpendicular to AD. By theorem 13, $AEFB$ is a quadrirectangle. Lay off $AG = a$ on AB. Construct GH perpendicular to AB. By theorem 13, $AGHE$ is a quadrirectangle, and its base and altitude are as required. See Fig. 276.

Intuitively, we make a bigger quadrirectangle and then snip off one of the right size.

Theorem 17. *If there exists* **one** *triangle whose angle-sum is 180°, then every* ***right*** *triangle has an angle-sum of 180°.*

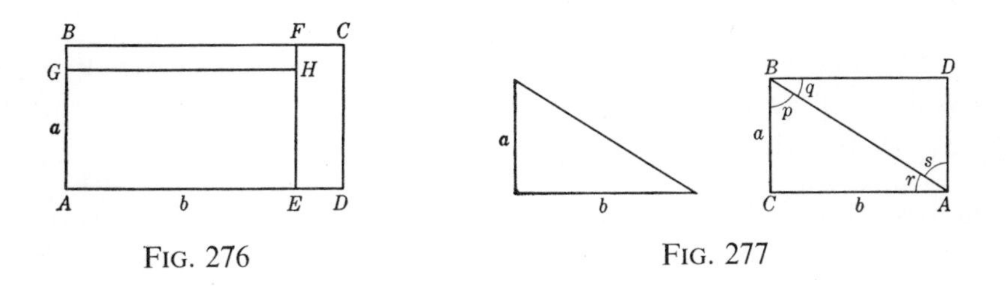

FIG. 276

FIG. 277

* By a base and an altitude of a quadrirectangle, we mean any two adjacent sides. One must not assume, however, that opposite sides of a quadrirectangle are equal.

Proof. Let the lengths of the legs of *any* given right triangle be a and b. By theorem 16, we can construct a quadrirectangle $ADBC$ with base and altitude equal to b and a, respectively (Fig. 277). Draw BA. Then triangle ABC is congruent to the given right triangle by theorem 1. Now we have $(C + p + r) + (q + s + D) = 360°$ and if one of these parentheses were less than half of 360° the other would have to be more than half of 360°. But each parenthesis is the angle-sum of a triangle which, by theorem 7, cannot be more than 180°. Hence ABC is a right triangle whose angle-sum is 180°. But the given right triangle is congruent to triangle ABC. Hence the angle-sum of the given right triangle is 180°. This completes the proof.

Theorem 18. *If there exists* **one** *triangle whose angle-sum is 180°, then* **every** *triangle has an angle-sum of 180°.*

Proof. Let ABC be any given triangle. From one of the vertices, say B, we can draw the perpendicular BD to the opposite side (Fig. 278). Then $A + p + r = 180°$ and $C + q + s = 180°$ by theorem 17. Hence $A + C + (p + q) + (r + s) = 360°$. But $r + s = 180°$. Hence, $A + C + (p + q) = 180°$ or $A + C + B = 180°$.

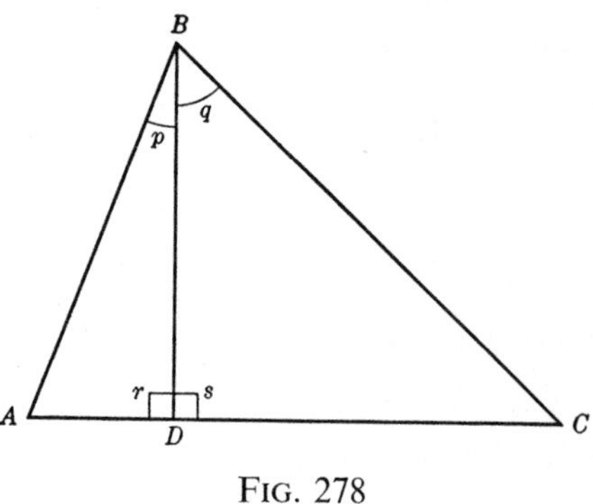

FIG. 278

Theorem 19. *If there exists* **one** *triangle whose angle-sum is less than 180°, then* **every** *triangle has an angle-sum less than 180°.*

Proof. By theorem 7, the angle-sum of every triangle is $\leqq 180°$. By theorem 18, if the angle-sum of *one* triangle were 180° then the angle-sum of *every* triangle would be 180°, contrary to the hypothesis. Thus the angle-sum of every triangle must be $< 180°$.

By virtue of theorem 19, in order to prove that the angle-sum of every triangle is less than 180° in Lobachevskian geometry, it will be sufficient to show that there is *one* triangle with angle-sum less than 180°.

Remark. All the previous theorems are common to Euclidean and Lobachevskian geometry since their proofs are based only on those postulates which are made in both geometries; that is, no parallel postulate of any kind has been involved. If we now introduced the Euclidean parallel postulate, we would get Euclidean geometry. We could then prove the following theorems (a), (b), and (c).

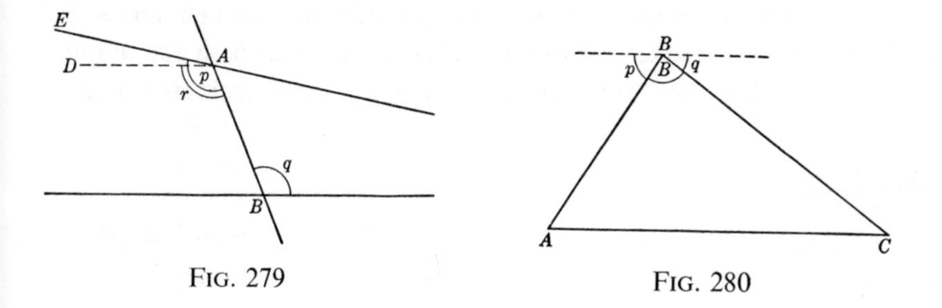

FIG. 279

FIG. 280

(*a*) *If two alternate interior angles made by a transversal to two lines are not equal, the lines are not parallel.*

Proof. One of the two unequal angles p and q (Fig. 279) is greater than the other; say $p > q$. Then at A construct angle $r =$ angle q. The AD is parallel to BC by corollary 4(*a*). But $p > r$, by substitution. Hence AD is different from AE and both lines pass through A. Hence AE cannot also be parallel to BC by the Euclidean parallel postulate.

(*b*) *If two lines are parallel, then any two alternate interior angles made by a transversal are equal.* (Converse of corollary 4(*a*).)

Proof. If there were a pair of unequal alternate interior angles, the lines could not be parallel, by (*a*).

(*c*) *The sum of the angles of any triangle is 180°.*

Proof. Let ABC be any triangle. At B (Fig. 280), draw the line parallel to AC. Then by (*b*), $p = A$, $q = C$. Hence $A + B + C = p + B + q = 180°$, since $p + B + q$ is a straight angle.

This is the familiar theorem of Euclidean geometry.

Instead of making the Euclidean parallel postulate, *let us now make the Lobachevskian parallel postulate*. We then get Lobachevskian geometry. We can now prove the following theorem.

Theorem 20. *There exists a triangle whose angle-sum is less than 180°.*

Proof. Let l be a line and Q a point not on l. Draw QP perpendicular to l (Fig. 281) and l' perpendicular to QP at Q. Then l' is parallel to l by corollary 4(*a*). By the Lobachevskian parallel postulate there exists another line m different from l', also parallel to l and passing through Q. By theorem 3, m cannot be perpendicular to QP since l' is perpendicular to QP. Hence one of the angles a made by m and QP must be less than 90°. Lay off $PR_1 = QP$ on l on the same side of the transversal QP as the acute angle a. Draw QR_1. Then $b_1 = c_1$ by corollary 1(a). By theorem 8, $c \geqq b_1 + c_1$. Substituting c_1

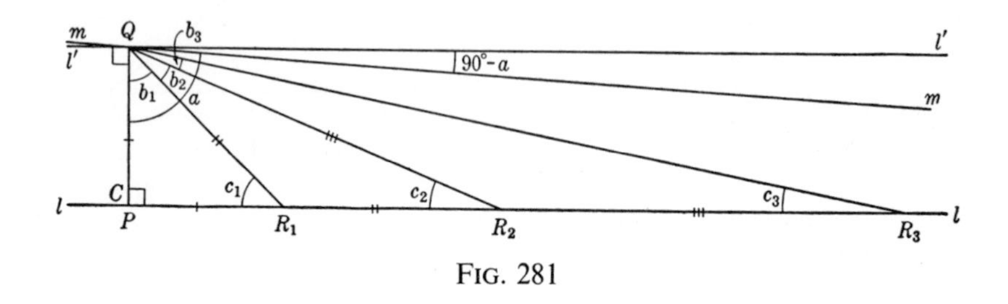

FIG. 281

for b_1, we have $c \geqq c_1 + c_1$, or $c \geqq 2c_1$, or $c_1 \leqq c/2$. But $c = 90°$. Hence $c_1 \leqq 45°$. Now lay off $R_1R_2 = QR_1$ and draw QR_2. Then $b_2 = c_2$ by corollary 1(a), and $c_1 \geqq b_2 + c_2$ by theorem 8; thus $c_1 \geqq 2c_2$, or $c_2 \leqq c_1/2$, or $c_2 \leqq (1/2)\cdot(c/2)$, or $c_2 \leqq c/2^2$, or $c_2 \leqq 22.5°$. Repeating this argument we get $c_3 \leqq 11.25°$, and so on. After n such steps, we have $c_n \leqq c/2^n$, or $c_n \leqq 90°/2^n$. By the remark preceding theorem 7, there exists a natural number n such that $90°/2^n$ is less than the positive quantity $90° - a$, no matter how small $90° - a$ may be. (For example, if a were 89°, $90° - a$ would be 1°, and we would have $c_4 \leqq 5.625°$, $c_5 \leqq 2.8125°$, $c_6 \leqq 1.40625°$, $c_7 \leqq .703125°$; thus $c_7 < 1°$ and $n = 7$ steps would be satisfactory in this example.) Hence, in triangle PQR_n, $\measuredangle PR_nQ = c_n < 90° - a$. Now, for every natural number n, $\measuredangle PQR_n < a$; for m does not meet l while QR_n does, so that QR_n lies below m. Finally $\measuredangle P = 90°$. Hence the angle-sum of triangle $PQR_n = \measuredangle P + \measuredangle PR_nQ + \measuredangle PQR_n < 90° + (90° - a) + a$; that is, the angle-sum of triangle PQR_n is less than 180°. (In our illustrative example, $\measuredangle a = 89°$. Hence $\measuredangle PQR_7 < 89°$, $c_7 = \measuredangle PR_7Q < 1°$, $\measuredangle P = 90°$ and therefore the angle-sum of triangle PQR_7 is $< 180°$.) This completes the proof.

Theorem 21. *The angle-sum of every triangle is less than 180°.*

Proof. Follows immediately from theorems 19 and 20.

Remark. The proofs in this section involve some theorems which were taken intuitively but which could have been proved logically from a complete set of postulates. In particular, they are riddled with inferences drawn from the diagrams or pictures. The derivation of Lobachevskian geometry, or, for that matter, Euclidean geometry, from postulates by strict logic without any pictorial inference is a difficult task which is best left for advanced courses. Your high school Euclidean geometry text took intuitively many things such as we slid over here. The references at the end of the chapter will provide places where one can find sound logical treatments of Euclidean geometry (especially, Veblen, and Forder).

Exercises

Prove in Lobachevskian geometry, that:

1. There exists no quadrilateral with an angle-sum of 360°.

2. If the angles of one triangle ABC are respectively equal to the angles of another triangle $A'B'C'$ (that is, if $A = A'$, $B = B'$, and $C = C'$), then the two triangles are congruent.* (Hint: suppose the contrary. Lay off one triangle on the other so that

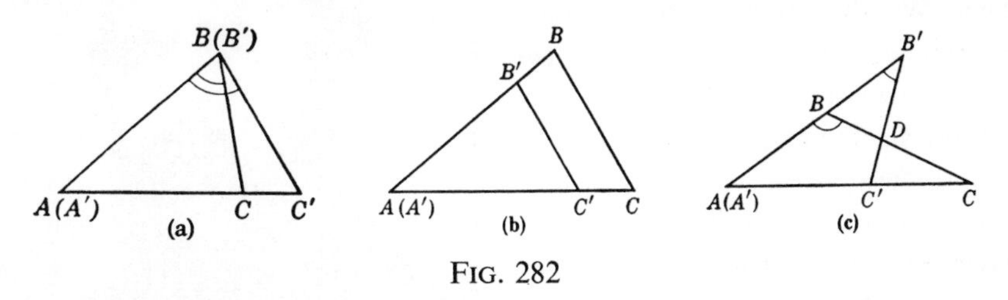

FIG. 282

$\measuredangle A$ and $\measuredangle A'$ coincide. Show that 8 of the 9 cases—3 are shown in Fig. 282—are impossible. E.g., Fig. 282 (*b*) is impossible because the quadrilateral $BCC'B'$ would have an angle-sum $= 360°$, contrary to exercise 1.)

3. If in a quadrilateral $ABCD$ we have $AD = BC$ and $A = B = 90°$, then the angles D and C are equal but acute. (Hint: draw DB and AC.)

4. Is the theorem "if two distinct lines are both parallel to the same line, then they are parallel to each other" true in Lobachevskian geometry?

189. RIEMANNIAN GEOMETRY

Riemann (1826–1866) developed many non-Euclidean geometries, different from Lobachevski's. In the two classic ones, called single-elliptic and double-elliptic geometry, respectively, one assumes instead of the Euclidean parallel postulate the following:

Riemannian parallel postulate. *There are no parallel lines.*

That is, any pair of lines must meet somewhere. Single-elliptic geometry is difficult to picture concretely, so we shall discuss here only the Riemannian

* It follows that in Lobachevskian geometry there are no similar but non-congruent figures. Hence, if space were really Lobachevskian, it would be fair to say that any picture of your sweetheart fails to do her or him justice, unless the picture were life-size.

geometry known as "double-elliptic geometry" which can be pictured easily. Double-elliptic geometry differs from Euclidean geometry not only by assuming the Riemannian parallel postulate instead of the Euclidean parallel postulate, but also contradicts another Euclidean postulate, namely, the one designated as postulate 2 (section 186). Postulate 1, however, is retained, so that, in this geometry, two distinct points may have one or more lines passing through them. We shall refer to this double-elliptic geometry as **Riemannian geometry** hereafter, since it is the only one of Riemann's geometries that we shall discuss.

Georg Friedrich Bernhard Riemann
1826–1866, German

To show that this Riemannian plane geometry is just as consistent as Euclidean geometry we can make a model of a Riemannian "plane" in Euclidean space, as follows. Consider the surface of a sphere in Euclidean space; call it a **Riemannian plane**. Let us make a concrete interpretation of the abstract logical system called Riemannian plane geometry as follows. The undefined term "point" in Riemannian plane geometry shall be interpreted as meaning an ordinary (Euclidean) point on the surface of the sphere. The undefined term "line" in Riemannian plane geometry shall be interpreted as meaning a great circle on the sphere (that is, a circle formed by the intersection of the sphere with a Euclidean plane passing through the center of the sphere). Then all Riemann's postulates can be seen to be verified (Fig. 283). If 2 points happen to be diametrically opposite on the sphere, then there are many "lines" (great circles) through them. For example, all the meridians of longitude lie along great circles through the North and South poles. Clearly, all "lines" (great circles) intersect.

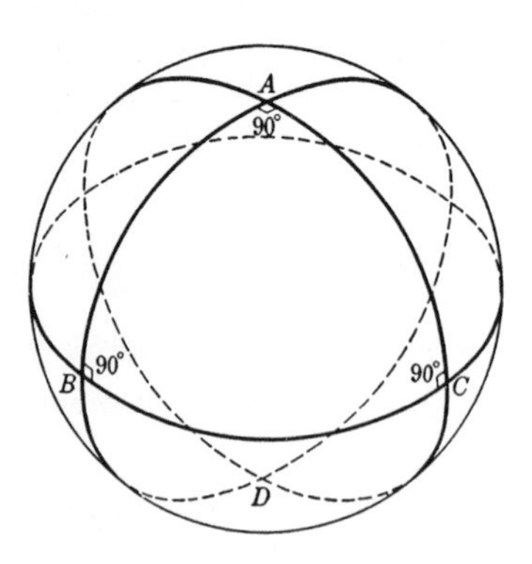

FIG. 283

It follows that Riemann's geometry is as consistent as Euclid's. For if Riemann's geometry involved any contradiction, the fact that we can have a model of Riemann's geometry in a Euclidean space would imply that the same contradiction must exist in the geometry of great circles on a sphere in Euclidean geometry.

As for applying to reality, the answer is much as before. In Riemann's system the sum of the angles of any triangle is more than 180°. For example, on the earth's surface, a triangle formed by the equator, the Greenwich meridian (0° longitude), and the meridian of 90° west longitude has in it three right angles (Fig. 283). But measurement does not reveal whether the sum of the angles of any physical triangle is exactly 180° or 180.000002° (or 179.99999876°). Therefore this test does not enable us to say that Riemannian geometry does not fit reality. In fact, suppose that what we think of as a plane were really a spherical surface of tremendously large radius. Then any "small" region of the surface would appear to be flat, just as small regions on the earth's surface appear to be flat within the limits of our ability to measure, although the earth is really approximately spherical. Thus surveyors, measuring small tracts of real estate, use the formulas of Euclidean plane geometry although they know that the earth is not flat, because in the small region of the earth's surface in which they are operating the differences between the two systems would not be measurable. Now "small" is a relative term and we can easily imagine a sphere of radius so large that a region on its surface whose size was greater than the range of our actual astronomical experience would appear to be flat within the limits of our ability to measure. Thus it might be that the geometry of "actual" space is really Riemannian. In fact, the discrepancies between the theorems of Euclidean and Riemannian geometry, in any limited region such as that of our actual experience, can be made too small to measure by merely supposing that the radius of the sphere is large enough.

On the other hand, we must not suppose that the surface of a Euclidean sphere is the only possible concrete interpretation of Riemannian geometry; just as we must not suppose that the interior of a Euclidean circle is the only possible concrete interpretation of Lobachevskian geometry. In fact, the whole point is that, as far as we can tell, the actual universe may be a concrete interpretation of Riemannian geometry. The spherical surface is introduced here merely to establish that Riemannian geometry is just as logically consistent as Euclidean.

Remark. On a flat surface (Euclidean plane), the shortest path joining 2 points is a straight line. It can be proved that on a spherical surface, the shortest path joining two points lies along the great circle passing through them. Hence, navigators on the ocean and aviators on long trips travel along great circles. Therefore it is not unnatural to expect great circles on a sphere to have properties analogous in many respects to the properties of straight lines in a (Euclidean) plane. Thus, in a sense Riemannian geometry is suggested by our practical experience. Of course, the geometry of the sphere was studied by the ancient Greeks. But it would not have occurred to them to interpret the undefined term "line" as meaning a great circle on a sphere, since they thought of lines as having the usual intuitive meaning and not as undefined terms at all.

190. CONCLUSION

We have seen that other abstract mathematical sciences than Euclidean geometry may apply equally well to the physical world. We have looked at two forms of non-Euclidean geometry, Lobachevski's and Riemann's. There are other geometries besides these which are also different from Euclid's. One such geometry has actually been found more convenient than Euclidean geometry in Einstein's physical theory of relativity. However, the discrepancies between the results of Einstein's theory and those of Newton's physical theory which is based on Euclidean geometry are so small in size that they cannot be measured except in connection with astronomical distances or extremely high velocities. Thus for practical work, on the earth, we continue to use Euclidean geometry and Newtonian physics since they are much simpler to handle.

However, this does not imply that non-Euclidean geometry is unimportant. In fact, it was the attempt to prove the Euclidean parallel postulate which led to the invention of non-Euclidean geometries which, in turn, led to a deep reconsideration of the nature of mathematics and forced mathematicians to arrive at a clear understanding of the difference between abstract mathematical sciences or pure mathematics and concrete interpretations or applied mathematics. It led to the overthrow of the idea that our assumptions are self-evident truths. It led to the understanding of the difference between truth and validity in connection with scientific theories. For, if one of these alternative geometries (Euclid's, Lobachevski's, or Riemann's) is actually *true* of the physical world, then the others are false, since they contradict each other. But they do not contradict themselves, and each of these logically consistent geometries seems to fit the real world as well as the others. Hence, one can no longer say that the axioms of Euclid are "absolute truths." It led to the wholesome practice (among scientists) of examining closely and challenging the underlying assumptions upon which our theories are based.

In stirring up these questions, and hence leading to a clear understanding of the nature of pure mathematics and applied mathematics, the study of non-Euclidean geometries performed its greatest service. These matters were discussed in Chapter 2, sections 8 and 9. Now that the reader has more mathematical background, we shall take them up again, and in greater detail, in the next two chapters.

References

Numbers refer to the bibliography at the back of the book.

Bell 20, 21
Blumenthal 31
Coxeter 59
Eves and Newsom 71
Forder 78
Hilbert 93
Lieber and Lieber 121
Moise 134
Robinson 161
Wolfe 213
Young 215
Young 216

18

Some Simple Mathematical Sciences

191. INTRODUCTION

Throughout the book we have called attention repeatedly to the nature of abstract mathematical sciences and their concrete interpretations or applications, and we have discussed many illustrations of these things. Beginning with Chapter 2, sections 8 and 9, we have seen that if one attempts to treat any subject matter logically one is inevitably led to base the treatment on some unproved assertions, called postulates, and some undefined terms; otherwise one becomes enmeshed in circular reasoning or circular definitions or both. When we do begin with unproved postulates and undefined terms, and we proceed to define new terms and prove new assertions by deductive logic, we obtain an abstract mathematical science or abstract logical system, and we have been engaged in postulational thinking. Thus an abstract mathematical science does not refer to any particular concrete subject matter. A concrete interpretation or application arises when we assign some meanings to our undefined terms. Of course, our postulates and undefined terms are usually suggested by experience and are chosen with some application in mind. But we have seen that one of the advantages of abstract mathematical sciences is that they may well be applicable to several different subject matters or concrete interpretations. See, for instance, the trivial examples 1 and 2 of section 8. Some of our work in algebra and geometry has been done in the form of abstract mathematical sciences. But we were unable to do all our work here on a strict logical basis because algebra and geometry are complicated abstract mathematical sciences based on many postulates. In this chapter we shall study some simple examples of abstract mathematical sciences and their concrete interpretations each of which is based on only a few postulates. We shall examine more closely some of the characteristics of postulational thinking.

192. GROUPS

We shall discuss here a simple but very important example of an abstract mathematical science and some of its concrete interpretations. Let us take as undefined terms a set G of undefined objects, called **elements** of G, which we denote by small letters a, b, c, ..., and an undefined operation denoted by $\circ$, whose properties will be given in the postulates. The significance of these postulates will become clearer as soon as some concrete interpretations are discussed, immediately below.

We now assume the following postulates.

Postulate 1. *To every pair of elements a and b of G, given in the stated order, there corresponds a definite (unique) element of G, denoted by* $a \circ b$. ***(Law of closure for the operation*** $\circ$.***)***

Postulate 2. *If a, b, c, are any elements of G, then* $a \circ (b \circ c) = (a \circ b) \circ c$. ***(Associative law for the operation*** $\circ$.***)***

Postulate 3. *There exists a unique element of G, denoted by e, having the property that, if a is any element of G whatever, then* $a \circ e = e \circ a = a$.

Definition. *The element e is called the **identity** element.*

Postulate 4. *To each element a of G there corresponds a unique element of G, denoted by a′, having the property that* $a \circ a' = a' \circ a = e$.

Definition. *The element a′ is called the **inverse** of a.*

A set G of elements with an operation satisfying these postulates is called a **group**. (Note that the word "group" is used here in a technical sense, not in the everyday sense as a synonym of set, collection, or assemblage). The group G is called **commutative** or **Abelian** (after Abel) if it also satisfies the following postulate.

Postulate 5. *If a and b are any elements of G, then* $a \circ b = b \circ a$. ***(Commutative law for the operation*** $\circ$***).***

Postulate 5 is not a logical consequence of the other postulates as may be seen below from the fact that some concrete interpretations of postulates 1, 2, 3, 4, namely, the sixth and seventh interpretations below, do not satisfy 5. For if 5 were a logical consequence of 1–4, then 5 would have to be true whenever 1–4 were true. We shall now exhibit several different concrete interpretations of the postulates for a group.

First interpretation. Let the set G be the set of all integers, 0, ± 1, ± 2, ..., and let the operation $\circ$ be addition. Then postulate 1 is satisfied since, to every pair of integers a and b, given in the stated order, there corresponds a definite (unique) integer, denoted by $a + b$. Postulate 2 is satisfied since if a, b, c, are any integers, $a + (b + c) = (a + b) + c$. Postulate 3 is satisfied since the integer 0, and no other integer, has the property that $a + 0 = 0 + a = a$ for any integer a. Hence, the identity element $\circ$ in this interpretation is zero. Postulate 4 is satisfied since to each integer a there corresponds a unique integer, namely, $(-a)$, such that $a + (-a) = (-a) + a = 0$. Hence the inverse of a in this interpretation is the negative of a. Thus we have a group. In fact, postulate 5 is also satisfied since $a + b = b + a$ for any integers a and b. Hence, the set of integers with the operation $+$ form a commutative group in which 0 is the identity element, and $-a$ is the inverse of a.

Second interpretation. Let G be the set of all positive rational numbers (fractions). Let the operation $\circ$ be multiplication. Then if 1 is taken as the identity element and $1/a$ as the inverse of a, all the postulates for a commutative group are satisfied. Postulate 1 is satisfied since if a and b are any positive rational numbers, there is a unique positive rational number $a \cdot b$. Postulate 2 is satisfied since if a, b, c are any positive rational numbers, then $a \cdot (b \cdot c) = (a \cdot b) \cdot c$. Postulate 3 is satisfied since $1 \cdot a = a \cdot 1 = a$ for any positive rational number a. Postulate 4 is satisfied since for each positive rational number a, there is a positive rational number $1/a$ such that $a \cdot (1/a) = (1/a) \cdot a = 1$. Postulate 5 is satisfied since $a \cdot b = b \cdot a$ for any positive rational numbers a and b.

However, if we interpreted G to be the set of all positive *integers* and the operation to be multiplication, all the postulates except 4 would be satisfied. But 4 would not, since the positive integer 3, for example would have no inverse. That is, there is no positive integer x such that $3x = x3 = 1$.

Exercise 1. Would all five postulates for a commutative group be satifised if G is taken to mean the set of positive integers and the operation is addition? Explain.

Exercise 2. Show that if G is the set of all even integers, the operation $\circ$ is addition, 0 is the identity element, and $-a$ is the inverse of a, then we have a commutative group. Write out all five postulates, replacing the undefined terms by their meanings in this interpretation.

Third interpretation. Let G be the set of all rational numbers and let $\circ$ be addition. Let 0 be taken as the identity element and $-a$ as the inverse of a.

Exercise 3. Verify that the postulates for a commutative group are satisfied in this interpretation. Write out all the postulates, replacing the undefined terms by their meanings in this concrete interpretation.

Exercise 4. Would all five postulates be satisfied if we let G be the set of all positive rational numbers and the operation is addition? Explain.

Fourth interpretation. Let G be the set of all rational numbers *except zero*, and let $\circ$ be multiplication. Let 1 be the identity element and let $1/a$ be the inverse of a.

Exercise 5. Verify that the postulates for a commutative group are satisfied in this interpretation. Write out all the postulates, replacing the undefined terms by their meanings in this concrete interpretation.

Exercise 6. Would all five postulates be satisfied if we let G be the set of all rational numbers *including zero*, and the operation is multiplication? Explain.

Fifth interpretation. Consider the dial in Fig. 284. Let the elements of G be the numbers 0, 1, 2, 3, 4, alone. Let the operation $\circ$ be "addition" understood in the following sense: the "sum" $2 + 1$ shall mean the number to which the dial hand points after rotating in the indicated direction (see Fig. 284), through two spaces starting from 0 and then through 1 space. Thus $2 + 1 = 3$. Zero is interpreted to mean do not rotate at all. In this way we get the "addition table":

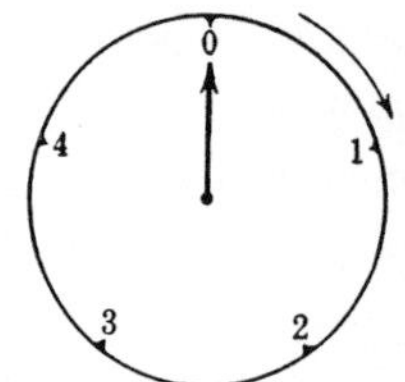

FIG. 284

$$\begin{array}{ccccc}
0+0=0 & 1+0=1 & 2+0=2 & 3+0=3 & 4+0=4 \\
0+1=1 & 1+1=2 & 2+1=3 & 3+1=4 & 4+1=0 \\
0+2=2 & 1+2=3 & 2+2=4 & 3+2=0 & 4+2=1 \\
0+3=3 & 1+3=4 & 2+3=0 & 3+3=1 & 4+3=2 \\
0+4=4 & 1+4=0 & 2+4=1 & 3+4=2 & 4+4=3.
\end{array}$$

Let 0 be the identity element. From the addition table we see that the inverse of 2 is 3 (since $2 + 3 = 3 + 2 = 0$), the inverse of 4 is 1 (since $4 + 1 = 1 + 4 = 0$), and so on. Thus all the postulates except postulate 2 can be verified easily by examining the table. The verification of postulate 2 is tedious since one has to examine all possible triplets formed by numbers 0, 1, 2, 3, 4. For example, to verify that $(2+4)+3=2+(4+3)$ we observe from the table that the left side is $1+3$ or 4 while the right side is $2+2$ or 4. This interpretation is called the **additive group of integers modulo 5.**

Exercises

7. Verify that $4+(3+4)=(4+3)+4$.

8. Verify that $2+(3+4)=(2+3)+4$.

9. Define $4 \cdot 3$ as $3+3+3+3$, $2 \cdot 4 = 4+4$, and so on; thus $4 \cdot 3 = 2$, $2 \cdot 4 = 3$, and so on. Make a "multiplication" table for the numbers on the dial above. Show that if we let the "elements of G" be the numbers 1, 2, 3, 4 (but not 0) and we let the operation $\circ$ be "multiplication," and we let 1 be the identity, then all the postulates for a commutative group are satisfied. Verify postulate 2 only for 3 or 4 instances.

10. Make up an "addition table" like that of the fifth interpretation for the numbers 0, 1, 2, 3, 4, 5 on a similar dial. Show that the postulates for a commutative group are satisfied with addition as the operation and 0 as the identity. Verify postulate 2 only for 3 or 4 instances.

11. Make up a "multiplication table" for the numbers on the dial of exercise 10, similar to that of exercise 9. Show that even though 0 is excluded, the elements 1, 2, 3, 4, 5 with "multiplication" as the operation $\circ$ and 1 as the identity do not satisfy all the postulates for a group. Which postulate is not satisfied? Verify postulate 2 only for 3 or 4 instances.

Sixth interpretation. Let G be the set of six letters e, p, q, r, s, t. Let the operation $\circ$ be defined by the following "multiplication table" (or "operation table"):

$e \circ e = e$	$e \circ p = p$	$e \circ q = q$	$e \circ r = r$	$e \circ s = s$	$e \circ t = t$
$p \circ e = p$	$p \circ p = q$	$p \circ q = e$	$p \circ r = s$	$p \circ s = t$	$p \circ t = r$
$q \circ e = q$	$q \circ p = e$	$q \circ q = p$	$q \circ r = t$	$q \circ s = r$	$q \circ t = s$
$r \circ e = r$	$r \circ p = t$	$r \circ q = s$	$r \circ r = e$	$r \circ s = q$	$r \circ t = p$
$s \circ e = s$	$s \circ p = r$	$s \circ q = t$	$s \circ r = p$	$s \circ s = e$	$s \circ t = q$
$t \circ e = t$	$t \circ p = s$	$t \circ q = r$	$t \circ r = q$	$t \circ s = p$	$t \circ t = e.$

By inspection of this table we see that postulates 1 and 3 are verified immediately, with e as the identity element. Similarly, 4 is obvious from the table; for example, the inverse of p is q since $p \circ q = q \circ p = e$, and the inverse of r is r since $r \circ r = e$. Postulate 2 has to be verified by tediously inspecting all 216 triplets of elements. For example, to verify $p \circ (r \circ t) = (p \circ r) \circ t$, we observe from the table that the left side is $p \circ p$ or q and the right side is $s \circ t$ or q. Note that postulate 5 is not satisfied; for example, $p \circ r = s$ while $r \circ p = t$. Hence this is a group but not a commutative group. The construction of this table so as to satisfy postulates 1 through 4 but not 5 may seem to be a remarkably ingenious feat, for if you try to make up such a table by random experiment, it will seem very difficult. In fact, however, the table given here was actually derived from the seventh interpretation below which is historically important. It can be shown that there is no simpler non-commutative group.

Exercises

12. What is the inverse: (*a*) of q; (*b*) of s; (*c*) of e; (*d*) of t?

13. Verify that $q \circ (s \circ t) = (q \circ s) \circ t$.

14. Verify that $q \circ (t \circ s) = (q \circ t) \circ s$.

Seventh interpretation. Let the numbers 1, 2, 3 represent volumes 1, 2, and 3 of a certain 3-volume work, respectively, standing in line on a shelf. Let us remove the books from the shelf and replace them in the order 3, 1, 2. The effect has been to replace volume 1 by volume 3, 2 by 1, and 3 by 2. Let the symbol

$$\begin{pmatrix}123\\312\end{pmatrix}$$

stand for the act of replacing volume 1 by volume 3, volume 2 by volume 1, and volume 3 by volume 2. Let us denote

$$\begin{pmatrix}123\\312\end{pmatrix}$$

by the letter p. In the same way, the symbol

$$\begin{pmatrix}123\\231\end{pmatrix}$$

stands for the act of replacing volume 1 by volume 2, volume 2 by volume 3, and volume 3 by volume 1. Denote

$$\begin{pmatrix}123\\231\end{pmatrix}$$

by q. Similarly, let

$$r = \begin{pmatrix}123\\213\end{pmatrix}, \quad s = \begin{pmatrix}123\\321\end{pmatrix}, \quad t = \begin{pmatrix}123\\132\end{pmatrix}, \quad e = \begin{pmatrix}123\\123\end{pmatrix}.$$

Thus, e stands for the act of replacing the books in the same order as they are, that is, of leaving the volumes as they are. Let $p \circ r$ mean perform the act p, then the act r. Thus, p replaces 1 by 3 and r replaces 3 by 3. Hence, $p \circ r$ replaces 1 by 3. Similarly, p replaces 2 by 1 and r replaces 1 by 2. Hence, $p \circ r$ replaces

2 by 2. Finally, p replaces 3 by 2 and r replaces 2 by 1. Hence, $p \circ r$ replaces 3 by 1. Thus,

$$\begin{pmatrix}123\\312\end{pmatrix} \circ \begin{pmatrix}123\\213\end{pmatrix} = \begin{pmatrix}123\\321\end{pmatrix}. \text{ Or, } p \circ r = s.$$

Exercise 15. Verify that the "multiplication table" for this interpretation is exactly the same as for the sixth interpretation. Hence this is a group but not a commutative group.

Eighth interpretation. Let G be the set of all vectors beginning at a given point in the plane. Let the operation $\circ$ be the addition of vectors (section 141); that is,

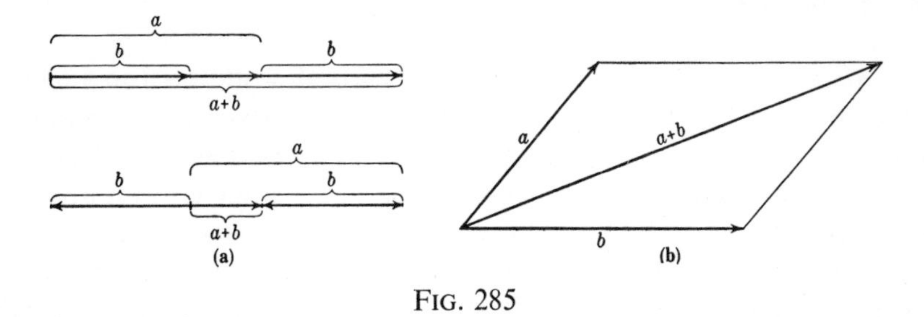

FIG. 285

the sum of two vectors is the vector represented by the diagonal of the parallelogram (except when the two given vectors have the same or opposite direction in which case they are added by placing one after the other). Let the identity element be a vector of "length" zero. Let the inverse of any vector be a vector of the same length in the opposite direction.

Exercise 16. Verify that all the postulates for a commutative group are satisfied in this interpretation. To verify the associative law (postulate 2) is a rather complicated exercise in geometry.

The study of groups originated in situations like that of the seventh interpretation toward the end of the eighteenth and the beginning of the nineteenth centuries. These were studied by Lagrange (1736–1813), Abel, Galois, and others in connection with the solution of equations (see section 44). They also came to be of central importance in geometry. Groups are now a very fundamental study in higher mathematics and physics in many different connections. Although no practical application of groups was known 100 years ago, groups are now studied in connection with quantum physics and crystallography.

It is clear that if we prove theorems in the abstract mathematical science based on postulates 1, 2, 3, 4, these theorems will apply automatically to all the different concrete interpretations of this abstract logical system. Hence, it is not necessary to prove these theorems over again in connection with each interpretation. This is one advantage of abstract or pure mathematics. It is a great unifying device which enables us to prove in one stroke results which apply to different subject matters. Furthermore, if a result is known in connection with one interpretation it may be discovered that the result depends only on our four postulates. This clarifies the nature of this result for our interpretation, and the result becomes automatically known for all other interpretations. In the next section we shall prove a few easy theorems about groups.

193. SOME THEOREMS ABOUT GROUPS

We shall prove some theorems on the basis of postulates 1 to 4 only. Of course, we must be careful not to use anything not given in the postulates. We do not assume postulate 5. We must recall that a statement of the form $a = b$ means that a and b represent the same element of the group G. That is, a and b are merely different symbols or names for the same element of G. Hence, if $a = b$, either symbol may be substituted for the other freely. Thus, from $a = b$ we may conclude that $a \circ c = b \circ c$ or $c \circ a = c \circ b$, by substitution. Similarly, if $a = b$ and $b = c$, we may conclude that $a = c$. Any inference of this sort will be referred to as "substitution."

Theorem 1. *If a and b are any elements of G, then $a \circ b'$ is an element of G.*

Proof. By postulate 4, b' is an element of G. By postulate 1, $a \circ b'$ is an element of G.

Theorem 2. *If a and b are any elements of G, then $a' \circ b$ is an element of G.*

Proof. We leave this as an exercise.

Theorem 3. *If $x = a' \circ b$, then $a \circ x = b$, all letters representing elements of G.*

Proof. If $x = a' \circ b$, then $a \circ x = a \circ (a' \circ b)$ by substitution. By postulate 2, $a \circ (a' \circ b) = (a \circ a') \circ b$. By postulate 4, $a \circ a' = e$. Hence, $a \circ x = e \circ b$ by substitution. But $e \circ b = b$ by postulate 3. Hence $a \circ x = b$ by substitution.

Theorem 4. *Conversely, if $a \circ x = b$, then $x = a' \circ b$, all letters representing elements of G.*

Proof. If $a \circ x = b$, then $a' \circ (a \circ x) = a' \circ b$ by substitution. By postulate 2, $a' \circ (a \circ x) = (a' \circ a) \circ x$. By postulate 4, $a' \circ a = e$. Hence, $e \circ x = a' \circ b$ by substitution. By postulate 3, $e \circ x = x$. Hence, $x = a' \circ b$ by substitution.

Theorem 5. *If $a \circ b = a \circ c$, then $b = c$, all letters representing elements of G.*

Proof. If $a \circ b = a \circ c$, then $a' \circ (a \circ b) = a' \circ (a \circ c)$ by substitution. By postulate 2, we obtain $(a' \circ a) \circ b = (a' \circ a) \circ c$. By postulate 4, $e \circ b = e \circ c$. By postulate 3, $b = c$.

Theorem 6. *If a and b are any elements of G, then $(a \circ b)' = b' \circ a'$.*

Proof. By postulate 1 and postulate 4, $a \circ b$ and $b' \circ a'$ are elements of G. Hence by postulate 1, $(a \circ b) \circ (b' \circ a')$ is an element of G. By postulate 2, $(a \circ b) \circ (b' \circ a') = a \circ [b \circ (b' \circ a')] = a \circ [(b \circ b') \circ a']$. By postulate 4 and substitution, $(a \circ b) \circ (b' \circ a') = a \circ (e \circ a')$. By postulate 3, $a \circ (e \circ a') = a \circ a'$. By postulate 4, $a \circ a' = e$. Hence, by substitution

$$(a \circ b) \circ (b' \circ a') = e. \tag{1}$$

By theorem 4, if $h \circ x = k$, then $x = h' \circ k$. Applying this to (1), with $h = (a \circ b)$, $x = (b' \circ a')$, and $k = e$, we have $b' \circ a' = (a \circ b)' \circ e$. By postulate 3

$$b' \circ a' = (a \circ b)'$$

which is what we had to prove.

Let us see what one of these theorems means in various interpretations. For example, when interpreted in the sense of our first interpretation (section 192), theorem 3 says "if $x = (-a) + b$, then $a + x = b$, all letters representing integers." When interpreted in the sense of the second interpretation, theorem 3 says "if $x = (1/a) \cdot b$, then $a \cdot x = b$, all letters representing positive rational numbers."

Many other theorems can be deduced from our four postulates. In fact, numerous books and articles in scientific journals are devoted to the study of the theory of groups.

Exercises

1. Restate theorems 1 to 6 above in terms of each of the first two interpretations of section 192.

2. Prove that if $x = b \circ a'$, then $x \circ a = b$.

3. Prove that if $x \circ a = b$, then $x = b \circ a'$.

4. Prove that if $b \circ a = c \circ a$, then $b = c$.

5. Prove that $(a')' = a$.

6. Restate exercises 2–5 in terms of the first two interpretations of section 192.

*194. INDIVIDUAL AND SOCIAL PREFERENCES

Consider a set A of alternatives which may be states of affairs or objects, denoted by small letters $x, y, z, \ldots$. Consider also a given individual named i. Given any pair of alternatives x and y we suppose that (a) i may prefer x to y, in symbols $x P_i y$; (b) i may prefer y to x, in symbols $y P_i x$; or (c) i may be indifferent between x and y, in symbols $x I_i y$. It is natural to assume the following postulates about the relations P_i and I_i.

Postulate 1. *For each pair x, y of alternatives, one and only one of the relations $x P_i y$, $y P_i x$, $x I_i y$ holds.*

Postulate 2. *If $x P_i y$ and $y P_i z$, then $x P_i z$; that is, P_i is transitive.*

Postulate 3. *For every alternative x, $x I_i x$; that is, I_i is reflexive.*

Postulate 4. *If $x I_i y$, then $y I_i x$; that is, I_i is symmetric.*

Postulate 5. *If $x I_i y$ and $y I_i z$, then $x I_i z$; that is, I_i is transitive.*

For brevity we may introduce a relation $x W_i y$ which is defined to mean either $x P_i y$ or $x I_i y$. We may read $x W_i y$ as i **weakly prefers** x to y. We term the relation W_i **weak preference** as distinguished from P_i which is termed **preference** or **strong preference**. We may call these relations the **preference pattern** of individual i.

The transitivity of preferences seems to be very widely agreed upon as a reasonable demand, for if i prefers coffee to tea and tea to milk, then it is hard to avoid the feeling that he must reasonably prefer coffee to milk. The transitivity of indifference is less plausible,† but, since it is technically difficult to do without, we shall assume it.

* This section may be omitted without disturbing the continuity.

† For instance, one might be indifferent between 1 spoonful of sugar in a cup of coffee and 1.1 spoonfuls, and indifferent between 1.1 and 1.2 spoonfuls, and indifferent between 1.2 and 1.3 spoonfuls, and so on up to indifferent between 2.9 and 3 spoonfuls, but one may not be indifferent between 1 and 3 spoonfuls as transitivity would imply.

As in the preceding section, we can deduce some theorems from our postulates.

Theorem 1. *If* $x\ P_i\ y$ *then* x *is different from* y.

Proof. By postulate 3, if x were the same as y, then $x\ I_i\ y$. Then by postulate 1, both $x P_i y$ and $y P_i x$ are false.

Theorem 2. *If* $x\ W_i y$ *then* $y P_i x$ *is false, and conversely.*

Theorem 3. *If* $x I_i y$, *then both* $x\ W_i y$ *and* $y\ W_i x$, *and conversely.*

Theorem 4. *For every pair* x, y *of alternatives, either* $x\ W_i y$ *or* $y P_i x$.

Theorem 5. *If* $x P_i y$ *and* $y\ W_i z$, *then* $x P_i z$.

The proofs of theorems 2–5 are left to the reader as exercises.

Suppose now that there are in a society a finite number n of individuals named 1, 2, 3, ..., n. The preference, indifference, and weak preference relations of the individual j will be denoted by P_j, I_j, W_j, respectively. For example, for the individual 3 they will be denoted by P_3, I_3, W_3, respectively. A difficult problem is to find suitable methods for amalgamating the possible preference patterns of the individuals 1, 2, 3, ..., n, *whatever they may be*, into a single "social preference pattern." Such a method is often called a **social welfare function** or **social decision method** in the literature. Of course, an easy way to achieve this is to choose one of the individuals as dictator and regard his preference pattern as that of "society" regardless of the preference patterns of the other individuals. Such a method may be termed **dictatorial**. Another easy way is to impose a preference pattern for society which will be what it is regardless of the preference patterns of *all* the individuals in the society. Such a method may be termed **imposed**. Both these methods are, of course, insensitive to the preference patterns of the members of the society (except the dictator if there is one).

The method of majority rule works well if there is only one pair of alternatives in A, as in the two-party system of American or British politics. But it has the awkward feature that if there are more than two alternatives in A, the resulting "social pattern" may fail to be transitive.

Example 1. Suppose there are three individuals 1, 2, 3 and three alternatives x, y, z. Suppose individual 1 prefers x to y and y to z, 2 prefers y to z and z to x, and 3 prefers z to x and x to y. Then a majority of individuals, namely, 1 and 3, prefer x to y; a majority of individuals, namely, 1 and 2, prefer y to z; but a majority of individuals, namely, 2 and 3, prefer z to x. This puts this society in the position of adopting a preference pattern which is not transitive.*

Example 2. Suppose a committee of three, named A, B, and C, wish to select by majority rule one of three alternatives x, y, z, and they do it by voting in turn on pairs of these alternatives, the losing alternative being eliminated. Suppose A ranks the alternatives in order of preference as x, y, z, B ranks them in order of preference y, x, z, and C ranks them in order of preference z, y, x.

Case 1. Suppose the committee first votes on the pair of alternatives y and z, and then the winning alternative is matched against x. Then on the first vote y has a majority over z. Having eliminated z, y then wins over x. Hence alternative y is the winner.

Case 2. Suppose, however, that on the first ballot A dissembles and votes for z instead of y, which he really prefers over z. Then z wins the first ballot, eliminating y, and on the second ballot z is matched against x. Thus x wins over z, so that A obtains his first preference by means of lying.

It is worth remarking that preferences or value-systems can be studied mathematically without supposing that of every pair of distinct alternatives one must be preferred to the other and without supposing that the preference scale can be reduced to numerical comparisons.

Exercises

1. Prove theorem 2.

2. Prove theorem 3.

3. Prove theorem 4.

4. Prove theorem 5.

5. Consider a society of three individuals 1, 2, 3, with three alternatives x, y, z, and majority rule. Suppose the preference pattern of 1 is $x\,P_1\,y$, $y\,P_1\,z$, $x\,P_1\,z$; the preference pattern of 2 is $z\,P_2\,x$, $x\,P_2\,y$, $z\,P_2\,y$; the preference pattern of 3 is $x\,I_3\,y$, $y\,I_3\,z$, $x\,I_3\,z$. Using P and I for the social preference and indifference, show that a contradiction arises since majority rule requires that $x\,P\,y$, and that $x\,I\,z$ and $z\,I\,y$ which imply $x\,I\,y$.

6. Consider a society of three individuals 1, 2, 3 with four alternatives x, y, z, w. Suppose they agree to assign weights 1, 2, 3, 4 with the lowest weight given to the least preferred alternative, and so on, and that the alternative with the highest total weight is to be elected. Suppose that individuals 1 and 2 assign weights 1, 2, 3, 4 to w, z, y, x, respectively, while individual 3 assigns weights 1, 2, 3, 4 to y, x, w, z, respectively. Then show that x is elected. But if y is withdrawn from the list of alternatives, and the same system used with weights 1, 2, 3, then x and z receive equal totals and the election is a tie (despite the fact that x is preferred to y by all individuals).

* Majority rule works well, however, if the individual orderings are sufficiently similar in the sense called "single-peakedness" developed by D. Black. On the other hand, it may be unrealistic to expect preferences to be transitive. See the works of K. J. Arrow, R. D. Luce and H. Raiffa, and J. H. Blau, cited at the end of this chapter, for further study.

195. CONSISTENCY AND INDEPENDENCE

To create an abstract mathematical science or abstract logical system, we have only to select some undefined terms, some unproved statements or postulates about them, and then define new terms in terms of the original undefined ones and prove new statements logically on the basis of the postulates. But it is essential that our postulates be consistent; that is, they must not be capable of leading to contradictory statements. How can we establish the consistency of a set of postulates? Clearly, the mere fact that we have deduced 100 or 10^{100} theorems without encountering any contradiction does not establish that we will *never* encounter one.

One way of proving the consistency of an abstract mathematical science is to exhibit a concrete interpretation of it; if concrete objects which satisfy the postulates actually exist, then the postulates cannot involve any contradiction. This faith in the logical consistency of the existing universe is so fundamental that it is hard to see how we could live without it. For example, the existence of the fifth or sixth interpertations of section 192 establishes the consistency of the postulates for a group.

However, such an exhibition of an interpretation using a finite number of concrete existing objects is not always possible. In particular, it is impossible if one of the consequences deducible from the postulates is that the number of elements (such as points or numbers) in the science is infinite (as happens, for example, in the case of the postulates for Euclidean geometry or in the case of Peano's postulates for the natural numbers).

Another method of proving the consistency of an abstract mathematical science is to give a concrete interpretation of it constructed within the framework of some other abstract mathematical science which is assumed to be consistent. In this way we established the consistency of the non-Euclidean geometries in Chapter 17, assuming that Euclidean geometry is consistent. To establish the consistency of Euclidean geometry, we exhibit the concrete interpretation of its postulates afforded by the number pairs, equations, etc., of analytic geometry (see section 105). This really establishes only that Euclidean geometry is as consistent as the number system. The consistency of the number system can be established if Peano's five postulates for the natural numbers are assumed to be consistent.*

* Properly speaking, besides the consistency of Peano's postulates, it is necessary to assume also the consistency of certain logical operations which are used in defining the real numbers in terms of the rational numbers. The validity of these logical operations has been seriously questioned in recent years by one school of mathematicians.

No satisfactory answer has been given to the question of the consistency of Peano's postulates. The fact that no one has seriously questioned their consistency seems to rest on a faith which goes beyond that in the logical consistency of the concretely existing universe. Intuitively, Peano's postulates arise from the counting process, which seems to be consistent; but this is hardly a consistency proof. (In fact, the counting process is always finite while Peano's postulates imply the existence of an infinite set.) The interpretation of Peano's postulates given by the finite cardinal numbers (section 185) establishes their consistency on the assumption of the consistency of certain logical operations involving sets; but that is no great progress, since these logical operations seem to be themselves more in need of justification than Peano's postulates.

Recently, consistency proofs for Peano's postulates for the natural numbers have been given, using a method, radically different from the method of giving a concrete interpretation, which depends on an analysis of the processes of deductive reasoning themselves by means of symbolic or mathematical logic. We cannot give here any more definite indication of the nature of these proofs. Suffice it to say that they also have their presuppositions and, the strength of these is such that no ultimate answer results to the question of the consistency of the elementary theory of the natural numbers. In any case, the subject of consistency has contributed to a rebirth of interest in symbolic or mathematical logic.

Another property of postulates for an abstract mathematical science which is aesthetically desirable, although not logically important, is independence. That is, if a postulate can be deduced from the remaining ones, it is said to be dependent on them. In this case, there is no need to include the statement in question among the postulates. It is uneconomical and aesthetically unsatisfactory to assume something that need not be assumed because it can be proved. In the same spirit as this is an economical principle which is a good working rule in science; that is, we do not like to use many or complicated assumptions or hypotheses if few or simple ones will do just as well. This principle is known as **Occam's Razor.*** For example, we do not like to accept a mythological theory of natural phenomena which ascribes the cause of each phenomenon to the whim of a separate supernatural spirit, because we prefer a theory which can explain all these phenomena on the basis of a few general principles or "laws of nature" (postulates). To show that a postulate P is independent of the others, we have only to show that the others together with a postulate P', contradictory to P, form a consistent set. For if P could be deduced from the others, this latter set would be inconsistent since the resulting logical system would contain P and P'.

* After William of Occam (English, fourteenth century) who did not state it quite this way.

Thus to show that Euclid's parallel postulate is independent of the other postulates of Euclidean geometry, we show that Lobachevskian geometry, which is based on all the postulates of Euclidean geometry (except the Euclidean parallel postulate) together with a parallel postulate contradictory to Euclid's, is consistent (see section 187). Similarly, to show that the commutative law is independent of the other four postulates for a commutative group, we exhibit concrete interpretations of the other four postulates which do not obey the commutative law (see section 192, sixth interpretation).

Remark. Two interpretations are *isomorphic* if their terms can be placed in one-to-one correspondence in such a way that all correct statements† in one interpretation are translated into correct statements* in the other interpretation by merely substituting terms which correspond to each other in this correspondence (dictionary). As an example, the sixth and seventh interpretations of the abstract mathematical science of section 192 are isomorphic. If all possible interpretations of an abstract mathematical science are necessarily isomorphic, the science is called *categorical.* The abstract science in section 192 is not categorical for we have some interpretations which have only a finite number of elements and others which have an infinite number of elements. This is sufficient to show that the system is not categorical, since the terms of a finite interpretation cannot be placed in one-to-one correspondence with the terms of an infinite interpretation at all, let alone in such a way that correct statements correspond to correct statements.

References

Numbers refer to the bibliography at the back of the book.

Arrow 7
Bennett and Baylis 23
Blau 30
Cohen and Nagel 55
Kershner and Wilcox 108
Littlewood 123
Luce and Raiffa 128
Russell 163
Stabler 184
Stein 185
Weyl 205
Wilder 210

* Within the science.

19

The Nature of Mathematics

196. PURE AND APPLIED MATHEMATICS

We return to the idea of an abstract mathematical science, or abstract logical system which has been illustrated many times throughout the book, perhaps most clearly in the preceding chapter. When we select some undefined terms, and a set of consistent postulates or assumptions about them, and proceed to define new terms in terms of the original undefined ones, and to deduce new statements logically from the preceding ones, we are creating an *abstract mathematical science*. If meanings are assigned to the undefined terms, then we have a *concrete interpretation* of our abstract mathematical science. The totality of all abstract mathematical sciences we call *pure mathematics*. The totality of concrete interpretations is called *applied mathematics*. Reasoning from postulates in this way is called *postulational thinking*.

This conception of mathematics is far broader than the common notion of what mathematics is, since it includes every subject in which you attempt to reason logically from explicitly recognized underlying assumptions, as you can hardly help doing, in all honesty, in any subject forming part of the search for truth.* For if you make an assertion in any subject whatever, you either assume it or must prove it. If you prove it, you deduce it from other assertions. If these are not to be assumed, they in turn must be deduced from still other statements. Sooner or later we must rest the entire structure on some unproved statements or postulates. We cannot prove all our statements unless we commit circular reasoning. Similarly, if we consider any term used in our original statement, we either use it without definition or we define it. If we define it, we do so by expressing it in terms of other terms. These in turn are either left undefined or are defined in

* The student is advised to review Chapter 2, sections 8 and 9, at this point.

terms of still other terms. Sooner or later we must rest all our definitions on some terms which are left undefined. We cannot define all our terms unless we use circular definitions. When we have organized our subject, whatever it may be, so that it begins with undefined terms and postulates and proceeds to define new terms and prove new statements, we have converted it into an abstract mathematical science. It you wish to attribute meanings (apprehended intuitively or some other way) to your undefined terms, you then obtain a concrete interpretation or application of your abstract science; that is, you then have a branch of applied mathematics.

Naturally, in passing from an abstract mathematical science to a concrete interpretation, we try to substitute such meanings for the undefined terms as will make true statements of the postulates. Needless to say, our abstract mathematical sciences are usually constructed with some application in mind. Of course whether or not a concrete interpretation really makes true statements of our postulates may not always be as certain as it was in section 192, say. In the case of Euclidean geometry, we have seen that it is far from certain that our intuitive meanings of "dot" and "streak" for the undefined terms "point" and "line," respectively, really satisfy the Euclidean postulates. As we saw in Chapters 2 and 17, the notion that our postulates are "self-evident truths" is not tenable. They are merely assumptions (whether or not they are suggested by experience, intuition, or creative imagination) and our theorems are deduced from the assumptions by logic.

But what of our rules of logic? Are they self-evident? There is hardly any doubt that most people even today would regard the rules of logic as self-evident and undeniable. But we have already burned our fingers in the fire of self-evidence in the case of the postulates of Euclidean geometry. A typical mathematical answer to the question of the self-evidence of logic itself is to formalize or formulate the rules of logic precisely and to say that we regard the logical rules as part of our assumptions. This leads to a careful study of formal, symbolic, or "mathematical" logic. Such studies go back to Leibniz, but the recent era in the development of symbolic logic begins with Boole, de Morgan, Peano, Frege, in the nineteenth century, and has been advanced by many contemporary workers such as Russell, Whitehead, Hilbert, Brouwer, Lukasiewicz, Tarski, Gödel, and others. Having taken the view that the rules of logic are assumptions and not self-evident truths, the possibility arises that *other* assumptions concerning logic may be consistent and useful. Thus arises the study of systems of logic different from the customary one; this is entirely analogous to the origin of non-Euclidean geometries. In fact, such logics have been studied in recent years and have actually been found useful in connection with quantum physics. This work is at present going on.

As we saw in section 195, the study of mathematical or formal or symbolic logic has also been stimulated by the question of the consistency of the mathematical sciences. In addition, the study of the foundations of logical reasoning has received impetus from the occurrence of concealed inconsistencies in apparently harmless statements, like the following.

(1) "In a certain town, there is a barber who must shave all those people and only those people who do not shave themselves" (Bertrand Russell). This seems harmless, but does the barber shave himself? Clearly, according to the rules, if he does, he mustn't; and if he doesn't, he must. (This sounds like the famous words of Tweedledee in Lewis Carroll's *Through the Looking Glass*, "If it was so, it might be; and if it were so it would be; but as it isn't, it ain't. That's logic.") This barber cannot exist and not even Occam's Razor will shave him.

(2) "It is a rule that all rules have exceptions." If this rule has an exception, then there must be some rule without an exception; but if this rule has no exception, the statement is false.

(3) "This statement is false." If it's true, it's false; and if it's false, it's true.

(4) "This sentence has six words" is false, but so, it seems, is its negation "This sentence has not six words."

Paradoxical statements like these indicate the necessity for a careful analysis of both logic and language. Perhaps the most paradoxical fact about modern mathematics is the fact that paradoxes have arisen within it. There is no general agreement concerning the resolution of some of these paradoxes. In fact, there are at present three different schools of thought concerning the logical foundations of mathematics and no reconciliation is in sight.

The King's advice to the White Rabbit to "begin at the beginning, and go on till you come to the end; then stop" does not apply to the development of mathematics. For the study of mathematics begins somewhere in its logical middle and progresses in two broad directions. One is the direction of further development of the logical consequences and applications of the various branches of the very ramified mathematical edifice. The other is the direction of further delving into the underlying foundations upon which the whole magnificent structure rests. Both directions of research are important and very much connected with each other. Every theorem of pure mathematics, from the elementary ones we have studied here to the most advanced ones available, is firmly cemented to the underlying assumptions by steps of strictly logical reasoning. There seems to be no end in either direction and, consequently, no possibility that mathematics can ever become completely worked out, dead, embalmed in books, and devoid of interest. Since the seventeenth century new results in mathematics have been produced at ever increasing speed. In recent years, periodicals devoted exclusively to the publication of new mathematical research have contained thousands of articles annually on many different subjects. The 1954 volume of *Mathematical Reviews*, a journal which publishes brief summaries of research papers appearing in reputable scientific journals the world over, used 1140 pages. Mathematics is far from the dead subject that some students think it is. In fact, in modern times, it has had something of the appearance of the furious young man who mounted his horse and rode off in all directions. Needless to say, not all of these myriad contributions survive. But neither are they all completely lost. Every so often, someone synthesizes numerous special results into a powerful general method. In fact, a subject sometimes begins its most interesting phase after it has been pronounced worked out and dead by a hasty coroner's jury. In any case, no mathematician is likely ever to voice Alexander's complaint concerning the scarcity of new lands to conquer.

197. MATHEMATICS AS A BRANCH OF HUMAN ENDEAVOR

The magnificent conception of mathematics as the study of all abstract logical systems or abstract mathematical sciences and their concrete interpretations or applications really justifies the statement that mathematics is basic to every subject forming part of the search for truth. In fact, mathematics, thus conceived, includes all subjects into which one injects logical structure. "To *mathematize* a subject does not mean merely to introduce equations and formulas into it, but rather to mould and fuse it into a coherent whole, with its postulates and assumptions clearly recognized, its definitions faultlessly drawn, and its conclusions scrupulously exact."* That is, to mathematize any subject means simply to put it in the form of an abstract mathematical science. As remarked in Chapter 2, and in the preceding section, this is unavoidable if one insists on organizing in a strictly logical way any subject matter at all. Realization of this should make us look into the assumptions underlying the things we assert. Examination of the underlying assumptions and the correctness of the reasoning by which we draw conclusions from them should serve to clarify our beliefs, to make us cognizant of the possibility of other tenable assumptions and other beliefs, and should therefore assist us on the road to tolerance, maturity, and wisdom. It is natural that, since antiquity, mathematics should have pointed the way toward these ideals of clarity since it has been comparatively free from the emotional confusion of prejudice and hatred; this is even more true since Lobachevski and others destroyed the sanctity of the notion that the axioms of Euclidean geometry constituted a self-evidently, absolutely true description of

* Fifteenth Yearbook of the National Council of Teachers of Mathematics.

physical space, a belief that was held with firm conviction by many people who scoffed at other "absolute truths." Mathematics today can still serve us as an ideal of intellectual honesty, of logical rigor and vigor and clarity, toward which to strive. Any applied science, for example, develops by evolutionary stages. First, the collection of data takes place; then the formation of hypotheses or postulates; then the deduction of the logical consequences of these postulates; then the checking of these consequences against the observed facts or data. If some consequence does not check with the facts, we attempt to revise the postulates and the process begins again. Ultimately the subject is put into the strict logical form of a mathematical science. Physics, chemistry, biology, and the social sciences have all followed this general evolutionary pattern, although biology and the social sciences are in the earlier stages of development, from this point of view.

As we have pointed out, mathematics is the backbone of all scientific (logical) subjects, whether physical, biological, social, or otherwise and, as such, is and must continue to be of the utmost importance to the civilized world. We have already remarked that pure mathematics is usually developed with some application in mind. Thus most of elementary mathematics originated in the social needs of commerce, surveying, engineering, etc. However, it would be a tragic mistake to censor or prohibit research in pure science merely because there was no immediate practical application visible. History has shown us many times that the applications may come much later than the pure science. For example, the conic sections were studied in ancient Greece for their own sake and came to be of overwhelming importance in physics only in the seventeenth century. Non-Euclidean geometry, developed for its own sake as pure mathematics early in the nineteenth century, was applied to the physical theory of relativity in the twentieth century. Similarly, the theory of groups, developed for its own sake as pure mathematics in the nineteenth century, was applied to the physical theory of quantum mechanics in the twentieth century. There can be no doubt that practical social needs have always had a great effect on the development of mathematics. Conversely, there can be no doubt that mathematics has had a great effect on the development of society, as, for example, in the case of the Industrial Revolution which would never have taken place without the technical applications of mathematics to engineering. Nor can there be any doubt that social conditions may well tend to stifle or stimulate scientific progress. Nevertheless, one should not lose sight of the fact that in pure mathematics we have a great structure of logically perfect deductions which constitutes an integral part of that great and enduring human heritage which is and should be largely independent of the perhaps temporary existence of any particular social or political conditions in any particular geographical location at any particular time. Euclid's geometry is far more important to us than the political ideas of Euclid's day. The enduring value of mathematics, like that of the other sciences and arts, far transcends the daily flux of a changing world. In fact, the apparent stability of mathematics may well be one of the reasons for its attractiveness and for the respect accorded it in a world wherein security is so elusive.

To a certain extent it is doubtless true, as has been maintained by Spengler in his *Decline of the West*, that the mathematics of any period is a good index of its culture. There is no doubt that much mathematical research has been definitely "in the air" and was not created out of whole cloth by any genius. This is indicated by the frequency with which similar results have been obtained by different men independently of each other. For example, no one has been greatly surprised by the invention of cheap television today although 50 years ago it would have been called impossible, and 500 years ago its inventor would have been burned at the stake. However, to conclude from this that the people who actually do the inventing are unimportant is an error that is more common than just. It is true that any two mathematicians will agree on the correctness of a mathematical theory, if they agree on the basic postulates. It may also be true, in at least some cases, that, if any given mathematician had not lived, his work might have been done by someone else, although perhaps much later; this opinion or conjecture has its defenders and its opponents. To this extent, mathematics may be independent of individual people. But to say that society or its needs "produced" a certain achievement is to ignore entirely that only one or a few individuals actually contributed to this achievement. To say that society or the human race "did it" is much like the remark of the baseball fan who says proudly that "we" won the ball game when he means that 9 athletes at most remotely connected with him won the ball game. In point of fact "society" does not always deserve such vicarious glory for it has sometimes seemed to do its best to censor, discourage, and hinder its best minds in every imaginable way.

We need not dwell on the manifold practical applications of mathematics, since these are, in a general way, well known to the reader, except to point out that the contempt in which the business man or "man of action" sometimes holds the pure scientist is totally unjustified. Such a person overlooks the fact that his daily life is full of the results of pure science. For example, the amount of pure astronomy, and hence mathematics, involved in the answer to the practical and important question "what time is it?", or in the navigation of ocean-going ships, might astound a "man of action." Of course the importance of pure science has been recognized by big business in recent years, and many large corporations support pure scientists in well-equipped laboratories in which they may pursue their researches, regardless of immediate applicability. Needless to say, the practical by-products of this research have amply justified the investment from a purely commercial standpoint. We have therefore stressed the importance of mathematics in the world of ideas, since this aspect may not be quite so familiar. Mathematics has been aptly called both the queen and the handmaiden of the sciences. Mathematics, likewise, has had a tremendous influence on philosophy as well as on the sciences. For example, mathematics has successfully dealt with the problems of infinity and has contributed greatly to the solution of problems of logic, all of which are problems that originated in philosophy. More than that, however, mathematics has clarified the notions of validity and truth, of pure and applied mathematics, and has led, especially since the study of non-Euclidean geometries, to a clearer understanding of the nature of human knowledge.

While we have stressed the scientific characteristics of mathematics and its relations to the sciences, it must be said that mathematics has relations with the arts as well, and has also the characteristics of an art. By this statement we do not refer merely to the obvious relations of geometry to pictorial design or architecture, or to the relations between numbers and musical harmonies which were known to Pythagoras (see section 34). We mean rather that the creation of new mathematics is itself an art and that the contemplation of well-wrought mathematical systems gives rise to genuine aesthetic satisfaction. It is easy to say that to construct an abstract mathematical science we have only to choose undefined terms and postulates and to define new terms and deduce new theorems. But what undefined terms, postulates, definitions shall we choose and which of the possibly infinite number of logical conclusions shall we deduce? Thus arises the problem of selection of materials to start with and the selection of a pattern or direction or mode of development of these materials. This is a problem of artistic composition requiring insight, taste, intuition, and creative imagination (that is, a problem of creative art), just as is the analogous problem of painting or musical composition, say, where one has to choose themes and modes of developing and interweaving them out of an infinite variety of possibilities. In mathematics we have, of course, the partial criterion that the resulting logical structure be consistent and preferably applicable to something; just as in music we have the criterion that the resulting composition be pleasing to the ear and perhaps emotionally satisfying. But to meet these criteria in either mathematics or music may well require artistic genius. For example, the genius of Newton was needed for his beautiful logical theory of gravitation which seemed to introduce order and harmony into the apparently chaotic movements of the entire physical universe so well that his work remained unchallenged for over 200 years, and is still a valuable and elegant logical composition. As for the statement that the contemplation of mathematics gives aesthetic satisfaction, you must understand that it is assumed that the contemplator has the training or background needed for such appreciation. This is the case in any art. A beginner in a foreign language cannot appreciate a great piece of literature if his knowledge of vocabulary and grammar is fragmentary. An untrained person does not get all he might from hearing a beautifully wrought symphony and gets nothing at all from seeing it in musical print, if he reads the individual notes or symbols with difficulty, while a well-trained person can read a score and enjoy it. Similarly, in mathematics, only when one passes the stage of reading the individual symbols with difficulty may one begin to see and appreciate in a mathematical composition the symphonic interplay of ideas, the economical simplicity of development, the subtle modulations and inversions of treatment, the inevitable sweep toward a climactic conclusion, and so on; just as in a musical composition one may see and appreciate the symphonic interplay of themes, the economical simplicity of development, the subtle modulations and inversions of treatment, the inevitable sweep toward a climax, and so on. The aesthetic satisfactions obtained in both instances by people whose background permits such appreciation are much akin. There can be no doubt that creative imagination has been needed for the invention of great mathematical works. In his *Philosophical Dictionary*, Voltaire wrote that "... there was far more imagination in the head of Archimedes than in that of Homer." Havelock Ellis, not a mathematician himself, says in *The Dance of Life** that "it is here [that is, in mathematics] that the artist has the fullest scope for his imagination." The mathematician is not even confined to the "actual" world. He is free, in a sense, to explore all possible worlds.

Needless to say, mathematics is the nearest thing to an international language that the human race possesses. The symbolism of mathematics is the same the world over, and work done in one part of the world is likely to be taken up and advanced further thousands of miles away. From another viewpoint, mathematics may be considered *the* most distinctively human of all human activities. For, as far as we know, man's social instincts, etc., are shared with other animals, but reflective logical curiosity and the important trait of being able to accumulate, organize, and add to wisdom and pass it on to the next generation for further improvement is distinctly human. It is our logical minds that serve to bind the future with the past and to give us whatever hope we have for progress. For example, the suspension bridge on which you cross a river rests not only on its pillars but on the calculus of Isaac Newton, the analytic geometry of Descartes, the algebraic researches of many centuries, the geometry of the ancient Greeks, and the primitive number-lore of our prehistoric ancestors. While our mathematical ideas change and progress, they do not do so by ignoring past achievements (although new developments often render past achievements obsolete). Real progress in any branch of the search for truth demands a degree of open-mindedness sufficient to combat both the unwise tendency to cling to old beliefs merely because they are old and the equally foolish tendency to embrace hastily

* Ellis, H. *The Dance of Life*, Houghton Mifflin, Boston, 1923.

every novelty merely because it is new. The history of mathematics and the physical sciences, for example, has shown many times the folly of both these policies. These cautions are obviously even more necessary in subjects which involve our emotions and in which the check of controlled experiments is either impractical or impossible. It is, however, worth pointing out that controlled experiments are seldom possible in astronomy. Yet in the course of many centuries, astonomical theories have been patiently and logically built up until astronomy may well be regarded as the most accurate and reliable branch of mathematical physics. To the appeal for rational thought it is sometimes objected that when a house is on fire there is no time to conduct a dispassionate scientific investigation. This argument, however, does not justify the too common contempt for the reflective scientist and the corresponding adulation of the "man of action." It rather points to the desirability for calm scientific investigation *before* the need for hasty action arises. While man's logical ability has been most highly developed in connection with numbers and diagrams, may we not hope that, despite the obvious difficulties, man may yet become reasonable about more complicated and emotionally confused subjects such as the social sciences? The standard of logical rigor set by mathematicians is a high ideal, but that scarcely justifies abandoning it. Man's faith in reason is so fundamental a need that to discard it lightly may be fairly regarded as a pathological symptom. But in order to strive toward this ideal, we must first understand and appreciate it. To give you such an understanding and appreciation, at least to some extent, has been one of the aims of this book. We hope that you are now able to see mathematics in its proper perspective as one of the greatest achievements of the human race.

References

Numbers refer to the bibliography at the back of the book.

Bell 18, 19, 20, 21
Benacerraf and Putnam 22
Bennett and Baylis 23
Braithwaite 36
Bronowski 41
Buchanan 43
Cohen 54
Dresden 65
Ellis 69
Eves and Newsom 71
Keyser 109, 110, 111, 112, 113
Kleene 114
Kline 117
Lieber and Lieber 122
Littlewood 123
Nagel 138
Nagel and Newman 139
Newman 140
Poincaré 148
Russell 163, 164, 165, 166
Sawyer 171
Smith 182
Stabler 184
Stein 185
Steinhaus 186
Stoll 187
Tarski 190
Weyl 204
Whitehead 206
Wilder 210

Selected Bibliography

1. Abbott, E. A., *Flatland, a Romance of Many Dimensions*, Boston: Little, Brown and Company, 1929.
2. Allen, R. G. D., *Mathematical Economics*, New York: St Martin's Press, Inc., 1956.
3. Allendoerfer, C. B. and C. O. Oakley, *Principles of Mathematics*, New York: McGraw-Hill Book Company, 1955
4. Archibald, R. C., "Outline of the history of mathematics," *American Mathematical Monthly*, Vol. 56, No. 1, 1949.
5. Arnold, B. H., *Logic and Boolean Algebra*, New Jersey: Prentice-Hall, Inc., 1962.
6. Arnold, B. H., *Intuitive Concepts in Elementary Topology*, New Jersey: Prentice-Hall, Inc., 1962.
7. Arrow, K. J., *Social Choice and Individual Values*, New York: John Wiley and Sons, Inc., 1951.
8. Ashby, W. R., *Design for a Brain*, New York: John Wiley and Sons, Inc., 1954.
9. Ashby, W. R., *Introduction to Cybernetics*, New York: John Wiley and Sons, Inc., 1956.
10. Attneave, F., *Applications of Information Theory to Psychology*, New York: Holt-Dryden, 1959.
11. Avondo-Bodino, G., *Economic Application of the Theory of Graphs*, New York: Gordon and Breach, Inc., 1962.
12. Ball, W. W. R., *Short Account of the History of Mathematics*, Macmillan, 1908.
13. Ball, W. W. R., *Mathematical Recreations and Essays*, New York: The Macmillan Company, 1962.
14. Baumol, W. J., *Economic Theory and Operations Analysis*, New Jersey: Prentice-Hall, Inc., 1961.
15. Beckenbach, E. and R. Bellman, *Introduction to Inequalities*, New York: Random House, Inc., 1963.
16. Bell, E. T., *Men of Mathematics*, New York: Simon and Schuster, Inc., 1937.
17. Bell, E. T., *Numerology*, Baltimore, Williams and Williams, 1933.

18. Bell, E. T., *The Development of Mathematics*, New York: McGraw-Hill Book Company, 1940.
19. Bell, E. T., *The Handmaiden of the Sciences*, Baltimore, Williams and Williams, 1937.
20. Bell, E. T., *The Queen of the Sciences*, New York, G. E. Stechert, 1938.
21. Bell, E. T., *The Search for Truth*, New York, Reynal and Hitchcock, 1934.
22. Benacerraf, P. and H. Putnam, *Philosophy of Mathematics: Selected Readings*, New Jersey: Prentice-Hall, Inc., 1964.
23. Bennett, A. A., and C. A. Baylis, *Formal Logic*, New Jersey: Prentice-Hall Inc., 1939.
24. Berge, C., *Theory of Graphs and its Applications*, New York: John Wiley and Sons, Inc., 1962.
25. Berkeley, E. C., Boolean algebra and application to insurance," *Record of American Institute of Actuaries*, Vol. 26, Oct. 1937.
26. Berkeley, E. C., *Giant Brains*, New York: John Wiley and Sons, Inc., 1955.
27. Berkeley, G., *The Analyst*, London, 1734.
28. Birkhoff, G. and S. MacLane, *A Survey of Modern Algebra*, New York: The Macmillan Company, 1953.
29. Blackwell, D. H., and M. A. Girshick, *Theory of Games and Statistical Decisions*, New York: John Wiley and Sons, Inc., 1954.
30. Blau, J. H., "The existence of social welfare functions," *Econometrica*, Vol. 25, 1957.
31. Blumenthal, L. M., *A Modern View of Geometry*, San Francisco: W. H. Freeman and Co., 1961.
32. Boole, G., *An Investigation of the Laws of Thought*, New York: Dover Publications Inc., 1951 (originally 1854).
33. Boulding, K., *Conflict and Defense*, New York: Harper and Bros., 1962.
34. Boulding, K. E. and W. A. Spivey, *Linear Programming and the Theory of the Firm*, New York: The Macmillan Company, 1960.
35. Bowden, B. V., *Faster than Thought*, New York: Pitman Publishing Corp., 1953.
36. Braithwaite, R. B., *Scientific Explanation*, New York: Cambridge University Press, 1955.
37. Braithwaite, R. B., *Theory of Games as a Tool for the Moral Philosopher*, New York: Cambridge University Press, 1954.
38. Breuer, J., *Introduction to the Theory of Sets*, (translated by Fehr, H. F.), New Jersey: Prentice-Hall, Inc., 1958.
39. Bridgman, P. W., *The Logic of Modern Physics*, New York: Macmillan Company 1946.
40. Brillouin, L., *Science and Information Theory*, New York: Academic Press, 1956.
41. Bronowski, J., "Science as Foresight," *in What is Science?* (J. R. Newman, ed.), New York: Simon and Shuster, 1955.
42. Bross, I. D. J., *Design for Decision*, New York: Macmillan Company, 1953.
43. Buchanan, S., *Poetry and Mathematics*, New York: John Day Company, 1929.
44. Burger, E., *Introduction to the Theory of Games*, (translated by Freund, J. E.), New Jersey: Prentice-Hall Inc., 1963.
45. Bush, R. R. and F. Mosteller, *Stochastic Models for Learning*, New York: John Wiley and Sons, Inc., 1955.

46. Cajori, F., A History of Elementary Mathematics, New York: Macmillan Company, 1917.
47. Cajori, F., A History of Mathematics, 2nd Ed. New York: Macmillan, 1929.
48. Cantor, G., *Contributions to the Founding of the Theory of Transfinite Numbers* (translated by Jourdain), La Salle, Ill.: Open Court Publishing Co., 1915.
49. Chernoff, H. and Moses, L. E., *Elementary Decision Theory*, New York: John Wiley and Sons Inc., 1959.
50. Cherry, C., *On Human Communication*, New York: John Wiley and Sons Inc., 1957.
51. Churchman, C. W., R. L. Ackoff, and E. L. Arnoff, *Introduction to Operations Research*, New York: John Wiley and Sons, Inc., 1957.
52. Cogan, E. J., *Foundations of Analysis*, New Jersey: Prentice-Hall, Inc., 1962.
53. Cohen, L. W. and G. Ehrlich, *The Structure of the Real Numbers*, New York: D. Van Nostrand Co., Inc., 1963.
54. Cohen, M. R., *Reason and Nature*, New York: Harcourt, Brace, and World, 1931
55. Cohen, M. R., and E. Nagel, *An Introduction to Logic and Scientific Method*, New York: Harcourt, Brace and World, 1934.
56. Cooley, H. R., D. Gans, M. Kline, and H. E. Wahlert, *Introduction to Mathematics*, New York: Houghton-Mifflin, 1937.
57. Courant, R., *Differential and Integral Calculus*, (translated by McShane, E. J.), New York, Nordemann, 1937.
58. Courant, R., and H. Robbins, *What is Mathematics*? New York: Oxford University Press, 1941.
59. Coxeter, H. S. M., *Introduction to Geometry*, New York: John Wiley and Sons, Inc., 1961.
60. Cramer, H., *Elements of Probability Theory*, New York: John Wiley and Sons, Inc. 1961.
61. Dantzig, G. B., *Linear Programming and Extensions*, New Jersey: Princeton University Press, 1963.
62. Dantzig, T., *Number, The Language of Science*, 4th Ed., Rev., New York: The Macmillan Company, 1954.
63. de Morgan, A., *Budget of Paradoxes*, La Salle, Ill.: Open Court Publishing Co. 1940.
64. Dorfman, R., P. A. Samuelson, and A. M. Solow, *Linear Programming and Economic Analysis*, New York: McGraw-Hill Book Co., 1958.
65. Dresden, A., *Invitation to Mathematics*, New York: Holt, Rinehart, and Winston, Inc., 1936.
66. Dresher, M., *Games of Strategy*, New Jersey: Prentice-Hall, Inc., 1961.
67. Eddington, A. S., *Space, Time and Gravitation*, New York: Cambridge University Press, 1920.
68. Einstein, A., and Infeld, L., *The Evolution of Physics*, New York: Simon and Shuster, 1938.
69. Ellis, H., *The Dance of Life*, New York: Houghton-Mifflin, 1923.
70. Eves, H., *An Introduction to the History of Mathematics*, New York: Holt, Rinehart and Winston, Inc., 1953.
71. Eves, H. and C. V. Newson, *An Introduction to the Foundations and Fundamental Concepts of Mathematics*, New York: Holt, Rinehart, and Winston, Inc., 1958.

72. Feller, W., *Probability Theory and its Applications*, New York: John Wiley and Sons, Inc., 1950.
73. Ficken, F. A., *The Simplex Method of Linear Programming*, New York: Holt, Rinehart, and Winston, Inc., 1961.
74. Fine, H. B., *College Algebra*, Boston: Ginn and Co., 1904.
75. Fine, H. B., *The Number System of Algebra*, Boston: Leach, Shewell, Sanborn, 1890.
76. Flament, C., *Applications of Graph Theory to Group Structure*, (translated by Pinard, M., Breton, R., and Fontaine, F.), New Jersey: Prentice-Hall, Inc., 1963.
77. Ford, L. R. jr. and D. R. Fulkerson, *Flows in Networks*, New Jersey: Princeton University Press, 1962.
78. Forder, H. G., *Euclidean Geometry*, New York: Cambridge University Press, 1927.
79. Fraenkel, A. A., *Abstract Set Theory*, Amsterdam, North Holland, 1953.
80. Fry, T. C., *Probability and its Engineering Uses*, New York: D. Van Nostrand Co., Inc., 1929.
81. Gale, D., *Theory of Linear Economic Models*, New York: McGraw-Hill Book Company, Inc., 1950.
82. Galileo Galilei, *Dialogue Concerning the Two Chief World Systems—Ptolemaic and Copernican* (translated by Drake, S., and foreword by Einstein, A.,), Berkeley: University of California Press, 1953.
83. Gamow, G., *One, Two, Three, ..., Infinity*, New York: Viking Press, 1947.
84. Gardner, M., *Mathematics, Magic and Mystery*, New York: Dover Publications, Inc., 1956.
85. Gardner, M., *The Scientific American Book of Mathematical Puzzles and Diversions*, New York: Simon and Shuster, 1959.
86. Gardner, M., *The Second Scientific American Book of Mathematical Puzzles and Diversions*, New York: Simon and Shuster, 1961.
87. Glicksman, A. M., *An Introduction to Linear Programming and The Theory of Games*, New York: John Wiley and Sons, Inc., 1963.
88. Hadley, G., *Linear Algebra*, Reading, Mass.: Addison-Wesley Publishing Co., Inc., 1961.
89. Hadley, G., *Linear Programming*, Reading, Mass.: Addison-Wesley Publishing Co., Inc., 1962.
90. Halmos, P., *Naive Set Theory*, New York: D. Van Nostrand Co., Inc., 1960.
91. Harary, F., R. Z. Norman, and D. Cartwright, *Structural Models: An Introduction to the Theory of Directed Graphs*, New York; John Wiley and Sons Inc., 1965.
92. Hausdorff, F., *Set Theory*, New York: Chelsea Publishing Co., 1957.
93. Hilbert, D., *Foundations of Geometry*, (translated by Townsend, E. J.), La Salle, Ill.: Open Court Publishing Co., 1921.
94. Hobson, E. W., et al., *Squaring the Circle, and Other Monographs*, New York: Chelsea Publishing Co., 1953.
95. Hohn, F. E., *Applied Boolean Algebra*, New York: The Macmillan Company, 1960.
96. Huff, D., *How to Lie with Statistics*, New York: W. W. Norton and Co., Inc., 1954.
97. Jacobson, H., "Information and life," *The American Scientist* Vol. 43, 1955.

98. Jaeger, A., *Introduction to Linear Algebra and Analytic Geometry*, New York: Holt, Rinehart and Winston, Inc., 1961.
99. Jeans, J. H., *Science and Music*, New York: The Macmillan Company, 1938. (Out of print.)
100. Jones, B. W., *Elementary Concepts of Mathematics*, 2d ed., New York: The Macmillan Company, New York: 1963.
101. Kamke, E., *Theory of Sets*, New York: Dover Publications, Inc., 1950.
102. Karlin, S., *Mathematical Methods and Theory in Games, Programming and Economics*, Reading, Mass.: Addison-Wesley Publishing Company, Inc., 1959.
103. Kasner, E. and J. Newman, *Mathematics and the Imagination*, New York: Simon and Shuster, 1940.
104. Kazarinoff, N. D., *Geometric Inequalities*, New York: Random House, 1961.
105. Kemeny, J. G. and J. L. Snell, *Finite Markov Chains*, New York: D. Van Nostrand Co., Inc., 1960.
106. Kemeny, J. G. and J. L. Snell, *Mathematical Models in the Social Sciences*, Boston: Ginn and Co., 1962.
107. Kemeny, J. G., J. L. Snell, and G. L. Thompson, *Introduction to Finite Mathematics*, New Jersey: Prentice-Hall, Inc., 1957.
108. Kershner, R. B. and L. R. Wilcox, *The Anatomy of Mathematics*, New York: Ronald Press Co., 1950.
109. Keyser, C. J., *Mathematical Philosophy*, New York: E. P. Dutton and Co., 1922.
110. Keyser, C. J., *Mathematics and the Question of the Cosmic Mind*, New York: Scripta Mathematica, 1935.
111. Keyser, C. J., *Pastures of Wonder*, New York: Columbia University Press, 1929.
112. Keyser, C. J., *The Human Worth of Rigorous Thinking*, New York: Columbia University Press, 1925.
113. Keyser, C. J., *Thinking About Thinking*, New York: E. P.: Dutton and Co., 1926.
114. Kleene, S. C., *Introduction to Metamathematics*, New York: D. Van Nostrand Co., Inc., 1952.
115. Klein, F., *Elementary Mathematics from an Advanced Standpoint* (translated by Hedrick, E. R. and Noble, C.A.) New York: The Macmillan Company, 1932. (Out of print.)
116. Klein, F., *Famous Problems of Elementary Geometry*, New York: Stechert-Hafner Co., 1930.
117. Kline, M., *Mathematics in Western Culture*, New York: Oxford University Press, 1953.
118. Koopmans, T. C., (ed.), *Activity Analysis of Production and Allocation*, New York: John Wiley and Sons, Inc., 1951.
119. Kraitchik, M. *Mathematical Recreations*, New York: Dover, Publications, Inc., 1953.
120. Lieber, L. R., *Infinity*, New York: Rinehart and Co., 1953.
121. Lieber, L. R. and H. C. Lieber, *Non-Euclidean Geometry*, Lancaster, Pa., Science Press, 1940.
122. Lieber, L. R. and H. C. Lieber, *The Education of T. C. Mits*, New York: W. W. Norton and Co., Inc., 1942.

123. Littlewood, D. E., *The Skeleton Key of Mathematics*, London, Hutchinson's University Library, 1949.
124. Luce, R. D., *Developments in Mathematical Psychology*, New York: The Free Press of Glencoe, 1960.
125. Luce, R. D., *Individual Choice Behavior*, New York: John Wiley and Sons, Inc., 1959.
126. Luce, R. D., R. R. Bush, and E. Galanter, *Handbook of Mathematical Psychology*, New York: John Wiley and Sons, Inc., 1963.
127. Luce, R. D., R. R. Bush, and E. Galanter, (eds.), *Readings in Mathematical Psychology*, New York: John Wiley and Sons, Inc., 1963.
128. Luce, R. D. and H. Raiffa, *Games and Decisions*, New York: John Wiley, and Sons, Inc., 1957.
129. Manning, H. P., *The Fourth Dimension Simply Explained*, New York, Munn, 1910.
130. McCoy, N. H., *Introduction to Modern Algebra*, New Jersey: Allyn and Bacon, 1960.
131. McDonald, J., *Strategy in Poker, Business and War*, New York: W. W. Norton and Co., Inc., 1950.
132. McKinsey, J. C. C., *Introduction to the Theory of Games*, New York: McGraw-Hill Book Co., Inc., 1952.
133. Miller, D. C., *The Science of Musical Sounds*, New York: The Macmillan Company, 1916. (Out of print.)
134. Moise, E. E., *Elementary Geometry from an Advanced Standpoint*, Reading, Mass: Addison-Wesley Publishing Co., Inc., 1963.
135. Moroney, M. J., *Facts from Figures*, New York: Pelican Books, 1951.
136. Morse, P. M. and G. E. Kimball, *Methods of Operations Research*, New York: John Wiley and Sons, Inc., 1950.
137. Mosteller, F., R. E. K. Rourke, and G. B. Thomas, Jr. *Probability with Statistical Applications*, Reading, Mass.: Addison-Wesley Publishing Co., Inc., 1961.
138. Nagel, E., *The Structure of Science*, New York: Harcourt, Brace and World, 1961.
139. Nagel, E. and J. R. Newman, *Gödel's Proof*, New York: New York University Press, 1958.
140. Newman, J. R., (ed.), *The World of Mathematics*, New York: Simon and Shuster, 1956.
141. Niven, I., *Numbers: Rational and Irrational*, New York: Random House, 1962.
142. Ore, O., *Cardano, The Gambling Scholar*, New Jersey: Princeton University Press, 1953.
143. Ore, O., *Graphs and their Uses*, New York: Random House. 1963.
144. Ore, O., *Number Theory and Its History*, New York: McGraw-Hill Book Co., Inc., 1948.
145. Ore, O., *Theory of Graphs*, Rhode Island: American Mathematical Society, 1962.
146. Peirce, C. S., *Chance, Love and Logic*, New York: Harcourt, Brace, and World, 1923.
147. Pfeiffer, J., *The Thinking Machine*, New York: J. P. Lippincott Co., 1962.
148. Poincaré, J. H., *The Foundations of Science* (translated by Halsted, G.B.), Lancaster, Pa., The Science Press, 1946.

149. Polya, G., *Mathematical Discovery*, New York: John Wiley and Sons, Inc., 1962.
150. Polya, G., *Mathematics and Plausible Reasoning*, New Jersey: Princeton University Press, 1954.
151. Quastler, H. (ed.), *Information Theory in Biology*, Urbana: University of Illinois Press, 1953.
152. Rademacher, H. and O. Toeplitz, *The Enjoyment of Mathematics*, New Jersey: Princeton University Press, 1957.
153. Rapoport, A., *Fights, Games, and Debates*, Ann Arbor: University of Michigan Press, 1960.
154. Rashevsky, N., "Life, information theory and topology," *Bulletin of Mathematical Biophysics*, Vol. 17, 1955.
155. Rashevsky, N., *Mathematical Biology of Social Behavior*, Chicago: University of Chicago Press, 1951.
156. Rashevsky, N., *Mathematical Biophysics*, Chicago: University of Chicago Press, 1948.
157. Rashevsky, N., "Topology and life," *Bulletin of Mathematical Biophysics* Vol. 16, 1954.
158. Richardson, M., *College Algebra*, 3rd Ed., New Jersey: Prentice-Hall Co., Inc., 1966.
159. Richardson, M., "Mathematics and intellectual honesty," *American Mathematical Monthly*, Vol. 59, 1952.
160. Richardson, M., *Plane and Spherical Trigonometry*, New York: The Macmillan Company, 1950.
161. Robinson, G. de B., *The Foundations of Geometry*, Toronto: University of Toronto Press, 1940.
162. Rosser, J. B., *Logic for Mathematicians*, New York: McGraw-Hill Book Co., Inc., 1953.
163. Russell, B., *Introduction to Mathematical Philosophy*, London: Allen and Unwin, 1920.
164. Russell, B., *Mysticism and Logic*, New York: Longmans, Green and Co., Inc., 1929.
165. Russell, B., *Our Knowledge of the External World*, London: Allen and Unwin, 1929.
166. Russell, B., *Principles of Mathematics*, New York: W. W. Norton and Co., Inc., 1938.
167. Russell, B., *The A B C of Relativity*, New York: Harper and Bros., 1925.
168. Ryser, H. J., *Combinatorial Mathematics*, New York: Mathematical Association of America, John Wiley and Sons, Inc., 1963.
169. Saaty, T. L., *Mathematical Methods of Operations Research*, New York: McGraw-Hill Book Co., Inc., 1959.
170. Sasieni, M., A. Yaspan, and E. Friedman, *Operations Research, Methods and Problems*, New York: John Wiley and Sons, Inc., 1959.
171. Sawyer, W. W., *Prelude to Mathematics*, New York: Penguin Books, 1955.
172. Schelling, T. C., *The Strategy of Conflict*, Cambridge, Mass., Harvard University Press, 1960.
173. Schrodinger, E., *What is Life?*, New York: The Macmillan Company, 1945. (Out of Print.)

174. Seshu, S. and Reed, M. B., *Linear Graphs and Electrical Networks*, Reading, Mass.: Addison-Wesley Publishing Co., Inc., 1961.
175. Shannon, C. E., "A chess-playing machine," *Scientific American*, February, 1950.
176. Shannon, C. E., and W. Weaver, *The Mathematical Theory of Communication*, Urbana: University of Illinois Press, 1949.
177. Shubik, M., (ed.), *Readings in Game Theory and Political Behavior*, New York: Doubleday, 1954.
178. Shubik, M., *Strategy and Market Structure*, New York: John Wiley and Sons, Inc., 1959.
179. Sluckin, W., *Minds and Machines*, New York: Penguin Books, Inc., 1954.
180. Smith, D. E., *A Source Book in Mathematics*, New York: McGraw-Hill Book Co., Inc., 1929.
181. Smith, D. E., *History of Mathematics*, Boston: Ginn and Co., 1923.
182. Smith, D. E., *The Poetry of Mathematics and other Essays*, New York: Scripta Mathematica, 1934.
183. Spivey, W. A., *Linear Programming*, New York: The Macmillan Company, 1963.
184. Stabler, E. R., *An Introduction to Mathematical Thought*, Reading, Mass.: Addison-Wesley, 1953.
185. Stein, S. K., *Mathematics, The Man-Made Universe*, San Francisco: W. H. Freeman and Co., 1963.
186. Steinhaus, H., *Mathematical Snapshots*, New York: Oxford University Press, 1938.
187. Stoll, R. R., *Sets, Logic, and Axiomatic Theories*, San Francisco: W. H. Freeman and Co., 1961.
188. Suppes, P., *Introduction to Logic*, New York: D. Van Nostrand Co., Inc., 1957.
189. Suppes, P. and R. C. Atkinson, *Markov Learning Models for Multiperson Interactions*, Stanford: Stanford University Press, 1960.
190. Tarski, A., *Introduction to Logic and the Methodology of the Deductive Sciences*, New York: Oxford University Press, 1941.
191. Thompson, J. E., *A Manual of the Slide Rule*, Boston: Chapman and Grimes, Inc., 1931.
192. Tucker, A. W., "Game theory and programming," (mimeographed), *Oklahoma A. and M. College* (Stillwater, Okla), 1955.
193. Tucker, A. W., and H. S. Bailey, Jr., "Topology," *Scientific American*, January, 1950.
194. Turing, A. M., "Computing machinery and intelligence," *Mind*, October, 1950.
195. Vajda, S., *An Introduction to Linear Programming and the Theory of Games*, New York: John Wiley and Sons, Inc., 1960.
196. Vajda, S., *Mathematical Programming*, Reading, Mass.: Addison-Wesley, 1961.
197. Vajda, S., *Readings in Linear Programming*, New York: John Wiley and Sons, Inc. 1958.
198. Vajda, S., *Theory of Games and Linear Programming*, New York: John Wiley and Sons, Inc., 1956.
199. von Mises, R., *Probability, Statistics and Truth*, New York: The Macmillan Company, 1939.

200. von Neumann, J., *The Computer and the Brain*, New Haven: Yale University Press, 1958.
201. von Neumann, J., *The General and Logical Theory of Automata* (in "Cerebral mechanisms in behavior," the Hixon Symposium, ed. by L. A. Jeffreys), New York: John Wiley and Sons, Inc., 1951.
202. von Neumann, J., and O. Morgenstern, *Theory of Games and Economic Behavior*, New Jersey: Princeton University Press, 1944.
203. Walter, W. G., *The Living Brain*, New York: W. W. Norton and Co., Inc., 1953.
204. Weyl, H., *Philosophy of Mathematics and the Natural Sciences*, New Jersey: Princeton University Press, 1949.
205. Weyl, H., *Symmetry*, New Jersey: Princeton University Press, 1952.
206. Whitehead, A. N., *An Introduction to Mathematics*, New York: Henry Holt and Co., Inc., 1911.
207. Whitehead, A. N., *Science and the Modern World*, New York: The Macmillan Company, 1925.
208. Wiener, N., *Cybernetics*, New York: John Wiley and Sons, Inc., 1948.
209. Wiener, N., *The Human Use of Human Beings*, New York: Houghton Mifflin Co., 1950.
210. Wilder, R. L., *Introduction to the Foundations of Mathematics*, New York: John Wiley and Sons, Inc., 1952.
211. Wilks, S. S., *Elementary Statistical Analysis*, New Jersey: Princeton University Press, 1951.
212. Williams, J. D., *The Compleat Strategyst*, New York: McGraw-Hill Book Co., Inc., 1956.
213. Wolfe, H. E., *Introduction to Non-Euclidean Geometry*, New York: Dryden (Holt), 1945.
214. Woodger, J. H., *The Axiomatic Method in Biology*, New York: Cambridge University Press, 1937.
215. Young, J. W., *Fundamental Concepts of Algebra and Geometry*, New York: The Macmillan Company, 1911. (Out of print.)
216. Young, J. W. A., *Monographs on Modern Mathematics*, New York: Longmans, Green and Co., Inc., 1911.
217. Zipf, G. K., *Human Behavior and the Principle of Least Effort*, Reading, Mass.: Addison-Wesley, 1949.
218. Zippin, L., *Uses of Infinity*, New York: Random House, 1963.

Table I
Common Logarithms

N	0	1	2	3	4	5	6	7	8	9
10	0000	0043	0086	0128	0170	0212	0253	0294	0334	0374
11	0414	0453	0492	0531	0569	0607	0645	0682	0719	0755
12	0792	0828	0864	0899	0934	0969	1004	1038	1072	1106
13	1139	1173	1206	1239	1271	1303	1335	1367	1399	1430
14	1461	1492	1523	1553	1584	1614	1644	1673	1703	1732
15	1761	1790	1818	1847	1875	1903	1931	1959	1987	2014
16	2041	2068	2095	2122	2148	2175	2201	2227	2253	2279
17	2304	2330	2355	2380	2405	2430	2455	2480	2504	2529
18	2553	2577	2601	2625	2648	2672	2695	2718	2742	2765
19	2788	2810	2833	2856	2878	2900	2923	2945	2967	2989
20	3010	3032	3054	3075	3096	3118	3139	3160	3181	3201
21	3222	3243	3263	3284	3304	3324	3345	3365	3385	3404
22	3424	3444	3464	3483	3502	3522	3541	3560	3579	3598
23	3617	3636	3655	3674	3692	3711	3729	3747	3766	3784
24	3802	3820	3838	3856	3874	3892	3909	3927	3945	3962
25	3979	3997	4014	4031	4048	4065	4082	4099	4116	4133
26	4150	4166	4183	4200	4216	4232	4249	4265	4281	4298
27	4314	4330	4346	4362	4378	4393	4409	4425	4440	4456
28	4472	4487	4502	4518	4533	4548	4564	4579	4594	4609
29	4624	4639	4654	4669	4683	4698	4713	4728	4742	4757
30	4771	4786	4800	4814	4829	4843	4857	4871	4886	4900
31	4914	4928	4942	4955	4969	4983	4997	5011	5024	5038
32	5051	5065	5079	5092	5105	5119	5132	5145	5159	5172
33	5185	5198	5211	5224	5237	5250	5263	5276	5289	5302
34	5315	5328	5340	5353	5366	5378	5391	5403	5416	5428
35	5441	5453	5465	5478	5490	5502	5514	5527	5539	5551
36	5563	5575	5587	5599	5611	5623	5635	5647	5658	5670
37	5682	5694	5705	5717	5729	5740	5752	5763	5775	5786
38	5798	5809	5821	5832	5843	5855	5866	5877	5888	5899
39	5911	5922	5933	5944	5955	5966	5977	5988	5999	6010
40	6021	6031	6042	6053	6064	6075	6085	6096	6107	6117
41	6128	6138	6149	6160	6170	6180	6191	6201	6212	6222
42	6232	6243	6253	6263	6274	6284	6294	6304	6314	6325
43	6335	6345	6355	6365	6375	6385	6395	6405	6415	6425
44	6435	6444	6454	6464	6474	6484	6493	6503	6513	6522
45	6532	6542	6551	6561	6571	6580	6590	6599	6609	6618
46	6628	6637	6646	6656	6665	6675	6684	6693	6702	6712
47	6721	6730	6739	6749	6758	6767	6776	6785	6794	6803
48	6812	6821	6830	6839	6848	6857	6866	6875	6884	6893
49	6902	6911	6920	6928	6937	6946	6955	6964	6972	6981
50	6990	6998	7007	7016	7024	7033	7042	7050	7059	7067
51	7076	7084	7093	7101	7110	7118	7126	7135	7143	7152
52	7160	7168	7177	7185	7193	7202	7210	7218	7226	7235
53	7243	7251	7259	7267	7275	7284	7292	7300	7308	7316
54	7324	7332	7340	7348	7356	7364	7372	7380	7388	7396
N	0	1	2	3	4	5	6	7	8	9

Table I [Contd.]

N	0	1	2	3	4	5	6	7	8	9
55	7404	7412	7419	7427	7435	7443	7451	7459	7466	7474
56	7482	7490	7497	7505	7513	7520	7528	7536	7543	7551
57	7559	7566	7574	7582	7589	7597	7604	7612	7619	7627
58	7634	7642	7649	7657	7664	7672	7679	7686	7694	7701
59	7709	7716	7723	7731	7738	7745	7752	7760	7767	7774
60	7782	7789	7796	7803	7810	7818	7825	7832	7839	7846
61	7853	7860	7868	7875	7882	7889	7896	7903	7910	7917
62	7924	7931	7938	7945	7952	7959	7966	7973	7980	7987
63	7993	8000	8007	8014	8021	8028	8035	8041	8048	8055
64	8062	8069	8075	8082	8089	8096	8102	8109	8116	8122
65	8129	8136	8142	8149	8156	8162	8169	8176	8182	8189
66	8195	8202	8209	8215	8222	8228	8235	8241	8248	8254
67	8261	8267	8274	8280	8287	8293	8299	8306	8312	8319
68	8325	8331	8338	8344	8351	8357	8363	8370	8376	8382
69	8388	8395	8401	8407	8414	8420	8426	8432	8439	8445
70	8451	8457	8463	8470	8476	8482	8488	8494	8500	8506
71	8513	8519	8525	8531	8537	8543	8549	8555	8561	8567
72	8573	8579	8585	8591	8597	8603	8609	8615	8621	8627
73	8633	8639	8645	8651	8657	8663	8669	8675	8681	8686
74	8692	8698	8704	8710	8716	8722	8727	8733	8739	8745
75	8751	8756	8762	8768	8774	8779	8785	8791	8797	8802
76	8808	8814	8820	8825	8831	8837	8842	8848	8854	8859
77	8865	8871	8876	8882	8887	8893	8899	8904	8910	8915
78	8921	8927	8932	8938	8943	8949	8954	8960	8965	8971
79	8976	8982	8987	8993	8998	9004	9009	9015	9020	9025
80	9031	9036	9042	9047	9053	9058	9063	9069	9074	9079
81	9085	9090	9096	9101	9106	9112	9117	9122	9128	9133
82	9138	9143	9149	9154	9159	9165	9170	9175	9180	9186
83	9191	9196	9201	9206	9212	9217	9222	9227	9232	9238
84	9243	9248	9253	9258	9263	9269	9274	9279	9284	9289
85	9294	9299	9304	9309	9315	9320	9325	9330	9335	9340
86	9345	9350	9355	9360	9365	9370	9375	9380	9385	9390
87	9395	9400	9405	9410	9415	9420	9425	9430	9435	9440
88	9445	9450	9455	9460	9465	9469	9474	9479	9484	9489
89	9494	9499	9504	9509	9513	9518	9523	9528	9533	9538
90	9542	9547	9552	9557	9562	9566	9571	9676	9581	9586
91	9590	9595	9600	9605	9609	9614	9619	9624	9628	9633
92	9638	9643	9647	9652	9657	9661	9666	9671	9675	9680
93	9685	9689	9694	9699	9703	9708	9713	9717	9722	9727
94	9731	9736	9741	9745	9750	9754	9859	9763	9768	9773
95	9777	9782	9786	9791	9795	9800	9805	9809	9814	9818
96	9823	9827	9832	9836	9841	9845	9850	9854	9859	9863
97	9868	9872	9877	9881	9886	9890	9894	9899	9903	9908
98	9912	9917	9921	9926	9930	9934	9939	9943	9948	9952
99	9956	9961	9965	9969	9974	9978	9983	9987	9991	9996
N	0	1	2	3	4	5	6	7	8	9

Table II
Trigonometric Functions

	sin	cos	tan	cot	sec	csc	
0°	.0000	1.0000	.0000	......	1.000	......	90°
1°	.0175	.9998	.0175	57.29	1.000	57.30	89°
2°	.0349	.9994	.0349	28.64	1.001	28.65	88°
3°	.0523	.9986	.0524	19.08	1.001	19.11	87°
4°	.0698	.9976	.0699	14.30	1.002	14.34	86°
5°	.0872	.9962	.0875	11.43	1.004	11.47	85°
6°	.1045	.9945	.1051	9.514	1.006	9.567	84°
7°	.1219	.9925	.1228	8.144	1.008	8.206	83°
8°	.1392	.9903	.1405	7.115	1.010	7.185	82°
9°	.1564	.9877	.1584	6.314	1.012	6.392	81°
10°	.1736	.9848	.1763	5.671	1.015	5.759	80°
11°	.1908	.9816	.1944	5.145	1.019	5.241	79°
12°	.2079	.9781	.2126	4.705	1.022	4.810	78°
13°	.2250	.9744	.2309	4.331	1.026	4.445	77°
14°	.2419	.9703	.2493	4.011	1.031	4.134	76°
15°	.2588	.9659	.2679	3.732	1.035	3.864	75°
16°	.2756	.9613	.2867	3.487	1.040	3.628	74°
17°	.2924	.9563	.3057	3.271	1.046	3.420	73°
18°	.3090	.9511	.3249	3.078	1.051	3.236	72°
19°	.3256	.9455	.3443	2.904	1.058	3.072	71°
20°	.3420	.9397	.3640	2.747	1.064	2.924	70°
21°	.3584	.9336	.3839	2.605	1.071	2.790	69°
22°	.3746	.9272	.4040	2.475	1.079	2.669	68°
23°	.3907	.9205	.4245	2.356	1.086	2.559	67°
24°	.4067	.9135	.4452	2.246	1.095	2.459	66°
25°	.4226	.9063	.4663	2.145	1.103	2.366	65°
26°	.4384	.8988	.4877	2.050	1.113	2.281	64°
27°	.4540	.8910	.5095	1.963	1.122	2.203	63°
28°	.4695	.8829	.5317	1.881	1.133	2.130	62°
29°	.4848	.8746	.5543	1.804	1.143	2.063	61°
30°	.5000	.8660	.5774	1.732	1.155	2.000	60°
31°	.5150	.8572	.6009	1.664	1.167	1.942	59°
32°	.5299	.8480	.6249	1.600	1.179	1.887	58°
33°	.5446	.8387	.6494	1.540	1.192	1.836	57°
34°	.5592	.8290	.6745	1.483	1.206	1.788	56°
35°	.5736	.8192	.7002	1.428	1.221	1.743	55°
36°	.5878	.8090	.7265	1.376	1.236	1.701	54°
37°	.6018	.7986	.7536	1.327	1.252	1.662	53°
38°	.6157	.7880	.7813	1.280	1.269	1.624	52°
39°	.6293	.7771	.8098	1.235	1.287	1.589	51°
40°	.6428	.7660	.8391	1.192	1.305	1.556	50°
41°	.6561	.7547	.8693	1.150	1.325	1.524	49°
42°	.6691	.7431	.9004	1.111	1.346	1.494	48°
43°	.6820	.7314	.9325	1.072	1.367	1.466	47°
44°	.6947	.7193	.9657	1.036	1.390	1.440	46°
45°	.7071	.7071	1.000	1.000	1.414	1.414	45°
	cos	sin	cot	tan	csc	sec	

Answers to Odd-numbered Problems

Section 3

1. 45 cents. **3.** Less. **5.** The second. In successive six-month intervals the first receives 900, 900, 1000, 1000, 1100, 1100, ... while the second receives, 900, 950, 1000, 1050, 1100, 1150, ... dollars.

Section 4

1. (*a*) Must be true. (*b*) May be true or false. (*c*) May be true or false. (*d*) Must be false. **3.** (*a*) Valid. (*b*) Must be false. **5.** (*a*) Valid. (*b*) Valid. (*c*) No. **7.** (*a*) Valid. (*b*) Various theologians and philosophers differ as to the truth of (1). Whether (2) is true or false is a question involving difficulties concerning historical evidence. Might Socrates be a fictional character invented by Plato? **9.** (*a*) Not valid. Although your opinion as to the truth of some of the statements may well be altered. **11.** (*a*) All not valid. **13.** (*a*) (2) is valid. Others not valid. **15.** (*a*) Invalid. **17.** (*a*) (1) Valid. Others not valid. **19.** Valid.

Section 5

1. All not valid. **3.** (*d*) is valid. Others not valid. **5.** (2) and (4) are valid. Others not valid. **7.** (*a*) (4), (5); (*b*) (3); (*c*) (2). **9.** Not valid. **11.** Not valid. **13.** Not valid. **15.** Sufficient. Not necessary. **17.** Both.

Section 11

1. (*a*) $\{x, y, z, w, v, r\}$ (*b*) $\{x, w\}$.
3. (*a*) The set consisting of all black chessmen together with the two white knights. (*b*) The set consisting of the two black knights.
5. (*a*) $\{a, b, c\}$, $\{a, b\}$, $\{a, c\}$, $\{b, c\}$, $\{a\}$, $\{b\}$, $\{c\}$, $\varnothing$. (*b*) All in (*a*) except the first listed. (*c*) $\{(a, a), (a, b), (a, c), (b, a), (b, b), (b, c), (c, a)\ (c, b), (c, c)\}$. **7.** (*a*) $P \cup Q$. (*b*) $P \cap Q$. **9.** (*a*) $\{2, 3, 4, 6, 8, 9, 10\}$. (*b*) $\{6\}$. (*c*) yes. (*d*) yes.

Section 12

1. None. **3.** Symmetric. **5.** Transitive. **7.** None. **9.** If x is west of y means that x can be reached by proceeding in a westerly direction from y, then the relation is reflexive, symmetric, and transitive. If x is west of y means that the shortest route from y to x is in a westerly direction, then it is none of them. **11.** Symmetric. **13.** All. Equivalence. **15.** Reflexive, symmetric. **17.** All. Equivalence. **19.** The class of 1965 of Yale College, for example.

Section 15

1. (*a*) Commutative law for addition of natural numbers. (*b*) Associative law for addition of natural numbers. (*c*) Commutative law for addition of natural numbers. (*d*) Associative law for addition of natural numbers. (*e*) Law of Closure for addition of natural numbers.

Section 16

1. (*a*) M_2. (*b*) M_3. (*c*) D. (*d*) D. (*e*) M_2. (*f*) M_3. (*g*) D. (*h*) D. **3.** (*a*) 10. (*b*) 14. (*c*) 17. (*d*) 20. (*e*) 16. (*f*) 20. (*g*) 56. (*h*) 28. (*i*) 226.

Section 18

1. $2 \cdot 5 = 10$. **3.** (*b*), (*c*), (*d*), (*e*). **5.** (*b*) a is greater than b; (*d*) a is a multiple of b.

Section 19

1. (*a*) yes. (*b*) yes. (*c*) yes. (*d*) yes. (*e*) no. (*f*) no.

Section 20

1. (*a*) $\frac{8}{21}$. (*b*) $\frac{7}{6}$. (*c*) 1. (*d*) 1. (*e*) 2. (*f*) $\frac{1}{3}$. (*g*) 1. (*h*) 1.

Section 21

1. (*a*) $\frac{25}{12}$. (*b*) $\frac{7}{12}$. (*c*) Impossible. (*d*) Impossible. (*e*) $\frac{9}{4}$. (*f*) $\frac{9}{4}$. **5.** Less than.

Section 22

1. (*a*) 26. (*b*) 1. (*c*) $1 + 3x$. (*d*) $\frac{5}{11}$. (*e*) 5. (*f*) $(ad + bc)/(ad - bc)$. (*g*) $\frac{4}{19}$. (*h*) $(b + a)/(ab - 1)$. (*i*) $(rv - su)/(sv + ru)$.

Section 24

1. 3. **3.** -3. **5.** -3. **7.** -10. **9.** 10. **11.** 4.

Section 25

1. No. If $a = -3$, for example, then $-a = +3$. **3.** -1. **5.** $-\frac{7}{6}$. **7.** $-\frac{2}{9}$. **9.** $-\frac{1}{2}$. **11.** $\frac{1}{2}$. **13.** -3. **15.** -9. **17.** $\frac{5}{6}$. **21.** (*a*) $-a + b$. (*b*) $a - b$.

Section 26

1. All except for division by 0 in (*d*). **3.** (*a*), (*c*)

Section 27

1. (*a*) 3. (*b*) 2. (*c*) 7. (*d*) 2. (*e*) 2. (*f*) 3. **3.** $a^2 + 2ab + b^2 = (a + b)^2$. **5.** $(a - b)^2 = a^2 - 2ab + b^2$. **7.** No, except when $x = y$ or $y = 0$. **9.** $\frac{1}{2}$. **11.** $\frac{1}{2}$. **13.** x^2. **15.** 18. **17.** 20. **19.** 38. **21.** 144. **23.** $8x$. **25.** $5x$.

Section 29

1. $q = 3$, $r = 1$. **3.** $q = 3$, $r = 3$. **5.** $q = 5$, $r = 2$. **7.** $q = 5$, $r = 0$. **9.** $q = -3$, $r = 2$.
11. $q = -5$, $r = 2$.

Section 31

1. (*a*) Between 1.732 and 1.733. (*b*) 1.73. **3.** (*a*) Between 1.259 and 1.260. (*b*) 1.26.
5. (*a*) Between 1.709 and 1.710. (*b*) 1.71. **11.** *c*, *b*, *a*, *d*.

Section 33

1. (*a*) $6 - 2i$. (*b*) $-2 - 3i$. (*c*) $-8 + 6i$. (*d*) $-1 + 5i$. (*e*) $\frac{2}{13} - \frac{3}{13}i$. (*f*) $\frac{2}{25} + \frac{11}{25}i$.
13. (*a*) Complex, imaginary. (*b*) Complex, real, rational, integral, positive, natural. (*c*) Complex, imaginary, pure imaginary. (*d*) Complex, real, irrational, positive. (*e*) Complex, real, irrational, positive. (*f*) Complex, real, rational, negative. (*g*) Complex, real, irrational, positive. (*h*) Complex, real, rational, integral, positive, natural.

Section 35

1. (*a*) Algebraic, irrational. (*b*) 4. **3.** (*a*) Algebraic, rational, polynomial. (*b*) $\frac{9}{2} + \sqrt{3}$.
5. (*a*) Algebraic, rational, polynomial. (*b*) 3. **7.** (*a*) Algebraic, rational. (*b*) $\frac{3}{10}$. **9.** (*a*) Algebraic, rational, polynomial. (*b*) 59. **11.** (*a*) Algebraic, rational (*b*) $\frac{1}{9}$. **13.** Rational. **15.** No.

Section 36

1. $7x^2 + 9x + 5$. **3.** $4x^3 + 4x^2 + 7x + 7$. **5.** $x^2 + 2xy + y^2$. **7.** $x^2 - 2xy + y^2$. **9.** $x^2 + \frac{b}{a}x + \frac{b^2}{4a^2}$.
11. $5x + 4xy - 3y^2$. **13.** $x^3 + y^3$.

Section 37

1. $2x(2x^2 + y + y^2)$. **3.** $(x + 4)(x - 4)$. **5.** $(x - 3)(x - 4)$.
7. $(4x + 3)(x - 2)$. **9.** $x(2x - 1)(x + 3)$. **11.** $(y + k)(y + k)$.
13. $(2ax + b)(2ax + b)$. **15.** $(x + y + 1)(x - y + 3)$. **17.** $(x + 6)(x + 5)$.
19. $(x + y - 6)(x + y + 2)$.

Section 38

9. 3. **11.** 2. **13.** Conditional. **15.** Conditional. **17.** Identity. **19.** Identity.

Section 39

1. -4. **3.** $\frac{7}{2}$. **5.** 1. **7.** 12. **9.** No solution.

Section 40

1. 3, -4. **3.** 7, -2. **5.** 2, $-\frac{9}{2}$. **7.** ± 4. **9.** $\pm\frac{1}{2}$. **11.** 0.

Section 41

1. 7. **3.** 4. **5.** 4, 20. **7.** No root. **9.** 2. **11.** -2. Note that $+2$ is extraneous. **13.** 25.
15. No root. **17.** $-\frac{1}{2}$. **19.** -6.

Section 42

1. 2, $\frac{3}{2}$; real, rational. **3.** $2 \pm \sqrt{3}$; real, irrational. **5.** $\pm\sqrt{-9}$ or $\pm 3i$; imaginary. **7.** 5, $-\frac{4}{3}$; real, rational. **9.** $-3 \pm \sqrt{17}$; real, irrational, **11.** $(-\sqrt{5} \pm 1)/2$; real, irrational. **13.** $2i$, $2i$; imaginary. **15.** $\sqrt{2}/2$, $\sqrt{2}/2$; real, irrational.

Section 45

1. $x = 3$, $y = 2$. **3.** $x = -3$, $y = -2$. **5.** $x = \frac{1}{2}$, $y = \frac{3}{2}$. **7.** $x = \frac{9}{13}$, $y = \frac{7}{13}$. **9.** $x = \frac{21}{17}$, $y = \frac{11}{17}$. **11.** Inconsistent. **13.** $x = (ce - bf)/(ae - bd)$, $y = (af - cd)/(ae - bd)$.

Section 46

1. $x = 5$, $y = 0$; $x = 3$, $y = 4$. **3.** $x = 3$, $y = 2$; $x = \frac{1}{5}$, $y = -\frac{18}{5}$. **5.** $x = -\frac{13}{3}$, $y = -4$; $x = -\frac{11}{9}$, $y = \frac{2}{3}$. **7.** $x = 3$, $y = 4$; $x = 4$, $y = 3$. **9.** $x = 3$, $y = 4$; $x = -3$, $y = -4$. **11.** $x = 3$, $y = 2$; $x = \frac{21}{4}$, $y = -\frac{19}{4}$.

Section 47

1. 16 yd., 12 yd. **3.** 96. **5.** 2. **7.** $3\frac{3}{4}$ days. **9.** 8 days. **11.** 40 ft., 10 ft. **13.** *A*, 10 days; *B*, 15 days. **15.** 40 ft., 10 ft. **17.** 2 hrs., 100 mi. **19.** $5\frac{5}{8}$ gals. **21.** 50 cts. per doz.

Section 50

1. (*a*) 24. (*b*) 44. (*c*) 26. (*d*) 30. (*e*) 33. (*f*) 40. (*g*) 120. (*h*) 220. (*i*) 11000. **3.** (*a*) 32. (*b*) 112. (*c*) 35. (*d*) 40. (*e*) 44. (*f*) 52. (*g*) 200. (*h*) 1012. (*i*) 100000. **5.** (*a*) 8. (*b*) 13. (*c*) 8. (*d*) 10. (*e*) 11. (*f*) 12. (*g*) 20. (*h*) 22. (*i*) 1000. **7.** (*a*) 62. (*b*) 146. (*c*) 26. (*d*) 222. **9.** (*a*) $2 + 10 = 12$. (*b*) $10 + 101 = 111$. (*c*) $2 + 12 = 21$. (*d*) $2 + 5 = 10$. (*e*) $2 + 5 = 7$. **15.** (*a*) 54. (*b*) 41. (*c*) *t*0. (*d*) *te*. (*e*) 11*e*. **17.** (*a*) 100101. (*b*) 111. (*c*) 1111. (*d*) 111001. (*e*) 1101111. **19.** 10000. **21.** 10101. **23.** 1000001. **25.** 110. **27.** 101. **29.** $x = 7$, $y = 5$. **31.** 8.

Section 52

1. a^6. **3.** a^4/b^3. **5.** a^2/b. **7.** 64. **9.** 24. **11.** 22. **13.** 54. **15.** 324. **17.** 72. **19.** 36. **21.** 3^5. **23.** 3^8. **25.** Correct.

Section 53

1. $\frac{1}{16}$. **3.** 8. **5.** 1. **7.** $\frac{1}{36}$. **9.** 1. **11.** 1. **13.** $\frac{2}{5}$. **15.** $3/x^2$. **17.** 4. **19.** $3b^2/a^3$. **21.** $(b + a)/(b - a)$. **23.** x^5/y^5.

Section 54

1. 3×10^5. **3.** 3.67×10^{11}. **5.** 5.6×10^{-2}.
7. 3×10^0. **9.** 100,000. **11.** 67,800,000.
13. 6.78. **15.** 468,000. **17.** 90.
19. 5×10^{14}. **21.** 220. **23.** 1.316385×10^{25} lbs.
25. 1.6×10^{-19}.

Section 55

1. 4. **3.** 2. **5.** $\frac{1}{4}$. **7.** $\frac{1}{4}$. **9.** $\frac{1}{64}$. **11.** $\frac{1}{243}$. **13.** $\frac{1}{3}$. **15.** $\sqrt[28]{x^{41}}$. **17.** $\sqrt[15]{x}$.

Section 56

1. $\log_5 25 = 2$. **3.** $\log_{10} 100 = 2$. **5.** $\log_8 2 = \frac{1}{3}$. **7.** $\log_5 (\frac{1}{25}) = -2$. **9.** $\log_7 1 = 0$. **11.** $2^4 = 16$. **13.** $10^{-2} = .01$. **15.** $10^0 = 1$. **17.** $5^3 = 125$. **19.** $10^{-1} = .1$. **21.** 5. **23.** $\frac{2}{3}$. **25.** 1. **27.** 0. **29.** $\frac{3}{2}$. **31.** 4. **33.** 5. **35.** .7781. **37.** .1761. **39.** 1.0791. **41.** −.6990. **43.** .6990.

Section 57

1. 2.0934. **3.** 8.0934–10. **5.** 1.5977. **7.** 8.6385–10. **9.** 6.5391–10. **11.** 2.5563. **13.** 7.6990–10. **15.** 33.2. **17.** .332. **19.** 49.8. **21.** .545. **23.** 9370. **25.** $10^{2.9355} = 862$; $\sqrt[10000]{10^{29355}} = 862$.

Section 58

1. 1.72. **3.** 2.59. **5.** .783. **7.** 40.7. **9.** 1280. **11.** .205.

Section 59

1. \$184. **3.** \$5,230,000. **5.** 197,000,000 sq. mi. **7.** 18 yrs. **9.** 2 sec. **11.** (*a*) \$328. (*b*) \$107. **13.** 35 yrs.

Section 62

1. 8. **3.** $\log_2 10 = 3.32$ approx.

Section 64

3. (*a*) PS. (*b*) QR. (*c*) PQ including Q. (*d*) RS including R. (*e*) $\varnothing$. (*f*) PS.

Section 66

1. (*a*) 1. (*b*) 1. (*c*) 1. (*d*) 1. (*e*) 1. (*f*) 0.

Section 67

1. Thinking is hard work and I was a fool to take this course. **3.** Thinking is not hard work and I was not a fool to take this course. **5.** Thinking is hard work and I was not a fool to take this course.

7.

p	$\sim p$	$p \vee (\sim p)$
T	F	T
F	T	T

9.

p	q	$\sim q$	$p \vee (\sim q)$
T	T	F	F
T	F	T	T
F	T	F	F
F	F	T	F

11.

p	q	$\sim q$	$(p \wedge q)$	$p \wedge (\sim q)$	$(p \wedge q) \vee (p \wedge (\sim q))$
T	T	F	T	F	T
T	F	T	F	T	T
F	T	F	F	F	F
F	F	T	F	F	F

25. $P \cup Q = Q \cup P$. **27.** $P \subset (P \cup Q)$. **29.** $P \cup P' = I$. **31.** $P \cap (Q \cup R) = (P \cap Q) \cup (P \cap R)$

Section 68

1. (*a*) (1) $a + (b + c)$; (2) $(a + b) + c$. (*b*) Associative law for addition.
3. (*a*) (1) $a + bc$; (2) $(a + b)(a + c)$. (*b*) Dual distributive law.

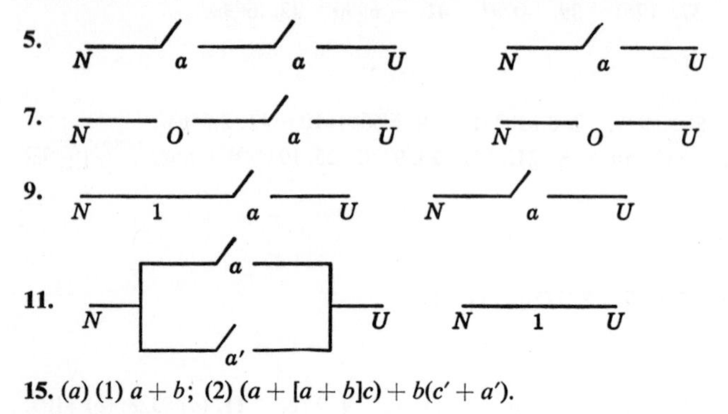

15. (*a*) (1) $a + b$; (2) $(a + [a + b]c) + b(c' + a')$.

Section 69

1. 10. **3.** 26. **5.** (*a*) 55. (*b*) 45. **7.** 10. **9.** 2 square feet.

Section 70

1. Minimal winning coalitions: $\{a,b,c\}$, $\{a,d\}$, $\{b,d\}$, $\{c,d\}$. Other winning coalitions: $\{a,b,c,d\}$, $\{a,b,d\}$, $\{a,c,d\}$, $\{b,c,d\}$, **3.** Exactly as in exercise 1. **7.** Minimal winning coalitions: the "Big Five" together with any 2 other nations. Blocking coalitions: any coalition of 5 or 6 nations; also any coalition to which at least one but not all the "Big Five" belongs (because of the veto).

Section 71

1. 15. **3.** (*a*) 380. (*b*) 400. **5.** 24. **7.** (*a*) 36. (*b*) 216. **9.** (*a*) 20. (*b*) 25.

Section 72

1. 720. **3.** 72. **5.** 72. **7.** 120. **9.** 60. **11.** 120. **13.** (*a*) 604,800, (*b*) 10,000,000. **15.** 6840. **17.** (*a*) 48. (*b*) 72. **19.** 576.

Section 73

1. 10. **3.** 190. **5.** 120. **7.** 35. **9.** 350. **11.** (*a*) 112. (*b*) 196. **13.** (*a*) 45. (*b*) 9. **15.** 403,200. **17.** (*a*) 3003. (*b*) 1001. (*c*) 2002. **19.** 15. **21.** 3024. **23.** 21.

Section 74

1. $x^7 + 7x^6h + 21x^5h^2 + 35x^4h^3 + 35x^3h^4 + 21x^2h^5 + 7xh^6 + h^7$. **3.** $p^9 + 9p^8q + 36p^7q^2 + 84p^6q^3 + 126p^5q^4 + 126p^4q^5 + 84p^3q^6 + 36p^2q^7 + 9pq^8 + q^9$. **5.** $32a^{15} + 240a^{12}b^2 + 720a^9b^4 + 1080a^6b^6 + 810a^3b^8 + 243b^{10}$. **7.** $a^3 - 3a^2b + 3ab^2 - b^3$. **9.** $a^5 - 5a^4b + 10a^3b^2 - 10a^2b^3 + 5ab^4 - b^5$. **11.** $\frac{9}{4}$. **13.** $\frac{625}{256}$. **15.** $680x^{14}h^3$. **17.** $3003x^{10}h^5$. **19.** $(15/2)a^{14}b^6$. **21.** $70a^4b^4$. **23.** $84b^3/a^6$. **25.** (*a*) 1.094. (*b*) .942. (*c*) 1.242. (*d*) .868.

Section 79

1. 15. **3** 12. **5.** 1.

Section 80

3. $2 \cdot 5 \cdot 11$. **5.** $2^4 \cdot 3^2 \cdot 5$. **7.** $3^3 \cdot 19$. **9.** $7^2 \cdot 11$.

Section 81

5. (*a*)

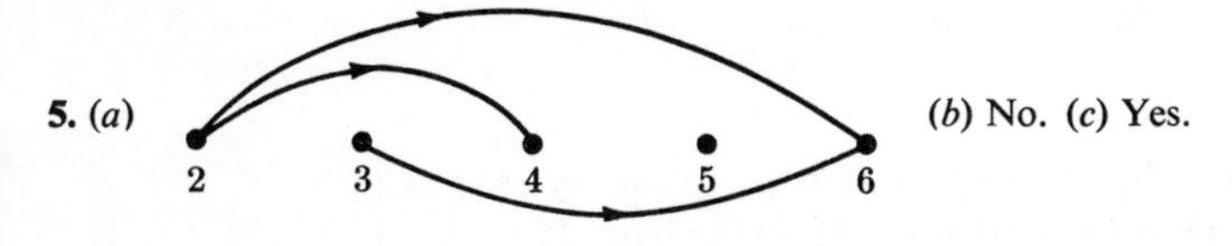

(*b*) No. (*c*) Yes.

Section 87

1. (*a*) 2. (*b*) 6. **3.** (*a*) 4. (*b*) -5. **5.** (*a*) 10. (*b*) 2. **7.** (*a*) 8. (*b*) 4. **9.** (*a*) 3. (*b*) $\frac{7}{2}$. **11.** 7
13. (*a*) $\frac{60}{7}$. (*b*) 70 lbs.

Section 88

5. 0. **7.** Equal. **9.** $(3, -3)$, $(-3, -3)$, $(-3, 3)$.

Section 90

1. 13. **3.** 4. **5.** 10. **7.** 4. **13.** (*b*) 5. (*c*) No. (*d*) No. (*e*) Yes. **15.** $(0, -3)$.

Section 91

1. (3,4). **3.** (*a*) $7, \frac{1}{2}\sqrt{85}, \frac{1}{2}\sqrt{85}$; (*c*) $\sqrt{26}, \frac{1}{2}\sqrt{221}, \frac{1}{2}\sqrt{65}$. **5.** $(-5, -1)$. **7.** $\left(\frac{a+c}{2}, \frac{b+d}{2}\right)$.

Section 92

3. (*a*) $-\frac{1}{5}, -\frac{7}{9}, 5$. (*b*) $\frac{3}{2}, \frac{4}{7}, -\frac{2}{3}$. (*c*) $-\frac{5}{12}$, 0, does not exist. (*d*) $0, \frac{7}{2}, -\frac{7}{2}$.

Section 94

1. (*a*) Yes. (*b*) No. (*c*) Yes. **15.** $y = -3$. **17.** $x = y$. **19.** $y = 2x$.

Section 95

1. $2x - y = 9$. **3.** $y = 2$. **5.** $y = x + 1$. **7.** $x = 2$. **9.** $y = 3x + 4$. **11.** $y = -x$. **13.** -1.
15. $m = \frac{3}{2}, p = \frac{1}{2}$.

Section 96

1. $\frac{2}{3}$. **3.** No slope. **5.** $-\frac{1}{2}$. **7.** $y = 0$; $x = 0$. **9.** $2x + y = 8$. **11.** (*a*) $y = 4x + 8$; $3y = x + 2$; $3x + 2y = 16$. (*b*) $3y = 2x + 4$; $x + 4y = 12$; $3x + y = 8$. (*c*) $4y = 5x + 10$; $7x + y = 8$; $2x + 5y = 18$. (*d*) $x + 4y = 15$; $y + 3x = 4$; $3y = 2x + 11$. **13.** $x + y = 5$; no; yes.
15. $x^2 + y^2 = 25$; yes; no.

Section 97

1. $(x + 1)^2 + (y - 3)^2 = 16$. **3.** $x^2 + y^2 = 4$. **5.** $(x + 2)^2 + y^2 = 4$. **7.** $(x + 2)^2 + (y + 3)^2 = 169$. **9.** $(2, -5)$; 4. **11.** (1,0); 3. **13.** (3,1); 2. **15.** $x^2 + y^2 = 25$; yes; yes. **17.** $x^2 + y^2 = 25$; yes; yes.

Section 98

7. $y^2 = 8x$. **9.** $9x^2 - 16y^2 = 144$.

Section 99

1. $x = y$. **3.** $4y - 4x = 15$.

Section 100

1. $(-1, -2)$. **3.** $(\frac{23}{17}, -\frac{1}{17})$. **5.** $(1,2)$. **7.** $(3,4)$, $(-3, -4)$. **9.** $(4,5)$, $(5,4)$.
11. $(1,1)$, $(\frac{9}{16}, -\frac{3}{4})$. **12.** No intersections. **13.** $(0,1)$, $(3,4)$. **15.** $(-3,2)$, $(-1,-2)$.
17. $(-3,-2)$, $(-1,2)$. **21.** (*a*) $(3,0)$, $(4,2)$, $(1,2)$. (*b*) $2y = x$; $2x + 5y = 12$; $4x + y = 12$. (*c*) $(\frac{8}{3},\frac{4}{3})$. **23.** (*a*) $x = 3$, $x = y + 2$, $x + 2y = 5$.

Section 102

1. $x = 3$, $y = 2$, $Q = 5$. **3.** $x = 2$, $y = 3$, $K = 14$. **5.** $x = 2$, $y = 2$, $C = 10$. **7.** $x = 8$, $y = 0$, $C = 8$. **9.** $x = 2$, $y = 6$.

11.

	S_1	S_2	S_3
W_1	0	7	3
W_2	5	0	1, min. cost = \$73.

Section 108

1. All real numbers. **3.** All non-negative real numbers. **5.** All real numbers between -3 and 3 inclusive. **7.** All real numbers except $x = 2$.
11. (*a*) 8; (*b*) 64; (*c*) 1; (*d*) 2; (*e*) $\frac{1}{4}$; (*f*) $\frac{1}{64}$.
13. (*c*) No. **15.** $2x + h$. **17.** $6x + 3h + 5$.
19. $-4 - 4x - 2h$.

Section 109

7. (*a*) $A = 20x - x^2$. **9.** (*a*) $A = 2x^2 + 256x^{-1}$. **11.** (*a*) $V = 84x^2 - 4x^3$.

Section 110

1. (*a*) 80 ft. per sec. (*b*) 112 ft. per sec. (*c*) 48 ft. per sec. (*d*) 64 ft. per sec.

Section 111

1. (*a*) 9.5. (*b*) 9.3. (*c*) 9.5. (*d*) 3.5. (*e*) 2. **3.** (*a*) 1.1804. (*b*) 1.1796. (*c*) 1.1797. (*d*) 1.1811.
5. (*a*) 49.25. (*b*) 492.25. (*c*) 492.75. **7.** \$227.53.

Section 112

1. (*a*) $y = 3x$. (*b*) 18. (*c*) y is tripled. **3.** (*a*) $r = v^2/6$. (*b*) 41,667 ft. (*c*) 600 ft. per sec.
5. 400 ft. **7.** 95.2 lbs. **13.** 2670 degrees. **15.** (*a*) 50. (*b*) 27.8.

Section 113

7. 3; between 1.4 and 1.5; between -1.4 and -1.5. **9.** Between -2.6 and -2.7. **11.** Between 1.2 and 1.3. **13.** Between 1.2 and 1.3.

Section 117

1. 3; 3. **5.** x has minimum element 1.

Section 118

1. 2.1, 2.01, 2.001, 2.0001, 2.00001. **3.** $\frac{1}{2}, \frac{3}{4}, \frac{7}{8}, \frac{15}{16}, \frac{31}{32}$. **5.** $-\frac{1}{2}, \frac{1}{4}, -\frac{1}{8}, \frac{1}{16}, -\frac{1}{32}$. **7.** $1, \frac{1}{2}, \frac{1}{3}, \frac{1}{4}, \frac{1}{5}$. **9.** $\frac{3}{2}, \frac{5}{4}, \frac{9}{8}, \frac{17}{16}, \frac{33}{32}$.

Section 119

1. 2. **3.** 1. **5.** 0. **7.** 0. **9.** 1.

Section 120

1. 1. **3.** 0. **5.** $3x^2$. **7.** $2x$. **9.** $8x + 3$. **11.** $-1/x^2$. **13.** $2/x^3$. **15.** $2ax + b$.

Section 123

1. (*a*) $6x$. (*b*) 12. (*c*) $y = 12x - 12$. **3.** (*a*) x. (*b*) 2. (*c*) $y = 2x - 2$. **5.** (*a*) $4x$. (*b*) 8. (*c*) $y = 8x - 3$. **7.** (*a*) $4x - 3$. (*b*) 5. (*c*) $y = 5x - 3$. **9.**(*a*) $-2/x^3$. (*b*) $-\frac{1}{4}$. (*c*) $x + 4y = 3$. **11.** (*a*) 2. (*b*) 2. (*c*) $y = 2x + 3$. **13.** (*a*) 1. (*b*) 1. (*c*) $y = x$. **15.** (*a*) $(-2)/(x-1)^3$. (*b*) -2. (*c*) $y = -2x + 5$. **17.** (*a*) $2cx + k$.

Section 124

1. (*a*) 64, 32, 0, -32 ft. per sec. (*b*) -32 ft. per sec. per sec. **3.** (*a*) $v = 100 - 20t$; $a = -20$. (*b*) 0, -100, -200 ft. per sec. **5.** $2\pi r$.

Section 125

1. $12x^2 + 12x$. **3.** $2x - 5$. **5.** $20x^3 + 6x^2 - 6x - 4$. **7.** $6x^2 - 6/x^4$. **9.** $2 - 8/x^3$. **11.** (*a*) 3. (*b*) $y = 3x - 2$. **13.** (*a*) 0. (*b*) $y = 2$. **15.** (*a*) 6. (*b*) $y = 6x + 18$. **17.** (*a*) -3. (*b*) $3x + y + 12 = 0$. **19.** (*a*) $\frac{1}{4}$. (*b*) $4y = x + 3$. **21.** 3, -2. **23.** (*a*) $6x^5$. (*b*) $2x$. (*c*) $4x^3$. (*d*) No. **25.** (*a*) $3x^2$. (*b*) $12x$.

Section 126

1. (3, -7) min. **3.** (2, 7) max. **5.** (-1, 1) max.; (4, -124) min. **7.** None.

Section 127

1. 25 ft. by 25 ft.; 625 sq. ft. **3.** 3 sec.; 144 ft. **5.** 4 ft. by 4 ft. by 4 ft. **7.** 6 sec.; 582 ft. **9.** 24 cm. by 32 cm. **11.** 20 in. by 10 in. by $\frac{20}{3}$ in.; $\frac{4000}{3}$ cu. in. **13.** \$3.00; \$9000.

Section 129

1. $\dfrac{x^2}{2} + 3x + C$. **3.** $5x + C$. **5.** $9x - 2x^3 + C$. **7.** $\dfrac{ax^2}{2} + bx + C$. **9.** $96t - 16t^2 + C$.

Section 130

1. $y = 3x + 1$. **3.** $y = x^2 - 4$. **5.** $y = x^2 - 3x + 5$. **7.** 80 ft. per sec. **9.** 80 ft. per sec.

Section 132

1. 34 $\frac{1}{2}$ square units. **3.** 10 $\frac{1}{2}$ square units. **5.** 21 square units.

Section 133

1. $98\pi/3$. **3.** 32π. **5.** $\pi/7$. **7.** $4\pi ab^2/3$. **9.** 21π. **11.** $625\pi/16$. **13.** 24π.

Section 134

1. .7833.

Section 137

1. $\pi/2$. **3.** $\pi/3$. **5.** $\pi/18$. **7.** $2\pi/3$. **9.** $\pi/10$. **11.** 180°. **13.** 30°. **15.** $\left(\frac{270}{\pi}\right)^\circ$ or 85.94°. **17.** $\left(\frac{90}{\pi}\right)^\circ$ or 28.65°. **19.** 54°.

Section 139

Where all six functions are required, they are given in the order sin, cos, tan, csc, sec, cot. **1.** $\frac{3}{5}, \frac{4}{5}, \frac{3}{4}, \frac{5}{3}, \frac{5}{4}, \frac{4}{3}$. **3.** $\frac{5}{13}, \frac{12}{13}, \frac{5}{12}, \frac{13}{5}, \frac{13}{12}, \frac{12}{5}$. **5.** $4/\sqrt{41}, 5/\sqrt{41}, \frac{4}{5}, \sqrt{41}/4, \sqrt{41}/5, \frac{5}{4}$. **7.** $\sqrt{3}/\sqrt{19}, 4/\sqrt{19}, \sqrt{3}/4, \sqrt{19}/\sqrt{3}, \sqrt{19}/4, 4/\sqrt{3}$. **9.** $\frac{1}{2}, \sqrt{3}/2, 1/\sqrt{3}, 2, 2/\sqrt{3}, \sqrt{3}$, **11.** 45°. **13.** 60°. **15.** 30°. **17.** $\frac{3}{5}, \frac{4}{5}, \frac{3}{4}, \frac{5}{3}, \frac{5}{4}, \frac{4}{3}$. **19.** $\frac{12}{13}, \frac{5}{13}, \frac{12}{5}, \frac{13}{12}, \frac{13}{5}\ \frac{5}{12}$. **21.** $\sqrt{7}/4, \frac{3}{4}, \sqrt{7}/3, 4/\sqrt{7}, \frac{4}{3}, 3/\sqrt{7}$. **23.** $\frac{4}{5}, \frac{3}{5}, \frac{4}{3}, \frac{5}{4}, \frac{5}{3}, \frac{3}{4}$. **25.** $5/\sqrt{34}, 3/\sqrt{34}, \frac{5}{3}, \sqrt{34}/5, \sqrt{34}/3, \frac{3}{5}$. **27.** $\frac{3}{5}, \frac{4}{5}, \frac{3}{4}, \frac{5}{3}, \frac{5}{4}, \frac{4}{3}$. **29.** $\frac{4}{5}, \frac{3}{5}, \frac{4}{3}, \frac{5}{4}, \frac{5}{3}, \frac{3}{4}$. **31.** $6/\sqrt{61}, 5/\sqrt{61}, \frac{6}{5}, \sqrt{61}/6, \sqrt{61}/5, \frac{5}{6}$. **33.** $2\sqrt{6}/7, \frac{5}{7}, 2\sqrt{6}/5, 7/2\sqrt{6}, \frac{7}{5}, 5/2\sqrt{6}$. **35.** (*a*) $\frac{1}{3}$. (*b*) $2\sqrt{2}/3$. (*c*) $2\sqrt{2}/3$. **37.** .454. **39.** 1.39.

Section 140

1. 105.0 ft. **3.** 46°. **5.** 67.3 ft. **7.** 235.6 ft. **9.** (*a*) 644.2 ft. (*b*) 145.1 ft. **11.** 4770 ft. **13.** 18,480 mi.; 1848 mi. **15.** 238,698 mi. **17.** 66°.

Section 141

1. 125 lbs.; 53° north of east. **3.** $100\sqrt{2}$ lbs. up the plane. **5.** 7.0 m.p.h.; 79.7 m.p.h. **7.** Any force greater than 845.2 lbs., up the ramp. **9.** 39°.

Section 142

1. 370°, 730°, 1090°, −350°, −710°. **3.** 420°, 780°, 1140°, −300°, −660°. **5.** 570°, 930°, 1290°, −150°, −510°.

Section 143

Where all six functions are required, they are given in the order sin, cos, tan, csc, sec, cot. **1.** $\frac{4}{5}, \frac{3}{5}, \frac{4}{3}, \frac{5}{4}, \frac{5}{3}, \frac{3}{4}$. **3.** $-\frac{4}{5}, -\frac{3}{5}, \frac{4}{3}, -\frac{5}{4}, -\frac{5}{3}, \frac{3}{4}$. **5.** $-\frac{3}{5}, \frac{4}{5}, -\frac{3}{4}, -\frac{5}{3}, \frac{5}{4}, -\frac{4}{3}$. **7.** 0, 1, 0, does not exist, 1, does not exist. **9.** $\frac{12}{13}, \frac{5}{13}, \frac{12}{5}, \frac{13}{12}, \frac{13}{5}, \frac{5}{12}$. **11.** $\frac{1}{2}, \sqrt{3}/2, 1/\sqrt{3}, 2, 2/\sqrt{3}, \sqrt{3}$. **13.** $-\sqrt{3}/2, -\frac{1}{2}, \sqrt{3}, -2/\sqrt{3}, -2, 1/\sqrt{3}$. **15.** $\frac{1}{2}, -\sqrt{3}/2, -1/\sqrt{3}, 2, -2/\sqrt{3}, -\sqrt{3}$. **17.** Same as ex. 13. **19.** $\sqrt{3}/2, \frac{1}{2}, \sqrt{3}, 2/\sqrt{3}, 2, 1/\sqrt{3}$. **21.** $1/\sqrt{2}, 1/\sqrt{2}, 1, \sqrt{2}, \sqrt{2}, 1$. **23.** $-1/\sqrt{2}, -1\sqrt{2}, 1, -\sqrt{2}, -\sqrt{2}, 1$. **25.** Same as ex. 21. **27.** −1, 0, does not exist, −1, does not exist, 0. **29.** 0, 1, 0, does not exist, 1, does not exist. **31.** II, III. **33.** III, IV. **35.** II, IV. **37.** $\frac{3}{4}, -\sqrt{7}/4, -3/\sqrt{7}, \frac{4}{3}, -4/\sqrt{7}, -\sqrt{7}/3$. **39.** $-3/\sqrt{34}, -5/\sqrt{34}, \frac{3}{5}, -\sqrt{34}/3, -\sqrt{34}/5, \frac{5}{3}$.

Section 145

Where all six functions are required, they are given in the order sin, cos, tan, csc, sec, cot. **1.** .1736, −.9848, −.1763, 5.759, −1.015, −5.671. **3.** −.1736, .9848, −.1763, −5.759, 1.015, −5.671. **5.** Same as ex. 1. **7.** .2588, .9659, .2679, 3.864, 1.035, 3.732. **9.** −.6018, −.7986, .7536, −1.662, −1.252, 1.327. **11.** −.2588, −.9659, .2679, −3.864, −1.035, 3.732. **15.** 147°. **17.** 120°. **19.** 147°. **21.** 150°. **23.** 110°.

Section 147

1. $C = 65°$, $a = 11.1$ ft., $b = 15.8$ ft. **3.** $B = 29°$, $b = 12.4$ ft., $c = 19.1$ ft. **5.** 83.3 yds. **7.** (*a*) 7160 ft. (*b*) 7439 ft. (*c*) 6847 ft. **9.** 1165 ft.

Section 148

1. $A = 38°$, $B = 22°$, $C = 120°$. **3.** $c = 21$, $A = 38°$, $B = 22°$. **5.** $b = 50.4$, $A = 55°$, $C = 46°$. **7.** $a = 25.6$, $B = 23°$, $C = 34°$. **9.** 35°, 86°, 59°. **11.** 2371 yds. **13.** 70 lbs.; 38° with 30-lb. force; 22° with 50-lb force. **15.** 411 yds.

Section 151

3. $\frac{1}{36}$. **5.** $\frac{1}{2}$; $\frac{3}{4}$; $\frac{1}{4}$; $\frac{1}{4}$. **7.** $\frac{3}{8}$; $\frac{3}{8}$; $\frac{1}{8}$, $\frac{1}{8}$; $\frac{7}{8}$; $\frac{1}{2}$. **9.** $\frac{1}{4}$; $\frac{1}{13}$; $\frac{1}{52}$. **11.** $\frac{13}{24}$; $\frac{11}{24}$; $\frac{7}{24}$.

Section 152

1. (*a*) $\frac{1}{5}$. (*b*) $\frac{3}{10}$. (*c*) $\frac{4}{5}$. **3.** $\frac{1}{12}$. **5.** $\frac{1}{3}$. **7.** (*a*) $\frac{5}{14}$. (*b*) $\frac{9}{14}$. (*c*) $\frac{3}{28}$. **9.** (*a*) $\frac{1}{2}$. (*b*) $\frac{1}{3}$. (*c*) $\frac{2}{3}$. **11.** (*a*) $\frac{13}{24}$. (*b*) $\frac{5}{12}$. (*c*) $\frac{2}{3}$. **13.** (*a*) 50%. (*b*) 60%. (*c*) 90%. **17.** 85%. **19.** (*a*) $\frac{3}{8}$; (*b*) $\frac{5}{8}$; (*c*) $\frac{1}{24}$; (*d*) $\frac{23}{24}$; (*e*) 0.

Section 153

1. $\frac{1}{36}$. **3.** (*a*) $\frac{1}{28561}$. (*b*) $\frac{1}{270725}$. **5.** (*a*) $\frac{3}{11}$. (*b*) $\frac{2}{33}$. **7.** $\frac{625}{3888}$. **9.** (*a*) $\frac{15}{128}$. (*b*) $\frac{121}{128}$. **11.** (*a*) $\frac{125}{3888}$. (*b*) $\frac{69}{1944}$. (*c*) $\frac{3875}{3888}$. **13.** (*a*) $\frac{1}{7776}$. (*b*) $\frac{1}{60466176}$, (*c*) No. **15.** $\frac{1}{3}$. **17.** (*a*) $\frac{53760}{9765625}$ or $\frac{1}{2}$ of 1% approx. (*b*) $\frac{62201}{9765625}$ or $\frac{2}{3}$ of 1% approx. **19.** (*a*) $\frac{1}{2}$. (*b*) $\frac{5}{12}$. (*c*) $\frac{1}{12}$. (*d*) $\frac{1}{2}$. **21.** $\frac{135}{512}$.

Section 155

1. As for illustrative example 2. **3.** *a* has $\frac{1}{2}$, others $\frac{1}{6}$. **5.** *a* has $\frac{1}{2}$, others, $\frac{1}{10}$. **7.** Dictator 1, dummies 0.

Section 156

1. (*a*) 0. (*b*) $\frac{1}{2}$ dollar. **3.** $-\frac{1}{8}$ dollar. **5.** 3 to 1.

Section 157

1. Row 1, column 2, value 0. **3.** Row 3, column 4, value 1. **5.** Each 0:2.

Section 158

1. Optimal mixed strategy for R is $(\frac{2}{3}, \frac{1}{3})$. Optimal mixed strategy for C is $(\frac{2}{3}, \frac{1}{3})$; value $\frac{2}{3}$. **3.** Optimal mixed strategy for R is $(\frac{3}{5}, \frac{2}{5})$. Optimal mixed strategy for C is $(\frac{7}{10}, \frac{3}{10})$; value $-\frac{1}{5}$. **5.** Optimal mixed strategy for R is $(0, \frac{3}{5}, \frac{2}{5})$. Optimal mixed strategy for C is $(\frac{2}{5}, \frac{3}{5}, 0)$; value $\frac{1}{5}$. **7.** Payoff matrix

$$\begin{array}{c c} & \begin{array}{cc} 1 & 3 \end{array} \\ \begin{array}{c} 1 \\ 2 \end{array} & \begin{bmatrix} -2 & -4 \\ 3 & 5 \end{bmatrix}. \end{array}$$

Optimal mixed strategy for R is (0, 1). Optimal mixed strategy for C is (1, 0). Value 3. This is a saddle-value.

Section 163

1. (*a*) 80. (*b*) 81.5. (*c*) 85. (*d*) 85–89. (*e*) 70–79. (*f*) 84. (*g*) 8. (*h*) 9.6 approx. **3.** (*a*) 84. (*b*) 87.5. (*c*) None. (*d*) 85–89. (*e*) 90–100. (*f*) 88.3. (*g*) 10. (*h*) 11.6 approx.

Section 164

1. 1. **3.** .75.

Section 169

13. $x_1 = 5 - 2a$, $x_2 = a$. **15.** $x_1 = -1$, $x_2 = -3$, $x_3 = 2$. **17.** Inconsistent. **19.** $x_1 = 5$, $x_2 = 2$. **21.** Inconsistent. **23.** $x_1 = 2 - 3a$, $x_2 = 4 + 7a$, $x_3 = a$. **25.** $x_1 = 0$, $x_2 = 0$, $x_3 = 0$. **27.** $x_1 = 7 - 4a - 2b$, $x_2 = -3 + 3a + b$, $x_3 = a$, $x_4 = b$. **29.** $x_1 = 1$, $x_2 = -1$, $x_3 = 2$, $x_4 = \frac{1}{3}$.

Section 170

1. [5, 4]. **3.** [6, 10]. **5.** [3, 2, 2]. **7.** [0, 7, −9]. **9.** $x = 2$, $y = -1$, $z = 3$. **11.** $x = 2$, $y = -1$, $z = -1$.

Section 171

1. (*b*) $X^{(1)} = \frac{2}{3}X^{(2)} + \frac{1}{3}X^{(3)}$; $X^{(2)} = \frac{3}{2}X^{(1)} - \frac{1}{2}X^{(3)}$; $X^{(3)} = 3X^{(1)} - 2X^{(2)}$.
3. (*b*) $X^{(1)} = \frac{2}{3}X^{(2)} + 0X^{(3)}$; $X^{(2)} = \frac{3}{2}X^{(1)} + 0X^{(3)}$.

Section 172

9. 2. **11.** 3. **13.** 3.

Section 173

1. (*a*) 4; no. (*b*) 0; yes. (*c*) 0; yes. (*d*) 0; yes. **3.** $|X| = 6$, $|Y| = 12$.

Section 174

1. $A + B = \begin{bmatrix} 3 & 1 \\ 3 & 7 \end{bmatrix}$, $AB = \begin{bmatrix} 2 & 5 \\ 6 & 9 \end{bmatrix}$. **3.** $A + B$ impossible, $AB = \begin{bmatrix} 9 & 0 \\ 8 & -4 \end{bmatrix}$.

5. $A + B$ impossible, $AB = \begin{bmatrix} 1 \\ -4 \\ 5 \end{bmatrix}$.

7. $A + B = \begin{bmatrix} 2 & 0 & 1 \\ 2 & 1 & 3 \\ 1 & 2 & 2 \end{bmatrix}$, $AB = \begin{bmatrix} 1 & 0 & 1 \\ 2 & -2 & -1 \\ 1 & 4 & 4 \end{bmatrix}$ **9.** $\begin{bmatrix} -1 & 0 \\ 9 & 12 \end{bmatrix}$.

11. $\begin{bmatrix} 2 & 4 & -2 \\ 1 & 8 & -6 \\ -4 & 2 & -5 \end{bmatrix}$. **13.** $\begin{bmatrix} 3 & 6 & 0 \\ 3 & -1 & 0 \end{bmatrix}$.

15. $AB = [a_1b_1 + a_2b_2 + \dots + a_nb_n]$,

$$BA = \begin{bmatrix} b_1a_1 & b_1a_2 & \dots & b_1a_n \\ b_2a_1 & b_2a_2 & \dots & b_2a_n \\ \dots\dots & & & \\ b_na_1 & b_na_2 & \dots & b_na_n \end{bmatrix}$$

Section 175

1. $A^2 = \begin{bmatrix} 1 & 0 & 2 & 2 \\ 1 & 0 & 1 & 1 \\ 0 & 1 & 2 & 1 \\ 1 & 0 & 0 & 1 \end{bmatrix}$, $A + A^2 = \begin{bmatrix} 1 & 1 & 3 & 3 \\ 1 & 0 & 2 & 2 \\ 1 & 1 & 2 & 2 \\ 1 & 0 & 1 & 1 \end{bmatrix}$.

3. (*a*)

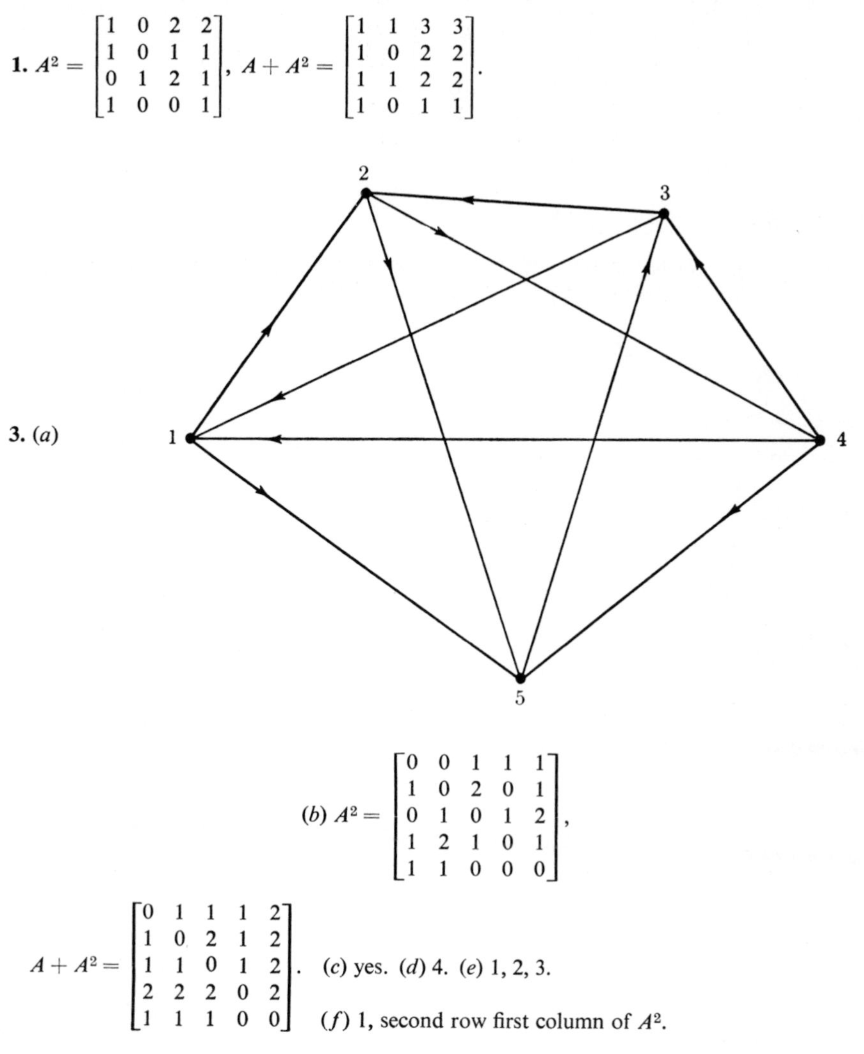

(*b*) $A^2 = \begin{bmatrix} 0 & 0 & 1 & 1 & 1 \\ 1 & 0 & 2 & 0 & 1 \\ 0 & 1 & 0 & 1 & 2 \\ 1 & 2 & 1 & 0 & 1 \\ 1 & 1 & 0 & 0 & 0 \end{bmatrix}$,

$A + A^2 = \begin{bmatrix} 0 & 1 & 1 & 1 & 2 \\ 1 & 0 & 2 & 1 & 2 \\ 1 & 1 & 0 & 1 & 2 \\ 2 & 2 & 2 & 0 & 2 \\ 1 & 1 & 1 & 0 & 0 \end{bmatrix}$. (*c*) yes. (*d*) 4. (*e*) 1, 2, 3.

(*f*) 1, second row first column of A^2.

Section 177

1. (*a*) $M^2 = \begin{bmatrix} \frac{7}{9} & \frac{2}{9} \\ \frac{1}{3} & \frac{2}{3} \end{bmatrix}$. (*b*) $\frac{2}{9}$. (*c*) $[\frac{1}{2}, \frac{1}{2}]$.
(*d*) $[\frac{2}{3}, \frac{1}{3}]$.

3. (*a*) $M^2 = \begin{bmatrix} \frac{1}{8} & \frac{1}{2} & \frac{3}{8} \\ \frac{1}{16} & \frac{9}{16} & \frac{3}{8} \\ \frac{1}{16} & \frac{1}{2} & \frac{7}{16} \end{bmatrix}$. (*b*) $[\frac{1}{12}, \frac{2}{3}, \frac{1}{4}]$.
(*c*) $[\frac{1}{12}, \frac{13}{24}, \frac{3}{8}]$.

Section 178

1. $\begin{bmatrix} -2 & 3 \\ 3 & -4 \end{bmatrix}$ **3.** $\begin{bmatrix} \frac{3}{10} & -\frac{1}{10} \\ -\frac{1}{5} & \frac{2}{5} \end{bmatrix}$. **5.** $\begin{bmatrix} 1 & 0 & 0 \\ -1 & \frac{1}{2} & 0 \\ 0 & -\frac{1}{2} & \frac{1}{3} \end{bmatrix}$.

7. $\begin{bmatrix} \frac{4}{5} & -\frac{1}{5} & -\frac{4}{5} \\ -\frac{6}{5} & -\frac{1}{5} & \frac{11}{5} \\ \frac{1}{5} & \frac{1}{5} & -\frac{1}{5} \end{bmatrix}$. **9.** $\begin{bmatrix} -\frac{3}{32} & 0 & \frac{1}{32} & \frac{1}{4} \\ \frac{15}{64} & -\frac{1}{2} & \frac{25}{64} & -\frac{1}{8} \\ \frac{11}{32} & 0 & \frac{7}{32} & -\frac{1}{4} \\ \frac{1}{32} & 0 & -\frac{11}{32} & \frac{1}{4} \end{bmatrix}$.

Section 181

1. (*a*) 20. (*b*) 300. (*c*) $4k$. (*d*) $4(k+1)$. (*e*) $4(k+6)$. **3.** (*a*) 9. (*b*) 149. (*c*) $2k-1$. (*d*) $2k+1$. (*e*) $2k+11$. **5.** (*a*) 15. (*b*) 225. (*c*) $3k$. (*d*) $3(k+1)$. (*e*) $3(k+6)$.

Index